HERMS'S
MEDICAL ENTOMOLOGY

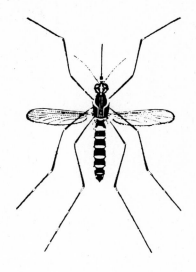

HERMS'S

MEDICAL

THE MACMILLAN COMPANY
COLLIER-MACMILLAN LIMITED, LONDON

ENTOMOLOGY

Sixth Edition

Maurice T. James, Ph.D.
Professor of Entomology,
Washington State University,
Pullman

Robert F. Harwood, Ph.D.
Professor of Entomology and Chairman,
Department of Entomology,
Washington State University,
Pullman

PRINTING   5678910   YEAR   3456789

Earlier editions entitled *Medical and Veterinary Entomology*, by W. B. Herms, copyright 1915 and 1923 by The Macmillan Company, copyright renewed 1943 and 1951 by William M. Herms. Earlier editions entitled *Medical Entomology* by W. B. Herms, copyright 1939 and 1959 by The Macmillan Company, copyright renewed 1967 by William M. Herms. Earlier edition entitled *Medical Entomology* by William B. Herms and Maurice T. James, © The Macmillan Company 1961. Library of Congress catalog card number: 69–12641

THE MACMILLAN COMPANY

COLLIER-MACMILLAN CANADA, LTD., TORONTO, ONTARIO

PRINTED IN THE UNITED STATES OF AMERICA

Dedicated to the Memory of

WILLIAM B. HERMS, Sc.D.
(*September 22, 1876–May 9, 1949*)

Late Professor of Parasitology, Emeritus, University of California, Berkeley; one-time Lecturer in Tropical Medicine, University of California School of Medicine, San Francisco; late Chairman, Division of Entomology and Parasitology, University of California, Berkeley

Preface to the Sixth Edition

The need to prepare this revision, after the passing of only a few years, is an indication of the rapidity with which knowledge in the field of medical entomology is advancing. The "one world" aspect of the subject is becoming increasingly apparent; consequently, the authors have given more emphasis to international considerations in the present edition. In this day of rapid and relatively easy transit, not only is there more travel abroad and to more distant parts of the world but also there is more opportunity for medically important arthropods and arthropod-transmitted pathogens to be imported into a given area. Consequently, both practical considerations and a general understanding of the subject demand that a provincial attitude be discarded.

The authors have changed the emphasis on control from one of specific measures to one of generalities. Thus, there is a more thorough account of principles and less information concerning the control of particular pests. In other words, major emphasis is placed on the more unchanging aspects of control rather than on the changing specifics, which may be the best that one can offer today but which may be wholly inadequate or for some other reason unsatisfactory tomorrow. Furthermore, all control information is now placed in one chapter (Chapter 6). The student will want to refer to this chapter when dealing with a particular insect or group of insects; nevertheless, the authors believe he will find it more useful to consider these control measures in relation to others that are applied in similar cases. For specifics, he will have to consult the more ephemeral literature.

Numerous changes, some sweeping in scope, many minor, will be found in this sixth edition. The amount of taxonomic material has been reduced somewhat. The authors believe this to be justified, now that adequate manuals are available from which the student can get such information. The amount of veterinary material has been increased slightly—not, however, at the expense of the medical. Some chapters have been combined, rearranged, or even added. The authors hope the present arrangement will prove to be a more serviceable one.

Citations not only document the work but also supply useful references for the serious student. The authors have particularly attempted to include pertinent review articles, because of their value to the student and also because such sources have been used extensively in writing this new edition.

The full responsibility for the book must be assumed by the authors. However, thanks are due the following individuals, who have made helpful suggestions and reviewed chapters or parts of chapters: R. D. Akre and C. A. Johansen, Washington State University, Pullman, Washington; D. W. Anthony and J. B. Hoy, U.S. Department of Agriculture; E. C. Bay, University of California, Riverside, California; J. G. Edwards, San Jose State College, San Jose, California; K. C. Emerson, Arlington, Virginia; D. P. Furman and W. C. Reeves, University of California, Berkeley, California; C. Garrett-Jones, B. Grab, and R. Pal, WHO, Geneva, Switzerland; J. D. Gregson, B. V. Peterson, and P. R. Wilkinson, Canadian Department of Agriculture; E. J. Hansens, Rutgers University, New Brunswick, New Jersey; W. L. Jellison, Rocky Mountain Laboratory, Hamilton, Montana; K. C. Kim and R. D. Price, University of Minnesota, St. Paul, Minnesota; M. Laird, Memorial University, St. John's, Newfoundland; H. Oldroyd, British Museum (Natural History), London, England; F. Perlman, Allergy Clinic, Portland, Oregon; H. D. Pratt, CDC, Atlanta, Georgia; R. E. Ryckman, Loma Linda University, Loma Linda, California; G. W. Ward, University of Sydney, Australia; and F. Zumpt, South African Institute for Medical Research, Johannesburg, South Africa. The authors are also indebted to Mrs. Anita Davis, who typed most of the manuscript for this sixth edition.

Maurice T. James
Robert F. Harwood

PULLMAN, WASHINGTON

Contents

HERMS'S
MEDICAL ENTOMOLOGY

1

INTRODUCTION

Medical entomology is the science that deals with the relation of insects, arachnids, and other arthropods to the causation of pathological conditions in man or to the transmission of organisms that are responsible for such pathological conditions. The arthropods involved may be the causal agents themselves, e.g., the scabies mite; intermediate hosts, as certain beetles that serve in this capacity for helminth parasites; or vectors, as *Anopheles* mosquitoes in relation to malaria. The science is directly concerned with the biology and control of the offending arthropods and with a recognition of the damage that they do. It contributes to the conservation of both public and individual health and well-being. Its relationship to veterinary entomology is very close; many of the problems of the two fields broadly overlap or are to a certain extent inseparable, in view of the fact that many arthropods attack both man and domestic animals, though sometimes in somewhat different ways or to a somewhat different extent. Medical entomology is also related to the broader general area of animal pathology and parasitology, because many arthropods transmit pathogens that are common to wild animals and to man; indeed, a very important aspect of medical entomology is the role wild birds and mammals play as reservoirs of human pathogens.

The name, medical entomology, as a designation for this field of knowledge apparently did not come into use until about 1909 (Herms, 1909).* Even at that late date there were those in high places who ridiculed the importance

* Bibliography located in back matter of book (see pp. 425–457).

of arthropods as vectors in spite of important entomologic discoveries relative to plague, malaria, yellow fever, and certain plant diseases. Today medical entomology is not only recognized as a science in its own right, but takes equal rank with some of the older sciences contributing to the fields of public health, tropical medicine, preventive medicine, and veterinary medicine.

Training. The medical entomologist must be thoroughly trained in general zoology; he must be particularly well trained in entomology and arachnology, as well as in protozoology, helminthology, virology, and bacteriology. He must be a parasitologist in the truest and widest sense. He must be well versed in field ecology. Because of the involvement of reservoirs and intermediate hosts, the medical entomologist must have a working knowledge of vertebrate zoology, particularly mammalogy, and a wider knowledge of invertebrates, particularly fresh-water forms, than is usually imparted in introductory courses in zoology and entomology. Familiarity with aquatic organisms is also helpful in determining public health implications when these organisms are found in domestic water supplies. Familiarity with insects consuming stored and dried foods and consuming or contaminating foods in general is valuable. A knowledge of house-invading animals is essential. Entomologic training must be built upon a sound basis of taxonomy and must emphasize the study of immature stages in the developmental cycle. Foundation work in arthropod toxicology and physiology should be included. Much direct benefit will be derived from many of the courses offered in medical, veterinary, and public health curricula, such as general anatomy, general physiology, epidemiology, pathology, histology, toxicology, and hematology. A substantial knowledge of chemistry is essential. To solve certain field problems involving arthropods such as mosquitoes and flies, knowledge of such phases of engineering as pertain to drainage and sewage disposal is useful. Familiarity with

these last named subjects will enable the medical entomologist to cooperate intelligently with other medical investigators and with engineers, or, on occasion, to make intelligent use of the professional services of physicians, engineers, epidemiologists, and other experts and specialists in the solution of complicated problems. For a more extended consideration of the preparation required for a career as a medical entomologist and of the demands that might be made of him in his chosen field, the student is referred to pertinent articles by Herms (1943) and Travis (1958).

Objectives. The aim of medical entomology is ultimately the prevention and, if possible, the eradication of human and animal diseases related to arthropod transmission and causation; to attain this objective, and consequently within the general scope of objectives, is the pursuit of knowledge of all kinds concerning the arthropods involved, their biology and control. There are many notable early examples of the service rendered by workers in this fertile field, such as the control of malaria and yellow fever in Cuba and the Panama Canal Zone (Le Prince and Orenstein, 1916) and the campaign against rats and fleas in San Francisco in 1907 (Todd, 1909). The eradication during 1939–1940 of *Anopheles gambiae* Giles from Brazil after its devastating introduction from tropical Africa (Soper and Wilson, 1943) and the control of lice and resulting suppression of typhus epidemics in Europe during World War II (Cushing, 1957) are excellent more recent examples. The benefit derived by animal industry is well illustrated in the control of the tick *Boophilus annulatus* (Say), which was responsible for transmitting the pathogen of Texas cattle fever in the southern United States. Current campaigns against malaria, yellow fever, filariasis, and the screw-worm point the way toward what we might hope to accomplish in the future.

Historical. Records from prehistory and early human history indicate man's awareness of medically important arthropods and of the diseases associated with them. The physician Susruta in Chapter XII of the *Susruta Samhita* recorded filarial infections in man in India as early as the sixth century B.C. (Raghavan, 1957). In approximately A.D. 1200 an American Indian artist unmistakably depicted, on Mimbres, New Mexico, pottery, a swarm of mosquitoes poised for an attack (Rodeck, 1932). It is interesting to note that the Flathead Indians of Montana were obviously aware of the fact that fly larvae metamorphosed into flies, since they used the same term, *xelmalten*, to designate both the "white maggot" and the fly (Weisel, 1952).

In the King James version of the Old Testament (Exodus 8:24) we read "… and there came a grievous swarm of flies into the house of Pharoah, and into his servants' houses, and into all the land of Egypt: the land was corrupted by reason of the swarm of flies." The Douay version reads, "and the land was corrupted by this kind of flies." Whether the term "flies" as used in this passage is coextensive with the modern use of the word may be questioned, but it is interesting to contemplate the implications. At any rate, it is a record of man's being annoyed by swarms of insects. As early as 1577 Mercurialis (Mercurialis, 1577) expressed the belief that flies carried the "virus" of plague from those who were ill or had died of the disease to the food of the well. Although we now know that this is not the usual mode of transmission of the plague pathogen, the principal role that flies play as vectors was correctly interpreted, that is, they are food contaminators.

Gabriel Soares de Souza (1587) stated that flies suck poison from sores (*Framboesia tropica*) and leave them in skin abrasions on healthy individuals, thus infecting many persons. Edward Bancroft (1769) advanced a similar theory, but it was Castellani (1907) who proved that these men had essentially the correct idea by demonstrating experimentally that flies do transmit *Treponema pertenue* Castellani, the causal agent of yaws. The role

of the house fly as a vector was, however, not fully appreciated until the Spanish-American War, when Veeder (1898) wrote

I have made cultures of bacteria from fly tracks and from the excrement of flies and there seems to be not the slightest difficulty in so doing. Indeed the evidence of every sort is so clear that I have reached the conclusion that the conveyance of infection in the manner indicated is the chief factor in decimating the army. Certainly so far as is known to the writer, nothing adequate has been said about it in current discussions.

Although popular beliefs in many parts of the world had for some time connected mosquitoes with various tropical fevers, no well-formulated ideas were advanced until Josiah Nott (1848) of New Orleans published his belief that mosquitoes gave rise to both malaria and yellow fever. Beauperthuy (1854), a French physician in the West Indies, formulated an excellent theory that mosquitoes were responsible for yellow fever. He believed, however, that the unknown disease factor was carried by the insect from certain decomposing matter and in turn was introduced by it into the human body.

Although early naturalists and physicians were fairly well informed concerning the larger intestinal parasites, such as roundworms and tapeworms, little information relating to microorganisms was available until after the development of the microscope in the latter part of the seventeenth century by Anton van Leeuwenhoek, who found that his "material contained many tiny animals which moved about in a most amazing fashion; the largest of these showed the liveliest and most active motion, moving through water or saliva as a fish of prey darts through the sea." This discovery led to the study of hitherto invisible organisms and eventually to the formulation of the "germ theory" by Pasteur in 1877.

Although according to Howard (1921) no standard medical treatise prior to 1871 mentioned any specific disease as related to insect transmission, Raimbert (1869) showed that by experimental inoculation of proboscids, wings, and other parts of nonbiting flies into guinea pigs anthrax could be so disseminated; this discovery had been foreshadowed by the theory of Montfils (1776) almost a century earlier. The first discovery of primary importance in the field of medical entomology, however, was made by Patrick Manson (1878), who, working in China, observed the development of *Wuchereria bancrofti* (Cobbald) in the body of the mosquito, *Culex pipiens quinquefasciatus* Say, and eventually, together with Bancroft, Low, and others, proved the mosquito to be the intermediate host and vector of the causal organism of filariasis.

The discovery by Laveran (1880) of the causal organism of malaria (*Plasmodium malariae*) living parasitically in the red blood cells of man marks an epoch in protozoology as well as in medical entomology. Ranking with Laveran's discovery of the malaria parasite is the discovery by Theobald Smith in 1889 (Smith and Kilbourne, 1893) of the causal protozoon, *Babesia bigemina*, of Texas cattle fever, also living parasitically within the red blood corpuscles of the host. Associated with Smith in the investigation was F. L. Kilbourne, and together in 1893 they made the second great fundamental discovery in the field of medical entomology, namely that the cattle tick, *Boophilus annulatus* (Say), is the necessary intermediate host of the causal agent of the disease. This knowledge, combined with Manson's discovery concerning mosquitoes and filariasis, established a new basis for the control and prevention of disease in both man and domestic animals.

In quick succession there followed a series of famous discoveries. Bruce (1895) investigated nagana and established the fact that the pathogen is conveyed from animal to animal through the agency of the tsetse fly, *Glossina morsitans* Westwood.

Ronald Ross (1897) announced that he had found the zygotes of the malaria parasite in two "dapple-winged mosquitoes" (anophelines) that he had bred from the larva and fed on a patient whose blood contained crescents. The chief contribution made by Ross, however, was the discovery of the complete life cycle of the causal organism of bird malaria in a culicine mosquito, with the establishment of the bird-to-mosquito-to-bird cycle. Grassi, Bignami, and Bastianelli (1899) proved that the human malaria parasites were transmitted by a particular genus of mosquitoes, namely *Anopheles*, and Sambon and Low (1900) demonstrated the fact of transmission beyond a doubt.

One of the world's outstanding achievements in the field of experimental medicine was that of the United States Army Yellow Fever Commission, consisting of Walter Reed, James Carroll, Jesse W. Lazear, and A. Agramonte, which in 1900, in Cuba, proved conclusively that the yellow fever pathogen is carried by the mosquito, *Aedes aegypti* (Linnaeus). Carlos Finlay, a Cuban physician, had, as early as 1880, propounded the theory and conducted experiments in an attempt to prove it; hence, he too amply deserves due credit and recognition. An extensive account of the foresight, courage, and careful experimentation that established the facts of mosquito transmission of this virus is given in the United States Senate Document number 822 (January 27, 1911). In the course of these experiments only one human life was lost. Doctor Lazear will always be remembered as the man who gave his life so that the curse of yellow fever could be conquered.

The two discoveries concerning malaria and yellow fever gave great impetus to the subject of mosquito control, although Howard had already demonstrated the value of kerosene as a larvicide in his experiments in the Catskill Mountains in 1892. Howard's pioneer book, *Mosquitoes: How They Live; How They Carry Disease; How They are Classified; How They May Be Destroyed*, appeared in 1901.

During almost a third of a century following these fundamental discoveries, little advance was made in the knowledge of malaria and yellow fever, and the complete solution of the problem of control of both diseases seemed to be within reach—that is, simply, mosquito control. However, malaria was again referred to as a mysterious disease by Hackett (1937) in his treatise *Malaria in Europe*: "... under close examination malaria becomes only more intricate and impenetrable, more protean in its character, more diverse in its local manifestations." The expression "anophelism without malaria" came into use, and malariologists became more interested, as Hackett points out, in the anophelines that did not transmit malaria than in those that did. The discovery by Falleroni (1926) that *Anopheles maculipennis*, so-called, was in reality separable into "races" on differences in the egg pattern, led Hackett, Martini, and Missiroli (1932) to the discovery that the "races" (now considered a complex of species and subspecies; see Chapter 11) differ markedly in their vector relationships to malaria, thus opening new avenues for research. So what appeared to be a clearcut situation in 1898 now became once more a malaria "puzzle."

More recent studies on the bionomics and taxonomy of mosquitoes have thrown considerable light on the question of why some species, or supposed species, are much more effective than others in the transmission of the malaria parasites. To these aspects of the problem must be added the significant advances in our knowledge of the parasites and their bionomics, notably the discovery of Huff and his associates of the exoerythrocytic cycle of the malaria parasite, and the advances in our knowledge of the epidemiology of the malarias.

Furthermore, the apparently well-solved problem of yellow fever control through the control of *Aedes aegypti* (Linnaeus) was again completely thrown open for further investigation by the discovery of Stokes, Bauer, and Hudson (1927) that experimental animals (monkeys) can be infected with yellow fever. Now, because of the availability of experimental animals, more than a dozen species of mosquitoes, instead of just one, are known to have the ability to transmit the virus by bite from monkey to monkey.

A type of yellow fever designated as jungle yellow fever (Soper, 1936) was first observed in 1932 in the Valle de Chanaan, Espirito Santo, Brazil. It differs from the previously known type of yellow fever, transmitted by *Aedes aegypti* (Linnaeus), only in that it occurs under conditions that suggest that infection takes place away from urban habitats and that man may not be an essential factor in the continuity of the infection. Indeed, "man may be but an accident in the course of an epizootic in the lower animals, or it may even be due to the persistence of the virus in invertebrate vectors for long periods of time." With the decreasing importance of classical yellow fever resulting from its successful control and the ever-imminent threat of the jungle type, increasing attention is being paid to the latter.

An historical account of plague is included in Wu, Pollitzer, and Wu (1936). Epidemics and pandemics of this disease have been known since ancient times. More than a thousand years before the time of Christ, the Philistines were afflicted with an outbreak of a disease that killed large numbers of their people, more than 50,000 in the city of Bethsames (Bethshemesh) alone, according to Old Testament accounts. The affliction with "emerods" suggests buboes, and, interestingly, an association was made with an abundance of "mice" (rats?). The great plague pandemic of Europe in the fourteenth century claimed 25,000,000 victims, one-fourth the population of the continent, and the London epidemic of 1666 killed 70,000 persons out of a population of 450,000.

Modern progress in the study of plague epidemiology dates from the success of Simond (1898) in transmitting the plague pathogen from a sick rat to a healthy one through the agency of fleas. The discovery was at first discredited, but the experiments were repeated successfully by Verjbitski (1908) in 1903 and Liston (1905) in 1904. The designation sylvatic (selvatic) plague, for the wild rodent or campestral form, was proposed by Jorge (1928) to specify plague of wild rodents in which fleas play an important role as reservoirs as well as vectors.

At this junction of the historical review of the subject, it is appropriate to call attention to the first comprehensive treatise dealing with arthropods in relation to disease, namely, the work of Nuttall (1899) entitled, *On the Role of Insects, Arachnids and Myriopods as Carriers in the Spread of Bacterial and Parasitic Diseases of Man and Animals: A Critical and Historical Study*. Nuttall deserves to be called the father of medical entomology.

Forde (1902) observed certain parasites in the blood of persons suffering from Gambian sleeping sickness, which Dutton (1902) recognized as trypanosomes and named *Trypanosoma gambiense*; and Bruce and Nabarro (1903) showed that *Glossina palpalis* (Robineau-Desvoidy) was the carrier, thus adding tsetse-transmitted pathogens to the list of arthropod-vectored parasites. Stephens and Fantham (1910) described *Trypanosoma rhodesiense* as the causal organism of Rhodesian sleeping sickness, and Kinghorn and York (1912) proved *Glossina morsitans* Westwood to be a responsible vector.

Graham (1902), working in Syria, found that dengue, or breakbone fever, a widely distributed disease particularly of warm climates, though frequently occurring elsewhere, was the result of mosquito transmission. He, and later Ashbury and Craig (1907), reported that possibly several species of mosquitoes, notably *Aedes aegypti*, are able to transmit the pathogen. A related disease is pappataci, also known as three-day fever and sand fly fever; Doerr, Rranz, and Taussig (1909) proved that transmission of its pathogen involved the sand fly, *Phlebotomus papatasii* Scopoli.

Approximately a decade after the pioneer work of Smith and Kilbourne, other important discoveries were made concerning the relation of ticks to human and animal diseases. Marchoux and Salimbeni (1903) proved that the pathogen of fowl spirochetosis, now known as *Borrelia anserina* (Sakharoff) Bergey, *et al.*, is tick borne and that its vector is *Argas persicus* (Oken), the common fowl tick. Dutton and Todd (1905) proved that the spirochete of African relapsing fever was transmitted to man by *Ornithodorus moubata* (Murray) and that it can be transmitted through the egg from the female tick to her offspring; the transmission to man was also discovered almost simultaneously by Dutton and Todd (1905). Wilson and Chowning (1902) had advanced for the first time the theory that the "wood tick" was involved in the transmission of Rocky Mountain spotted fever, but it was Ricketts (1906), working in Montana, who proved conclusively that *Dermacentor andersoni* Stiles (which he believed to be *D. occidentalis* Neumann) was the vector of the pathogen.

Although lice have for centuries been associated in the mind of man with filth and disease, apparently little thought was given to these insects as possible vectors, even though Melnikoff (1869) had shown that the biting dog louse, *Trichodectes canis* De Geer, was an intermediate host of the double-pored tapeworm, *Dipylidium caninum* (Linnaeus), which also occasionally occurs in humans. Aubert (1879) considered that lice were spreaders of impetigo and the cause of prurigo, pityriasis, and so forth. Also, in experiments conducted by Dewèvre (1892) lice were shown to carry the specific microorganisms mechanically on their front legs, and infection was thus accidentally transmitted to healthy persons. Furthermore, Flugge (1891) and Ticitin (1897) both supposed that disease might be carried by vermin and conducted experiments with bed bugs. Mackie (1907), working in India, found that the relapsing fever organism was transmitted by, and multiplied in the body of, the body louse, *Pediculus humanus humanus* Linneaus.

Nicolle, Comte, and Conseil (1909), working in Tunis, and Ricketts and Wilder (1910), working independently in Mexico, proved experimentally that the body louse is a carrier of the typhus fever organism, which was isolated, described, and named *Rickettsia prowazeki* by Da Rocha Lima (1916).

Members of the family Reduviidae, the assassin and conenose bugs, have long been known for their bloodthirstiness and for their fierce bites, but it was apparently not until 1909 that insects of this group were experimentally proven to be pathogen carriers. In that year Chagas (1909), who had already described the causal organism of Chagas' disease as *Schizotrypanum cruzi,* demonstrated that this organism is carried by the conenose bug *Panstrongylus megistus* (Burmeister).

Flies of the family Tabanidae (horse flies, gad flies, deer flies) were looked upon with suspicion as early as 1776, but apparently no satisfactory evidence against them was forthcoming until 1913, when Mitzmain (1913), working in the Philippine Islands, demonstrated transmission of the surra pathogen of the carabao by *Tabanus striatus* Fabricius, which he regarded as the principal vector. Strong evidence against tabanid flies of the genus *Chrysops* as intermediary hosts of the nematode *Loa loa* (Cobbold) was advanced in the same year by Leiper (1913).

Bloodsucking gnats of the dipterous family Simuliidae are a terrible scourge to both man and beast in many parts of the world and have long been under suspicion as vectors of disease-producing organisms. Blacklock (1926) reported *Simulium damnosum* Theobald as the vector of the filarial worm *Onchocerca volvulus* (Leuckart), the causal agent of human onchocerciasis. O'Roke (1934) reported *Simulium venustum* Say to be a vector of the protozoon *Leucocytozoon simondi* Mathis and Léger, the causal organism of a disease of ducks.

Tularemia, also known as Pahvant Valley plague or deer fly fever, was shown by Francis and Mayne (1921) to be carried from rodent to rodent by the tabanid *Chrysops discalis* Williston, and presumably from rodent to man in the same manner. The causal organism, *Francisella tularensis,* was described in 1911 by McCoy and Chapin as the cause of a plague like disease of California ground squirrels. The involvement of arthropods in the transmission of this bacillus and the discoveries of Francis, Mayne, McCoy, and Chapin are significant, even though arthropod transmission is not the chief factor in the epidemiology of the disease.

Kelser (1933) succeeded in transmitting the virus of equine encephalomyelitis from inoculated guinea pigs to a horse by the bite of the mosquito *Aedes aegypti*. The isolation of the virus from wild *Culex tarsalis* Coquillett by Hammon, Reeves, and their associates (Hammon, *et al.,* 1941) and the subsequent establishment of the role of this species as the vector of western equine encephalitis virus constitute landmarks in the study of the epidemiology and epizootology of that disease.

The discovery of the insecticidal value of DDT represents the beginning of a new era in the prevention of insect-associated diseases pertaining to both plants and animals, particularly to such a devastating disease of man as malaria. It also represents the beginning of a new concept in insect control—the use of a *residual* insecticide, with its relatively long-lasting effects, and which can be applied in relatively small quantities. DDT was first synthesized by Othmar Zeidler in 1874 at Strasbourg, Germany. Zeidler was apparently ignorant of its insecticidal properties. It was not until about 1939 that Paul Müller, then a member of the scientific staff of Geigy Company in Basle, Switzerland, discovered this remarkable insecticidal value. For this discovery Müller was awarded the Nobel Prize in Medicine for 1948.

A significant discovery that profoundly affects control programs against medically important arthropods was that insects may develop resistance to residual insecticides. This was demonstrated by Speich in house flies in northern Sweden in 1946, and by

Mosna in the mosquito, *Culex pipiens molestus* Forskål, in Italy, in 1947. Since that time, insect resistance to chlorinated hydrocarbons and other insecticides has become commonplace knowledge.

A historical review would not be complete without a consideration of the change of attitude that has accompanied the development of medical entomology as a science. A classical example of this involves the supposed effect of the bite of the European spider that became known as the tarantula (not to be confused with the American tarantulas). In Italy, in the vicinity of Taranto, there occurred a spider scare during the seventeenth century that gave rise to a condition known as "tarantism." The following account is from the *Cambridge Natural History*, Volume 4, page 361:

The bite of the spider was supposed to induce a species of madness which found its expression—and its cure—in frantic and extravagant contortions of the body. If the dance was not sufficiently frenzied, death ensued. In the case of survivors, the symptoms were said to recur on the anniversary of the bite. Particular descriptions of music were supposed to incite the patient to the exertion necessary for his relief; hence the name "Tarantella."

In the middle ages epidemics of "tarantism" were of frequent occurrence and spread with alarming rapidity. They were seizures of an hysterical character, analogous to the ancient Bacchic dances, and quite unconnected with the venom of the spider from which they took their name. The condition of exaltation and frenzy was contagious, and would run through whole districts, with its subsequent relapse to a state of utter prostration and exhaustion. The evil reputation of the Tarantula appears to have exceedingly little basis in fact.

More recent changes in attitude involve such household pests as the house fly and such intimate companions of man as the lice that infest him. West (1951) has pointed out that our early attitude toward the house fly was one of "friendly tolerance"; a few flies "were nice things to have around, to make things seem homelike.... Those that were knocked into the coffee or the cream could be fished out; those that went into the soup or the hash were never missed." (Doane, quoted by West.) This attitude prevails today to an extent among primitive peoples, who may look upon head lice, for instance, as something akin to household pets. During the last quarter of the nineteenth century there came a period of incrimination, during which many signal successes in research connected arthropods with the transmission of many disease-producing organisms.

During the period that followed, that of "popular education," preceding World War I, the public became aware of the situation through the writings of such men as L. O. Howard. The stimulation of the great successes led to some blind alleys, however, such as the attempts to link the "transmission" of poliomyelitis with the stable fly, that of pellagra with the buffalo gnat, and that of cancer with cockroaches.

Between World War I and World War II there was a diminution of activity resulting from "false security," followed by the period of "stern necessity" during World War II, when the conquest of typhus, scrub typhus, dengue, malaria, and other arthropod-associated diseases became an essential part of the war effort. Unlike the aftermath of World War I, the importance of medical entomology is continuing to be recognized to an intense degree and on a worldwide scale. Three aspects of this recognition are particularly important: first, the idea of the "one world" as applied to this science, in which problems of one continent or geographical area should be considered as actually or potentially applying to others; secondly, the idea of eradication, rather than control, as applying either to arthropods themselves (e.g., *Anopheles gambiae* Giles and the primary screwworm) or to arthropod-transmitted pathogens (e.g., those of malaria and filariasis); and thirdly, the recognition that we should also think of *pest* control or eradication in terms of improving standards of living, comfort, and mental health. Thus, the trend in attitude has completely reversed itself, from the idea that a few flies were "nice things to have around," through the idea that they were carriers of dangerous pathogens, finally to the modern desire to get rid of them, whether or not a disease threat may be involved, purely because they are an annoyance factor.

Medical Importance of Arthropods. The ways in which arthropods relate to human and animal health and well-being are almost as numerous as the species of responsible arthropods themselves. Each species, however similar to its next of kin, has certain characteristics that affect the host differently. It is nevertheless possible to classify the relationships of arthropods to health by putting them into two divisions, each of which is subject to further differentiation. The relationships may be designated as follows:

A. Arthropods as direct agents of disease or discomfort.
   1. Entomophobia (including delusory parasitosis).
   2. Annoyance and blood loss.
   3. Accidental injury to sense organs.
   4. Envenomization.
   5. Dermatosis.
   6. Myiasis and related infestations.
   7. Allergy and related conditions.
B. Arthropods as vectors or intermediate hosts.
   1. Mechanical carriers (transmission being more or less accidental).
   2. Obligatory vectors (involving some degree of development, cyclical or propagative, within the arthropod).
   3. Intermediate hosts (in a passive capacity; if an intermediate host bites or otherwise seeks out the definitive host of a pathogen it will be considered a vector, under category no. 2).

As our subject develops in the remaining chapters of this book, the student will determine the way or ways in which the particular groups of arthropods fit into the scheme presented here.

Entomophobia. Insects, spiders, and other arthropods, even though they may be wholly innocuous, frequently cause man acute annoyance and worry that may eventually lead to a nervous disorder, sometimes with sensory hallucinations. The offending arthropod, if such ever existed, may disappear and be replaced in the mind of the patient by small "bugs" that jump and produce skin irritation and itching. Such disturbances of long duration are termed entomophobia, or, if no actual arthropod is involved, the term "delusory parasitosis" may be used (Waldron, 1962).

Cases of this nature are from time to time brought to the attention of the medical entomologist either directly or through reference by physicians, or they may be handled by qualified pest control operators, on the basis that one who has knowledge of the control of tormenting insects may either be able to remove the cause of the disturbance or, if the latter is imaginary, may show the patient that such is the case. The subject has been ably discussed by Pomerantz (1959) and Waldron (1962), with descriptions of typical case histories.

Entomophobia and delusory parasitosis should not be dismissed as trivial and should not be confused with mere squeamishness. On the other hand, these conditions should be viewed sympathetically, with the recognition that their treatment may require the help of medical personnel and other professional individuals.

Annoyance and Blood Loss. It is difficult to estimate the importance of annoyance by insects, yet everyone is aware of this source of nuisance and discomfort at one time or another. A blow fly, buzzing through the house, may be very irritating, particularly to small children or to elderly persons, and a swarm of flies alighting on screen doors or hovering in the house can be very annoying to almost anyone. "Fly worry" and "tick worry" are recognized entities that result in reduced production of animals because of interference with their normal feeding and rest. Ants may spoil a picnic; so may the threat of yellow jackets and hornets, even though one might not actually be stung by them. Blood loss from insect bites usually is not of much importance so far as man is concerned (though allergic responses to such bites may be); but in livestock it may cause economic loss, even the death of the animals.

Even Collembola (springtails) may be a source of annoyance to man. Scott, *et al.* (1962) list nineteen Nearctic species that have been reported as being intimately associated with man. One of these, *Orchesella albosa* Guthrie, was reported to have infested the head and pubic areas of a Texas family but without causing dermatitis; however, Scott, *et al.* cite records involving the Australasian *Entomobrya tenuicauda* Schött and the cosmopolitan *E. nivalis* (Linnaeus) in which dermatitis did occur.

Accidental Injury to Sense Organs. Various species of insects, like other minute objects, may accidentally enter the eye; this is most likely to be true of small flying insects. Some of these, notably several species of rove beetles, Staphylinidae, cause extreme pain because of an irritating secretion. Many species of insects discharge odoriferous fluid or vapor, and in some instances the fluid is so forcibly ejected that it may be thrown some distance from the insect. Stewart (1937) records the case of a phasmid walking stick, *Anisomorpha buprestoides* (Stoll), squirting fluid a distance of two feet and striking a person in the eye. The pain was severe and vision was impaired for about five days, but no permanent ill effects resulted. Roth and Eisner (1962) have reviewed the subject of the usage of squirting mechanisms of insects, with some original observations.

Injury to the human eye is often caused by the spiny larvae of the sheep bot fly, *Oestrus ovis* Linnaeus. The fly normally deposits active larvae in the nostrils of sheep, and persons working in the field with sheep are occasionally "struck" in the eye by the fly,

with one or more larvae being deposited. Another source of eye injury, which may even result in blindness, comes from urticating hairs of caterpillars; these, either attached to the cast skin of the caterpillar or free, may be carried by the wind and so come in contact with the eye.

Envenomization. Envenomization is discussed in detail in Chapter 20.

Dermatosis. Various skin irritations are caused by arthropods, either by bites or by skin invasions. Some of these irritations could appropriately be classified as envenomizations. Skin irritations commonly result from the bites of such insects as mosquitoes, fleas, lice, and bed bugs. Various species of burrowing mites cause skin irritations known as *acariasis.* Among these are various scabies mites, itch mites, chigger mites, and others. For further discussion of dermatoses, refer to the chapters dealing with the various arthropods involved.

Myiasis and Related Invasions. An invasion of organs and tissues of man and animals by the larvae of Diptera is called *myiasis.* This subject is developed in Chapter 16. Similar invasions by beetle larva (*canthariasis*), moth larvae (*scoleciasis*), and others are known to occur but are rare.

Allergy Caused by Insects. The condition of being specifically hypersensitive to certain insect proteins is a fairly common and widespread phenomenon. This is discussed in Chapter 20.

Arthropods as Vectors. The general role of arthropods as vectors of pathogens and as intermediate hosts of parasites is discussed in Chapter 4.

Literature. The literature of medical entomology has become so voluminous that it is difficult for the worker in one field to keep abreast of even major developments in other fields. It has been our aim to supply the student with important citations under the individual topics discussed, but such citations have had to be selective, and some soon become obsolete with the passage of time. Some of the more important sources and general references are mentioned here.

The *Annual Review of Entomology*, the first volume of which was published in 1956, contains review articles with extensive lists of citations; each of the first thirteen volumes (1956–1968) has included articles that review recent developments in some field of medical entomology, as well as others of pertinent interest. The similar *Annual Review of Microbiology* (first volume, 1947), the *Annual Review of Medicine* (first volume, 1950) and the *Annual Review of Genetics* (first volume, 1967), will also repay examination. Articles dealing with various aspects of medical entomology will be found in a wide range of entomological and other biological periodicals, but there is now a publication dealing specifically with the subject, the *Journal of Medical Entomology* (first volume, 1964), published through the Bishop Museum, Honolulu, Hawaii. Various indexing and abstracting media are available; one of these, an abstracting journal, deals specifically with the subject, namely the *Review of Applied Entomology, Series B* (first volume, 1913).

For the identification of medically important arthropods, beyond the limits of this text, the student must, for the most part, refer to manuals, monographs, comprehensive reviews, and other important works in the specific fields. Two useful general works are those of Smart (fourth edition, 1965, now undergoing a new revision) and of Beklemishev (1958, in Russian).

In regard to pathogens, Richardson and Kendall's (1957) text in veterinary protozoology is a very useful reference, as are Horsfall and Tamm's (1965) *Viral and Rickettsial Infections of Man* and Dubos and Hirsch's (1965) *Bacterial and Mycotic Infections of Man*.

Names of bacteria have been used according to Bergey's *Manual of Determinative Bacteriology* (Breed, *et al.*, 1957). For scientific and common names of insects, with few exceptions where special considerations warrant a deviation, we are following the list prepared by the Committee on Common Names of Insects of the Entomological Society of America (Blickenstaff, 1965). For names of insects not included in that list, we have attempted to follow either what seems to be the best standard usage or that which seems taxonomically most acceptable. The common names list for Australian insects has proven quite useful (Gay, 1966).

2

STRUCTURE, DEVELOPMENT, AND CLASSIFICATION OF INSECTS AND ARACHNIDS

THE INSECTA (HEXAPODA)

The Insecta (Hexapoda) constitute the largest class in numbers of species in the phylum Arthropoda, which in turn comprises a greater number of species than all other phyla of the animal kingdom combined. Various estimates as to the number of described species of insects in the world range from about 625,000 to 1,500,000 and the number ultimately known will probably be much greater. As members of the phylum Arthropoda, insects share the following arthropod char-

acteristics: segmented body with paired, segmented appendages; bilateral symmetry; dorsal heart; ventral nerve cord; and chitinous exoskeleton. Insects have the body divided into three more or less distinct parts, the *head*, the *thorax*, and the *abdomen*. There are eighteen to twenty-one segments in the insect body, the variable number resulting from differences in the interpretation of the embryologic evidence; but owing to the specialization of the head and posterior terminal segments, the number of clearly recognizable ones is usually much smaller. The *head* of the adult insect bears a pair of antennae, the mouth parts, and the eyes. The *thorax* bears the locomotor appendages, namely, three pairs of segmented legs, and in addition usually two pairs of wings (which are morphologically not appendages), one or both of which may be absent or nonfunctional as locomotor structures. The *abdomen* bears no appendages except the terminalia, sometimes cerci, and, in the Collembola, specialized locomotor structures. Respiration is effected by means of a complex system of microscopic tracheal tubules opening through the body wall and carrying air directly to all parts of the body of the insect.

Immature insects belonging to many of the orders differ markedly from the mature forms; e.g., maggots of flies, but almost all possess tracheal tubules.

To familiarize himself with the external anatomy of insects (Fig. 2-1), especially with the parts upon which classification is mainly based, the student should study carefully some large hard-bodied insects, such as the horse fly, cricket, or cockroach. He should give sufficient time to this exercise in the laboratory to become thoroughly informed.

Wings. The earliest systems of insect classification were based on wing characters; today these, together with mouth parts and metamorphosis, still afford the major elements in the bases for modern classification. The venation of insect wings is so markedly characteristic for most species that even a part of a wing is sometimes all that is necessary for identification. The winged insects are usually referred to as the Pterygota and may be either *Exopterygota* (wings developing externally), e.g., cockroaches, or *Endopterygota* (wings developing internally), e.g., beetles. There are

typically two pairs of wings present, situated on the mesothorax and metathorax, although in many parasitic insects, such as the bed bugs, lice, fleas, certain louse flies, and so forth, the wings are absent. The wingless insects just mentioned should, of course, not be included with the *Apterygota*, which are a group of primitively wingless (apterous) forms, of which only one order, the Collembola (now considered by some to be distinct from the insects), will be given any consideration here.

In form the wing presents a more or less triangular appearance. The three sides are called margins: the *costal* margin is anterior, the *anal* margin is posterior, and the apical (outer) margin is between these. The three angles connecting the margins are *humeral* (at the base), *apical* (apex of wing), and *anal* (between the apical and anal margins). Generally the fore and hind wings differ considerably in size; the fore wing in some groups, such as the mayflies, many butterflies and moths, and the bees and wasps, is larger than the hind wing; in the grasshoppers, cockroaches, beetles, and some others, however, the fore

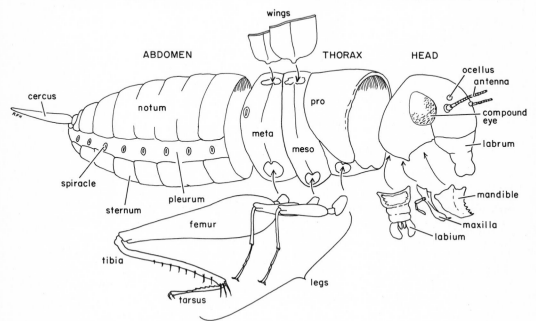

Fig. 2-1 General external structure of an insect.

wing is narrow and serves largely as a cover to the hind wing, which folds fanlike. In the dragonflies, termites, and antlions the fore and hind wings are nearly equal. In the flies, the hind pair of wings is replaced by club-shaped structures known as *halteres*, leaving consequently only one pair of wings, hence the name Diptera (two-winged). In the calyptrate Diptera and some other flies there are present two pairs of lobes (*squamae*, also called *alulae* or *calypters*) at the junction of the wings and the thorax. One of these squamae, the *thoracic*, is more closely associated with the wall of the thorax; the other, the *alar*, is more closely associated with the base of the wing.

There are some differences in the structure of the wings within an order, although for each order a certain general pattern prevails; e.g., the Neuroptera have thin membranous wings, often quite filmy, and with numerous veins and cells; however, the wings of Diptera and many Hemiptera have the same texture throughout, but possess fewer and differently arranged veins. Most Diptera can, of course,

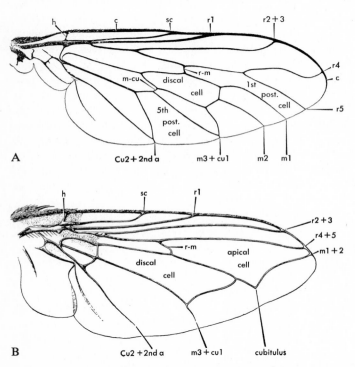

Fig. 2-2 Application of the Comstock-Needham system of nomenclature to two types of dipterous wing (see also Fig. 10-1). The longitudinal veins (with the nomenclature used by those dipterists who follow the old system of numbered veins given in parentheses) are as follows: *c*, costa (costal); *sc*, subcosta (auxillary); *r*, radius (*r1* = 1st longitudinal, *r2* + 3 = 2nd longitudinal, *r4* and *r5* = 3rd longitudinal); *m*, media (*m1* and *m2* = 4th longitudinal, *m3* = part of 5th longitudinal); *cu*, cubitus (*cu1* = part of 5th longitudinal, *cu2* = part of 6th longitudinal); *2nd a*, 2nd anal (part of 6th longitudinal). The 1st anal vein occurs only as a fold in the membrane. The cross veins are: *h*, humeral; *r-m*, radiomedial (anterior or small cross vein); *m-cu*, mediocubital.

A. Wing of Thereva, illustrative of the more primitive type of venation. (U.S.D.A. photograph.)

B. Wing of *Cochliomyia hominivorax*, illustrative of the muscoid type. (U.S.D.A. photograph.)

be readily distinguished from all but a few insects (such as the male coccids, the Strepsiptera, and the two-winged mayflies) by the presence of but a single pair of wings. In winged Hemiptera of the suborder Heteroptera the front wings are thickened at the base and the apical portion is membranous. In the Hemiptera of the suborder Homoptera, the two pairs of wings are of more or less even texture throughout.

The *venation* of the insect wing is an important element in classification, because of the great variety of arrangements and the reliability of this character for the identification of the family, genus, and sometimes even the species. The *veins* are hollow, riblike structures that give strength to the wing. The areas of membrane between the veins are called *cells*; they are said to be *open* if the membranous area extends to the wing margin, and *closed* if the cell is surrounded on all sides by veins. By a careful study of the evidence, a fundamental type of wing venation has been constructed by Comstock and Needham and revised by Tillyard. Figure 2-2 will illustrate this nomenclature as applied to a primitive type of dipterous wing (Fig. 2-2*A*) and as modified in the muscoid type (Fig. 2-2*B*).

Metamorphosis. To achieve the size and development of the parent, the young insect undergoes greater or less change in size, form, and structure. This series of changes is termed *metamorphosis*. The least change is found in the primitively wingless Apterygota (e.g., silverfish, springtail), hence, the newly emerged young individual is externally unlike the parent mainly in size; this type of development, i.e., *without metamorphosis*, is termed *direct development* (Fig. 2-3),

A slightly more obvious metamorphosis occurs in such insects as the true bugs. Not only is there a great difference in size, but also the absence of wings in the young is at once apparent. To reach the winged condition, the young individual casts its skin at intervals and with each *ecdysis* achieves longer wing pads until, after a certain number of molts,

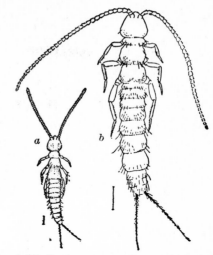

Fig. 2-3 Illustrating primitive metamorphosis. *a.* Young of *Campodea* (Order Entotrophi). *b.* Adult of same. (After Kellogg.)

the fully developed wings appear. The following stages may be recognized: (1) *egg*; (2) *nymph*; and (3) *imago*, or sexually mature adult. There is, of course, a series of nymphal forms, or *instars*, one after each molt. This type of metamorphosis is called *simple* or *incomplete* (Fig. 2-4) and the orders in which this type occurs are known as the *Heterometabola*.

The greatest difference between the newly hatched young and the parents occurs in such forms as the housefly (Fig. 2-5) and the flea. In these forms the newly hatched insect has no resemblance whatsoever to the adult, but in many cases bears a close resemblance to a segmented worm. However, the internal anatomy and certain other features are distinctly insectan. The fact that the young are mandibulate and the adults haustellate in Diptera and Siphonaptera indicates an adaptation to different ways of life in the immature and adult forms. To attain the winged condition of the adult, the wingless, wormlike form must undergo many profound changes, and a new stage is interjected, the *pupa*, or resting stage, in which this transformation is accomplished. The newly hatched young insect emerging

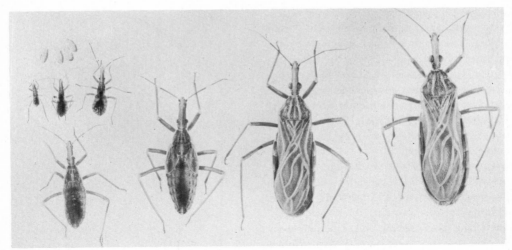

Fig. 2-4 Incomplete metamorphosis of a bug, *Rhodnius prolixus.* Eggs, nymphs, and adult male and female. (Photograph by Roger D. Akre.)

from the egg is called a *larva*, hence the following stages: (1) egg, (2) larva, (3) pupa, and (4) imago. As in insects with simple metamorphosis, there is here again a series of larval instars. This type of metamorphosis is termed *complex* or *complete* metamorphosis, and the orders in which it occurs are known as the *Holometabola*.

Functional wings, and consequently the ability to fly, occur only in adult insects, with one exception, the mayflies, order Ephemeroptera. In this order, the preadult, fully winged subimago molts once more to form the adult. The dried subimaginal skins may be carried in large numbers by the wind and may cause allergic responses in susceptible persons.

Importance of Knowing Internal Anatomy.
It is important that the student familiarize himself with the internal anatomy of insects (cf. Snodgrass, 1935), giving special attention to the digestive system and its accessory structures, such as the salivary glands. The following two cases illustrate the reason for this.

First, the simplest condition in which internal organs of insects are involved in pathogen transmission is in the case of the common house fly, in which pathogenic organisms may be sucked up with infectious dejecta from those ill with cholera or typhoid fever. These organisms will then pass out with the feces of the fly—which may be deposited on human

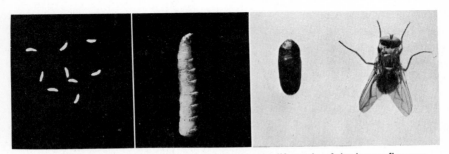

Fig. 2-5 Illustrating complete metamorphosis in the life cycle of the house fly: egg, larva, pupa, adult.

food—either in their original virulent condition or more or less attenuated. Regurgitation on the part of the insect may be equally effective. In this example simple passage through the digestive tract is involved, and not much knowledge of its special anatomy is required.

Second, a more complicated situation exists in the case of the *Anopheles* mosquito, which sucks up pathogenic organisms (plasmodia) with its meal of human blood, whereupon these parasites undergo vital sexual changes within the body of the insect, eventually finding lodgment in the salivary glands before final introduction by the "bite" into the next victim. The insect in this case is the essential natural vector. An understanding of the part of the cycle of the plasmodium within the mosquito requires at least a basic knowledge of the digestive system of the insect and its spatial relations to other parts of the body.

Digestive System. There are three distinct regions to the insect intestine (Fig. 2-6); namely, (1) the *foregut*, consisting of the mouth, pharynx, esophagus, crop, and proventriculus; (2) the *midgut*, comprising the stomach; and (3) the *hindgut*, consisting of the ileum, colon, rectum, and anus. In bloodsucking insects, such as the conenose bug and the mosquito, the pharynx, including its pumping organ, becomes associated with the sucking tube of the proboscis. In the mosquito the esophagus has three diverticula that serve as reservoirs for sugars. The crop is merely a widened portion of the esophagus in the more generalized forms and serves as a food receptacle. In the more specialized groups, such as adult Diptera and Lepidoptera, the crop is expanded into a capacious pocket or pouch. In such forms as the cockroach and grasshopper the proventriculus consists of a highly muscular dilation provided internally with sclerotized teeth for grinding or straining food. The stomach is a simple sac into which open *gastric caeca*, generally few in number, which are important sources of digestive

enzymes. At both ends of the stomach are located valves that control the flow of the food. Much variation is seen in the length and the degree of convolution of the hind intestines, but usually the three regions—ileum, colon, and rectum—can be located. The *Malpighian tubules*, which vary in number and length in the several groups of insects, empty into the ileum. These are excretory, not digestive organs, but they are often discussed along with the digestive system because of their location in respect to that system.

The *salivary apparatus* consists of a pair of salivary glands, which may be lobed; they are situated usually within the thorax. Generally each gland empties into a *salivary duct* and the two ducts discharge into a common duct that opens into the mouth at the base of the labium. In many species of insects a pair of *salivary reservoirs* is present; these may be located near the opening of the common duct and then present a compound condition, or may be situated on either side of the esophagus at the end of a long slender duct.

Insect Larvae and Pupae. When insect larvae, parasitic or accidental, are encountered in the body of man or beast, confusion may arise because of the wormlike appearance of the invaders; e.g., muscoid fly larvae may be incorrectly mistaken for worms. These larvae are short and plump and have eleven or twelve well-marked segments. Microscopic examination of fragments will reveal tracheal tubules, which are not present in worms. The student of medical entomology must be thoroughly familiar with the immature stages of those arthropods that are or may become pathogenic.

Although the larvae of insects belonging to the order Diptera (flies, mosquitoes, and so forth are characteristically legless and frequently have an undeveloped or poorly developed head, the variations within the order are considerable. *Maggots* of muscoid flies, for example, are usually smooth, with the body tapering to the apparently headless anterior end, which bears hooklike mouth

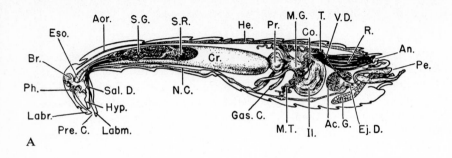

A

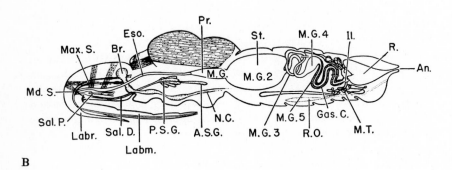

B

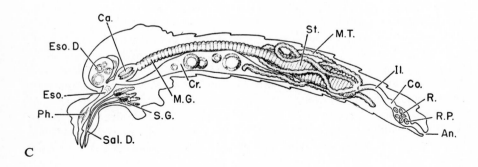

C

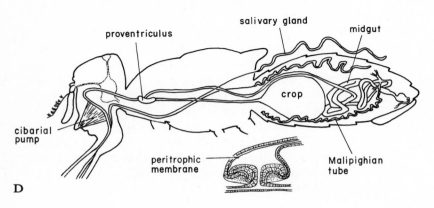

D

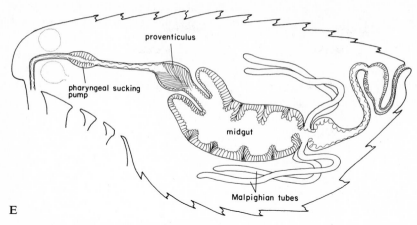

proventiculus

pharyngeal sucking
pump

midgut

Malpighian tubes

E

Fig. 2-6 Showing digestive tract of the cockroach, Order Blattaria (*A*); of assassin bug, Order Hemiptera (*B*); of anopheline mosquito, Order Diptera (*C*); of tsetse, Order Diptera (*D*); and of flea, Order Siphnaptera (*E*). Explanation of abbreviations: *Ac.G.* accessory gland; *An.*, anus; *Aor.*, aorta; *A.S.G.*, accessory salivary gland; *Br.*, brain; *Ca.*, cardia; *Co.*, colon; *Cr.*, crop; *Ej.D.*, ejaculatory duct; *Eso.*, esophagus; *Eso. D.*, esophageal diverticula; *Gas.C.* gastric caeca; *He.*, heart; *Hyp.*, hypopharynx; *Il.*, ilium; *Labm.*, labium; *Labr.*, labrum; *Max.S.*, maxillary stylet; *Md.S.*, mandibular stylet; *M.G.*, midgut; *M.T.*, Malpighian tubules; *N.C.*, nerve cord; *Pe.*, penis; *Ph.*, pharynx; *Pr.*, proventriculus; *Pre.C.*, preoral cavity; *P.S.G.*, principal salivary gland; *R.*, rectum; *R.O.*, reproductive organ; *R.P.*, rectal papilla; *Sal.D.*, salivary duct; *S.G.*, salivary gland; *Sal.P.*, salivary pump; *S.R.*, salivary reservoir; *St.*, stomach; *T.*, testis; *V.D.*, vas deferens. (*A* after Miall; *B* after Elson; *C* after Herms; *D* after Glascow; and *E* after Faarch.)

parts; in contrast, the larvae (*wrigglers*) of mosquitoes have a well-sclerotized, freely moving, conspicuous head with faceted eyes, and both the head and body bear many hairs and setae. The larvae of fleas (Siphonaptera) are also legless; the well-sclerotized head is well developed; and each of the thoracic and abdominal segments is well armed with a band of bristles. The larvae of beetles (order Coleoptera) commonly have three pairs of legs on the thorax only; the head is well developed; the body may be hairy, spiny, or naked. Some beetles larvae are legless. The larvae of moths and butterflies (order Lepidoptera) have three pairs of thoracic legs and two to five pairs of abdominal prolegs; the head is prominent, and the mouth parts are usually well developed and mandibulate; they are called *caterpillars* and are hairy, spiny, or naked. The larvae of bees, ants, and wasps (order Hymenoptera) are without legs (apo-

dous); the head is more or less well developed; the body is usually fairly smooth and gourd-shaped.

Insect pupae are classified as: *Obtect*, in which the appendages are closely appressed to the body and held in place by a tightly fitting envelope, e.g., moths; *exarate*, in which the appendages are free from the body, e.g., many beetles; and *coarctate*, in which the appendages are concealed by an enveloping pupal case, or *puparium*, e.g., the higher flies. The obtect pupa is sometimes, as in many of the Lepidoptera and Hymenoptera, covered by a silky case, or *cocoon*. The puparium of the higher Diptera is formed from the hardened integument of the third stage larva, and encloses the developing pupa; the terms puparium and pupa should not be used interchangeably, as is frequently done. In fact, there is a fourth molt and a fourth instar within the puparium before the formation of the true pupa. The puparium bears the most characteristic features of the third stage larva, such as the feeding apparatus (cephalopharyngeal skeleton and mouth hooks), the spinous bands, and the anterior and posterior spiracles, so identification of the puparium, and consequently the pupa, can be made from these on the same basis as the larva.

Insect Classification. The medical entomologist must be able to place the insect at hand correctly in at least its proper order and family; in the case of insects of importance in medical entomology he should be able to identify most specimens down to species with the aid of keys, illustrations, and descriptions. To determine the order to which an insect belongs one need usually know only the venation and structure of the wings, if present, the type of mouth parts, the type of metamorphosis, and sometimes one or two other structural characters. Unfortunately, the parasitic forms have undergone many modifications such as reduction or loss of wings and great alteration in form, but generally the mouth parts, coupled with a salient character or two, will serve as a ready means of crude identification. Before passing to a list of the orders of insects of medical importance, the usual bases for classification may be tabulated as follows:

1. Wings: (a) presence or absence; (b) form; (c) structure; (d) venation.

2. Mouth parts: (a) biting (mandibulate); (b) sucking (haustellate, of several subtypes).

3. Metamorphosis: (a) primitive (lacking); (b) simple (incomplete); (c) complex (complete).

4. Special characteristics, such as the modification of the ovipositor as a stinging apparatus in the Hymenoptera.

The Orders of Insects. The student may be confused by the fact that different authorities recognize different numbers of insect orders and that, consequently, the assignment of an insect to a particular order may vary with the authority; e.g., some workers consider the cockroaches as constituting a separate order, Blattaria, whereas others consider them a part of the Orthoptera. The following list includes only those insects that are of some known medical importance. For a more complete listing of insect orders and a key to separate them, the student is referred to any good textbook of general entomology or to *Classification of Insects* by Brues, Melander, and Carpenter (1954).

1. Order Collembola (Col-lem′ bo-la) (*colla*, glue, *embolos*, wedge or peg): springtails, snowfleas. Biting mouth parts, withdrawn into the head; primitive metamorphosis; wingless. These animals have a number of peculiarities: the abdomen is only six-segmented, without external genitalia; and appendages of a peculiar nature are present on the first, third, and fourth abdominal segments in the form of a collophore, a catch, and a spring, respectively. Some authorities consider the Collembola a class of Arthropoda separate from the insects.

2. Order Blattaria (Blat-tar′ ia) (*blatta*, insect that shuns the light): cockroaches. Fore wings modified into leathery wing covers, or *tegmina*, often shortened; biting mouth parts; simple metamorphosis. The body is rather flattened dorsoventrally, and the pronotum extends forward over the head, usually concealing it from dorsal view; the legs are fitted for running, the hind femora not being thickened as they are in the jumping Orthoptera.

3. Order Mallophaga (Mal-loph′ a-ga) (*mallos*, a lock of wool; *phagein*, to eat): biting lice. Wingless; biting mouth parts: simple metamorphosis.

4. Order Ephemeroptera (Eph-em′ er-op′ ter-a) (*ephemeros*, living but a day; *ptera*, wings): mayflies, dayflies. Two, sometimes one, pair of triangularly shaped, net-veined, membranous wings; vestigial mouth parts; metamorphosis simple, but involving a preadult, fully-winged form (subimago) found only in insects of this order.

5. Order Thysanoptera (Thy' san-op' ter-a) (*thysanos,* fringe; *ptera,* wings): thrips. Wingless or with very narrow, elongated wings, fringed posteriorly with long hairs, and almost without veins; rasping-sucking mouth parts; simple metamorphosis.

6. Order Anoplura (An' o-plu' ra) (*anoplos,* unarmed; *oura,* tail): sucking lice. Wingless; piercing-sucking mouth parts; simple metamorphosis.

7. Order Hemiptera (He-mip' ter-a) (*hemi,* half; *ptera,* wings): bugs, cicadas, treehoppers, leafhoppers, aphids, scale insects, and others. Wings two pairs (rarely one) or none, either both membranous (Homoptera) or the fore pair thickened only on the basal half (Heteroptera); piercing-sucking mouth parts; simple metamorphosis.

8. Order Trichoptera (Tri-chop'ter-a) (*thrix,* hair; *ptera,* wings): caddisflies. Two pairs of mothlike wings, clothed with hairs (not with scales, as in the moths); biting, though often vestigial, mouth parts; complex metamorphosis.

9. Order Coleoptera (Col'e-op'ter-a) (*coleos,* sheath; *ptera,* wings): beetles, weevils. Fore wings thickened into hardened wing covers, or *elytra* concealing the hind wings when at rest; biting mouth parts; complex metamorphosis.

10. Ordera Diptera (Dip'ter-a) (*dis,* two; *ptera,* wings): flies, gnats, mosquitoes. One pair of wings, the hind pair being replaced by knoblike structures known as halteres; sucking mouth parts; complex metamorphosis.

11. Order Hymenoptera (Hy'men-op' ter-a) (*hymen,* a membrane; *ptera,* wings): bees, wasps, ants, sawflies, horntails, and others. Two pairs of membranous wings (sometimes lacking), the anterior pair the larger; chewing or lapping-sucking mouth parts; complex metamorphosis.

12. Order Siphonaptera (Si'phon-ap' ter-a) (*siphon,* a tube; *aptera,* wingless): fleas. Wingless; piercing-sucking mouth parts; complex metamorphosis. Body flattened laterally; hind legs usually enlarged, fitted for jumping.

13. Order Lepidoptera (Lep'i-dop'ter-a) (*lepidos,* scale; *ptera,* wings): moths, butterflies. Two pairs of wings (rarely absent), clothed with scales; sucking (siphoning) mouth parts; complex metamorphosis.

THE ARACHNIDA

The class Arachnida includes the ticks, mites, spiders, scorpions, and related forms. Among the species of arachnids are some of the most important parasites and vectors of pathogens to man and beast; for example, the ticks, which carry the causative organisms of spotted fever and relapsing fever of man, Texas cattle fever, and bovine anaplasmosis. Parasitic mites cause acariasis, often serious, such as mange, scabies, and various forms of itch, and may, like the ticks, serve as vectors, particularly of the scrub typhus rickettsia.

The more important arachnids lack distinct segmentation of the body, e.g., ticks, mites, and spiders; scorpions, pseudoscorpions, and a few others are clearly segmented. The body is divided into two parts (Fig. 2-7): first the *cephalothorax* (prosoma) composed of combined head and thorax, and second the *abdomen* (opisthosoma). In the ticks and mites there is a strong fusion of the cephalothorax and the abdomen so that the body becomes saclike in form.

Adult arachnids with few exceptions (such as the eriophyid mites, in which only the first two pairs of legs are developed) have four pairs of legs, though the larvae of ticks and most mites have but three pairs. In spiders there is a pair of *pedipalpi,* which may resemble an additional pair of legs; in the scorpions, whipscorpions, and pseudoscorpions these are chelate (that is, the terminal segment of the limb is opposed to the preceding segment, an adaptation for grasping). All arachnids are

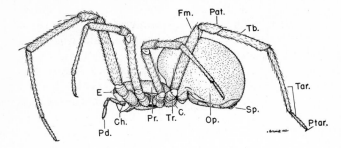

Fig. 2-7 Showing external anatomy of a spider. *C.,* coxa; *Ch.,* chelicera; *E.,* eyes; *Fm.,* femur; *Op.,* opisthosoma; *Pat.,* patella; *Pd.,* pedipalp; *Pr.,* prosoma; *Ptar.,* pretarsus; *Sp.,* spinnerets; *Tar.,* tarsus; *Tb.,* tibia; *Tr.,* trochanter.

devoid of wings and antennae. Eyes, when present, are simple. The mouth parts usually consist of a pair of piercing *chelicerae*, the *pedipalpi*, and in ticks and some mites, a *hypostome*. The respiratory system of many arachnids, particularly ticks and mites, is tracheal as in insects, except that there is usually but one pair of spiracles. In spiders the respiratory organ is a combination of lung books and tracheae. There is frequently a strong sexual dimorphism in the arachnids; the males are commonly smaller than the females.

In general, arachnids are predatory or parasitic, although many mites are plant-feeders or scavengers. Most of them are terrestrial, although aquatic mites are of common occurrence.

Arachnid Development. All orders of Arachnida deposit eggs except for the scorpions and some mites (e.g., *Pediculoides*), which are viviparous. Eggs are usually numerous, particularly in the ticks, which may deposit as many as 18,000 per female. The newly hatched individuals have the general form of adults, although the number of legs may vary, e.g., newly hatched ticks and mites usually have three pairs of legs. Metamorphosis is simple, as in cockroaches and grasshoppers. Molting takes place as in insects, the various stages being termed instars as in the Insecta. The longevity of many arachnids is remarkable: certain ticks have been known to live for as many as fourteen years, and some species are able to endure starvation for several years.

Internal Anatomy. The digestive tract of arachnids (Figs. 2-8, 2-9) is characterized by various types of diverticula and branched tubules. The diverticula, which diverge from the tract between the sucking organ of the pharynx and the mesenteron, range, according to Savory (1935), from two short simple sacs directed forward in the cephalothorax to a condition of five pairs, four of which extend laterally, reaching the bases of the legs and entering the coxae for a short distance; also there is a very complex type that branches and divides and becomes very large. Leading from the mesenteron is a complex system of branched tubules that occupy most of the

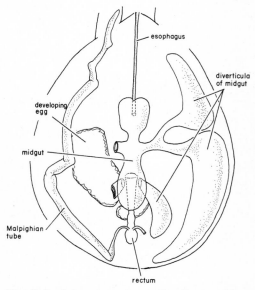

Fig. 2-8 Internal anatomy of spiny rat mite, *Echinolaelaps echidnius.* (After Jakeman.)

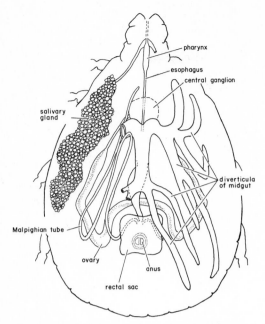

Fig. 2-9 Internal anatomy of *Dermacentor andersoni*. (After Douglas.)

abdomen and function partly as a digestive gland and partly as a reservoir. The Arachnida are thus enabled to store large quantities of food and to undergo long periods of fasting.

The excretory organs of the arachnids are *Malpighian tubules*, which empty into the gut, and *coxal glands*, which empty excretory products into tubules and discharge to the exterior from openings that vary in relation to the coxae among the several orders.

Arachnid Classification. Some authors include among the Arachnida the Pycnogonida (Pantopoda), sea-spiders, the Tardigrada, waterbears, and the Pentastomida (Linguatulida), tongue-worms. These and three small terrestrial orders, namely the Palpigradi, Schizomida, and Ricinulei, as well as the marine Xiphosura, kingcrabs or horseshoecrabs, are omitted from this discussion and from the key to the orders. For a good discussion of these and other arachnids, the student is referred to Cloudsley-Thompson (1958).

The following orders, all terrestrial, may be considered in a classification for the purpose of this work, namely, (1) *Scorpionida*, scorpions; (2) *Araneida* (Araneae), spiders; (3) *Pedipalpida*, whipscorpions; (4) *Phrynichida* (*Amblypygi*), tailless whipscorpions; (5) *Chelonethida* (*Pseudoscorpionida*), pseudoscorpions; (6) *Solpugida* (*Solifugae*), sunspiders; (7) *Phalangida* (*Opiliones*), harvestmen or harvestspiders; (8) *Acarina* (*Acari*) mites and ticks.

Among the more important characters used to separate the terrestrial arachnids into orders are the following: *segmentation* of the body; presence or absence of the *pedicel*; presence or absence of *telson*; *chelicerae*, large or small; *pedipalpi*, chelate or unchelate; location and form of *spiracles*.

KEY TO THE TERRESTRIAL ORDERS OF THE CLASS ARACHNIDA

1. Abdomen distinctly segmented 2
   Abdomen with segmentation obscured . . 7
2. Abdomen with taillike prolongation 3
   Abdomen without taillike prolongation . . 4
3. Tail stoutly armed with a sting at end . . . .
   . . . . *Scorpionida* (scorpions)
   Tail slender, without sting . . . .
   . . . . *Pedipalpida* (whipscorpions)
4. Pedipalpi chelate . . . .
   . . . . *Chelonethida* (pseudoscorpions)
   Pedipalpi not chelate 5
5. Abdomen constricted at base and narrowly joined to the cephalothax . . . .
   . . . . . . *Phrynichida* (tailless whipscorpions)
   Abdomen not constricted at base and broadly joined to cephalothorax 6
6. Legs very long and slender, body hairless, whole body fused together . . . .
   . . . . *Phalangida* (harvestmen)
   Legs moderate, body hairy, appearing to be in three divisions . . . .
   . . . . *Solpugida* (sunspiders)
7. Abdomen constricted at base and joined to cephalothorax by a narrow stalk (pedicel) . . . . *Araneida* (spiders)
   Abdomen fused with cephalothorax . . . . .
   . . . . *Acarina* (ticks and mites)

3

THE FEEDING APPARATUS OF INSECTS AND ACARINA

The entire complex of the feeding apparatus, at the anterior end of the digestive tract, is of importance in understanding the commonest route of acquisition and transmission of pathogens by medically important arthropods. For a working knowledge one needs to know: (1) the structure of mouth parts and their means of penetrating tissues; (2) the pharyngeal or esophageal pumping apparatus that draws up blood or other fluid; (3) the relationship of salivary glands to the mouth parts, and how these structures may be involved in storage and introduction of pathogens; (4) the possi-

bility of regurgitation of infectious fluid from the arthropod's digestive tract into vertebrate tissue or onto the food of vertebrates. At this point discussion will largely be limited to the mouth parts alone, other portions of the feeding apparatus being covered in Chapter 2.

Importance of Mouth Parts. No doubt all insects possessing mouth parts capable of piercing the skin may be regarded as potential vectors of human and animal pathogens, even though bloodsucking is not a normal habit of those insects. Nonpiercing insects obviously cannot introduce pathogens directly into the circulation, but they can do so through natural orifices of the body or through previously injured surfaces. Thus the house fly, which possesses nonpiercing mouth parts, is a vector of *Trypanosoma hippicum* Darling, a blood-inhabiting organism causing murrina of horses and mules. It carries the parasites on its proboscis, which becomes contaminated while it is feeding from bleeding wounds, and conveys the organisms thence to open wounds on healthy animals.

Piercing-sucking mouth parts of insects have the functional portion that actually enters the host developed into a single, often interlocked unit termed the *fascicle*. The fascicle may be separated into its component parts that are called *stylets*. The actual functioning of the fascicle in tissue has been largely a matter of speculation, based on microscopic examination and surmise on the role of each component part, and on histological examination of mouth parts fixed in tissue. Such an approach provided the impression that the fascicle was a relatively rigid structure incapable of much directional control. Techniques developed to actually observe mouth parts within living tissue have shown that the fascicle may be extremely flexible and capable of changing the path of its thrust, and have also clarified the function of individual stylets (Gordon and Lumsden, 1939). By this means it has also become possible to determine the specific site of blood uptake. The use of an electronic device promises further sophistication in recording penetration, salivation, engorgement, and withdrawal (Kashin, 1966).

With respect to the specific site of blood acquisition, Lavoipierre (1965) has proposed the terms *solenophage* for a *vessel feeder* that generally obtains blood directly from venules or small veins, and *telmophage* for a *pool feeder* that obtains blood from a blood pool resulting from the laceration of blood vessels. The method of blood feeding must surely be of consequence in both acquisition and introduction of pathogens. In filariasis there is evidence that the parasites are found at a higher rate in the blood within a mosquito's stomach than in blood withdrawn from animals by puncture in sampling for parasites. Likewise the introduction of a pathogen directly into a blood vessel should ensure its distribution throughout a vertebrate much more rapidly than is possible if release occurs into tissues surrounding vessels.

The medical entomologist will soon find that he must be familiar with the feeding habits of an insect in all stages of its life cycle. Larvae of many sucking insects have mandibulate (biting-chewing) mouth parts. The biting mouth parts of the worm-like flea larva enable it to ingest particles of excrement or other matter in which eggs of the double-pored dog tapeworm occur, and it thus becomes an intermediate host of this worm, retaining the infection as an adult flea, which, if ingested by a suitable host, becomes the agent of infection. Insects with complete metamorphosis frequently change from chewing mouth parts in the larval stage to the sucking type in the adult. Most insects with simple metamorphosis, such as the cockroaches and bugs, have the same general type of mouth parts in all active stages of development, although in the aquatic groups the mouth parts may change considerably from the larval type (dragonflies and damselflies), or become vestigial in the adult (mayflies). Snodgrass (1944) describes in great detail the feeding apparatus of biting and sucking insects affecting man and animals.

Classification of Mouth Parts. All adult insect mouth parts, however highly specialized, have been derived from a simple primitive chewing type such as exists with some modification in the cockroach. Insect mouth parts are commonly divided into two broad classes: (1) mandibulate (biting and chewing) as in cockroaches, grasshoppers, and beetles; and (2) haustellate (sucking) as in bugs, flies, butterflies, and moths. This classification is far too general for a real understanding of function. For example, the house fly, *Musca domestica* Linnaeus, and the stable fly, *Stomoxys calcitrans* (Linnaeus), both possess haustellate mouth parts and are both in the family Muscidae; yet by virtue of its efficient piercing proboscis the stable fly pierces the skin and sucks blood, becoming a direct infector; whereas the house fly cannot pierce the skin because of the structure of its proboscis and is therefore only indirectly responsible for infection, i.e., it is more particularly a food contaminator.

Obviously insects could be grouped on the basis of mouth parts and feeding habits, into (1) piercing, as in mosquitoes, and (2) non-piercing, as in cockroaches. This, however, is too great an oversimplification and provides no information on morphological and detailed functional aspects. For an inclusive classification of arthropod mouth parts Metcalf, *et al.* (1962), should be consulted. A more limited scheme, with examples restricted to medically important arthropods that actually feed on vertebrates or serve as intermediate hosts of parasites is provided here.

1. *Orthopteran type* (biting and chewing): generalized mouth parts consisting of opposable mandibles used in biting and chewing; upper and lower lips easily recognized. Orders Blattaria, cockroaches; Coleoptera, beetles; Mallophaga, chewing lice; and others.

2. *Thysanopteran type* (rasping-sucking): mouth parts minute in size; approaching the biting form, more particularly rasping, but functioning as suctorial organs; the right mandible is greatly reduced or possibly even absent, causing a peculiar asymmetry. Order Thysanoptera, thrips.

3. *Hemipteran type* (piercing-sucking): mouth parts comprising four stylets closely ensheathed within the elongated labium, forming a three- or four-segmented proboscis. Order Hemiptera, true bugs.

4. *Anopluran type* (piercing-sucking): mouth in a sac concealed within the head but evertible when functioning. Three stylets consisting of united maxillae, hypopharynx and labium; mandibles vestigial. Order Anoplura, sucking lice.

5. *Dipteran type* (suctorial and piercing or nonpiercing): no single representative is available to illustrate the entire order Diptera, hence the following subtypes may be recognized.

    a. First subtype: mouth parts consisting of six stylets, loosely ensheathed within the labium; as in the *mosquito*.

    b. Second subtype: mouth parts consisting of six short bladelike structures, four of which are used for piercing and cutting, all loosely ensheathed within the labium; as in the *horse fly*.

    c. Third subtype: piercing stylets reduced to two in number, closely ensheathed within the labium; as in the *stable fly*.

    d. Fourth subtype: mouth parts consisting of a muscular proboscis, not suited for piercing; stylets rudimentary; as in the *house fly*.

    e. Fifth subtype: mouth parts closely related to those of the third subtype, but the haustellum is fitted for piercing the skin; as in the *sheep ked*.

6. *Siphonapteran type* (piercing-sucking): mouth parts consisting of a pair of broad maxillary lobes bearing long palpi, a pair of broad maxillary lacinial stylets; a slender labium with parallel palpi, and a median unpaired stylet, the "epipharynx" (the labrum is difficult to interpret, Snodgrass). Order Siphonaptera, fleas.

7. *Hymenopteran type*: mouth parts consisting of suctorial, lapping organs, mandibles specialized for portage, combat, and other nonfeeding purposes. Order Hymenoptera in part; bees, wasps, and ants.

8. *Lepidopteran type*: mouth parts consisting of a suctorial coiled tube, the maxillary galeae. Order Lepidoptera; butterflies and moths.

STRUCTURE AND FUNCTION OF THE FEEDING APPARATUS

Orthopteran Type. The cockroach may be used to illustrate the orthopteran type of mouth structure. This type, the mandibulate or chewing-biting, is the generalized or primitive form and will serve as a basis for later comparisons and derivations. Its main importance in medical entomology is to furnish a model for understanding the haustellate or sucking types.

If the head of a cockroach (Fig. 3-1) is viewed from the side and again from the front,

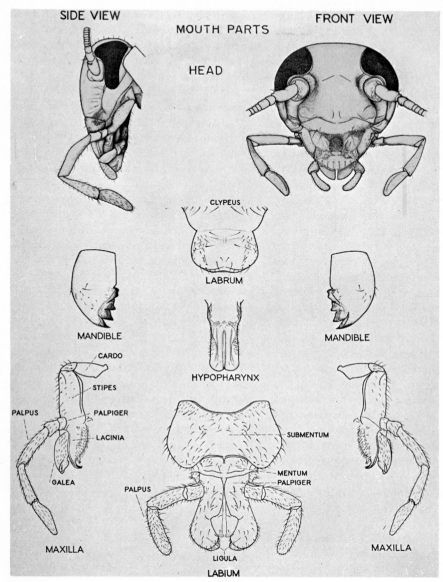

SIDE VIEW   MOUTH PARTS   FRONT VIEW

HEAD

CLYPEUS

LABRUM

MANDIBLE   HYPOPHARYNX   MANDIBLE

CARDO

STIPES

PALPUS   PALPIGER

LACINIA   SUBMENTUM

GALEA

MENTUM
PALPIGER

PALPUS

MAXILLA   LIGULA   MAXILLA

LABIUM

Fig. 3-1   Head and mouth parts of a cockroach. Orthopteron (mandibulate) type mouth parts.

the relative position of the separate mouth parts will be better understood. Separating the individual parts, the following structures will be observed. In front, low down on the head, hangs the *labrum* or anterior lip, easily lifted as one would raise a hinged lid, the hinge line

being at the lower edge of the sclerite or plate known as the *clypeus*.

The labrum functions to draw food toward the mandibles and to cover the anterior mouth opening. In this the labrum is greatly aided by a rough structure called the *epipharynx*, which forms the inner lining of the labrum and clypeus. Because of the close association of these two structures, they are often referred to as a double organ, the *labrum-epipharynx*. Removing the labrum, a pair of heavy, opposable jaws, the *mandibles*, is exposed. These are biting structures par excellence. They are toothed and movable laterally. Dislodging the mandibles brings into view the pair of maxillae, or accessory jaws. These organs are known as *maxillae* (first maxillae). They are composite structures separable into *cardo, stipes, lacinia, galea*, and *palpus*, which should be carefully observed, inasmuch as they undergo great modification in the remaining types of mouth parts. The two supporting sclerites of the maxillae are *cardo* (basal) and *stipes* (the second); the distal lobes are (1) the *maxillary palpus* (a jointed structure) with sensory functions; (2) the *galea* (median and fleshy); (3) the *lacinia* (inner and toothed), capable of aiding in comminuting food.

Underneath the maxillae and forming the floor of the mouth lies the posterior lip or *labium*, a structure frequently called the *second maxilla* because it resembles a pair of maxillae fused at the base. On the same plan as the maxillae, the labium consists of a basal sclerite, the *submentum*, followed by the *mentum*, upon which rest the *labial palpi* (a pair of outer, jointed structures to the right and left), and the *prementum* bearing the *ligula* (a pair of straplike plates that together correspond to the lower lip). The labium functions as the back wall of the mouth opening, and is also subject to much modification in insects.

The fleshy organ still remaining in the mouth cavity after the parts just described have been removed is the *hypopharynx*, an organ of taste comparable in a measure to the tongue of higher animals. The salivary duct enters near the base of the hypopharynx, and in highly modified piercing-sucking mouth parts the salivary duct may be located within the hypopharyngeal stylet.

The mandibles are most useful landmarks because they are almost universally present in insects, from the strong mandibles of certain beetles (Lucanidae) to the vestigial structures of fleas (Siphonaptera). In the Hymenoptera, even though the order is largely haustellate, the mandibles are nevertheless important structures, serving, however, in the honey bee as wax implements and organs of defense, and in the ants as organs of portage, cutting, and combat. In Hemiptera and many Diptera the mandibles are converted into piercing organs, and the maxillae are also greatly changed in form.

Thysanopteran Type. The thysanopteran type (Fig. 3-2) is interesting as it combines the features of biting-chewing and piercing-sucking mouth parts. The very minute thrips, order Thysanoptera, possess this transitional type of mouth parts. Authors disagree as to the identity of the parts; some believe that the right mandible is reduced, others consider it to be entirely wanting, making the head and mouth parts asymmetrical. The left mandible, both maxillae, and the hypopharynx are elongate, suggesting stylets of the piercing type adapted to move in and out through a circular opening at the apex of the head. No food channel is formed, but the sap from plants is lapped up as it exudes from the abraded surface. Thrips are mentioned because they will on occasion be troublesome, biting man when they accidentally land on the skin.

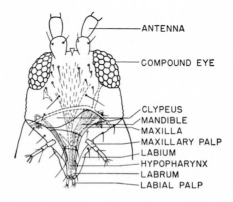

Fig. 3-2 Head and mouth parts of a thrips. Thysanopteran type. (After Borden.)

Hemipteran Type. A very different sort of feeding apparatus from those described previously is found in the order Hemiptera (Fig. 3-3). Here the cylindrical labium forms a prominent beaklike proboscis that is usually three- or four- (rarely one- or two-) segmented. It is devoid of palpi. The proboscis encloses a fascicle comprised of a pair of *mandibles*, often terminally barbed, and a pair of *maxillae*; all four are efficient piercing stylets, the maxillae operating as a unit and the mandibles functioning separately. The maxillae are closely apposed, forming the food and salivary tubes (Fig. 3-3*A*); the mandibles may aid rigidity. The *labrum* is quite short and inconspicuous. The *hypopharynx* consists of a small complicated lobe at the base of the other mouth parts.

Hemiptera, as represented in studies of the triatomine bug *Rhodnius* (Lavoipierre, *et al.,* 1959) and the bed bug *Cimex* (Dickerson and Lavoipierre, 1959), are solenophages. However there is a basic difference in the manner in which the fascicle operates. In *Rhodnius* the barbed mandibles simply anchor into the superficial skin tissue and it is the maxillary bundle that penetrates to enter a blood vessel (Fig. 3-3*B*). The tips of the maxillae also differ in symmetry, one being hooked and the other spiny, so that in sliding on one another a very curved path may be followed through the tissue. In *Cimex* the basic details of mandibular and maxillary construction are quite similar, but the mandibles penetrate deeply into the region of the blood vessels (Fig. 3-3*C*). In triatomines the labium is swung forward from its resting position under the body, but in the act of feeding it does not bend (Fig. 3-3*D*). In *Cimex* the labium folds back at the basal segments. Bennet-Clark (1963) calculated that

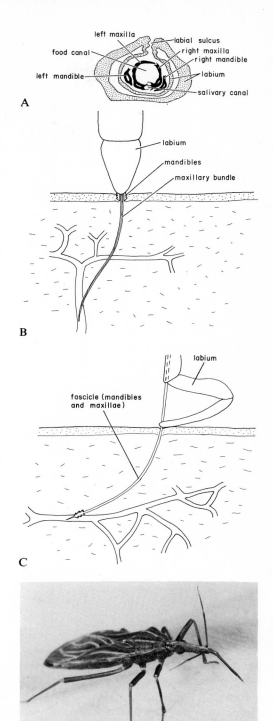

Fig. 3-3 *A.* Cross section of fascicle sheathed in labium of *Rhodnius*. *B.* Maxillary bundle of *Rhodnius* in blood vessel; note mandibles stay at skin level. *C.* Fascicle of *Cimex* penetrated deep into host's tissues. *D. Rhodnius* feeding; note that labium is not bent back. (*A-C* after Lavoipierre and Dickerson; photograph *D* by Roger D. Akre.)

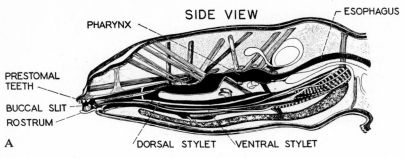

SIDE VIEW

PHARYNX · ESOPHAGUS

PRESTOMAL TEETH

BUCCAL SLIT

ROSTRUM

A   DORSAL STYLET   VENTRAL STYLET

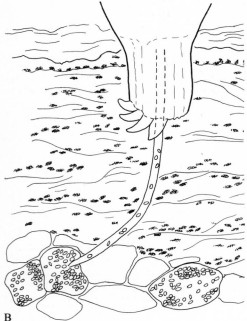

B

Fig. 3-4 *A*. Head and mouth parts of sucking louse. *B*. Fascicle of *Haematopinus suis* in host's tissue. (After Lavoipierre.)

Rhodnius must exert a suction equivalent to at least two atmospheres, possibly as much as nine, to ingest blood at the recorded rate.

Anopluran Type. The mouth parts of the Anoplura (sucking lice) are distinctly piercing-sucking in function, but lie in a sac concealed within the head (Fig. 3-4). The prestomal opening is situated at the extreme anterior portion of the tiny snoutlike proboscis and is encircled with minute sclerotized recurved retractile hooklets, which serve as anchorage when everted. The eversible proboscis is said

to be formed of the *labrum*, which is armed internally with the small recurved teeth just mentioned. The piercing fascicle (three stylets) lies within a long sac and consists of the united maxillae situated dorsally; the *hypopharynx* and the *labium* are attached posteriorly to the walls of the enclosing sac. The mandibles are vestigial. The apposed maxillae form the food duct, and the hypopharynx forms the salivary channel. In the act of biting, these parts are pushed forward into the skin by muscular action when firm attachment has been made by means of the circlet of oral evertible teeth. Salivary secretion is poured into the wound, and the cibarial and pharyngeal pumps draw blood into the pharynx and into the intestine of the louse. In studying the action of the fascicle of the hog louse, *Haematopinus suis*, Lavoipierre (1967) notes that feeding is exclusively from a small blood vessel (solenophagy).

Dipteran Type. The dipteran type of mouth parts is divided into five subtypes: (1) mosquito; (2) horse fly; (3) stable fly; (4) house fly; and (5) sheep ked.

First Subtype, the Mosquito. A generalized type of dipteran mouth parts is found in the mosquito (Fig. 3-5); hence, the maximum number of stylets is present, loosely ensheathed within the elongated *labium*, the whole forming a prominent beak or proboscis. The six stylets represent the two *mandibles*, the two *maxillae* (distinctly serrated distally), the *hypopharynx*, and the *labrum-epipharynx*. The palpi are conspicuous structures in all mosquitoes. These represent the maxillary palpi of the cockroach; the pair of flattened lobelike

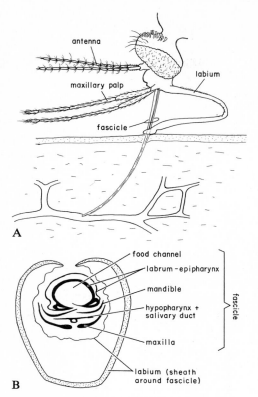

Fig. 3-5 Mosquito mouth parts. *A.* Fascicle thrust deep into host's tissue with labium bent back. *B.* Cross section of mouth parts. (After Waldbauer.)

organs forming the distal portion of the proboscis are said to represent the *paraglossae* and are called the *labella*.

Gordon and Lumsden (1939) observed that the fascicle is highly flexible, and though vessels might be punctured to form a blood pool, feeding takes place from the lumen of a vessel. Earlier authors showed the food channel is formed by the labrum-epipharynx and hypopharynx, but studying the large mosquito *Psorophora ciliata*, Waldbauer (1962) found the mandibles to be interposed between these two structures (Fig. 3-5*B*). He also cited other authors who had observed the same stylet relationship in other mosquitoes. The labium bends back in the act of feeding, and is not inserted into the host's tissue (Fig. 3-5*A*).

Second Subtype, the Horse Fly. Though retaining the same number of mouth parts as the mosquito, the horse fly subtype is characterized by the flattened bladelike condition of the stylets (Fig. 3-6). The *labium* is the conspicuous median portion loosely ensheathing the blades and terminating in a pair of large lobes, the *labella*. The mandibles, movable transversely, are distinctly flattened and saber-like, and the *maxillae* are narrower and provided with conspicuous palpi. Both the *hypopharynx* and *labrum-epipharynx* are lancet-like. In the males these piercing parts are very weakly developed. Mouth parts of simuliids are similar to those of the horse fly.

Studying the fascicle of the tabanid *Haematopota pluvialis* in action in a live host, Dickerson and Lavoipierre (1959) showed that penetration is by means of a thrusting action, with mandibles and maxillae lacerating the tissues. The mandibles move with a scissorlike motion, and the maxillae thrust and retract (Fig. 3-6*C*). The result is a rupture of small and large blood vessels, with the fly feeding on the pool of blood formed in the tissues (telmophagy).

Third Subtype, the Stable Fly. The stable fly subtype (Fig. 3-7) is represented by a group of flies in which the mouth parts are distinctly specialized for piercing. In addition, these flies show, together with the next subtype, to what extent these structures may become modified within the same family of insects.

The proboscis at rest is carried at the position of a bayonet at charge and is therefore provided with a prominent muscular elbow or knee. This conspicuous organ (the proboscis) is the *labium* terminating in the *labella*, which are provided with a complex series of rasping denticles. The proboscis is forced into the flesh of the victim by a strong thrust of the head and body. Within the folds of the labium, and easily removable through the upper groove, lie two stylets: the *labrum-epipharynx*, the uppermost and heavier, and the *hypopharynx*, a lower and weaker one, the two

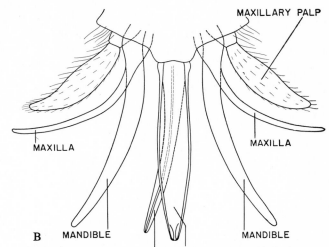

HEAD
SIDE VIEW

ANTENNA   COMPOUND EYE

LABELLA
LABIUM

MAXILLARY PALP

A

LABIUM REMOVED

MAXILLARY PALP

MAXILLA   MAXILLA

MANDIBLE   MANDIBLE
HYPOPHARYNX   LABRUM-EPIPHARYNX

B

salivary canal

hypopharynx

food canal

labrum

mandible

maxilla

C

Fig. 3-6 Mouth parts of a horse fly. *A*. Side view of head. *B*. Mouth parts spread apart. *C*. Diagram showing thrusting and cutting action of stylets. (*A* and *B* after Snodgrass; *C* after Dickerson and Lavoipierre.)

entire structure is highly muscular, and may be either protruded in feeding or partially withdrawn while at rest. Lying on top of the grooved labium is the inconspicuous spadelike *labrum-epipharynx* that forms, with the *hypopharynx*, a sucking tube, supported by the labium. The maxillae have evidently become fused with the fleshy elbow of the proboscis, and only the prominent *maxillary palpi* remain.

On the bottom surface of the labella are lines of open tubes, formed by sclerous partial rings termed pseudotracheae, serving as a sponge through capillary action. The free ends of the pseudotracheal rings may be somewhat abrasive in action as has been noted in the feeding of some species of *Hippelates*.

Fifth Subtype, the Sheep Ked. The sheep ked and other louse flies, members of the family Hippoboscidae, have mouth parts closely related to those of the third subtype, the stable fly; the characteristic tubular or cylindrical haustellum is adapted for penetration into the skin of the host (Fig. 3-9). The

forming a sucking tube supported within the folds of the labium. The maxillary palpi are located at the proximal end of the proboscis. Lavoipierre (1965) states that *Stomoxys calcitrans* (Linnaeus) is a telmophage.

Fourth Subtype, the House Fly. In the house fly subtype (Fig. 3-8) the prominent fleshy proboscis consists mainly of the *labium*, which terminates in a pair of corrugated sponging organs, the *labella*, and is attached in elbowlike form to the elongated head. The

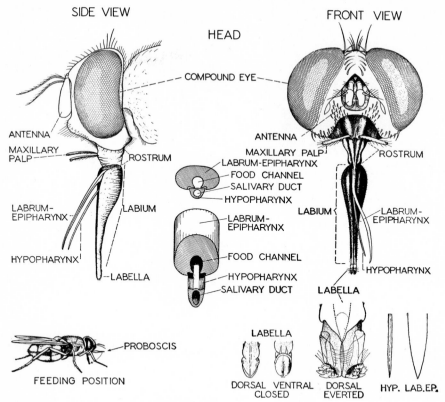

SIDE VIEW

HEAD

FRONT VIEW

COMPOUND EYE

ANTENNA

MAXILLARY PALP

ROSTRUM

LABRUM-EPIPHARYNX

FOOD CHANNEL

SALIVARY DUCT

HYPOPHARYNX

LABRUM-EPIPHARYNX

FOOD CHANNEL

HYPOPHARYNX

SALIVARY DUCT

ANTENNA

MAXILLARY PALP

ROSTRUM

LABRUM-EPIPHARYNX

LABIUM

HYPOPHARYNX

LABELLA

LABIUM

HYPOPHARYNX

LABELLA

PROBOSCIS

FEEDING POSITION

LABELLA

DORSAL VENTRAL CLOSED

DORSAL EVERTED

HYP. LAB. EP.

Fig. 3-7 Head and mouth parts of a stable fly.

labrum-epipharynx is stylet-shaped; its proximal portion is strongly sclerotized and rigid, whereas the distal end is membranous and very flexible (Jobling, 1926). The hypopharynx in two common species, *Pseudolynchia canariensis* (Macquart) and *Melophagus ovinus* Linnaeus, is nearly as long as the combined haustellum and labellum and is a very slender and hyaline mouth part.

Larval Mouth Parts of Diptera. Although not directly involved in transmission of pathogens, two types of larval mouth parts in the Diptera are of interest to the medical entomologist. The more primitive feeding apparatus of mosquito and black fly larvae is involved in removing particulate material from water, a fact that can be used in their control; the mouth hooks of cyclorraphous Diptera are most frequently involved in myiasis.

MOSQUITO AND BLACK FLY FEEDING APPARATUS. In the larvae of aquatic Nematocera the external mouth parts, which are developed for drawing in particulate matter, generally are in the form of brushlike structures that bring a current of water and suspended particles into the pharynx. The significant feature is the development of the pharynx into a pump with internal screens (Fig. 3-10). These screens have closely arranged spacings that permit removal of very fine suspended material (Harwood, 1952).

MOUTH HOOKS OF CYCLORRAPHA. The mouth hooks of maggots are attached to a prominent pharyngeal sclerite (Fig. 13-3). Unlike opposed mandibles that have a biting action, mouth hooks move parallel to each other in a more or less tearing motion. There is some question as to their derivation,

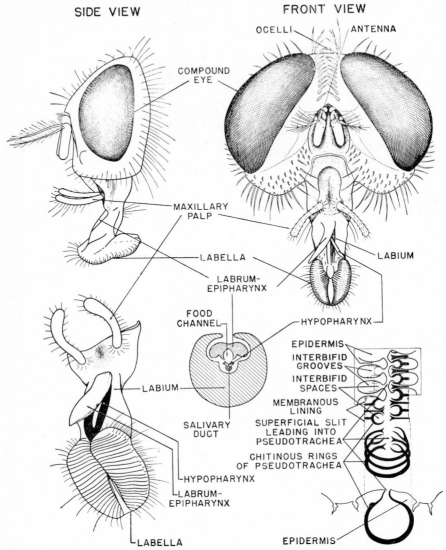

SIDE VIEW

FRONT VIEW

OCELLI — ANTENNA

COMPOUND
EYE

MAXILLARY
PALP

LABELLA

LABRUM-
EPIPHARYNX

LABIUM

FOOD
CHANNEL

HYPOPHARYNX

EPIDERMIS

INTERBIFID
GROOVES

INTERBIFID
SPACES

MEMBRANOUS
LINING

LABIUM

SALIVARY
DUCT

SUPERFICIAL SLIT
LEADING INTO
PSEUDOTRACHEA

CHITINOUS RINGS
OF PSEUDOTRACHEA

HYPOPHARYNX

LABRUM-
EPIPHARYNX

LABELLA

EPIDERMIS

Fig. 3-8   Head and mouth parts of the house fly. Lower right-hand figure shows detailed cross section of a pseudotrachea in the labella.

authors variously considering them to consist of mandibles or fused mandibles and maxillae. Some muscoid larvae, such as *Musca domestica* and *Stomoxys calcitrans*, have only a single mouth hook. In studying the metamorphosis of a fly's head, Snodgrass (1953) states that, if not mandibles, the mouth hooks cannot be homologized with any other structures in insects.

Siphonapteran Type.   The mouth parts of the Siphonaptera (fleas) (Fig. 3-11), though typically of a piercing-sucking type, are peculiar to this order of insects. The broad *maxillary lobes* bearing long palpi are conspicuous landmarks; the other organ (slender) bearing long parallel palpi is the *labium*. The principal bladelike piercing organs are a pair of independently movable structures commonly

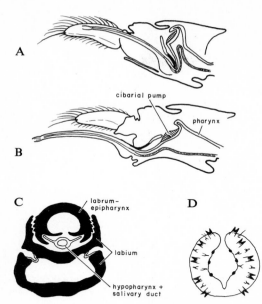

Fig. 3-9 Mouth parts of a hipoboscid, *Pseudolynchia canariensis. A.* Mouth parts retracted. *B.* Mouth parts protracted in the act of feeding. *C.* Cross section of haustellum. *D.* Tip of labellum with prestomal teeth. (After Bequaert.)

referred to as mandibles, but are said by Snodgrass and others to be *maxillary laciniae.* The mandibles are believed to be rudimentary in fleas. The median stylet (unpaired) is said to be the *epipharynx,* not the labrum of many authors, the labrum being difficult to demonstrate. The epipharynx is closely embraced by the lacinial blades. The three stylets that form the fascicle (the pair of maxillary laciniae and the epipharynx) are held in the channel by the labium. The labium is rudimentary, and the existence of a hypopharynx is not demonstrable. The wound is made by the protraction and retraction of the maxillary laciniae. As soon as the blood begins to flow, it is drawn up into the pharynx by the action of both the cibarial and the pharyngeal pump. From studying the fascicle operating within the tissues of a living host, it has been determined that fleas are normally solenophages (Lavoipierre and Hamachi, 1961).

Hymenopteran Type. In the hymenopteran type the two general classes of mouth structures, the *mandibulate* and *haustellate,* find full development in the same species, though the mandibles in many representatives are not involved in the feeding process. The honeybee serves as an example of the fully mandibulate and suctorial condition, details of which may be seen in Snodgrass (1935). A similar full development of mandibulate and suctorial mouth parts is found in vespoid wasps, which have been suspected of contaminant transfer of pathogens on meat, as occurs with the house fly. In ants the mandibles may be greatly developed into effective biting organs.

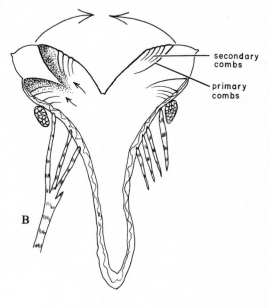

Fig. 3-10 Pharyngeal straining apparatus in mosquito larvae. *A.* Electron micrograph of primary straining combs. *B.* Section across pharynx showing suspended matter strained out on left side.

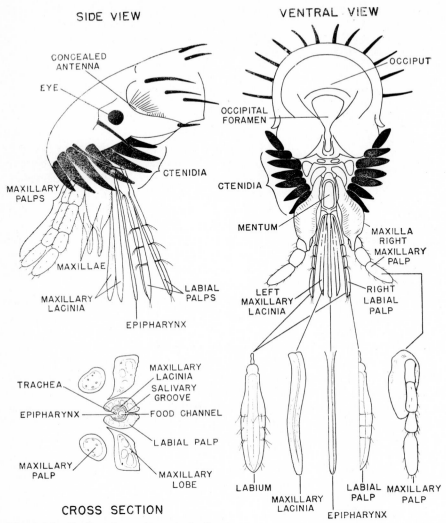

SIDE VIEW

VENTRAL VIEW

CONCEALED ANTENNA

EYE

OCCIPUT

OCCIPITAL FORAMEN

CTENIDIA

MAXILLARY PALPS

CTENIDIA

MAXILLAE

MENTUM

MAXILLA RIGHT

RIGHT MAXILLARY PALP

MAXILLARY LACINIA

LABIAL PALPS

LEFT MAXILLARY LACINIA

RIGHT LABIAL PALP

EPIPHARYNX

TRACHEA

MAXILLARY LACINIA

SALIVARY GROOVE

EPIPHARYNX

FOOD CHANNEL

LABIAL PALP

MAXILLARY PALP

MAXILLARY LOBE

LABIUM

MAXILLARY LACINIA

LABIAL PALP

EPIPHARYNX

MAXILLARY PALP

CROSS SECTION

Fig. 3-11 Head and mouth parts of a flea.

Lepidopteran Type. Represented by ordinary butterflies and moths, the lepidopteran type is typically a coiled sucking tube capable of great elongation. It functions as a siphoning type. Taking the cabbage butterfly, *Pieris rapae* (Linnaeus), as an example (Fig. 3-12), the *labrum* is seen to be greatly reduced, and the mandibles are absent. Mandibles may be weakly present in the lower Lepidotera. The only obvious portions of the maxillae are the galeae, which by close approximation of their inner grooved surfaces form the long, coiled proboscis. The double structure of the proboscis can be easily demonstrated by manipulation. The labium is represented by the *labial palpi*. In eye-frequenting Lepidoptera (see Chapter 5) the typical coiled proboscis is present, but in light of reported irritation of

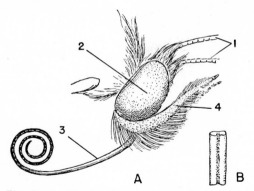

Fig. 3-12 Head and mouth parts of a butterfly (*Vanessa sp.*). *A.* Side view: suctorial coiled tube, Lepidopteran type. (*1*) antennae; (*2*) compound eye; (*3*) proboscis consisting only of galeae; (*4*) labial palpus. *B.* Section of proboscis showing double nature.

eye membranes during the act of feeding the terminal portion should be closely examined for the presence of rasping surfaces.

Arachnid Mouth Parts. In his excellent study of the feeding organs of Arachnida, Snodgrass (1948) points out that arachnids come from an ancestral line that never acquired organs for mastication, and even today have no true jaws, hence are forced to subsist on liquids. A liquid diet requires an ingestion pump, and with all arachnids a highly developed sucking apparatus constitutes an essential part of the feeding mechanism. The *chelicerae* (a pair) are the first postoral appendages of the arachnid (see Chapter 18), and although functioning more or less as "jaws" they are not homologous with the mandibles of insects; they are used for grasping, holding, tearing, crushing, or piercing. In spiders the venom glands are associated with the chelicerae (Fig. 20-18). The leglike *pedipalps* are the second postoral appendages of the Arachnida and are the homologs of the mandibles of mandibulate arthropods (Snodgrass). These organs are modified in various ways, functioning as organs of prehension, protection, and, in male spiders, as sperm-carrying organs. In

the scorpions the pedipalps are chelate and serve for catching, holding, and crushing the prey.

FEEDING APPARATUS OF TICKS. According to Snodgrass, the lobes or processes often associated with the distal part of the hypostome (Fig. 3-13) are the only features that cannot be homologized with structures present in other Arachnida. It is generally believed that the chelicerae serve as cutting structures that gain entrance, and the recurved spines of the hypostome serve as an anchoring device. According to Sutton and Arthur (1962), three phases of feeding consist of (1) blood entry, (2) lymph and tissue liquefaction by salivary secretion, and (3) hemorrhage to produce blood. Extensive laceration of blood vessels is characteristic of feeding by argasid ticks, the result being that feeding occurs rather rapidly from a pool of blood (Lavoipierre and Riek, 1955).

Ixodid ticks, while feeding, characteristically remain attached for a longer time than do argasids. Gregson (1960) showed that in *Dermacentor andersoni* Stiles attachment was aided by cementing with a free-flowing white fluid, presumably from the salivary glands (Fig. 3-13), though he later observed (Gregson, 1962) that at least some of the salivary fluids produced are sucked back with alternate withdrawals of blood. It was confirmed in *Ixodes ricinus* (Linnaeus) that salivary gland extracts have anticoagulant and edema-producing properties (Foggie, 1959); also, copious salivary fluid production (increasing the likelihood of introducing pathogens) may be a means of excreting excess water (Tatchell, 1967).

FEEDING APPARATUS OF MITES. The mouth parts of mites resemble those of ticks. In mites possessing a hypostome, that structure is not armed with teeth. Among trombidiform mites the chelicerae become progressively adapted for piercing by a transformation of the movable digits into hooks or stylets (Fig. 19-19). Mites tend to feed on lymph and tissues other

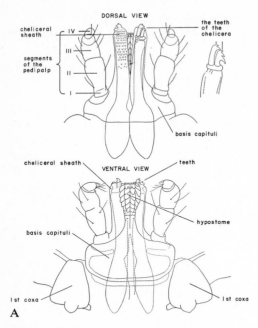

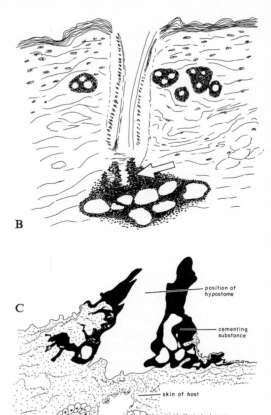

Fig. 3-13 Mouth parts of tick. *A*. Overall view. *B*. Section of mouth parts in host's tissue, showing feeding on a pool of blood at arrow (after Lavoipierre and Riek). *C*. Cementing substance that holds mouth parts of *Dermacentor andersoni* against host's skin (after Gregson).

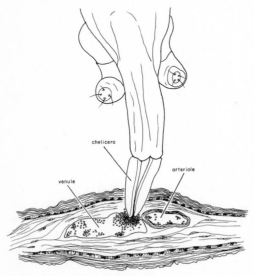

Fig. 3-14 The mite *Chiroptonyssus* feeding in bat wing membrane. (After Lavoipierre.)

than blood. Trombiculids remain attached for some time, and around the inserted mouth parts a feeding tube or *stylostome* forms. The stylostome is thought to be developed in part from host tissue reactions, but by feeding through artificial membranes its source is shown to be a fluid (salivary?) introduced by the mite (Schumaker and Hoeppli, 1963; Cross, 1964). The macronyssid mite *Chiroptonyssus*, feeding in bat wing membrane as the adult female, teases a hole in the wall of a small venule and feeds rapidly (Fig. 3-14); as the protonymph it feeds for a prolonged time on tissue fluids before likewise feeding from a venule (Lavoipierre, 1968).

4

EPIDEMIOLOGY

application of techniques for determining and controlling vector populations.

Vectors are intimately associated with both pathogens and vertebrate hosts, and these associations must be understood. What is desired is a comprehension of those factors that make an arthropod (vector) susceptible to receiving and maintaining a pathogen in the first place, and what will then allow the vector to transfer the pathogen to the host under study, be it man or domestic or wild animal. The development of parasitism among medically important arthropods and the mouth parts for feeding on a host, both important for the success of vectors, are discussed in Chapters 3 and 5.

VECTORS

Epidemiology is that branch of medicine that treats of epidemic diseases; the breaking out, suddenly and more or less unpredictably in a particular area, of a disease that affects many individuals at the same time. In its broadest sense the study of epidemiology consists of a more or less applied ecology, wherein all factors of the natural history of a disease are of interest. In the area of medical entomology such a broad view includes the biology and behavior of vectors as well as the study of pathogens. A further important area of medical entomology encompasses the learning and

Vectors, as used here in the simplest sense, are those arthropods that are capable of transmitting a pathogen that causes disease. Mere capability, however, is of little significance in understanding how an arthropod-transmitted pathogen is maintained in any specific place at times of high or low incidence.

It is useful to distinguish between primary vectors—primary in the sense of principal responsibility for infecting man or other animals whether or not they show clinical evidence of disease—and secondary vectors that may normally be unimportant, but assume significance during outbreaks or during proximity of the host under unusual circumstances. These distinctions can be illustrated by the occurrence of malaria in an area where many species of *Anopheles* mosquitoes are present, yet frequently a single species proves to be principally responsible for transmission. In such a case other vector species may be very susceptible to *Plasmodium* development, but under existing conditions they are secondary because of infrequent contact with man. That such conditions may change is shown by the acquisition of a primary role in malaria transmission by *Anopheles sacharovi* Favre and *Anopheles hispaniola* (Theobald) in Sardinia following eradication measures against the former primary vector, *Anopheles labranchiae labranchiae* Falleroni (Aitken and Trapido, 1961). A primary vector that may not be responsible for clinical disease in humans could be illustrated by a mosquito that maintains an arbovirus in its basic cycle in wildlife.

In addition to simply verifying many arthropods as being of medical importance, further studies have identified a number of factors useful for evaluating the potential of a given species. Some of those factors bear discussion.

INCRIMINATING THE VECTOR

In instances where a disease of unknown cause is occurring, certain general characteristics help identify it as arthropod-borne. The time of occurrence, nearly always immediately following a time of great arthropod growth and activity, is a common clue. Even in cases where an arthropod harbors a pathogen throughout the year, there will be no transmission without active feeding, and diseases resulting solely from the attack or presence of arthropods occur at high rates only when the stages proximal to man are at peak numbers.

The environment in which a disease occurs provides further clues. Characteristically many arthropod-associated diseases are connected with wilderness areas, or areas disturbed by agriculture or deforestation, though urban concentrations of humans near such areas may be affected. Malaria, scrub typhus, and diseases transmitted by ticks fit within this general description. By contrast, however, diseases such as plague, yellow fever, dengue, St. Louis encephalitis, and typhus may have characteristic urban foci.

Due to prior information amassed in the field of medical entomology, in most cases an investigator has some indication of the likely vector or vectors of a disease. This may be due to recognition of the pathogen as one known to be arthropod transmitted. The site of feeding may be diagnostic; marks in the form of characteristic welts or more long lasting lesions at the site of attack, as occur with the bites of triatomine bugs, chigger mites, ticks, and black flies, can provide important clues. A persistent lesion caused by the pathogen itself at the site of feeding is characteristic of certain diseases such as cutaneous leishmaniasis, anthrax, scrub typhus, and tick-borne typhus.

In addition to the broad geographic coincidence of a disease and its vectors, identification of specific *temporal and spatial overlap* will help pinpoint the vector. Temporal coincidence occurs when a vector is observed to build up to maximum numbers, with a proportion of the population infective at a period just prior to the time the disease is at its highest incidence (Fig. 4-1). In most arthropod-borne diseases the interval between successive vertebrate infections includes the incubation period of the disease-producing organism in a vector before it is capable of transmission, and an incubation period in the vertebrate host before disease is expressed. A more specific temporal coincidence is

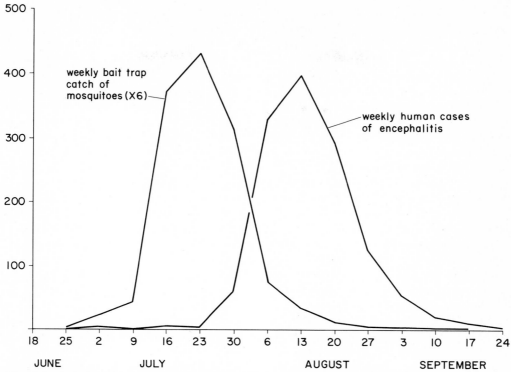

Fig. 4-1 Relationship between mosquito vector populations and Japanese encephalitis. (After Barnett.)

present if a vector is found to be active at the time of day the host is most readily attacked. Spatial coincidence relates a characteristic zone of activity of the vector with its host, such as tsetse flies in a thicket transmitting trypanosomes between mammalian hosts found there, arboreal mosquitoes transmitting yellow fever virus among monkeys, or *Anopheles* mosquitoes entering dwellings to transmit malaria.

Barnett (1960) lists the basic criteria for incriminating a specific arthropod with transmission of the causal agents of disease. Briefly stated these are (1) demonstration of feeding or other effective contact with the host under natural conditions, (2) a convincing biological association in time and/or space of the suspected arthropod species and occurrence of clinical or subclinical infection in the host, (3) repeated demonstrations that the arthropod, under natural conditions, harbors the

infectious agent in the infective stage, (4) transmission of the agent under controlled conditions.

Experimental Transmission. Transmission of a pathogen by an arthropod under laboratory conditions to any susceptible animal is another means of incriminating vectors. However, transmission under such conditions can really help only to delimit potential vectors; to show those potentially capable of transmission. Suspect vectors may be exonerated if transmission proves impossible experimentally, though for leishmaniasis it has frequently been difficult to obtain experimental transmission. Difficulty in transmission as suggested by low titer of pathogen, or prolonged developmental time before transmission will occur, can reveal suspect arthropods as probably being of insignificant importance in nature. When experimental transmission occurs readily with a vector not found where the disease occurs, the danger of introducing an infected host into its range is clear. Insight into various complications of arthropod transmission of viruses can be gained by reading the reviews of Hurlbut (1965), Day (1955), and Chamberlain and Sudia (1961).

In ordinary transmission tests a naturally infected animal, or one infected by injecting a pathogen, is fed on by suspect arthropods. These presumably infected arthropods are then permitted to feed on other susceptible animals, generally first allowing the pathogen time to develop to the extent that it is in sufficient quantity to be infective on biting (*the extrinsic incubation period*) or is at high level in the feces or other fluid products, such as coxal fluid of argasid ticks. Since arthropods do not regulate their body temperature, environmental temperature during the incubation period greatly influences the length of incubation. Once the presumed infectious arthropod has fed or otherwise infected the host, the latter is then observed for the appearance of characteristic clinical evidence or other evidence of infection.

Rather extensive facilities may be required if the normal route of accession and transmission of pathogens by feeding of a vector is attempted. Such facilities can include quarters for rearing arthropods as well as a variety of host animals. A compilation of colonization and mass rearing procedures for arthropods by Smith (1966), as well as one developed for vectors by the World Health Organization (1964, "Symposium on culture procedures for arthropod vectors and their biological control agents." *Bull. WHO* **31**:433–622) is most useful.

Methods have been developed to cope with cases where the arthropod will not feed readily on a host in the laboratory. Thin membranes, usually derived from animal structures, or fine cloth fabrics, have been found suitable for feeding arthropods upon infectious materials (Tarshis, 1958). The infectious materials are mixed with attractive substances such as blood or sugar solutions, and are usually made more acceptable by warming to simulate the temperature of a mammal or bird. A variant of this procedure has been to place a capillary tube of infectious fluid over the stylets of *Phlebotomus* and mosquitoes (Hertig, 1927), or the hypostome and chelicerae of ixodid ticks (Burgdorfer, 1957). Introduction of pathogens into the terminal end of the gut has been used to infect *Glossina* with trypanosomes and various arthropods with arboviruses. Almost certain acquisition of viruses, rickettsiae, and bacteria is possible by direct introduction into the hemocoele. This latter procedure bypasses the gut and therefore does not really incriminate a vector if successful.

RELATIONSHIPS OF VERTEBRATE PATHOGENS TO VECTORS

The great number and variety of vertebrate pathogens transmitted by arthropods suggests a longstanding relationship. These pathogens are generally well adapted within the vector, causing no measurable adverse effects, but pathogenicity is noted in some instances, a matter discussed further in Chapter 5.

There is increasing interest in identifying those factors that make blood- or tissue-feeding arthropods suitable for development of a specific pathogen. Anatomical features are easily conceived of as being significant, yet in few cases are structural characteristics known to be of importance. Physiological differences, whereby the vector host is specifically suited to meet nutritional, respiratory, and other requirements of the pathogen, are readily visualized, but are also difficult to prove. By and large the available evidence is suggestive rather than irrefutable.

Gut Morphology and Susceptibility. The digestive system and its associated structures are anatomical features of particular interest. It has been shown repeatedly that bypassing the gut by injections of viruses, rickettsiae and bacteria into the hemocoele will permit development of a transmissible titer within the arthropod at a much lower dose than is required by acquisition through the normal digestive tract route. As an example, Řeháček (1962) found 21 per cent of *Ixodes ricinus* (Linnaeus) to transovarially transmit the pathogen of Central European tick-borne encephalitis after direct inoculation, in contrast to only 3.3 per cent of females fed on viremic mice.

Other examples of gut morphology in relation to susceptibility of a vector to a vertebrate pathogen are known or have been suggested. In tsetse flies the peritrophic membrane must be transected or bypassed by trypanosomes to gain access for passage through the midgut wall. It was suggested that the nature of the peritrophic membrane, particularly its mechanical resistance, might affect susceptibility, explaining why recently emerged flies are more readily infected (Wijers, 1958). Further studies have shown that the trypanosomes pass through the fluid secretion that forms the peritrophic membrane (Fairbairn, 1958) (Fig. 2-6*D*). A similar relationship has been surmised for mosquitoes and other Diptera (Stohler, 1961). Likewise the oocysts of malaria develop on the midgut, and resistance or susceptibility to infection may be ascribed to this structure in mosquitoes (Howard, 1962). Proventicular spines in the gut of the flea *Xenopsylla cheopis* (Rothschild) are prominent structures (Fig. 17-4) that are the site of blockage by plague bacilli, with resultant back pressure forcing pathogens into the tissues of the vertebrate host during the act of feeding.

VARIABILITY OF VECTORS IN ACQUIRING AND MAINTAINING VERTEBRATE PATHOGENS

Within a species of vector arthropod there may be great variations in its role within different geographic areas. Close observation has generally proved such variations to be due to behavioral differences or basic differences in susceptibility to establishment of the vertebrate pathogen. Ultimately genetic differences have further been shown to be present, often to the point of differentiating subspecies, but even in the absence of so distinct a genetic isolation it is possible to show natural variance in susceptibility and to develop changed susceptibility by selection. The whole problem of genetics of vector susceptibility to establishment of vertebrate pathogens is reviewed by Macdonald (1967).

Behavioral changes of vectors, some of which are discussed in Chapter 6, may occur in response to selection. The variety of vertebrates fed upon by a vector species is highly dependent upon the kinds of hosts available, and behavioral characteristics of a vector strain will greatly affect its efficiency as a vector. Insight into such behavioral relationships may be gained from Mattingly's article (1962) on mosquito behavior in relation to disease eradication programs.

PHYSIOLOGY OF THE VECTOR

Many physiological characteristics of arthropods have been studied in those of medical importance. In fact the blood-feeding habit serves as a tool for studying such features as digestion, nitrogenous excretion, and hormonal mechanisms. Certain physiological findings discussed here have contributed to an understanding of the importance of vector species.

Age Grading Studies. Longevity during the blood-feeding stage of a vector insect is an important consideration in determining its potential. In general the longer the life span of a species that does not continuously infest a host, the better is its chance of acquiring and transmitting a pathogen. This is so from the standpoint of number of hosts fed upon, and from the fact that most pathogens require an incubation period within a vector before they can be transmitted.

Various external signs, though of poor

specific accuracy, provide evidence of longevity. These signs of wear can be used to advantage with more accurate methods in that they are rather easily seen. As examples a recently emerged insect is perfect in its scale and setal covering, and its color pattern is distinct. Within a few days of active life many scales and setae are lost and colors may become comparatively dull. Further aging is characterized by wear of the tips and back edges of wings in flies and mosquitoes, and the spur like ctenidial combs of fleas may become worn or broken off. Corbet (1960) has discussed some of the readily utilized external characters of mosquitoes, showing that aging techniques can be greatly accelerated with little loss of accuracy if some screening by external characteristics is used before applying techniques requiring dissection.

Obviously, except in cases of transovarial carryover, a vector must feed more than once to transmit a pathogen. Many arthropods, such as ticks and lice, feed on blood as a sole source of food so that the achievement of growth beyond the earliest postembryonic stage automatically implies blood feeding has occurred. However, blood feeding in the adult stage, generally for the purpose of egg development, is characteristic of vectors such as most bloodsucking Diptera. It is this relationship of blood meals to egg development that has proved of specific value in age grading. A complicating factor is *autogeny*, a condition whereby a proportion of a vector population can develop a first batch of eggs without a blood meal. This phenomenon is known for many bloodsucking arthropods; it is a genetically controlled characteristic that requires ideal nutritional and environmental conditions for maximum expression, and it is controlled by hormonal factors (see Clements, 1963, and more recent authors).

After a blood meal the ovaries of most adult female insects increase greatly in size, with shrinkage after oviposition. The ovarian tissues thereby undergo changes that are permanent and diagnostic in determining whether any egg development (*parous*) or no egg development (*nulliparous*) has occurred.

Permanent changes in fine endings of tracheoles coincide with advanced ovarian development. As with insect tissue in general, the ovaries are supplied with tracheoles to meet the oxygen requirements of cellular respiration. Tracheolar proliferation into the cellular sheath of the ovaries is particularly rich to meet high oxygen requirements during the growth of eggs. The increase in size of oocytes to form fully developed eggs permanently stretches the knotlike endings of fine tracheoles within the ovarian tissue. Thus, unraveled or stretched tracheolar endings indicate the parous condition, whereas knotted endings are typical of nulliparity (Fig. 4-2). Another indication of parity that is quickly recognized is the finding of eggs that are developed but have failed to be laid and may be partially or entirely unresorbed (*relict eggs*). Parity, because of the complicating factor of autogeny, does not always mean that blood feeding has occurred.

Numbers of Blood Meals. Further information on the significance of a vector species can be gained by learning how many times individuals feed on blood. Again specific evidence is found within the ovary. Oocytes develop sequentially within ovarian tubes (ovarioles). In most blood-feeding insects only the basal oocyte within each ovariole develops with a blood meal, and generally a single blood meal is sufficient to mature one series of basal oocytes, though there are cases where more than one blood meal between ovipositions is common. As the oocyte expands to form a mature egg it stretches the epithelial sheath surrounding the ovariole. After oviposition the flaccid epithelium of the sheath in each recently functional ovariole shrinks, leaving a small knot like dilatation, termed the corpus luteum (reminiscent of the same named structure in the vertebrate ovary, though not known to have a similar hormonal function). The number of dilatations on the ovariole corresponds to the number of previous ovipositions (Fig. 4-3).

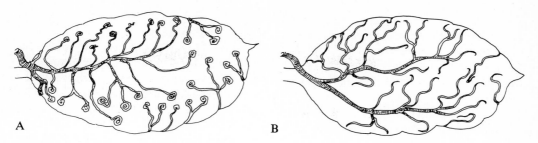

Fig. 4-2 Tracheole changes in mosquito ovaries as a consequence of ovarian development and egg laying (after several authors). *A.* No ovarian development has occurred (nulliparous) and tracheole endings remain in tight coils. *B.* Eggs have been laid (parous) and tracheole endings are permanently stretched.

Ovarian dilatations are not always usable as an indicator of blood feeding. Autogeny will cause a first dilatation. Also in certain species of vectors successive dilatations cannot be observed.

Colless and Detinova have been very instrumental in the development of these methods and the latter has prepared a monograph (1962) and a review article (1968) that analyze their

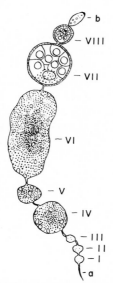

Fig. 4-3 Diagram of ovariole from a multiparous mosquito. Dilatations I through VI are decreasingly old tissue remains from prior ovipositions. Items VII and VIII are undeveloped oocytes. *b* is the germarium. (Courtesy of World Health Organization.)

utility in Culicidae, Simuliidae, Tabanidae, Ceratopogonidae, and other insects. Even where a corpus luteum is difficult to discern, as in *Anopheles gambiae* Giles, a small cord of interfollicular tissue indicates previous ovarian developments (Lewis, 1957).

With the proven utility of these earlier findings, changes in ovarian structure, fat body cells and pigmentation, digestive tract cells, and clarity of the halteres have been shown to indicate parity in many groups of medically important arthropods, including some that do not feed on blood. A representative listing includes ticks (Rasumova, 1962), cockroaches (Plyater-Plokhotskaya, 1962), cyclorraphous Diptera (Anderson, 1964), Hippoboscidae (Saunders, 1964), and fleas (Kosminskii, 1960).

Colless (1958) has shown that information derived from parity studies can indicate changed survival rates; of particular significance during control campaigns. In his hypothetical situation a knowledge of any three of the following criteria permits calculation of the fourth: (1) daily survival rate, (2) days from emergence to first feed, (3) days taken to develop eggs up to first deposition, and (4) item three plus days from oviposition to the next feed.

In studying the possibility that overwintering females of the mosquito *Culex tarsalis* Coquillett comprised the mechanism for survival of encephalitis viruses, it was evident that actual isolations of viruses were rare and at best the exception rather than the rule. This was fully confirmed by studies of Burdick and Kardos (1963) and Nelson (1964), which showed on the basis of ovarian structure that blood feeding in the overwintering mosquito population was rare.

Survival Under Difficult Conditions. The vast variety and abundance of insects and related arthropods attest to their many adaptations for survival under often harsh environmental conditions. Certain of these adaptations, namely cold and drought resistance, autogeny, and prolonged starvation relate to pathogen survival in the vector as well as the overall problem of vector activity and size and potential survival of vector populations. The onslaught of insecticides is increasingly a feature of the vector's environment, and adaptations to this situation are mentioned in Chapter 6.

Though hematophagous arthropods (and the pathogens they transmit) are often thought to be characteristic of tropical zones, they may also be extremely abundant at northern latitudes. In such cases feeding activity is restricted to the spring through late summer period, or infrequently occurs in the warm habitations of man in winter. Winter survival of arthropods is generally accomplished by cessation of growth, a condition known as *diapause*. Diapause may be typified by a prolonged period in an immature stage, or by reproductive cessation in the adult condition. In cases where only a single generation per year is found, as at extreme north and south latitudes (see Downes, 1965), diapause is said to be *obligatory*. At mid northern and southern latitudes (approximately 35–65 degrees) multiple generations are possible, and cessation of growth after a few generations is referred to as *facultative* diapause. In these latter cases the arthropod responds to environmental clues such as lowered temperatures of autumn or shortened day length. Further information on the subject of diapause can be obtained from Lees (1956), cold hardiness from Salt (1961),

and photoperiodism from Danilevskii (1965) and Wilde (1962).

The winter survival of ticks and adult mosquitoes has been most thoroughly investigated to determine whether pathogens they transmit are maintained during this season. General aspects of the life history of these arthropods are discussed in the sections on their biology, but a summary of the diapause condition is appropriate here.

Most species of *Culex* and *Anopheles* mosquitoes overwinter as inseminated adult females. Soviet investigators (see Danilevsky, 1965, and Clements, 1963) have found that preparation for winter in these species is characterized by increased fat body size as a response to short day length. There is either no blood feeding, or blood utilization results in increased fat rather than ovarian development (gonotrophic dissociation). In a study of photoperiod-induced diapause of the *Anopheles maculipennis* complex in Russia, lots from 65–40 degrees north latitude commenced diapausing in the extreme north at 20.25 hours, in the extreme south at 12.5 hours; approximately 1 to 1.5 hours change in critical photoperiod for each five degrees change in latitude (Shipitsina, 1959). In North America *Culex tarsalis* Coquillett (Harwood and Halfhill, 1964; Anderson and Harwood, 1966) and *Anopheles freeborni* Aitkin (Depner and Harwood, 1966) respond to day length, the latter showing latitudinal variation. Japanese *Culex tritaeniorhynchus* Giles likewise diapauses in response to short photoperiod (Bullock, *et al.*, 1959). Photoperiod length is also the key factor in egg and larval diapause in the North American treehole mosquito *Aedes triseriatus* (Say) (Baker, 1935; Love and Whelchel, 1955).

Most *Aedes* mosquitoes overwinter in the egg stage, having a single generation in northern and alpine regions with short summer periods, and several generations where prolonged summer high temperatures prevail. In the Soviet Union diapause initiation and termination of *Aedes caspius dorsalis* (Meigen) is affected by photoperiod and temperature (Khelevin, 1959), and in California *Aedes nigromaculis* (Ludlow), *Aedes dorsalis* (Meigen) (Telford, 1963), and *Psorphora confinnis* (Lynch-Arribálzaga) (Gunstream, 1965) show a temperature-diapause relationship.

The same species of mosquito may have quite different environmental adaptations in different regions. Büttiker (1959) found that in the cold climate of Afghanistan *Anopheles culicifacies* Giles precedes winter inactivity (*hibernation*) by blood feeding resulting in fat body development and cessation of ovulation; in eastern India, where winters are mild, there is a semi-hibernation with repeated blood meals converted to fat; in northern Ceylon and central Burma summer inactivity (*aestivation*) begins at the start of the dry season. In North America adult activity of *Culiseta inornata* (Williston) is confined to summer in Canada, to spring and autumn in the northern United States, and to winter in the southern United States and Mexico (Horsfall, 1955).

Some confusion accompanies studies of adult reproduction of the tick *Dermacentor marginatus* (Sulz.) in the Soviet Union. This univoltine species appears to undergo an obligatory diapause that is eliminated after cold exposure whatever the previous conditions of diapause (Belozerov, 1964).

Adaptations to hot and dry climates are largely behavioral, with activity of vectors confined to a period of likely encounter with a host, or to times when temperature and humidity are favorable. Behavioral and physiological changes are undertaken by arthropods in dry environments because their small size and relatively large surface area make desiccation an acute problem (Edney, 1957). A few examples will suffice as illustrations. The mosquito *Aedes vittatus* (Bigot) breeds in rockholes. In northern Nigeria it was found that its eggs resist desiccation at normal temperature for at least ten weeks, indicating sheltered rock holes should permit survival in a relatively dry season (Boorman, 1961). Rozeboom and Burgess (1962) studied

survival of several mosquito species during extended drought conditions in Liberia. In their investigation of plant cavities and banana leaf axils there was evidence that *Aedes simpsoni* Theobald could survive as larvae in the minute film of water on opposing surfaces of the leaf base and trunk. In Tanzania the mosquitoes *Anopheles gambiae* Giles and *A. pharoensis* Theobald rest during the day in low vegetation, and in soil cracks especially during the dry season (Smith, 1961). In Central America the mosquito *Sabethes chloropterus* (Humboldt) can survive, feed, and transmit yellow fever virus over many weeks, explaining maintenance of this disease through the dry season (Galindo, 1958). The desert-inhabiting argasid tick *Ornithodoros savignyi* (Audouin) of South Africa is very susceptible to desiccation, but digs itself into deep sand under large, shady trees (Theiler, 1964).

Hematophagous arthropods for the most part require frequent blood meals. However, many of those associated with mammalian burrows, dens, or bird roosts, have evolved an ability to withstand prolonged starvation. This phenomenon is discussed further in Chapter 5.

Blood Meal Sources. One means of determining the significance of a potential vector in maintenance and spread of a given disease is the identification of its blood meal sources. Where the disease is present such information not only verifies that a potential vector feeds on the host animal in question, but also other identified blood meals can suggest where the pathogen is being acquired or maintained.

Both general and specific techniques are required to successfully determine blood meals. It is first of all desirable to obtain fresh blood, generally recognizable as still being red in color rather than a brownish to blackish cast. As blood becomes digested it progressively loses its distinctive morphological and antigenic properties. The morphological characters of blood cells are only of general use; nucleated red blood cells are those of birds, reptiles, or amphibians and enucleated erythrocytes are from a mammalian source.

Proteins in the blood serum contain specific antigens. According to the sensitivity of the type of test employed, as well as the specificity and diversity of the antisera prepared, it is possible to identify blood down to a closely related group of animals, or in some cases even to species of origin. The general reliability of immunological methods is indicated by their increasing use by taxonomists to determine relatedness of animals, and by the flourishing field of immunochemistry.

A normal procedure for blood source determination is to inject blood serum from a donor animal into a host animal whose immunity mechanisms will respond (become sensitized) by forming antibodies. The immune serum then reacts to specific antigens in a characteristic way, such as precipitation, when mixed with even small amounts of blood serum from the same or a related sensitizing species of animal. Experience is required to distinguish nonspecific responses that may occur. Rabbits or guinea pigs have been used extensively to produce precipitin antisera, but Tempelis and Lofy (1963) have found chickens to be more satisfactory for providing a wide range of specific antisera. Procedures and their interpretation require more background than can be appropriately dealt with here though the interested student can consult texts or the excellent review article by Weitz (1960).

Another development is the "inhibition test" procedure (Weitz, 1956). In this method erythrocytes of a normal rabbit are coated with tannic acid and then sensitized with the serum of the animal tested for. These cells are agglutinated by the corresponding antiserum and this reaction is specifically inhibited by the serum of the homologous species. Under suitable conditions the serum proteins of the blood meal inhibit the reaction, thus the specific inhibition of agglutination by a blood meal extract indicates the identity of the blood.

Weitz has published a number of papers utilizing this method to determine the blood meal source of tsetse flies.

One particular shortcoming to be avoided is bias in obtaining arthropods with a fresh blood meal. A freshly engorged arthropod usually seeks secluded resting places, often near its recent blood meal, for the blood to digest and eggs to mature. It is a natural human failing to obtain engorged arthropods where they are most easily collected, but more diligent generalized searching is required to identify all types of hosts fed on in an area. For example, a preponderance of engorged mosquitoes resting within a cattle shelter will usually contain cattle blood, those within houses will contain human blood.

Terms have been developed to identify the preferred blood source of vectors. *Anthropophilous* (Gr. *philos*, loving) or *anthropophagous* (Gr. *phagein*, eat) species of arthropods are those that are attracted to feed on man, *zoophilous* forms (generally meaning mammal-feeders) prefer other animals, and *ornithophilous* arthropods prefer birds. *Exophagous* species usually feed outdoors, and *endophagous* species enter houses or other man-made shelters to feed.

Reeves (1965) has discussed studies that determined the vertebrates providing blood meals for the mosquito *Culex tarsalis* Coquillett, particularly as they might serve to infect the vector with western and St. Louis encephalitis viruses. Although the mosquito will feed on almost any vertebrate in its environment, in most circumstances it feeds by preference on avian hosts. In areas highly endemic to these viruses as much as 84 per cent of blood meals are from birds, and where other vertebrates are fed on extensively their low virus titer appears to disrupt serial transmission of virus.

POPULATION STUDIES

Awareness of the kinds and numbers of medically important arthropods within a given study area is of paramount importance. The objectives are (1) to identify all suspect vectors, (2) to gain some idea of the relative numbers of each species, and (3) to determine whether populations are relatively stable or in a state of flux. Increasing numbers of vectors may alert one to the imminent development of an epidemic. In vector control programs, and particularly during eradication campaigns, a fairly continuous estimate of population size is needed to indicate the measure of success.

Collecting Methods. Many techniques, each with particular utility for specific situations, have been developed for collecting medically important arthropods. In the case of ectoparasites it is generally sufficient to capture and examine vertebrate hosts; ectoparasites may then be obtained by brushing them off their hosts, causing them to let loose by using anesthesia such as ether, or by washing them off with detergent solution. For actively flying or crawling arthropods a standardized trapping procedure such as light trapping may be used, but it has the drawback of capturing an excess of irrelevant insect material that must be sorted out. Methods that capitalize on specific behavior or attraction to a host are more discriminating but require time and effort during capture, or require maintenance of vertebrate hosts.

Surveys of other than the bloodsucking stage of development can be useful. For example, in mosquito control it is common practice to determine the presence of the aquatic larvae and pupae, particularly as this is the stage against which control measures are most frequently directed. Knight (1964) has evaluated mosquito larval survey procedures.

The specific behavior of arthropods is sometimes utilized. Hard-shelled ticks (Ixodidae) frequently climb onto grass and low shrubs to transfer to passing hosts (Fig. 4-4). They may be collected by *flagging*, dragging coarse cloth such as flannel, to which they cling, through the shrubs. Many mosquitoes

rest in shaded environments during the day, and can be surveyed by placing artificial shelters and capturing the resting individuals. A variety of such shelters have been developed, such as wooden nail kegs, artificial huts, earth-covered barrels, and artificial pit shelters. A foot-square wooden box painted red with one open side has proved simple and effective for many species. In surveying for the presence of *Aedes aegypti* (Linnaeus), particularly where the populations are low, placing containers with water where they can oviposit is helpful; by this means fewer man-hours are needed than in trying to capture adults and presence of eggs or larvae in the placed containers indicates the need to search for obscure natural breeding sites (Fay and Eliason, 1966). Likewise, artificial containers have been developed to determine numbers of treehole-breeding mosquitoes.

A variety of light traps has been designed to sample flying insects. In mosquito surveys

Fig. 4-4 A questing tick, *Dermacentor andersoni,* waiting on a blade of grass to attach to a host. Orientation may also be upside down. (Photograph by Roger D. Akre.)

the New Jersey light trap (Fig. 4-5) is widely used. It has an incandescent bulb as attractant and a fan to draw nearby insects down into a killing chamber. Tests to determine the optimum fan suction and size of bulb indicate that for some species the light itself provides little attraction, and though bright lights are more attractive (Barr, *et al.*, 1960) the sixty watt size is commonly employed. As with insects in general, bright moonlight is competitive and will lower light trap catches (Provost, 1959). Black light traps employing a fluorescent tube with high ultraviolet output are very successful with many insects but have little advantage for mosquitoes. However, black light traps have proven very attractive for some ceratopogonid bloodsucking midges and black flies.

A portable battery-operated modification of the New Jersey type of light trap has proved to be extremely useful for arbovirus surveillance (Sudia and Chamberlain, 1962). This particular design has a live trapping chamber so that the catch can be used to determine the presence of vertebrate pathogens.

Traps for flying bloodsucking insects may be baited with various hosts to yield specific information on host preference, as well as

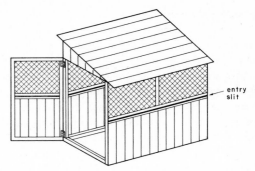

Fig. 4-6 Magoon trap, usually baited with a calf or other large animal. (Courtesy of World Health Organization.)

data to provide an index of the population attracted. One widely used design is the Magoon or stable type trap (Magoon, 1935) (Fig. 4-6), which is essentially a large screened cage having side entrance baffles. Magoon traps are often baited with a calf or donkey. Smaller baffle entrance traps have proved useful in studying host preference in the wild. Lumsden (1958) developed a trap that permits insects to be attracted to a host and then at predetermined intervals draws them by suction into a trapping chamber. A striped and moving black and white visual pattern with suction is useful for species attracted largely by vision (Haufe and Burgess, 1960). One type of experimental trap permits use of animal attraction, moving visual patterns, or light, but is more for research use than routine surveys (Harwood, 1961).

Carbon dioxide is produced during the normal respiration of vertebrate hosts. It has been used, particularly in the form of dry ice, to attract many bloodsucking arthropods and has been especially effective for certain species of mosquitoes. The amount of carbon dioxide released can be a selective factor determining which mosquito species will predominate in the catch. Reeves (1953) studied the effect of three carbon dioxide release rates, those equivalent to the amounts produced by chicken, by man, and by cow or horse. Three species of mosquitoes were attracted somewhat differently to the three release rates.

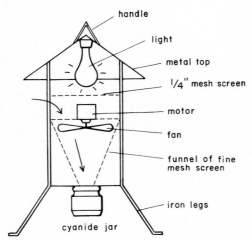

Fig. 4-5 A New Jersey light trap. (Courtesy of World Health Organization.)

Specific methods permit assessment of the presence and numbers of flies that breed in organic matter. For filth-breeding flies an attractant such as meat is used, over which an upward pointing screen cone funnels departing insects into a trap chamber. Fly resting sites called grids are another means of rapidly assessing populations of house flies and filth-infesting flies (Scudder, 1947).

All trapping procedures have some bias with respect to where and how the trapping is done. Such bias may be intentional and therefore useful, as with malaria studies that employ traps to capture mosquitoes entering huts to determine endophily of vectors; but if general information is sought less discriminating traps or procedures should be used. In comparing relative attractiveness of various hosts or baits, the traps used may be evenly spaced on a slowly rotating turntable, thus eliminating bias of immediate position. Turntable procedures have been profitable for studying mosquitoes and eye gnats (Dow, 1959; Mulla, *et al.*, 1960). The Malaise trap, a trap that has sidewalls and a funneling top of fabric or screen has proven extraordinarily successful with a great variety of flying insects (Marston, 1965). Breeland and Pickard (1965) collected twenty-seven of twenty-nine known species of mosquitoes in western Kentucky by Malaise trap, in comparison to nineteen, sixteen, and thirteen species by light trap, biting collection, and resting site examination, respectively. Other flying bloodsucking insects would likely be similarly sampled by Malaise traps. Moving nets indiscriminately sampling insects flying in a given zone have been used on a rotating axis to capture mosquitoes, or mounted on a driven vehicle to sample *Culicoides*, mosquitoes, and other flying insects (Bidlingmayer, 1961; Sommerman and Simmet, 1965).

As can be noted, from the variety of trapping methods mentioned, the procedure employed depends on the species of vectors sought and the objectives of the capture. Effective attractants and traps are of prime importance, and if

an analysis of infected vectors is sought it will be necessary to use a method that obtains a live catch.

When sampling data have been collected various statistical procedures may be employed if the goal is to indicate population size and trends. One common objective is to obtain a relative index of population size, a sort of running seasonal and yearly account of trends.

Absolute population size estimates are sometimes desired, and may be obtained most accurately by marking and releasing a known number of insects, recapturing and identifying the proportion of marked to unmarked individuals to proportionally calculate the absolute size of the population. This is an oversimplified description of what is known as the *Lincoln index*, widely used in estimating absolute numbers of all kinds of animals (see Morris, 1960). Statistical methods for population estimates may be referred to in Watt (1962).

Marking Methods. Marking procedures identify insects released from, or known to have developed in, a given area. Radioactive isotopes or dyes are most commonly used. Isotopes of phosphorus (P^{32}) and sulfur (S^{35}) are useful because of high specific activity, moderate half-life (14.3 and 87.1 days respectively), availability, and widespread occurrence of their natural analogs in insect diets. Tagging may be by surface treatment, but there is a likelihood of loss by wear and contamination of originally unmarked material. Addition of isotopes to the diet as practiced with screw worm and mosquito larvae incorporates radioactivity internally and is therefore more long lasting. Tagging procedures and other uses for radiosotopes in ecological and biological studies are reviewed by Jenkins (1962).

Surface staining is advantageous because radioactive monitoring equipment is not required to identify marked individuals, and permits that control the use of isotopes are not necessary. The proper kinds of dyes are needed, however, to minimize loss by wear and to not interfere with normal insect activity. Liquid fluorescent stains or dye powders have proved useful, although determining stained arthropods requires a dark area and an ultraviolet light source. Reeves, *et al.* (1948), used fluorescent markers to determine the flight range of a number of mosquitoes, and Bailey and Baerg (1967) used dyes to study the flight range of *Anopheles*.

Mobility and Rate of Spread. In determining the necessary limits of control procedures, and for quarantine purposes, the mobility of insect vectors must be determined. The problem of transport of vectors through man's activities is discussed in Chapter 6.

Information on natural spread is gained by inference (for example by knowing certain insects are outside their breeding sites) or by marking and releasing from a specific area and then recapturing at known distances from release. Both methods have yielded greater flight distances than originally supposed. One must distinguish between these distance records, which are rather like Olympic sports records, and average dispersal. Under any circumstances the natural movement of vectors will bring arthropod-borne pathogens into uninfected centers.

Inferential methods have yielded some surprising distances of spread. W. D. Haufe (Canada Department of Agriculture, personal communication to Harwood) has found species of *Aedes* mosquitoes such as *dorsalis* Müller, *flavescens* (Müller), *campestris* Dyar and Knab and *pionips* Dyar far from known breeding grounds as a consequence of atmospheric convections; likewise, records for *Culiseta alaskaensis* (Ludlow) at Fort Churchill, Manitoba, indicate dispersal at least 300 miles in association with weather disturbances along the polar front; and a similar situation pertains to *Aedes punctor* (Kirby) and *A. hexodontus* Dyar. Horsfall (1954) observed *Aedes vexans* Meigen to migrate 90 to 230 miles from Wisconsin to Illinois in a weather front situation. Garrett-Jones (1962) attributed

a 1959 malaria outbreak in widely separated Israeli settlements to migrations of *Anopheles pharoensis* (Theobald) from the Nile delta, a maximum possibility of 175 miles. Migrations of salt marsh mosquitoes in the southeastern seaboard of the United States are well known, *Aedes taeniorhynchus* (Wiedemann) in Florida dispersing into populated areas at least sixty miles away (Harden and Chubb, 1960).

Specific marking procedures have shown spread by flight may be rapid and encompass great distances. A study in Lake County, Oregon (Eddy, *et al.*, 1962) recaptured marked muscoid flies five miles from release in less than two hours.

Determining the Proportion of Infected and Transmitting Vectors in a Population. In epidemiological studies of specific diseases it is necessary to know what proportion of naturally occurring vectors are infected in addition to estimates of population size. For all pathogens other than viruses the vectors may be dissected and parts examined by compound microscopy, provided pathogens are present in sufficient numbers. Thus in malariology the salivary glands and midguts of *Anopheles* mosquitoes are examined for sporozoites and oocysts, respectively (Figs. 11-18 and 11-19), trypanosomes are sought in the salivary glands and digestive tract of tsetses (or digestive tract of triatomine bug vectors), *Leishmania* are looked for in the salivary glands and digestive tract of *Phlebotomus* sand flies, and microfilariae are searched for throughout the body of their dipteran vectors (Fig. 12-4). Fresh dissection and examination is desirable, but when large numbers are encountered storage by freezing has shown promise for later assessment of malaria in mosquitoes (Ward, 1962).

Pathogens that do not require achievement of a specific developmental stage to be pathogenic may be found by grinding individual or pooled vectors in diluents. The suspensions are then injected into intact susceptible hosts such as suckling mice, guinea pigs, or chick embryos, which are subsequently observed for typical clinical evidence of disease. Similarly, such suspensions may be introduced into susceptible tissue culture systems, which are then observed for cytopathological effects. These techniques have been most helpful in determining if vectors are infected with viruses and rickettsiae. It is beyond the scope of the present discussion to indicate differences found by site of injection, use of splenectomized hosts, titer of infectivity, and other complications that must be understood to properly utilize these methods. The interested reader should consult articles and textbooks in immunology and virology.

In surveying for numbers of infected vectors, particularly in studying viruses, wild-caught vectors are collected and ground while fresh, or stored at temperatures well below freezing until processed. The number of vectors in a group, known as a *pool*, is recorded. Each pool is preferably composed of a single species, or species as closely related as identification at the time of collection will allow. A pool of vectors is triturated in a diluting fluid of physiological saline and serum or other blood protein product. Antibiotics generally are added to reduce bacterial contamination, and the suspension is injected into susceptible hosts or distributed in tissue cultures. Statistical treatment, as outlined by Chiang and Reeves (1962) for mosquito vector populations, permits estimation of infection rates.

The actual transmission rate in nature is a more important fact to be known than the infection rate alone. Reeves, *et al.* (1961), described a method for determining this item in encephalitis virus transmission, using single-night exposures of susceptible chickens in traps. By this method the risk of virus infection of susceptible hosts can be ascertained.

Where direct visual observation of pathogens within a vector is difficult, as with rickettsiae and viruses, the fluorescent microscope and specific fluorescent antibody conjugates (immunofluorescence) have proved useful (Burgdorfer and Lackman, 1960). Although these methods are promising they require further development before they will find routine use. In this technique soluble specific antibodies for a known pathogen are combined with fluorescent compounds, and such conjugated antibodies are flooded over vector or vertebrate host tissues. After rinsing, any concentrations of fluorescing substance, as observed by fluorescent microscope, indicate the presence of pathogens (Fig. 18-25).

Methods used for determining salivary gland sporozoite infection rates of *Anopheles* are treated in textbooks on malariology. Because individual mosquitoes must be dissected and examined, and actual infection rates may be very low, as many as two to three thousand dissections may be required for an accurate assessment. Transmission rates are usually seasonally variable, making it advisable to examine collections made several times in a year. The World Health Organization has prepared a number of pertinent publications, the two volume treatise printed in 1963 entitled *Practical Entomology in Malaria Eradication* (WHO/PA/62.63) being very useful.

Vector Effectiveness. In all natural situations where arthropods transmit pathogens there are primary or major vectors, sometimes limited, to be sure, to a specific geographic area. Much effort has been directed toward analyzing those factors that make a given species or strain of singular importance in a particular disease situation. Through epidemiological and laboratory investigations it has been possible to identify factors that predilect a vector to play a primary role. Factors known to be of importance are listed below.

1. *Pathogen Receptivity.* Except in cases of mechanical transmission a vector must be able to support the pathogen, though such support may not always have to be efficient. The pathogen must develop (filariae) or multiply (most pathogens), and be suitably concentrated to cause infection when introduced into a vertebrate host. The vector's contribution to pathogen development then, is to provide a suitable physical and chemical milieu.

The vertebrate host also provides a developmental medium, but in the vertebrate immunity develops whereas infection is lifelong in most vectors. As an example the efficient malaria vector, *Anopheles gambiae* Giles, is particularly receptive to human *Plasmodium*. The genus *Anopheles* includes the only vector for the pathogens of human malaria, and tick vectors of relapsing fever spirochetes may be suitable for only specific strains of the pathogen.

2. *Host Specificity.* Pathogens causing diseases exclusive (or nearly so) to a specific vertebrate host, such as human malaria and filariasis, are best transmitted by vectors that feed preferentially on such hosts. There are many cases known where *Anopheles* mosquitoes will readily develop the pathogens of human malaria, but they do not serve as natural vectors because of their preference for feeding on livestock. Also in North American mosquito-transmitted arboviruses the normal hosts are birds, and man or other susceptible mammals are only tangentially involved when fed on by infective vectors. Thus factors that increase feeding of vectors on susceptible hosts are of prime importance. Pathogens that develop in a number of vertebrate hosts may have wide host range arthropods as principal vectors. The argasid ticks *Ixodes persulcatus* Schulze and *Ixodes ricinus* Linnaeus have proved to be potent vectors of tick-borne encephalitis complex viruses, which they transmit to a great variety of rodents, birds, intermediate sized and large mammals, and man.

3. *Longevity.* Except in cases of transovarial and transstadial transmission, as occurs with mites and ticks, a vector must feed more than once to transmit pathogens. Basic to this requirement is the need for a vector to live for a sufficient period of time. MacDonald (G. MacDonald, 1957) has emphasized the importance of vector longevity in malaria transmission, a situation reasserted by Garrett-Jones and Grab (1964). In addition to a minimal longevity required for transmission, maximal longevity permits vectors to serve as essential parts of the reservoir, well illustrated by relapsing fever and ticks (see Chapter 18).

4. *Frequency of Feeding.* Vector-host contact of a frequent nature may increase the effectiveness of a vector, though frequent contact can adversely affect vector survival. In mechanical transmission of anthrax and tularemia by tabanid flies the frequent interruption of feeding by the host, due to irritation, is a factor aiding the spread of these diseases. Likewise, a flea with digestive tract blocked by plague organisms will feed many times before death, increasing its chances of feeding on more than one host. One factor making *Anopheles gambiae* Giles an effective vector is the fact that this mosquito will seek a blood meal in the same night it oviposits, whereas other vectors may wait a day or more before refeeding after oviposition. Such rapid refeeding is of no consequence until after the incubation period in the vector is completed, and if the first blood meal is not infectious the likelihood that a vector will function is markedly reduced.

5. *Mobility.* The ease with which a vector makes contact with a number of hosts, to provide opportunities for feeding, is significant in determining its effectiveness. Superior mobility aids in the rapid dissemination of disease over a wide area so that it is not as limited and focal in nature. Mobility is obvious in insects with good flying ability, but may also be a characteristic of wingless ectoparasites such as fleas, lice, mites, and ticks that are distributed by the mobility of their hosts.

6. *Numbers.* Sheer population density, enormous numbers making contact with susceptible hosts, will permit some vectors that are otherwise poor hosts to a pathogen to be of significance. Such is clearly the case in certain instances of active malaria transmission. For example *Anopheles culicifacies* Giles in South India and *A. albimanus* Wiedemann and *A. aquasalis* Curry in Central America have been shown to be principal vectors of malaria plasmodia through density of populations, even though salivary gland infections

proved to be less than one per thousand dissections. Additionally, when large numbers of a vector are present the chance of feeding on, and infecting other than, the preferred hosts is increased; of great consequence in mosquito transmission of North American encephalitis viruses.

7. *Physiological and Behavioral Plasticity.* Under the pressure of insecticides used extensively in control schemes, successful vectors have been those that developed the ability to resist destruction by physiological (biochemical) and behavioral means. Such ability generally is found to be under genetic control. This problem is dealt with more thoroughly in Chapter 6.

ARTHROPOD-TRANSMITTED PATHOGENS

Parasitism among arthropods places them in frequent, intimate, and often dependent association with vertebrates. This has resulted in the transmission of a wide variety of pathogens. The better-known agents transmitted by arthropods can be grouped as follows:

1. **Protozoa**

    a. *Entamoeba histolytica* Schaudinn, the dysentery amoeba, along with other non-pathogenic intestinal protozoa, may be transmitted by contamination between fecal sources and foodstuffs by cockroaches and muscoid flies. These and other contaminative pathogens are usually transferred by routes involving poor sanitation, and arthropods usually play only a minor role.

    b. Sporozoa blood parasites of man and many other higher vertebrates, such as *Plasmodium* species transmitted by *Anopheles* to man, and by many mosquitoes to other vertebrates. Others include *Babesia* and *Theileria* transmitted to large domestic animals by ticks, *Hepatocystis* of monkeys transmitted by *Culicoides*; *Leucocytozoon* species of fowl transmitted by black flies and *ceratopogonid* midges, *Haemoproteus* of birds transmitted by hippoboscid flies.

    c. *Trypanosoma* blood flagellates of man, domestic animals, and other vertebrates transmitted by tsetse flies and triatomine bugs; tabanid flies (mechanically), by fleas to rodents, and by the sheep ked to sheep.

    d. *Leishmania* transmitted by *Phlebotomus* to man, dogs, rodents, and other wild vertebrates.

2. **Helminths**

    a. Various insects, mites, and crustaceans serve as intermediate hosts of tapeworms (Cestoda), flukes (Trematoda), roundworms (Nematoda), and spiny-headed worms (Acanthocephala). Filth flies and cockroaches may convey helminth eggs on the body surface or in the digestive tract.

    b. Vectors of filarial worms of man and other vertebrates. Mosquitoes and *Wuchereria* and *Brugia*; tabanid flies and *Loa*, ceratopogonid midges and *Acanthocheilonema*, simuliid flies and *Onchocerca*.

3. **Bacteria** (Terminology according to Dubos and Hirsh, 1965)

    a. Mechanical contamination by filth flies of food poisoning *Shigella* and *Salmonella*; and the spirochete *Treponema pertenue* of yaws by *Hippelates* gnats. Mechanical transmission by bite of *Bacillus anthracis* (anthrax) by tabanid flies, and *Francisella tularensis* (tularemia) by the same.

    b. Bacteria multiplying within a vector and transmitted in the act of feeding. The plague organism, *Pasteurella* ($=$ *Yersinia*) *pestis*, transmitted by fleas. Some twenty-two "species" of *Borrelia* (relapsing fever spirochetes) transmitted by *Ornithodoros* ticks; tick transmission of the tularemia organism. *Bartonella bacilliformis* (Oroya fever and verruga of man) transmitted by *Phlebotomus* sand flies.

4. **Rickettsiae;** microorganisms somewhat intermediate between bacteria and viruses that multiply only in cells of susceptible species

(except *Rickettsia quintana*). The grouping used is adapted from that listed by Hoogstraal, 1967:

a. Typhus group

1. Louse-borne typhus, caused by *Rickettsia prowazekii*, transmitted by the louse *Pediculus humanus* to man. A zoonosis with a tick-mammal cycle is known.

2. Murine typhus, *R. mooseri*, transmitted by fleas from rats to man.

b. Spotted fever group (Lackman, *et al.*, 1965)

1. Rocky Mountain spotted fever, *R. rickettsi*, transmitted by ticks. Siberian tick typhus, *R. siberica*, of man and domestic and wild animals, transmitted by ticks.

2. Boutonneuse fever, *R. conorii*, of man and dogs, transmitted by ticks. Maculatum agent, *R. parkeri* (closely related to *R. rickettsi*), found in livestock and ticks.

3. Rickettsialpox, *R. akari*, of domestic and wild rodents and man, and the mite *Liponyssoides sanguineus* (Hirst). Queensland tick typhus, *R. australis*, transmitted to man by ticks.

4. Eastern Montana agent (*R. montana*) and Western Montana agent, two apparently nonpathogenic rickettsiae isolated from *Dermacentor* ticks.

c. Scrub typhus, *R. tsutsugamushi*, transmitted to man and rodents by trombiculid mites.

d. Trench fever, *R. quintana*, found in man and the body louse.

e. Q fever, *Coxiella burnetii*, primarily a zoonosis acquired by various contaminant routes, but also transmitted to man by ticks and known from other arthropods.

5. **Viruses**

a. Transmission of poliomyelitis virus by filth flies and cockroaches; Coxsackie viruses and Echoviruses and possibly trachoma virus by filth flies. Mechanical transmission of myxoma virus (myxomatosis) of rabbits and avian pox virus by blood-sucking arthropods.

b. Arboviruses; arthropod-borne viruses transmitted by hematophagous arthropods. These produce viremia in one or more vertebrates, multiply in a blood-feeding arthropod, and are transmitted by the infected arthropod upon feeding. The more than 200 arboviruses described are classified by a combination of immunological characteristics and epidemiological grounds such as circumstances of isolation and effects on laboratory animals and tissue cultures. They have usually been named by geographic site of first isolation, general geographic distribution, vector from which isolated, or native name for the disease produced. The groupings, initially developed by Casals and Brown (1957), are reviewed in Horsfall and Tamm (1965), and Melnick and McCombs (1966):

1. Group A: All mosquito-transmitted. Antigenic subgrouping into complexes is possible.

a. Semliki forest virus, Mayaro virus, chikungunya virus, o'nyong-nyong fever.

b. Venezuelan equine encephalitis (VEE), Pixuna, Mucambo.

c. Western encephalitis (WE), Sindbis, Aura.

d. Miscellaneous: includes Eastern encephalitis (EE), Middelburg, and Ndumu.

2. Group B: Mosquito- and tick-borne viruses. Immunologically related groupings are:

Mosquito-Borne

a. Yellow fever.

b. Dengue; four types recognized.

c. St. Louis encephalitis (SLE), Japanese encephalitis (JE, JBE), Murray Valley encephalitis (MVE), West Nile virus, Ilheus virus.

d. Wesselsbron virus of sheep, also affecting humans.

Tick-Borne

e. Tick-borne encephalitis (TE, Russian spring-summer encephalitis, RSSE). Louping ill (primarily of sheep), Omsk hemorrhagic fever, Kyasanur Forest disease (KFD), Powassan virus.

3. Group C: Mosquito-borne viruses causing disease of man, but neither serious illness nor epidemics. Nine entities described from Brazil, Panama, and Trinidad, and antibodies in man found in Africa, Puerto Rico, and the U.S.S.R. Named Apeu, Caraparu, Itaqui, Madrid, Marituba, Marutuca, Nepuyo, Oriboca, Ossa.

4. Miscellaneous: Antigenic relationships place some 100 viruses of man, domestic, and wild animals into eighteen subgroups, and more than forty-five into an ungrouped category. The better known diseases include *Phlebotomus* fever; African horse sickness, and bluetongue of sheep transmitted by ceratopogonid midges; Colorado tick fever, Crimean-Central Asian hemorrhagic fever (Hyalomma tick fever), and Quaranfil fever transmitted by ticks; Rift Valley fever of cattle and sheep transmitted by mosquitoes; California encephalitis group transmitted by mosquitoes.

Pathogen Development in Arthropods. Basically, as Chamberlain and Sudia assert (1961), vectors transmit pathogens mechanically or biologically. In mechanical transmission the vector is no more than a carrier that transmits with contaminated mouthparts. Rather obviously the act of feeding in itself should permit some degree of success in mechanical transmission by any blood-feeding arthropod, provided a vertebrate-infective stage of the pathogen is acquired. Arboviruses provide excellent examples of mechanical transmission as a consequence of interrupted feeding. Chamberlain and Sudia showed that the mosquito *Aedes triseriatus* (Say) infected

chicks with eastern (equine) encephalitis virus, after brief feeding on viremic chicks, with about the same degree of success as a jab with an infective pin. Although this is an artificial situation, it points out the consequences of disrupted feeding. Mechanical transmission is the normal, and apparently only, method of transfer for myxoma virus by a variety of vectors, and avian pox virus by mosquitoes.

In biological transmission the arthropod serves a necessary role in the growth or development of the pathogen. By far the greater number of arthropod-transmitted diseases of vertebrates are transmitted biologically. Further complexities of biological transmission have been listed by Huff (1931) as:

1. *Cyclo-propagative Transmission.* The causal organisms "undergo cyclical changes and multiply" in the body of the arthropod, as in the transmission of malaria plasmodia by anopheline mosquitoes and in the transmission of *Babesia bigemina* of Texas cattle fever by the Texas fever tick, *Boophilus annulatus*.

2. *Cyclo-developmental Transmission.* When the causal organisms "undergo cyclical change but do not multiply" in the body of the arthropod, transmission may be classified as *cyclo-developmental*, as in mosquito transmission of the worm *Wuchereria bancrofti*, causal organism of bancroftian filariasis.

3. *Propagative Transmission.* When "the organisms undergo no cyclical change, but multiply" in the body of the vector, transmission is said to be *propagative* only. The transmission of bubonic plague is probably propagative, as it is known that the causal organism, *Pasteurella pestis*, can multiply in the gut of the flea. It is also very probable that the transmission of relapsing fever by ticks falls into this category.

It is still uncertain into which category the arthropod transmission of rickettsiae and arboviruses should be placed. Because of their very small size, observations on development of these agents are difficult and they are generally included with propagative transmission.

The diagrammatic representation in Figure 4-7 illustrates the sequence of events involved in arthropod acquisition and dissemination of pathogens.

Mention should be made of pathogen interaction in cases where a vector might be a host to two different pathogens simultaneously; a not unlikely situation where arboviruses and malaria coincide. Concurrent infection of canaries and *Culex tarsalis* with avian malaria and western encephalitis virus resulted in a significant suppression of virus titer in such birds, but did not alter ability of the mosquitoes to transmit the virus (Barnett, 1956). It has also been noted that *Aedes aegypti* can harbor bird malaria and Semliki Forest virus without evidence of interactions except when the vector is under stress or physiologically deficient (Bertram, *et al.*, 1964).

VERTEBRATE HOSTS

Vertebrates are hosts to arthropods and to the pathogens they disseminate, whether in a normal parasitic relationship or by chance. In medical entomology the infections of prime concern are those in man, but other vertebrates such as domestic animals and wildlife may show the same disease or discomfort relationships.

Various characteristics of man have helped create public health problems, no less so in vector borne than in other disease situations. Man is unquestionably the greatest environmental disrupter of all living things and consequently may unintentionally create problems of enormous complexity and gravity. As with other forms of life, any tendency to over-populate finally meets with population-limiting controls; the medically important arthropods and the pathogens they transmit are simply one of many biotic population-limiting forces. Man views population-con-

trolling diseases with alarm and as unnatural, but such diseases have no doubt had, and still have, a role as forces shaping the evolutionary course of man into his present state. One well-known example of an evolutionary force influenced by an arthropod-transmitted disease is sickle cell anemia, a genetically controlled hemoglobin aberration of man that is generally harmful but has some protective value against malaria, which probably accounts for its prevalence in Negroes (Wiesenfeld, 1967). Historical aspects of arthropod transmitted diseases are dealt with in Chapter 1. Especially noteworthy is the role of diseases such as typhus, relapsing fever, malaria, dengue, and yellow fever in early military campaigns, and plague as a factor that reshaped society.

Human Habits and Disease Prevalence. An understanding of human characteristics that promote or prevent arthropod-borne diseases is vital, for often a relatively minor change in existing practice can significantly modify a problem. Each disease situation has such human elements, making it cumbersome to cite many here; a few examples will suffice as illustrations.

Disposal of waste and unwanted articles creates acute problems. Mosquitoes that normally breed in the water of rock holes and tree cavities are found in car and airplane tires, tin cans, and other artificial containers. Improper disposal of garbage provides breeding sites for filth-breeding flies as well as rats and their attendant ectoparasites (see Chapter 14). Organic contamination of waters is a further complication, as shown in Salt Lake County, Utah, where it was demonstrated that the population of mosquito larvae increases as pollution increases (Graham and Bradley, 1963). Mattingly (1962) analyzes the growing evidence that populations of *Culex pipiens quinquefasciatus* Say (=*fatigans* Wiedemann), the primary vector of *Wuchereria* filariasis, have increased in both Africa and Asia. Two major factors are the spread of urbanization, which provides favorable habitats for this essentially urban mosquito, and

ARTHROPOD

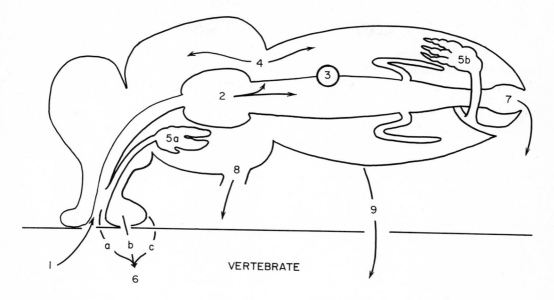

Fig. 4-7 Diagram of acquisition, development, and transmission of pathogens by medically important arthropods.

1. Pathogen and blood or tissues of vertebrate host ingested. More or less accidental ingestion of helminth eggs also possible.

2. Pathogens in lumen of gut may be "inactivated" (digested or adsorbed) or multiply here as with fleas and plague bacillus or *Leishmania* in *Phlebotomus* flies.

3. Passage directly through gut wall as with filarial worms in biting flies and *Borrelia* in lice and ticks, or development in the epithelial layer as in sporozoan Protozoa, and probably most arboviruses, or development on the epithelial layer as in malaria.

4. Transport by hemolymph to tissues.

5. Tissue concentration such as (*a*) salivary gland concentration of many arboviruses and the sporozoites of malaria and (*b*) invasion of epithelium and oocytes of ovary for transovarian transmission as with tick vectors of spirochetes and viruses, and tick and mite vectors of rickettsiae.

6. Introduction into the vertebrate host by (*a*) back pressure of digestive tract as with plague bacillus by fleas and *Leishmania* by *Phlebotomus,* or introduction of saliva in act of feeding (see *5a*), or (*b*) escape of pathogens through the body wall as in transmission of filariae, or (*c*) by contaminated mouth parts or other body surfaces; tularemia and *Chrysops,* avian pox virus and mosquitoes, myxoma virus and various bloodsucking insects, dysentery organisms, and filth flies.

7. Infected feces egested onto skin of host where pathogens enter cuts, are scratched in, or rubbed onto conjunctiva (*Trypanosoma cruzi* and triatomine bugs).

8. Infective fluids may be excreted from glands, for example, viruses and spirochetes from the coxal glands of argasid ticks.

9. Vertebrate may acquire pathogen by ingesting or crushing infected arthropod. Examples include ingestion of arthropod intermediate hosts of helminths, *Trypanosoma lewisi* or rats obtained by ingestion or crushing of fleas, or crushing of *Borrelia*-infected lice by vertebrates.

increasing use of persistent insecticides, which has led to disregard of conventional sanitary measures with consequent proliferation of suitable breeding places.

Water management problems are also a failing of man. Irrigated agriculture has increased, often with little regard for disposal of excess water. Standing water provides breeding sites for mosquitoes, ceratopogonid midges, and tabanid flies; and if such water becomes saline, the breeding of brackish water forms that are vicious biters may become a further complication. Water stored for domestic use in containers, promoting development of *Aedes aegypti* and attendant outbreaks of urban yellow fever, illustrates a classic example of water mismanagement. Another type of human water use problem concerns the development of fish ponds for providing a source of food. In the Hollandia area of New Guinea it was found there was almost no mosquito development in well-managed ponds in which food fishes kept the surface free of algae and floating plants, and where predator fishes ate mosquito larvae. In poorly managed ponds, on the other hand, *Anopheles farauti* Laveran and three other known vectors of malaria plasmodia were prevalent (Dijk, 1960).

Nomadic habits of less-developed human cultures have proved to be a block in the final eradication of malaria. Infected persons in nomadic tribes of Africa have reinfected stable human populations through vectors where control had been achieved. Likewise people of remote mountainous areas in Asia and New Guinea have served as a residual means of survival of the parasites, occasional contact with uninfected vectors in malaria-free zones permitting a recurrence of transmission. Jungle agricultural communities are characterized by frequent moving so that any vector control program dependent on treatment of dwellings with residual insecticides is hampered because new huts are built but unrecorded, and so are missed in treatment schedules.

Man's activities are directly responsible for introduction of vector arthropods, along with the pathogens they transmit. This problem is further dealt with in Chapter 6. It is worth noting that four of the six internationally quarantinable diseases are arthropod-borne. It is also well to know for the United States, and many other countries, that vector *Anopheles* mosquitoes are still often abundant even though human malaria is absent. For this reason continued vigilance is required to prevent reintroduction of the pathogens.

Response of Vertebrate Hosts to the Pathogen. Vertebrates commonly develop immunity once exposed to disease. For this reason the number of unexposed susceptibles is a major factor determining whether an outbreak of epidemic proportions can occur. Reeves, *et al.* (1962, 1964), analyzed factors involved in epidemics of western equine and St. Louis encephalitis. In these diseases there are many instances where vector mosquitoes have relatively high virus infection rates, but no clinical evidence of disease is present and the human population is found to have high specific antibody rates. Even disease eradication programs have inherent dangers, as disruption of a program can expose a large number of susceptibles to attack. As an example, a hurricane on the southern peninsula of Haiti occurred in October, 1963, in the fourth six-month cycle of spraying to control *falciparum* malaria transmitted by *Anopheles albimanus* Wiedemann. The parasite rate index before control had been 10 per cent, was down to 0.8 per cent in the course of the control program, and rebounded to 17 per cent after the hurricane, with the occurrence of 75,000 cases in a three- to four-month period (Mason and Cavalie, 1965).

Diseases of Wild Animals. The same groups of arthropod-transmitted pathogens causing disease in man are serious problems for his domestic animals and for wild vertebrates. Diseases of domestic animals due to arthropod transmission of pathogens will be dealt with more fully in discussing specific groups of vectors and the diseases with which they are associated.

From an epidemiologic standpoint wildlife without evident disease are very important sources of vector infection with pathogens causing human disease. Thus many species of mice can serve as primary resistant hosts of plague bacilli that affect rats and man, and snowshoe hares are rarely affected by the tularemia pathogen in marked contrast to its effect on cottontail rabbits and man. Birds are well adapted to western and St. Louis encephalitis, but man may be seriously affected. Myxoma virus kills the European rabbit but does not kill its normal American rabbit hosts. From these illustrations it can be seen that man or affected animals of any kind are often merely tangential hosts in a normal cycle involving vertebrates that are usually unaffected by arthropod-borne pathogens.

In general we are rather poorly aware of the effect of arthropod-transmitted diseases on wildlife. Myxomatosis, a virus disease of rabbits and hares, is an outstanding example of the known effects of disease on wild animal populations (Fenner and Ratcliffe, 1965). There is little doubt that diseases of animals transmissible to man, termed *zoonoses*, have had a significant effect on the survival and evolutionary development of wild vertebrates, though only the most extensive epidemics in wild animal populations (*epizootics*) tend to be recorded. A few illustrations will suffice.

Plague, caused by a flea-transmitted bacillus, has frequently decimated wild rodent populations in addition to its well known effects on domestic and commensal rats. For example, Lechleitner and others (1962) describe an epizootic of plague that exterminated an isolated colony of Gunnison's prairie dog, *Cynomys gunnisoni gunnisoni*, in Chubbs Park, central Colorado.

Hoogstraal (1966) cites a paper describing an epizootic in muskrats (*Ondatra*) in the Omsk area of the Soviet Union. These animals had been introduced and became numerous along streams, but large numbers died off between 1960 and 1962 due to Omsk fever virus and the bacterium of tularemia, the former apparently being transmitted between muskrats and other rodents by gamasid mites.

Bird malarias likely have a very significant effect on avian populations. In the United States it has been noted that annual Audubon Society bird census figures have increased in recent years, especially swamp and salt marsh inhabiting species such as blackbirds. There has been some conjecture that improved control of marsh-breeding mosquitoes by insecticides and other means has resulted in reduced bird malaria and bird filariasis, permitting better survival of marsh- and swamp-inhabiting birds. Warner (1968) has developed an hypothesis, well supported with experiments and observations, that the extinction of nearly half the native Hawaiian bird species (drepaniids), and present restriction of the remainder remnant populations to a few high mountain forest sanctuaries, is a consequence of introduction of the mosquito *Culex pipiens fatigans* (probably by the ship *Wellington* in 1826), which transmits avian pox virus and bird malarias from introduced avian species.

Contributions of Vertebrates to Arthropod-Transmitted Disease Studies. In addition to their rather obvious use in transmission studies, laboratory and wild vertebrates have been utilized to gain an understanding of approaches in controlling arthropod-transmitted diseases. One noteworthy contribution is their use in chemotherapy investigations. Chicks and canaries infected with plasmodia have aided in the screening of thousands of compounds for antimalarial activity, and promising drugs thus discovered have been tested on malarious monkeys before final clinical testing on humans. Candidate trypanocides may be screened initially against *Trypanosoma lewisi* in the common laboratory rat, and antifilarial agents tested against microfilariae of *Litomosoides carinii* (Trav.) in the cotton rat *Sigmodon hispidus* Say and Ord.

Vertebrates previously unexposed to a pathogen under study may provide information on existing transmission rates by vectors under more or less normal conditions. Animals used in this manner are referred to as *sentinel hosts*; for instance exposed chickens are termed sentinel flocks. Because the vertebrate used may be more attractive (or under greater exposure) to a vector than is man, routine use of sentinel animals can warn of a potential epidemic before the first human cases occur. Such methods have been most useful in studying arboviruses; routine sampling of the serum of exposed sentinel animals indicating acquisition of a virus by *viremia* (virus actively circulating in the peripheral circulation) or by the development of specific antibodies.

RESERVOIRS

The theory of the role of reservoirs for arthropod-transmitted pathogens has been developed to explain the maintenance of infection during times when active transmission is not occurring. As Philip and Burgdorfer (1961) note, reservoirs are more a feature of temperate climates where vectors become dormant or hibernate; in the tropics there may be continuous passage between susceptible hosts and vectors. Where a reservoir is indicated it is looked for in (1) the principal vector(s), (2) clinically susceptible hosts, which would generally be man or domestic animals, (3) wild vertebrates, and (4) possibly secondary vectors. Whichever of these hosts maintains the pathogen in question for a lengthy period is considered a part of the *reservoir*. The term reservoir is somewhat loose and can include any or all of these four factors in various situations. The sum of host relationships previously outlined, along with the pathogen maintained, is referred to as a *biocenosis* (pl. biocenoses).

Discovering the reservoir in any given situation may be difficult, though the actively feeding stage of many vectors is so brief, except in cases of diapause, that pathogen survival in long-lived vertebrate hosts is clearly indicated.

A few examples illustrate variations in the role of different hosts as reservoirs for specific infections. Philip and Burgdorfer (1961),

Philip (1961, 1963), and Burgdorfer and Varma (1967) have further documented the role of arthropods as reservoirs.

In cases where only mechanical transmission by arthropods is known it is probable that the vertebrate hosts serve as reservoirs. In such instances a prolonged presence of the pathogen in the blood (viremia or bacteremia) or premunition within vertebrates, or prolonged survival of the pathogen away from a host, seems the likely method of survival. Myxomatosis of rabbits fits this situation, in that the role of mosquitoes and other biting arthropods in transmitting myxoma virus is solely mechanical.

Q fever, a worldwide infection of domestic and wild animals, and tangentially of man, is caused by the rickettsia *Coxiella burnetti* (Derrick) and has a varied reservoir. Transmission in heavily populated regions can occur readily by contact between vertebrates through a number of contaminant routes, and certain vertebrate hosts develop long-term carrier states. In more natural or wild environments various species of ticks are vectors, and some of these constitute a reservoir by transmitting the rickettsiae to their offspring. Natural foci of tick reservoirs have been demonstrated in Queensland (Australia), Morocco, and Montana (United States).

Chagas' disease, a trypanosome affliction of man and certain wild vertebrates in the Americas, also has a reservoir that includes vectors and vertebrates. The pathogens undergo cyclic development and persist throughout the relatively long life span of the triatomid bug vectors. Spread between vectors occurs through the habit of harmless bloodfeeding by unfed bugs upon those recently engorged. As is true of trypanosomiases in general, the parasites also persist in an active condition within the vertebrate host.

In filiariases (nematode blood parasites) and malaria (protozoan blood parasites), mosquito vectors are for the most part too short-lived to serve as reservoirs. The vertebrate hosts are long-lived, and in both diseases their parasites may persist for years without fresh introduction into the host.

Ticks provide a classic example of an arthropod reservoir, serving in that capacity in maintaining the Rocky Mountain spotted fever rickettsia. An example of a human reservoir is provided by epidemic typhus, in which man maintains the rickettsia under certain circumstances for years though this pathogen is often decidedly detrimental to, and is not maintained for long periods by, the louse vector.

5

THE EVOLUTION OF ANIMAL TISSUE FEEDING AND PATHOGEN TRANSFER BY ARTHROPODS

Insects and related arthropods preceded man on earth by at least 400 million years, and microorganisms were present long before that. In fact the origins of microorganisms and insects occurred so far in the past, and the fossil records provide such meager evidence of their beginnings, that we cannot clearly perceive how medically important arthropods came to occupy their position of major importance as causal agents of disease and transmitters of pathogens affecting man and other terrestrial vertebrates. The uncertainties, however, are by no means limited to arthropods

and vertebrates, for an even more extensive similar relationship exists between the insecta, certain Acarina, and terrestrial plants. From this fact, and from our recognition that insects are singularly adapted to exploit all types of terrestrial and freshwater environments, we can reasonably assume that the medical and veterinary involvement of insects and Acarina was a natural consequence of their ability to adapt to and occupy all available habitats.

The development of parasitism by arthropods, utilizing vertebrates as hosts, is the basis for their medical and veterinary importance. What is perhaps unique in this relationship is the extent of the role of arthropods in disseminating pathogens of vertebrates, often as the only means of transfer. The complexity of these associations, then, has evolved from relationships of a more or less accidental coincidence to dependent relationships between two forms of life (arthropods dependent on vertebrates), to the exploitation of these dependent relationships by microorganisms or metazoan parasites. It seems important to try and understand how these situations have arisen to better appreciate the factors underlying their present complexity. What is sought, then, is a base for understanding the very restricted parasitology of medically important insects and acarines. It will be impossible to present more than an exposure to some of the main ideas here.

Parasitology, the study of parasitism, like many other disciplines in biology, was first largely confined to a descriptive phase. It became necessary to develop terms that categorize the variety of parasitic relationships. From these simpler descriptive observations there naturally arose much conjecture as to how parasitic relationships evolved. The descriptive terms used are defined here, and may be further examined in any modern textbook of parasitology.

First, the term *parasitism* merely denotes the fact that two species of organisms are living in intimate association. Usually there is a disparity in size of the two organisms, the larger form being the *host*, and the smaller one the *parasite*. If this relationship is only occasional, with the parasite appearing to normally exist in a free-living condition, for example as in scavenger flies, the condition is termed *facultative parasitism* or *accidental parasitism*. If the parasite is always dependent on a host for its development the relationship is termed *obligatory parasitism*. *Temporary parasites* visit the host for only a short time to feed, as is the case with most biting flies, most ticks, and bed bugs. *Continuous parasites* characteristically infest one host, for example scabies and mange mites, sucking and chewing lice. Continuous parasitism with a change of hosts is typical of many helminth parasites, and in medical entomology is illustrated by filarial worms and sporozoan malaria parasites alternating between mosquito vectors and a vertebrate host.

The site of infestation has also been used to classify types of parasitism. *Ectoparasitism* includes those forms on the body surface of the host, *endoparasitism* entails those parasites not visible on the surface; for example, within the skin tissues, the host's blood, the digestive tract, respiratory passages, or other internal sinuses. The artificiality of site of infestation as a means of classification is suggested by the fact that a parasite of the outer ear canal would probably be termed an ectoparasite, whereas one in the lung passages would generally be thought of as an endoparasite. Dogiel (1966) cites an instance of possible transition from ecto- to endoparasitism as observed by Dubinin, wherein the chewing louse *Tetrophthalmus titan* of the pelican feeds on blood within the pouch, but still moves out to the feathers to lay its eggs.

The degree of host specificity is another consideration in studying parasitism. In medical entomology this situation applies to arthropods as disease-causing agents, to vectors of vertebrate pathogens, and to the pathogens themselves as they relate to arthropod vectors and to vertebrate hosts. As examples various mites may be exclusively restricted to a single vertebrate host, whereas mosquitoes transmitting *Wuchereria bancrofti* (bancroftian filariasis) may feed on a number of hosts, though the nematode develops in man alone. As terms describing the degree of dependency on a vector, *obligate transmissible diseases* are those wherein the vector is the sole natural means of transmission (i.e., malaria, piroplasmas); *facultative transmissible diseases* are those wherein a vector may be only one of the possible routes of dissemination (i.e., anthrax, tularemia).

The Origins of Parasitism. Parasitism involves a bewildering complexity of adaptations; yet if we examine a species or limited group of parasites, especially among the Insecta and Acarina, we can often surmise how the parasitic habit originated. The origins of parasitism may be suggested from the behavior of related groups, indeed within some families (or even genera) there may be both free-living and parasitic forms.

In the terrestrial Arthropoda, parasitism of vertebrates has occurred chiefly and most successfully in lairs, nests, and other host habitations. Such sites provided a very specific and stable environment that permitted exploitation of the host, though intitially progenitors of the arthropods in question may have inhabited this environment as scavengers or as predators. When the parasitic means of existence evolved in such environments many of the parasites retained their relationship with the host's home, hiding in adjacent cracks and crevices to conceal themselves from the host's attempts to rid itself of its guests, and often approaching the host only at night. Other parasites probably transferred permanently to a life upon the host under lair or nest conditions, thus becoming less dependent on the host's return. At any rate the parasitic mode of existence resulted in the loss of some general abilities, and the development of specific adaptations for existence in association with a new, specific environment, the host. The lair or nest association is readily evident in gamasid mites, feather mites, argasid ticks, triatomid bugs, bed bugs (Cimicidae), chewing lice, fleas, and the Hippoboscidae or louse flies among the higher Diptera.

Scavenging on debris within lairs, burrows, or nests seems a logical route for development of the parasitic habit. On the floor of such environments there is an accumulation of litter containing wastes and remnants of the host's meal whether of plant or animal nature. Such a rich environment could readily have been utilized by mites and lice, and fleas still consume this detritus during larval development. As candidates for possible future parasitic association one can envision the oribatid mites and psocids as being suitable by virtue of their scavenging habits and their abundance in animal habitations. In fact, oribatids and various ectoparasitic mites may have had a common ancestry, and Hopkins (1949) believes that lice were derived from psocid-like ancestors.

Predatory habits appear in some cases to have preceded blood feeding on vertebrates. The bloodsucking triatomine bugs illustrate this view, in that they are obviously close morphological relatives of the predaceous Reduviidae. One can imagine, considering how readily many predaceous reduviids will bite when in close contact with humans, that an ancestral type became associated with lairs or burrows where it preyed on other arthropod associates, subsequently finding the mammalian inhabitants quite tasty and perhaps more available. Very little bodily change was required to make the transition, but one outcome was the development of an essentially painless bite in contrast to the painful attack of predaceous reduviids. In the Ceratopogonidae the "predaceous" to parasitic transition can be seen in existing genera, with *Culicoides* and *Leptoconops* being bloodfeeders on vertebrates, and other genera, including *Forcipomyia*, feeding on the hemolymph of insects. There is evidence that this latter genus may be in transition, in that species are known that feed on vertebrate blood (Pechuman and Wirth, 1961). The dipteran genera *Symphoromyia* and *Suragina* in the family Rhagionidae feed on mammals, whereas most rhagionids are predaceous on insects.

In all the examples from predation to parasitism cited, the predation consists of feeding on liquid contents of prey rather than consumption of the entire prey. Thus the morphological modifications of mouth parts to permit sucking of vertebrate blood had already been largely accomplished. If mouth part adaptation is a requirement it seems possible that predaceous immature Neuroptera, such as lacewing larvae, could evolve a parasitic relationship with vertebrates, for they commonly bite when in contact with the skin. What may preclude the appearance of parasitism in this case is that contact occurs rather infrequently in the field—frequent contact such as is provided by a lair association may be necessary. Severe biting attacks may also be observed when man comes in contact with normally predaceous free-living Hemiptera.

A general willingness to feed when a substrate of attractive physical or chemical constituency is encountered may serve as a feature leading to parasitic dependence. Several plant feeders commonly bite man, and presumably other vertebrates as well, as is noted in the case of thrips and leafhoppers in Chapter 20. Likewise, phytophagous Hemiptera may engage in blood sucking, and the chemical differences between blood and plant juices may not be as great as one would suppose (Usinger, 1934).

Chance feeding encounters, perhaps initially on proteinaceous secretions, can be carried a step further into a more purposive relationship in the case of certain eye-frequenting Lepidoptera. In Uganda a noctuid moth, *Arcyophora longivalvis* Gn. was seen to feed in large numbers on lachrymal secretions of cattle, and was thought to be the primary agent disseminating *Moraxella* (*Hemophilus*) *bovis*, the causal organism of infectious keratitis that blinded many cattle (Guilbride, *et al.*, 1959). Similarly, in Cambodia and Thailand the noctuids *Arcyophora sylvaticus*

Büttiker and *Lobocraspis griseifusa* Hmps., along with four other noctuids and a lycaenid, were found to feed on the eyes of cattle, water buffalo, sambar (a large deer, *Cervus unicolor*), and other large mammals (Büttiker, 1959, 1962, 1964). Some of these Asiatic species will also feed in the eyes of man (Fig. 5-1).

The present-day feeding on a given host may have been by way of transfer from a different kind of host. As examples one can cite the feeding of some Mallophaga on mammals, whereas most of these chewing lice attack birds; fleas are nearly entirely restricted to mammals, yet a small fraction of the total number of species attacks birds; the two species of bed bugs in the genus *Cimex* that are definitely associated with man may have transferred to this host from bats at a time when man lived in caves, remaining with man when he left this environment to build his own habitations (Usinger, 1966).

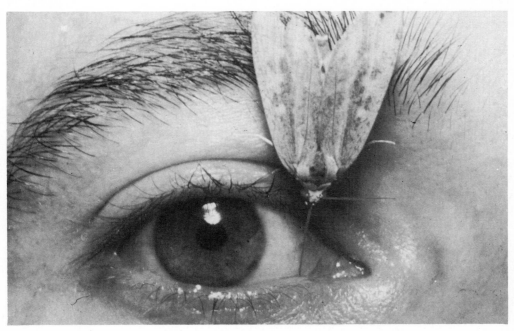

Fig. 5-1 An eye-frequenting lepidopteran from Thailand. (Photograph by Bänziger; courtesy of World Health Organization.)

Synanthropy, a close association with man without actually feeding on him, is in a sense a loose form of parasitism. The house fly, house-infesting species of cockroaches, and various species of ants are found in this type of association, and all of these are particularly in contact with man's food and are naturally suspect in the contaminative transfer of microorganisms and helminths. Other synanthropes include silverfish and firebrats, dermestid beetles, and clothes moths, though none of these latter guests are as clearly associated with man's food, and therefore the likelihood that they will be of medical importance, other than as sources of allergenic substances, is not great. Greenberg (1968) and others have discussed the problem of synanthropy in the Diptera.

Secondary hematophagy may provide a route for the development of blood feeding on vertebrates, though persuasive evidence for such a pathway is lacking. It is worth mentioning, nonetheless, that feeding on blood at sites of accidental injury, or where blood oozes from an arthropod's feeding wound, is by no means rare. As an example, the muscid flies *Fannia flavipalpis* Stein and *Hydrotaea armipes* (Fallén) have been observed in California to be in association with, and imbibing blood made available by, tabanids (Garcia and Radovsky, 1962). The face fly *Musca autumnalis* De Geer, *M. larvipara* Portschinsky, and *M. tempestiva* Fallén will feed on free blood when it is available (West, 1951). Diptera commonly need a protein source as adults for eggs to develop; as a consequence they are attracted to tissue fluids. Even blood-sucking forms such as black flies may be attracted to meat baits (Davis and James, 1957). It requires but little modification of dipteran mouthparts from the sponging condition that can feed on free liquids to the development of rasping structures able to scarify tissue to release more fluids, as found in *Hippelates* gnats. A further progression along this line of development is conceivably

involved in the mouthparts found in tsetse and stable flies.

The partaking of vertebrate blood by one arthropod feeding on the contents of another recently engorged arthropod, a form of cannibalism for which the term *haematoklepty* has been proposed (Phillips, 1960), occurs frequently enough to suggest that it may have developed initially through accidental probing. Such a habit has been observed among triatomine reduviid bugs, where it can serve as a means of increasing the reservoir of Chagas' disease.

Size is a factor that could favor endoparasitism by mites. Species such as scabies mites, mange mites, and follicular mites, living within or beneath the skin of their host, could have initially developed such a habit with little structural modification if they were derived from free-living ancestors small enough to fit within so limited an environment. Even less in the way of structural modifications would be required of mites living in respiratory passageways and ear canals. Diminutive size as a factor permitting ectoparasitism is suggested by the finding that free-living insects such as the collembolan *Orchesella albosa* Guthrie may infest hairy surfaces of the body in humans (Scott, *et al.,* 1962).

One of the most interesting parasitic associations is *phoresy*, transfer from one site, in this context the host, to another by attaching to a passing animal. Such behavior may be relatively simple; for example, the attachment of Mallophaga by mouthparts to hippoboscid flies, probably in response to overcrowding on their bird host or to a drop in temperature when the host dies (Fig. 5-2). In such a case the survival advantage is obvious. Considerably more complicated is the attachment of eggs to arthropods by the torsálo fly, *Dermatobia hominis*, with the eggs then being carried to a suitable vertebrate host (Fig. 16-19). Survival advantage is again deducible, the vertebrate host is less likely to associate attack with the presence of any of a number of

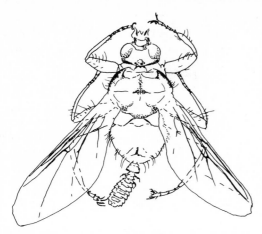

Fig. 5-2 A chewing louse (Mallophaga) attached to a louse fly for phoretic transfer. (Redrawn from a photo in Bequaert, 1953-1957.)

common arthropods than with the approach of the large and rather distinctive bot fly. The real puzzle lies in how utilization of an intermediate agent of transfer could have evolved from a possibly accidental occurrence into a fixed habit.

Finally, a dietary requirement for protein is another factor favoring development of parasitism. Protein as a constituent of the adult diet required for egg development is common throughout Insecta. Predaceous and parasitic insects are particularly associated with this need, and also among phytophagous insects pollen may serve as a rich source of protein that promotes egg maturation. In the Diptera an entire spectrum of protein requirement can be found. In primitive free-living forms, such as Chironomidae, sufficient protein is consumed during immature growth so that adults are short lived and do not feed. Their relatives, the ceratopogonid midges, black flies, and mosquitoes, partake of blood as adults, though in these bloodsuckers an adequate protein supply as larvae may permit some eggs to be developed. In higher Diptera adult protein sources may not be required (tachinid parasites of insects) or may be obtained from meat juices and other proteinaceous sources (Muscidae, Calliphoridae, Sarcophagidae), or

there may be complete dependence on blood alone as an adult foodstuff (tsetses, stable flies, horn flies).

Morphological Adaptations. A plethora of structural modifications is evident among medically important arthropods. Most obvious of these, where pathogens are transferred in the act of biting, is the feeding apparatus. The mouthparts are considered of sufficient importance to be treated separately in Chapter 3.

Characteristically there is flattening of the entire body in ectoparasites. Such a body form permits the parasite to remain close to the host's skin without being easily dislodged and to move readily through the obstructive maze of hairs or feathers. Fleas, nearly exclusively found on mammals, are bilaterally compressed and can thereby move rapidly through the fur. Dorsoventral compression is commonplace among other ectoparasites, requiring less extreme modification of the usual arthropod body form. Such dorsoventral flattening is present in chewing and sucking lice, ticks, bed bugs, and most parasitic mites. Extreme flattening is found in some mites that live under the scales of snakes and lizards.

Along with the development of ectoparasitism the need for flight has been lost by many insects. Flightlessness may be found among representatives of normally winged insects, presumably to insure that they will not become lost from an especially suitable though limited environment. Such an interpretation seems correct since in free living insects flightlessness is characteristic of areas with a very limited suitable environment, such as is the case with grasshoppers living at high altitudes on mountain slopes, or insects in Arctic or island environments. There is a real survival advantage if the insect cannot be readily blown away from its very limited suitable habitat, as would be possible if the insect were in flight. For ectoparasites the entire environment, namely the host, is likely to remove itself if the parasite is temporarily away. If flight is retained an efficient host-seeking system must be developed, whereas if flight is lost a special host-seeking sensory system is less of a necessity if the parasite remains on the host most of the time. For ectoparasites the wingless condition probably also permits easier movement on the skin surfaces.

Among insect ectoparasites may be found extremes of variation from complete loss to full retention of wings. In fact this degree of variability may be seen in the hippoboscid flies, with the fully winged condition occurring throughout life, but with reduced functional ability in some cases, or a transitional condition in which wings are functional but may be shed once a suitable host is reached, or a completely wingless condition typified by the sheep ked *Melophagus ovinus* (Bequaert, 1954). Many of the Heleomyzidae (Diptera) inhabit caves and burrows, already noted as a habitat favoring the development of parasitism. In the genus *Lutomyia*, associated with chipmunk burrows, adults remove the major portion of the wings once they become associated with a suitable habitat (Sabrosky, 1949), which confirms the previously stated belief that winglessness serves as a means of confining an insect to a favorable environment. Permanent winglessness is found in fleas and chewing and sucking lice. Since all Acarina are wingless, this feature may have helped predispose them toward development of the parasitic habit.

Loss or reduction of structures is a common feature of ectoparasites. The essential loss or very great reduction in size of legs, particularly of the last pair, is found in some mites that infest the skin. This is especially evident among the dermanyssid mites. Eyes may be greatly reduced or lacking entirely, as can be seen to be the case with fleas and Acarina. Antennae could be troublesome if they projected as much in ectoparasites as with free-living insects, therefore antennae of biting and chewing lice are much reduced in size and those of fleas fit closely to the body in grooves. There may be an addition or specialization of certain structures aiding the ectoparasitic existence. The first pair of legs of many mites and of ticks seems to function rather like insect antennae, with special sensory receptors located on these appendages. A tarsal construction particularly adapted to clinching onto hairs or bristles of mammals is a type of specialization found in sucking lice. Setae facing backward to permit rapid passage through hairs or feathers is a common feature of many ectoparasites. In addition, among fleas there may be the development of groups of backward-facing combs or ctenidia.

Where the ectoparasitic habit consists of a prolonged attachment to the skin, anchoring capabilities of mouthparts is seen. This situation is typical of permanently attached species of fleas and of many ticks. Secondarily the feeding ectoparasite may cause host tissue to grow, surrounding the site of attachment to form special enclosing structures reminiscent of gall formation associated with some plant-feeding arthropods. In this category can be included the chigoe flea, *Tunga penetrans*, and mites developing within the wing membranes of bats (Lavoipierre, *et al.*, 1967).

One obvious adaptation associated with the blood-feeding habit is extensibility of the gut and body wall. This capability is particularly developed in those cases where feeding occurs rather infrequently, and seems best represented in blood-feeding Hemiptera and in female ixodid ticks. The latter arthropods are especially noteworthy for the really prodigious expandibility of the body wall.

More or less permanent ectoparasites associated with aquatic vertebrates have developed structural modifications designed to help meet the needs of such a habitat. Seal lice in the genera *Lepidophthirius* and *Antarctophthirius* have scales on the dorsal body surface to retain air when the host dives (Fig. 5-3), but *Echinophthirius* is enclosed within the nostrils and lacks such scales (Baer, 1952). Beetles in the family Leptinidae, including the Platypsyllidae of certain authors, are parasitic on beavers. Their general body structure is streamlined and rather resembles some of the

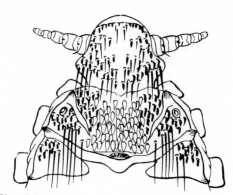

Fig. 5-3 Head and thorax of a seal-infesting sucking louse, *Antarctophthirius*. Note flattened scales. (Courtesy of U.S. Public Health Service.)

free-living aquatic beetles. These unusual coleopterans, incidentally, are believed to have adopted this parasitic habit from a prior scavenger existence in the host's lodges.

Reproductive Adaptations. Adaptation of reproduction is generally considered from the standpoint of fecundity. In short the question arises as to how many eggs or live offspring the female will produce. Considering that under normal conditions the reproductive potential of insects is approximately proportional to the risk experienced by growing forms before they reach reproductive age, we can see that permanent ectoparasites tend to lay rather few eggs, those arthropods that produce partially grown postembryonic forms also have a low reproductive potential, and the highest reproductive rate is found where eggs are more or less indiscriminately scattered and the likelihood of the immature feeding stages finding a suitable developmental site is remote. Such conditions are also evident among plant-feeding arthropods as well as with those parasitic on other arthropods. A really high egg production is found among ixodid ticks that simply disgorge a mass of as many as 18,000 eggs at the ground level wherever the female happens to be when the eggs have matured.

Among permanent ectoparasites that undergo all of their development on the host, eggs are firmly attached. Eggs of sucking lice are glued to hair shafts, those of chewing lice are attached to feathers or hairs, and those of permanently parasitic mites are stuck to the hairs or feathers, or deposited within the skin.

It is noteworthy that viviparity is a common, though by no means exclusive, feature of parasitic Diptera. One can speculate that viviparity under these circumstances is especially possible because of the rich proteinaceous diet of blood or tissue fluids consumed by the mother. An advanced form of viviparity is characteristic of the families Hippoboscidae and Glossinidae. Other higher Diptera may larviposit or lay eggs that hatch almost at once. Though relatively few offspring may be produced by each female, the survival rate must be high, particularly when offspring are deposited directly onto the host.

Biochemical Adaptations. A number of biochemical oddities, or correlates, may be found among medically important arthropods. These may signify relatedness between groups, parallel evolution, or merely biochemical adaptation in response to the parasitic way of life.

Cross antigenicity of bites and stings, and as inhalant allergens, is a problem of biochemical relatedness that still requires more investigation. This subject is alluded to in Chapter 20. One characteristic of bites among medically important arthropods is that they are often painless, and blood in the bite wound may clot slowly. Though the biochemical nature of these observations is largely unknown, there have obviously evolved salivary secretions that do not immediately irritate the host (thereby having survival value for the parasite) and that often contain anticoagulins (thereby permitting easier and more prolonged feeding).

Difficulties encountered in respiration by internally parasitic horse bots in the genus *Gasterophilus* probably account for the presence of hemoglobin in the larvae, which most likely is a biochemical oddity because this compound appears to be found elsewhere in insects only in free-living aquatic Hemiptera and larval chironomid flies. Furthermore, when the oxygen carrying capacity of the hemoglobin of *Gasterophilus* is compared with that of chironomids there is evident disparity, presumably an indication of molecular differences, and neither one is particularly close to vertebrate hemoglobin (Gilmour, 1961). Another instance of respiratory adaptation in internal parasites of vertebrates concerns the cattle grubs, where larvae during their internal wandering stages appear to have anaerobic respiration.

One consequence of parasitism is a loss of unnecessary digestive enzymes, the number lost increasing as the relationship has become more obligate. Such can be shown to be the case among higher Diptera where the whole range of transformation from scavengers to facultative parasites to obligate parasites is found. Kamal (1959) tested for the presence of particular digestive enzymes in thirteen species of calliphorids and sarcophagids, showing that the more obligately parasitic the relationship the fewer enzymes were found, a consistent consequence of a highly restricted type of food supply. Among Diptera that are internally parasitic on body tissues, special enzymes may be present to meet the demands of this particular environment. Thus collagenase that will attack the protein collagen, a typical constituent of connective tissue, has been found in larvae of the cattle grub *Hypoderma bovis* (Lienert and Thorsell, 1955), and in *Phaenicia* (=*Lucilia*) *cuprina* that can infest living tissues of sheep (Waterhouse and Irzykiewicz, 1957).

Finding the Host and Feeding on it. Terrestrial arthropods parasitic on vertebrates utilize a number of host-associated cues for locating their victims. Their ability to find hosts can be separated into (1) factors that operate at a distance, (2) factors to which the parasite responds when relatively near the host, and (3) factors when on the host that will cause a biting response and actual engorgement. Each of these items appears to be involved in flying species and in some arthropods that intermittently attack a host, but understandably only the latter two factors are noted among permanent ectoparasites.

Generalized seeking activity, expressed as flight or locomotion, may be a feature common to host-seeking behavior that will automatically increase the chance of encounter. Such activity tends to occur at a particular time of day, for instance activity of many mosquitoes after nightfall, either in response to environmental cues such as daily light or temperature changes or to innate or circadian rhythms. The great selective ability and precision of such feeding periods is suggested by the fact that in human bancroftian and brugian filariasis the microfilariae of periodic forms are found in the peripheral blood of the vertebrate host at times coinciding with the feeding activity of the mosquito vector.

Once flight or locomotion is initiated there may be characteristics of the host or its environment that attract a blood-seeking arthropod at a rather great distance. Attraction to the host environment is strongly indicated in the behavior of anthropophilic vectors (attracted to humans) of human malaria, which have a marked tendency to enter, feed, and rest within habitations such as huts. A striking example of vectors associating specific (olfactory?) cues with a host is provided by the attraction of *Chrysops silacea* and *C. dimidiata*, vectors of *Loa loa*, to smoke in jungle habitats, thus leading them to men clearing vegetation (Duke, 1959).

Visual cues are evident among bloodsucking species that attack during daylight. It has often been noted that dark colors invite attack by bloodsucking Diptera. Movement and dark colors have been demonstrated by Sippel and Brown (1953) to be especially attractive for female *Aedes* mosquitoes, and significantly larger numbers of horn flies are attracted to the side of white cattle that is dyed black (Franks, *et al.*, 1964). More specifically Wenk and Schlörer (1963) demonstrated that two species of black flies normally feeding on the ears of horses and cows, and a species that normally feeds on the ventral parts, were attracted to the same regions of a horse silhouette trap. Likewise when a bird-feeding species was included in the tests along with a dummy crow, bird and large mammal feeders were preferentially attracted to shapes resembling their normal hosts.

Attraction to the host when in close proximity has been documented in a wide variety of blood-feeding arthropods. Heat above ambient temperature is a factor attractive to many vectors, being noted for some but not all species of fleas, ticks, mites, mosquitoes, and tabanids. A near universal attractant of variable importance is the production of carbon dioxide by the host, shown to be attractive for more bloodsucking arthropods than any other single factor. In most cases carbon dioxide appears to initiate non-directed seeking activity (see Sasa, 1961), but the tick *Ornithodoros coriaceus* Koch seems to respond to a gradient (Garcia, 1962).

Although common chemical and physical attractants are responded to by vectors, little evidence clearly implicates specific factors that delimit host preference. This condition is not altogether surprising when it is realized that most flying insects such as mosquitoes are not exclusively restrictive in their choice of hosts. Therefore the matter of host choice is often affected by availability. Host preference must generally be due to a favorable combination of several factors (see review by Brown, 1966, for mosquitoes). A narrow range of hosts is virtually immutable in many ecto-parasitic arthropods, and in a few cases even flying bloodsucking insects show similar restrictions. One illustration of exclusive attraction is found in the response of the bird-feeding black fly *Simulium euryadminiculum* to the extractable odoriferous materials of loons (Fallis and Smith, 1964). Presumably, as with broader general types of host restriction (such as fleas to mammals), the cases of uniquely specific attraction are a consequence

of an evolutionary pattern whereby host and parasite evolved together. Evolution of appropriate sensory structures may also be involved in group specific attraction, as suggested by the observation of Jamnback (1965) that primarily bird-feeding ceratopogonids have eight or more antennal segments bearing sensory pits whereas six or fewer antennal segments of mammal feeders have such pits. That specific chemicals can restrict the attraction of arthropods to certain vertebrates is not particularly unique when one considers the well-documented instances of limitations between insects and certain plant hosts and the proven role of specific plant chemicals.

Evidence suggests that apparent specificity is usually a combination of host availability and a mixture of attractive factors, but the question arises as to whether such preferences are relatively fixed in a species or can change under selective pressure. Both possibilities have been shown to operate under experimental conditions. For example the mosquito *Anopheles pharoensis* Theobald still showed a marked preference for humans after being raised for twenty generations on guinea pigs (Mahfouz, 1963), and a highly man-attracted strain of species A in the *Anopheles gambiae* complex segregated according to feeding responses to calf or human showed significant differences in preference within seven generations (Gillies, 1964).

Once the host is reached, and single or combined factors of warmth, moisture, odor, and skin texture initiate the feeding probe, then chemicals associated with blood or other tissue fluids are required to cause engorgement. For mosquitoes, feeding is enhanced by certain adenosine nucleotides in combination with an osmotic pressure close to blood and the presence of sodium ions (Hosoi, 1959; Galun, *et al.*, 1963). The tick *Ornithodoros tholozani* (Laboulbène and Mégnin) engorges on solutions at an osmotic pressure near that of plasma, and containing the reduced tripeptide glutathione (Galun and Kindler, 1965). That such engorgement is in response to the need for protein to develop the ovaries is suggested by a parallel situation in the female house fly, which will feed on guanine nucleotide and derivatives, or on protein when the fly is sufficiently matured, as well as on certain amino acids (Robbins, *et al.*, 1965; Yamamoto and Jensen, 1967).

Associations of Vertebrate Pathogens with Arthropods. The question arises as to whether pathogens transmitted by arthropods are essentially vertebrate parasites utilizing vectors as a means of transfer from one host to another, or whether they were originally parasites of arthropods. The prevailing evidence, on a number of grounds, suggests that the associations were first between arthropods and pathogens. At least as far as concerns man and his immediate progenitors, microorganisms and insects long preceded him, and therefore had undoubtedly been in intimate association for some time. Another type of evidence relates to the comparative pathogenicity of microbial associates, the general impression being that long term associations reduce pathogenicity. Here again the priority of arthropods with their parasites is suggested. Andrewes (1957), in discussing arthropod-borne viruses, makes the interesting suggestion that as early man was probably not a very social creature the arthropod-borne route became a means of spreading these pathogens. For a general review of the types of associations of microorganisms with insects the reader may consult Steinhaus (1946).

The majority of studies show that vertebrate pathogens transmitted by arthropods generally do not harm their vector. Literature on this subject is too extensive to dwell on, but the interested reader is referred to an excellent review by Kramer (1963) that covers both plant and animal pathogens and arthropod vectors. Mussgay (1964) has dealt more specifically with viruses and vector arthropods. In summation, vertebrate viruses appear to have no significant effect on arthropods even though many of the vector's tissues may be heavily infected; rickettsiae of epidemic typhus shorten the life span of louse vectors, but other

rickettsiae do not adversely affect their natural vectors; plague bacilli cause a deleterious blockage of the fleas's gut and are pathogenic in bed bugs (*Cimex*) and ticks, tularemia bacilli may be fatal to tick vectors and to human lice, *Salmonella* are deleterious to a wide variety of vectors, and spirochetes of relapsing fever are generally harmless to ticks; trypanosomes and *Leishmania* affect a small portion of their normal vectors, malaria parasites can cause adverse effects to mosquitoes when infection rates are high, other blood sporozoans have proved to be fatal to ticks or mites in heavy infestations; filarial worms are frequently detrimental to the vector.

The development of arthropod tissue cultures has provided a useful means of examining virus development. In studying ixodid tick tissue cultures Řeháček (1964) has noted that many A group viruses readily multiply in these cells though normally they are isolated from mosquitoes; the tick-borne B group viruses such as those causing Russian spring-summer encephalitis and Kyasanur forest disease also develop in tick tissue cultures whereas mosquito-borne B group viruses multiply but do not reach a high infective level. At the very least, a general arthropod-related specificity was shown in that viruses not belonging to a known arbovirus group, such as poliomyelitis, did not multiply. No cytopathic effects of viruses on tick tissues were noted, and if we hold the view that pathogenicity is a reflection of recent parasitic relationships, then ticks and viruses must illustrate an ancient association. Progress in insect vector tissue cultures has not been as great, but studies with this technique as well as examination of arthropod-borne viruses by using fluorescent antibody techniques and by electron microscope suggest that extensive growth of viruses occurs in tissues with no evidence of pathogenicity. The specificity of such a nonpathogenic relationship is evident when one considers that many viruses are known that are highly detrimental to insects.

Rickettsiae may represent another long-term association with arthropods, as noted by Steinhaus (1946). Transovarian passage of the rickettsiae of Rocky Mountain spotted fever in ticks, and scrub typhus in chiggers, is evidence of a very intimate relationship.

Spirochetes causing relapsing fever are at least strain specific and in tick vectors are transmitted transovarially. Consult Chapter 18 for further details on these relationships.

The vertebrate protozoan pathogens transmitted by arthropods have progressed to the point where, in the sporozoa, elaborate developmental cycles may be present. Intuitively, because of the complexity of the developmental cycle of human malaria and restriction of the vectors to a single mosquito genus, it would appear that the mosquito host provides physical and chemical conditions that are absolutely unique. Nonetheless, studies of the most detailed sort do not clearly identify what specific factors are necessary. Ball (1965) identifies some of the conditions he and others have found in studying avian plasmodia. He concludes that the stomach (midgut) and salivary glands, specific sites of normal development, are not necessary in a physiological or biochemical sense in that oocysts dissected out of the stomach wall could be grown *in vitro* and would develop sporozoites infective for canaries when injected directly. The blood cell stages die out after a few asexual generations, but sexual stages in the mosquito and exerythrocytic stages in the vertebrate seem to provide trace substances that stimulate further development. Withdrawal of blood, as would occur when the vector feeds, seems to release some plasma factor that activates exflagellation of male gametes. The sexual stages and zygotes do not withstand a low temperature challenge, but oocysts, which are the next developmental stage in the mosquito, show resistance to temperatures well below those found in the vertebrate host. Finally, adaptation of the malaria parasite in the mosquito to the higher temperature it will encounter in the vertebrate host is only gradually acquired during its life cycle.

The evolution of malaria is of considerable interest, but too speculative and extensive in the literature to deal with in great detail here. Initial vertebrate or insect parasitism have both been proposed as the origin of malaria parasites. Manwell (1955) reasons that malaria parasites originated from coccidia in the intestine of reptiles, which preceded the bloodsucking Diptera, and at a more recent date insects became involved. The parasites reached birds from reptiles, and malaria is still very common in these two groups of vertebrates; introduction into mammals was more recent and infections are therefore less frequent and more pathogenic. Huff (1945) argues that Haemosporidiidea were originally parasites of Diptera and to the present they all possess dipterous hosts in which they pass a similar life cycle. These invertebrate hosts form a much closer group than do their more diverse vertebrate hosts. Human *Plasmodium* is believed by Bruce-Chwatt (1965) to have originated in tropical Africa, spreading up the Nile valley to eventually reach India and China and other parts of the world. As applied to the genus *Plasmodium* of mammals, Garnham (1966) notes that an Old World origin is indicated by the fact that the related genus *Hepatocystis* is apparently absent from the New World, and *Plasmodium* in the New World is confined to two species in monkeys despite its exuberant speciation among primates elsewhere.

From studying life cycles in existing nematodes, Anderson (1957) proposes that filariae evolved as follows: A common ancestor inhabited the gut of vertebrates in a simple life cycle. Ancestors established themselves in the eye socket region and larvae accumulated in lachrymal secretions from which they were taken up by arthropods and carried to the eyes of other hosts (*Thelazia*). Adult worms established in subcutaneous tissue and released infective larvae that were transferred by arthropods feeding on ulcerated skin lesions (*Stephanofilaria*). Adults and larvae developed in the skin where the latter were removed by bloodsucking insects (*Onchocerca*). Finally larvae accumulated in the peripheral blood and adult nematodes were free to colonize deeper tissues of the host (*Wuchereria* and *Brugia*).

Various observations on pathogens maintained under artificial and natural conditions for prolonged periods yield some insight into the stability of pathogenicity. After twenty-three years of cyclical transmission of *Trypanosoma rhodesiense* by *Glossina morsitans* through sheep, one strain of the pathogen remained infective for man (Ashcroft, 1959). In fact this finding suggested that *T. rhodesiense* is basically the same parasite as *T. gambiense*, but the former maintains a reservoir in wild animals whereas the latter is specifically a human pathogen. In comparing a strain of *T. rhodesiense* syringe-passaged for twenty years through rats and mice versus the same pathogen cyclically transmitted for a similar period by *Glossina morsitans* in sheep, Ashcroft (1960) found the syringe-passaged line to be consistently monomorphic in all animals whereas the fly-transmitted line was polymorphic. The syringe-passaged line would not infect man and was less virulent to several other mammals but was more virulent to rats. Recovery from the syringe-passaged line did not confer immunity against the fly-transmitted line, and the syringe-passaged line could no longer develop in *G. morsitans*. According to this author, differences noted were great enough to consider the two strains as separate species by criteria commonly applied to trypanosomes. In his review of transmission of relapsing fever spirochetes by ticks, Varma (1962) notes that prolonged mechanical passage in laboratory hosts results in partial or total loss of ability to develop in arthropod vectors.

Origins of Tissue Feeding or Internally Infesting Arthropods. The origins of major groups of arthropods of medical and veterinary importance have been sufficiently investigated, on the basis of paleontological and structural evidence, to permit summarization. The paleontological statements that follow, unless otherwise stated, are based on the publication of Rohdendorf (1962). The geologic terminology he uses is related to western terminology, which can in turn be placed on a more absolute time scale by consulting geological or paleontological texts. Comment will be restricted to tissue feeding or internally infesting arthropods, as these are related to the problem of parasitology and the associated transmission of vertebrate pathogens. The groups discussed will be in the same order as that adopted later in the main body of this text.

Bed bugs in the genus *Cimex* have been described from fossil remains, but these are of questionable identification. Usinger (1966), in his *Monograph of Cimicidae*, has commented at length on his own findings, and those of others, on the evolution of this family. These bugs are believed to be related to Anthocoridae, which prey on insects and mites and may occasionally bite warm-blooded animals, and to the Polyctenidae, which are permanent ectoparasites of bats. About half of the known genera are associated exclusively with bats, and nearly half of the remaining genera are associated exclusively with birds. The two human-infesting species of *Cimex* have followed man since the dawn of recorded history, but this association is relatively recent and is thought to have begun when man, bats, and bugs lived together in caves somewhere in the Middle East. It seems likely that permanent association occurred during man's movement from cave to village to city, say 8,000–5,000 B.C. Incomplete adaptation to man is suggested by the finding that feeding on a variety of animals and on man reveals that lowest egg production and longest developmental time results from utilizing the blood of man. Man's use of fire made him a more suitable host in temperate regions during winter, and tremendous increases in *C. lectularius* populations in northern European cities in the early twentieth century were undoubtedly favored by the use of central heating.

The triatomine Reduviidae, or *conenose bugs*, are known from Baltic amber, and a few of the existing genera are represented from the oldest Cenozoic of Europe and North

America. As this group is not exclusively associated with man or domestic animals, it seems to be composed of a predaceous group that adopted blood feeding on wild reptiles, birds, and mammals.

Rohdendorf speculates that *lice* arose from a psocopteran stem in the upper Carboniferous or Permian. Phylogeny of this group is stated briefly in Chapter 9.

The bloodsucking nematocerous Diptera, comprising *black flies* (Simuliidae), *sandflies* (*Phlebotomus*), and *mosquitoes* (Culicidae), have been placed by Rohdendorf in different superfamilies in the infraorder Tipulimorpha, with its origin in the Triassic. The fossil Simuliidae are represented by one genus from the Paleogene (Paleocene, Eocene, and Oligocene of western authors) of Europe, and the Baltic amber (Oligocene) and Neogene (Miocene and Pliocene of western authors) of western Europe. *Phlebotomus* are known from the Paleogene to the present. Culicidae are also represented from the Paleogene to the present, with three present day genera found in fossil beds of western Europe and North America. Ross (1964) has provided a well-documented analysis that includes phylogenetic lines of development for mosquitoes, and he concludes that for North America the ancestors of the major genera occurred during the Cretaceous period perhaps 100 million years ago.

The *horse flies* and *deer flies* (Tabanidae) and *snipe flies* (Rhagionidae) are grouped in a superfamily Tabanidea of the infraorder Asilomorpha that is itself separated from a bibionid stem in the Triassic. The Tabanidae are represented by a large number of genera, with three present genera from the Paleogene of Europe, and the Baltic amber and Neogene of western Europe. Some aspects of the evolution of Tabanidae are mentioned in Chapter 12. The Rhagionidae include extinct genera in the Jurassic. Five extant genera are found in the Neogene of Europe and from Baltic amber.

Muscoid flies, in general the Cyclorraphous Diptera, are represented by a stem derived from the Asilomorpha in the middle of the Cretaceous. The family Muscidae is of ancient origins; twenty genera that include about 400 species of the present fauna have been found in the Paleogene. Presence of the genus *Musca* in the tertiary fauna has not been confirmed. The tsetses, genus *Glossina*, presently restricted to Africa, are of considerable interest because four extinct species are known from the Oligocene Florissant shale beds of Colorado, United States (Buxton, 1955). Evolutionary trends in myiasis-causing flies have been documented by Zumpt (1965), and are also summarized in Chapter 16. Based on the finding of a fossil hippoboscid fly of advanced characteristics in Upper Oligocene shales of the Rhineland, Germany, Bequaert (1954) believes this family had much earlier origins, stating that "... primitive higher muscoid flies, of types that might have given rise to both the ancestral Proto-Hippoboscidae and Proto-Glossinidae, were already fairly abundant during Cretaceous times, if not earlier."

The *fleas* or Siphonaptera are included in fossil remains from the Paleogene to recent times. Two of the existing genera are represented by fossils from western Europe and the Baltic amber of Europe. Hinton (1958) places the origin of fleas from a mecopteran stem, stating that on the basis of larval structure they have been derived from a *Boreus*-like ancestor. Holland (1964) presents the view that although their actual origins are obscure, their isolated position as a distinct group, the existence of small families isolated on ancient continents, and distribution on hosts of all continents including the Arctic and Antarctic, all indicate a long history of dispersal and evolution.

Parasitic Acarina, namely the *ticks* and *mites*, appear to have had a common origin with ticks separating from the mesostigmatid mites at the beginning of the Permian. Parasitic mites are believed to have developed during the Devonian. The present ixodid tick genera *Ixodes* and *Dermacentor* are known from the Oligocene of North America.

6

CONTROL OF MEDICALLY IMPORTANT ARTHROPODS

The control of medically important arthropods employs many of the same principles used in controlling pests of agricultural importance. However, factors underlying the need for control may be quite different. The reader should bear in mind that discussion here will concentrate on arthropod control, *not disease control*, though controlling arthropod vectors may in some cases be the chief means of combating a given disease

Unique Aspects of Control in Medical Entomology. The basic purpose in controlling medically important arthropods is simply to

protect man. The control of arthropods to protect crops and livestock is fundamentally an economic matter in which costs must not exceed the value of increased production. The protection of human lives and the promotion of human physical comfort cannot be measured by monetary considerations alone because man views his personal welfare as priceless. Economic factors do enter the picture, however, because available resources for control are limited and most emphasis therefore centers on diseases of major importance. Furthermore such widespread debilitating diseases as malaria and Chagas' disease, causing death and considerable loss in productivity, can be an important factor blocking economic development in underdeveloped countries. Whole areas, including all the public and private land therein, are generally involved; and controlling arthropods that directly torment man gains ready support. One readily sees, therefore, that political interests and public relations also influence what will be controlled and at what costs.

Productivity of animals or animal products does provide a base for deciding whether control procedures are profitable on livestock. Loss of production may be due to pathogens transmitted by arthropods, or to the direct effects of arthropod attack. Where death or crippling disability of livestock results from arthropod-transmitted disease, the need for control is clear. In such cases, however, the disease may often be most readily controlled through immunization rather than control of the vector; as examples, immunization of horses is more effective than mosquito control in preventing losses from western encephalitis; likewise immunization reduces losses of poultry from avian pox virus.

The amount of reduced productivity of animals annoyed or debilitated by the attack of arthropod parasites may be difficult to determine, particularly in instances where attack is occurring under more-or-less natural conditions such as in range or pasture land. Livestock management will also have some bearing on whether losses are experienced. As an example, on dairy cattle in Pennsylvania, Cheng and Kesler (1961) found that controlling biting and merely annoying flies with sprays and aerosols had no significant effect on milk production of well-managed herds provided with supplementary feed, though a poorly managed herd with less pasture responded favorably. Where biting fly populations are heavy, increased income well beyond the cost of control by sprays may be realized for dairy herds (Granett and Hansens, 1957). One study on the chicken body louse *Menacanthus stramineus* (Nitzsch) indicated experimental infestations yielded a fifteen per cent reduction in egg production over a fourteen-week period (Gless and Raun, 1959), whereas another study found no differences in egg production or other factors (Stockdale and Raun, 1960). An example of a debilitating pest is the tick, *Boophilus microplus* (Canestrini), which causes serious damage to rangeland cattle in Australia. In Queensland, Little (1963) found that average daily infestations of forty to eighty engorged ticks of this species through the season would reduce expected annual weight increases of heifers by 56 to 160 pounds.

Large-Scale Campaigns. The need for widespread and thorough area control of arthropods in many disease control programs also imposes certain problems. Increasingly the effective implementation of programs for medically important arthropods requires comprehensive areawide measures, seldom achievable through the voluntary cooperation of individuals. Supervision has evolved from local governments, such as city governments, to somewhat larger units of county or state governments, to national governments, to hemispheric multinational units like the Pan American Health Organization (PAHO), to the ultimate supervision of an international agency such as the World Health Organization (WHO). With international agreements the objectives have also expanded to include schemes as extensive as worldwide eradication of malaria, and worldwide eradication of the mosquito *Aedes aegypti*. For a discussion of universal eradication schemes the student is referred to Hinman (1966).

The use of pesticides introduces further complications concerning public domain and the rights and well being of individuals. Because of the long term persistence of many toxicants, the biological concentration of some toxicants, and the dangers to fish, birds, and mammals (including man) attendant upon their improper use, much research and adequate safeguards as well as appropriate public education are needed before embarking on schemes requiring the widespread use of pesticides. Agencies responsible for control of arthropods in recreational areas, forests, marshlands, and other public lands must have the responsible use of pesticides as one of their main objectives. By now it has been extensively documented that it is nearly impossible to apply pesticides without directly or indirectly affecting forms of life other than the intended target.

Unique characteristics of the life history and behavior of many medically important arthropods provide specific methods for their control. For example the immature stages of many medically important Diptera are limited to water, making water management an especially effective means for controlling mosquitoes, black flies, ceratopogonids, and tabanids. The vector's habit of entering dwellings in search of a human host provides unique opportunities for controlling many of the most potent mosquito vectors of malaria. Arthropods highly dependent on a vertebrate host can be effectively controlled by methods that take advantage of this dependency, such as using animal systemic insecticides for cattle grub and ectoparasite control, or the frequent laundering and changing of garments to control the human body louse.

The mere alleviation of annoyance has been a prime motivating factor responsible for many control programs; particularly for many of the mosquito abatement districts that include coastal salt marshes of the United States. Increased use of coastal lands for recreational, residential, and agricultural purposes, and attendant increases in property values, has been possible only with the development of effective mosquito-control schemes in the states of New Jersey, Delaware, Florida, and California. With such developments malaria has disappeared, though *Anopheles* control was often not the main purpose for starting control districts. Continued effective control by abatement agencies is very likely a deterrent to arthropod-borne virus (arbovirus) transmission, and the organizational resources available can be immediately mobilized to reduce vector populations in the event of outbreaks. Annoyance occasioned by household contaminators such as house flies, cluster flies, and cockroaches has been a motivating force in the development of urban public health agencies.

The spread of vectors to areas where they do not ordinarily exist, or from where they have been eradicated, is a matter of great concern. Rapid transport of vectors, even at intercontinental distances, is an increasing possibility; the more so because of projected rapid expansion in international jet aircraft traffic. Even before extensive air travel, the introduction of *Anopheles gambiae* Giles from Africa caused catastrophic epidemics of malaria in Brazil that threatened all the Americas until the mosquito was finally eradicated (Soper and Wilson, 1943).

Control programs may have as their objective the reduction of a vector population below a level that can maintain a disease. Though it is theoretically possible for a single infective vector to transmit a pathogen (a fact readily demonstrable in the laboratory), to keep a stable level of a disease in nature requires a minimal size of vector population; and to create epidemics large increases of vector populations in contact with the host are necessary. In malaria eradication schemes, reduction, but not eradication, of the vector population has often been an attainable goal. It is being successfully accomplished by applying residual insecticides to surfaces on which *Anopheles* rest in human dwellings throughout much of Asia and South America.

Eradication of medically important arthropods, or arthropod-transmitted pathogens, on a definable area basis or as a worldwide goal, is technically feasible in certain instances. In all cases thus far proposed or attempted, technical skills and monetary supports have been sufficient to focus control procedures on a given vector species; or organizational skills have been adequate to concentrate on reducing the pathogen incidence to an unsustainable level, consolidating cleared areas, and further concentrating on remaining affected areas. It is noteworthy that in the major schemes proposed, man and the vector(s) constitute either the entire reservoir or the most significant portion of the biocenose.

METHODS OF ARTHROPOD CONTROL

Controlling arthropods generally implies reduction in their numbers, but as used here it also includes methods preventing them physical access to a vertebrate host. Prevention of annoyance, as directly applied to man and his domestic animals, may be broadly grouped under the heading of personal protection.

PERSONAL PROTECTION

Under personal protection three general categories may be distinguished: (1) *physical barriers* between a vertebrate and arthropods; (2) *chemical barriers* that repel an arthropod from actually biting; and (3) *arthropod toxicants* that are applied directly to or within a vertebrate. The subject of arthropod toxicants will be dealt with shortly in discussing insecticides, acaricides, formulations, and application equipment.

Physical Barriers. Screening fabricated of metal or durable plastic placed at potential entrances to man's dwellings (and those of his domesticated animals) is one of the most effective means of reducing arthropod attack. Use of screening, for the purpose of barring mosquitoes and houseflies, was decidedly a contributing factor in the decline of malaria in the United States. Bacillary dysentery outbreaks and intestinal myiasis were also undoubtedly reduced when this procedure denied access of house flies and other filth flies to food in homes and at the point of processing and vending. There is little doubt that widespread use of screening in less technologically developed nations would greatly reduce arthropod-related disease, but though the basic costs of such procedures are reasonable, cultural acceptance is required, and, particularly in the tropics, the construction of dwellings would often have to be altered. Even in so-called advanced cultures there may be apathy toward the use of window and door screening in the belief that screening reduces excessively the exchange of fresh air. In certain areas fine screening should be used to prevent passage of very small biting flies, such as *Phlebotomus* and Ceratopogonidae.

Where circumstances do not permit house screening, fabric netting may be practical.

In the tropics, sleeping under bed nets is effective in reducing malaria, filariasis, and dengue where these diseases are transmitted primarily by nocturnally active vectors. Likewise, protection against hordes of Arctic tundra mosquitoes and other biting flies is possible with appropriate clothing and a head net that is kept away from the skin. Leggings, particularly when treated with repellents, can prevent immediate access to the skin on the lower body and thereby delay attack by ticks and mites.

Other physical barriers have been used in specific situations, and doubtless still more could be developed. The increased use of air conditioning, primarily for man's comfort at high temperature, has reduced insect attack within buildings because windows and doors must be closed for efficient operation of the air conditioner. The Congo floor maggot, *Auchmeromyia luteola* (Fabricius), feeds on warm-blooded animals in contact with the floor or ground. Protection from this insect can be achieved merely by using a bed, a sleeping platform off the floor, or a hammock.

Chemical Barriers. By chemical barriers are meant substances that, when applied to a vertebrate host or to clothing, will repel attacking arthropods. These substances are commonly called *repellents.* Repellency is generally not effective at a great distance, and there may still be considerable annoyance through persistent flying or crawling. The main feature of repellency is that arthropods leave without actually feeding. Rate of loss of repellents varies, the main causes being absorption and abrasion (Smith, *et al.*, 1963). Some insecticides that are essentially nontoxic to man can act as repellents, but the materials commonly used are also of low toxicity to arthropods. Repellents found effective against blood-sucking arthropods are generally of little use against merely annoying species such as filth flies or *Hippelates* eye gnats. An effective repellent is reported against the bush fly, *Musca vetustissima* Walk, a notorious pest attracted to human eyes and lips in Australia (Waterhouse, 1966).

Certain features are essential in repellents. They must be (1) highly repellent to blood-sucking arthropods but not unpleasant to humans; (2) long lasting; (3) nontoxic and non-irritating to skin; (4) stainless. Additional desirable features include innocuous tactile qualities (for example do not feel sticky or greasy), low cost, and no solvent action on plastics or synthetic fiber.

Most repellents in common use at the present time meet the essential requirements listed. Some of the eleven commercial products listed in Kenaga (1966) are used to protect livestock. Two compounds, commonly in use for humans in the United States, are mentioned here because of their particular value in preventing attack by mosquitoes and other biting flies. The compound termed *deet* (N, N-diethyl-m-toluamide) is the active ingredient in many proprietary products. It is noted for its essential odorlessness, water-like texture, and long-lasting effectiveness. It causes a burning sensation in eyes, cuts, and membranous areas, and will damage some plastic and synthetic fibers.

deet

Another well-known product is ethyl hexanediol (2-ethyl-1, 3-hexanediol; 6–12®). Its qualities are similar to *deet*, though it is generally not as long lasting.

ethyl hexanediol

Both repellents may be formulated in liquid or paste-like form for application, or as a pressurized spray; the latter formulation is advantageous for application to clothing. Clothing may also be treated by saturating garments in 5 per cent emulsion, or 5 per cent solution of repellent in a volatile solvent.

ENVIRONMENTAL MANIPULATION

Environmental manipulation includes all procedures that specifically modify the environment in which an arthropod breeds so that it is no longer suitable for that purpose. Environmental modification may consist of complete and permanent change—for example draining mosquito-producing waters—or less-permanent change such as that which occurs when a salt marsh is diked and kept flooded for several months to control mosquitoes and *Culicoides* (Rogers, 1962). Thorough knowledge of the life history and biology of the vector in question is required for a successful program. It is also necessary to be certain that the modification practiced will not provide favorable conditions for a different pest.

Where otherwise compatible with man's uses, environmental modification is a desirable goal because of its permanent nature. It is also termed *source reduction* when it prevents a buildup of vectors by denying the growth stages a place to develop. Initial costs of source reduction programs such as deforestation barrier zones, drainage ditching, or landfill may be high, but the permanent effectiveness of such programs (perhaps with some annual maintenance) reduces the need for temporary measures that must be applied seasonally.

Permanent source reduction is often consistent with good agricultural practice. In fact, poor agronomic practices can result in a potential for mosquito production (Davis, 1964). Drainage that solves marshy conditions in fields, to remove mosquito breeding, will frequently simultaneously increase yields of many crops and allow equipment more ready access for tillage. Suggestions for water

Fig. 6-1 Breaks in the irrigation ditch are responsible for considerable inundation, producing favorable breeding places for mosquitoes. Similarly, seepage from such ditches into borrow pits or low-lying areas may be highly productive of mosquitoes. The rapidly running water in the ditch is unfavorable for breeding.

Fig. 6-2 Seepage water below impoundment (O'Sullivan Dam, Grant County, Washington; the dam is out of the picture, to the left). Seepage water, producing large numbers of *Anopheles freeborni,* is encroaching upon a road where, 2 or 3 years before, the dominant vegetation was sagebrush. (Photograph by Harry G. Davis.)

resource management may be consulted in *Prevention and control of vector problems associated with water resources,* Washington, U.S. Department of Health, Education, and Welfare, 1965.

One type of effective environmental manipulation consists of pasture rotation to reduce populations of certain ticks attacking livestock. The object is to remove stock so that ticks that have left the host to molt will not find a blood meal for the next stage, thereby experiencing heavy mortality before stock is returned. In arid areas this method can be particularly effective because a hot and dry environment is detrimental to ticks. In addition, the periodic "spelling" of grazing lands permits good regrowth of forage.

Certain other types of environmental modification can be listed as examples. The removal of nests and nesting places for pigeons and other birds is an effective means of preventing annoying numbers of bird mites from entering homes and biting humans. Water level management in reservoir systems as practiced in the Tennessee Valley Authority (United States) has been long recognized as an effective means of reducing *Anopheles* breeding. In this case reservoirs are filled to capacity with spring runoff, then are drained in sudden steps throughout the summer to prevent floating debris and plant growth at the margins. By this means sheltered sites that protect *Anopheles* larvae from wave action are reduced. Most species of tsetse will not readily fly across open zones. In control schemes areas are separated by corridors cleared of trees and brush vegetation, thereby preventing reinvasion of freed areas from regions still harboring flies.

An area free from certain vectors, either naturally or as a consequence of control programs, may need protection from invasion. This protection is recognized to be of increasing importance with the expanding amount and speed of air traffic. The matter has become of such concern that the World Health Organization has devoted much effort toward controlling the problem and has recommended routine insecticidal treatment of aircraft traveling between countries. Again, in preventing transport of tsetse flies, it has been necessary to place vehicle check points on roads entering control zones. At these points vehicles are sprayed with insecticide to prevent the flies from traveling in or on them.

A few examples will indicate how serious are recent problems of vector introduction. Eradication of *Aedes aegypti* was achieved in

Fig. 6-3 Drainage water resulting from faulty irrigation, a source of numerous mosquitoes.

Fig. 6-4 Storage sump collects extra irrigation water to be used again. This prevents water from standing in fields in shallow puddles. (Photograph by Roy McCarrell; courtesy of the Delta Mosquito Abatement District, Visalia, California.)

French Guiana in 1952, but a reinfestation was discovered in 1959. This reinfestation extended 125 miles in two months, nearly 3,000 square miles were affected in seven months, and the evidence suggested spread by land vehicles (Fontan and Fauran, 1961). Interceptions of traffic arriving at international airports in the United States and Puerto Rico for the years 1947–60 revealed 20,000 mosquitoes of eighty-seven species; forty-eight were indigenous and four species were alive when found (Hughes, 1961). *Aedes nocturnus* (Theobald), a potential vector of Japanese encephalitis, was intercepted a number of times in Hawaii on quarantine inspection of aircraft. In 1962 this species was taken at light traps and subsequent examination showed it to be spread throughout most of the island of Oahu and also established on Kauai (Joyce and Nakagawa, 1964). Quarantine inspections of bananas imported from Mexico revealed chigger mites and a tick (on small mammals), nine species of cockroaches, four species of scorpions, and the mosquito *Culex pipiens quinquefasciatus* Wiedemann (Eads, *et al.*, 1966). The tsetse, *Glossina palpalis* (Rob-

ineau-Desvoidy), was eradicated from the island of Principe but was later reintroduced, presumably from the island of Fernando Po some 125 miles distant (Azevedo, *et al.*, 1956).

BIOLOGICAL CONTROL (BIOCONTROL)

All animal populations, including those of medically important arthropods, are reduced in numbers by certain other forms of life. For arthropods these destructive control agents are categorized as predators (both vertebrate and invertebrate), parasites (generally meaning metazoan arthropods or nematodes), or pathogens (viruses, rickettsiae, bacteria, fungi, protozoa). Though biocontrol agents occur under natural conditions, without the aid of man they seldom reduce vector populations to a level too low to maintain a disease. Even when these agents drastically reduce vector populations, they do not ordinarily do so until after the vectors have reached an undesirably high level. For this reason biological control agents are manipulated in the hope that they can more effectively control vector populations.

Biological control is often most effective when agents found naturally in the area of origin are introduced to control an imported pest.

Principles and procedures involved in using biological agents to control medically important arthropods are the same as those used in controlling agricultural pests; such methods are discussed at length in Steinhaus (1963) and DeBach (1964). Further sources of information include reviews of biocontrol in Australia and Australian New Guinea (Wilson, 1960, 1963), a survey of fungal diseases of insects (Müller-Kogler, 1965), and an annotated bibliography of the pathogens, parasites, and predators of medically important arthropods (Jenkins, 1964). Biological control is a field of much current activity, and new developments are frequent.

Because of the lag in development of effective populations of biological control agents, major effort may be directed toward their rearing and release. Other means of improving biocontrol include better distribution of naturally occurring agents, or the provision of environments that favor their survival. An awareness of naturally present biocontrol agents is important to prevent, as much as possible, their destruction when any control procedures are used.

Biocontrol has some of the same advantages as environmental manipulation, namely once controlling agents have been successfully established in an area they may remain as permanent vector suppressants. Furthermore, biocontrol agents such as predators or parasites can have the specific advantage of actively seeking out prey; or their life history may be so intimately coordinated with that of their host that they respond to the same environmental factors that cause renewed growth and development. Examples of the latter situation occur with mermithid nematodes, which parasitize *Culicoides*, and certain South American egg-laying fishes that are predators on mosquito larvae, both of which occur as resistant eggs that hatch with the flooding that initiates development of their prey. Adaptation, unfortunately, often causes controlling agents to become less effective; one common feature of parasitism is that long-term association of host and parasite tends to reduce the effectiveness of the latter. In a study of parasitism of the house fly by the wasp *Nasonia vitripennis* (Wlk.), reproductive capacity of the latter over a period of nearly three years declined from about 135 to 39 per female, with an overall 50 per cent decrease in average parasite density (Pimentel and Al-Hafidh, 1965).

Environmental modification and improved biological control can be linked effectively; for example, keeping waterways free of emergent vegetation provides fish and predaceous aquatic insects ready access to mosquito larvae and pupae.

INSECTICIDES AND ACARICIDES

Effective, long-lasting contact insecticides were developed during World War II. During that conflict DDT was found to be spectacularly effective against human body lice, mosquitoes, and various muscoid flies, and was credited with controlling outbreaks of malaria, typhus, and dysentery. The historical aspects of the development of DDT and its use in human and veterinary medicine are covered in Simmons (1959).

Since World War II there has been a vast proliferation of many kinds of organic chemical control agents, until, by 1966, some 210 compounds actually used or extensively field tested, were listed for the United States (Kenaga, 1966). This number includes plant and synthetic products, insecticides, acaricides (effective against ticks and/or mites), repellents, attractants, fumigants, synergists, and chemosterilants. The listing by Kenaga is used here, and is extremely helpful because it provides common names of compounds approved by the Entomological Society of America and by *Chemical Abstracts*, in addition to providing other names and trademarks, structural formulas, manufacturers, and mammalian toxicity. This listing, in the *Bulletin of the Entomological Society of America,* has been revised about every three years. The World Health Organization also prepares lists of chemicals used to control medically important arthropods.

Many nations restrict the use of pesticides, and publish frequently revised listings that provide official limitations on types and amounts of chemicals that can be used for specific purposes. Agricultural Handbook 331, "*Suggested Guide for the Use of Insecticides to Control Insects Affecting Crops, Livestock, Households, Stored Products, and Forest Products,*" published annually by the United States Department of Agriculture, includes useful information. The *Summary of Registered Agricultural Pesticide Chemical Uses,* with its frequent revisions, available from the Superintendent of Documents, U.S. Government Printing Office, Washington, D.C., provides current information on official pesticide tolerances for the United States.

SYSTEMIC INSECTICIDES

Specific mention must be made of the systemic insecticides that have been developed to provide outstanding control of livestock pests, most notably of cattle grubs. Development of systemics has been a great achievement. Systemic insecticides, as the name implies, are toxicants that can be absorbed by an animal and circulate through its body to control pests internally and at some distance from the area of absorption. A future challenge lies in the possibility of developing satisfactory systemic insecticides and repellents for treating man. Systemics work well on internal parasites, and on ectoparasites that depend wholly on frequent feeding upon the blood and tissues of the host. Though systemics may also render blood toxic for flying insects, they could not exert much control unless the host was a more or less exclusive food source of the vector in question. Some requirements for good systemics are: (1) high toxicity for arthropods and low toxicity for

the vertebrate host; (2) elimination of the toxicant from the vertebrate so that its meat and products do not contain harmful residues; (3) ease of application, particularly for animals on range. Systemic insecticides are administered by: (a) forced feeding of a bolus (large pill), not used much because easier methods of application are known; (b) thorough spraying or dipping to cause absorption through the skin; (c) pouring a concentrated formulation along the back of the animal (pour-on-treatment); or (d) adding to feed or mineral salt. A largely historical review of methods used in the development of animal systemics is provided by Bushland *et al.,* 1963.

Obviously, the objectives of a control program govern the kind of chemicals used, the type of application equipment, the formulation of insecticide, and the extent of the area to be treated. *Source treatment,* applying pesticide to the area where immature forms are developing, is generally conceded to be more efficient as a control measure than application aimed at adults, especially if the adults are flying insects. The nature and extent of the source, however, are of prime importance. Where sources are aquatic environments harboring valuable fish and wildlife, or are difficult to identify as in jungle environments, or are at some distance as may be the case with flying insects, it may be simpler to aim control methods at the adult stage. Insecticidal control of flying vectors is generally practiced by (1) treating a limited area on which the vector habitually rests (such as walls of houses), or (2) laying down a barrier zone around a community in the knowledge that flying insects will frequently rest on vegetation during their flight activities, or (3) using finely dispersed sprays to treat large portions of the aerial environment. Whatever methods are used, protecting man and other organisms from the effects of pesticides, and preventing food crop residues, must always be kept in mind.

The attempt is made here to provide a classified list, mainly from the inclusive work of Kenaga (1966), of only those compounds used to control arthropods affecting man and animals. Additions to this listing will doubtless occur in the future. Repellents have been discussed under personal protection.

BOTANICALS AND DERIVATIVES

Rotenone is derived from *Derris* and *Lonchocarpus* plants; it has extremely low dermal, and rather low oral, mammalian toxicity.

rotenone

Pyrethrum is a mixture of four compounds, termed pyrethrins, principally obtained from the plant *Chrysanthemum cinariaefolium*. The nature of the four compounds is dependent on the chemical groups or radicals added to the points designated as *R* in the basic pyrethrum formula shown below. Extremely low dermal toxicity and rather low oral toxicity to warm-blooded animals, slight insect repellency, and rapid knockdown are characteristics.

pyrethrum

Allethrin is a synthetic analog of pyrethrum with many of the same characteristics.

Nicotine (1-1-methyl-2-(3-pyridyl)-pyrrolidine) is an alkaloid from the tobacco plant. It has moderate dermal and oral mammalian toxicity. Nicotine sulfate is used to paint roosts of domestic fowl to control mites.

SYNERGISTS

Particularly when used with pyrethrum and derivatives, certain compounds that in themselves are essentially nontoxic will greatly synergize or activate toxicity for arthropods. These synergists are commonly used with pyrethrum to reduce costs. Some seven compounds are noted for their synergistic properties, the three most common being *piperonyl butoxide* (a-[2-(2-butoxyethoxy)ethoxy]-4,5-methylenedioxy-2-propyltoluene; Butocide®); *sesamex* (acetaldehyde 2-(2-ethoxyethoxy)ethyl 3,4-methylene-dioxyphenyl acetal; Sesoxane®) and *sulfoxide* (1,2-methylenedioxy-4-[2-(octyl-sulfinyl)propyl] benzene; Sulfox-Cide®).

MISCELLANEOUS COMPOUNDS

Some compounds not readily classifiable under main groupings have shown promise for controlling arthropods. Two thiocyanates are noted for quick knockdown of flies, and have found use in livestock sprays and in fogging for adult mosquitoes. The compound 2-(2-butoxyethoxy)ethyl thiocyanate (Lethane 384®) has relatively low mammalian toxicity, and isobornyl thiocyanatoacetate (Thanite ®) has extremely low mammalian toxicity.

DDT RELATIVES (DIPHENYL ALIPHATIC CHLORINATED HYDROCARBONS)

DDT (1,1,1-trichloro-2,2-bis(p-chlorophenyl ethane) is probably the best known of all synthetic insecticides. Its desirable features are outstanding properties as a contact insecticide, utility against a wide variety of insects, long-lasting residue, and relatively low mammalian toxicity. Drawbacks include persistence when found where not desired, the tendency to be concentrated in certain organisms in food chains, and the ability of many arthropods to develop high resistance to it.

DDT

A close relative of DDT is *methoxychlor* (1,1,1-trichloro-2, 2-bis(p-methoxyphenyl)ethane; methoxy DDT, Marlate®), differing from the parent compound in that each chlorine atom attached to the phenyls is replaced by a methoxy group. It has extremely low mammalian toxicity and is rapidly excreted by mammals.

Certain other relatives of *DDT*, namely Dimite®, *dicofol* (Kelthane®), and *chlorobenzilate*, are noted for specific mite toxicity and low mammalian toxicity. These have been largely limited to experimental control of acarines affecting man and animals.

CHLORINATED ARYL HYDROCARBONS (SIX OR MORE CHLORINES)

Chlorinated aryl hydrocarbon compounds also have relatively long residual toxicity, and are for the most part mainly contact in action. They vary from rather low mammalian toxicity (*chlordane* and *mirex*) to quite high mammalian toxicity (*lindane, heptachlor, toxaphene, dieldrin*, and *endrin*).

Best known of these compounds, for controlling medically important insects, is *dieldrin* (85 per cent or more of 1,2,3,4,10,10-hexachloro-6,7-epoxy-1,4,4a,5,6,7,8,8a-octahydro-1, 4-*endoexo*-5, 8-dimethanonaphthalene). This compound has found widespread use as a residual application on resting sites for mosquitoes, but rapid resistance has developed in some cases, and improper use has resulted in a number of human poisoning incidents.

dieldrin

Compounds rather related to *dieldrin* are *chlordane* (1,2,4,5,6,7,8,8-octachloro-3a,4,7,7a-tetrahydro-4,7-methanoindane), *heptachlor* (1, 4,5,6,7,8,8-heptachloro-3a,4,7,7a-tetrahydro-4,7-methanoindane), and *toxaphene* (chlorinated camphene containing 67 to 69 per cent chlorine).

The gamma isomer of benzene hexachloride (BHC), called *lindane* (99 per cent or more γ

isomer of 1,2,3,4,5,6-hexachlorocyclohexane), is used as a contact insecticide with rather prolonged residual properties; crude BHC made up of mixed isomers has similar properties but is generally restricted to outdoor application because of a disagreeable musty odor.

lindane

The compounds *mirex* (dodecachlorooctahydro-1,3,4-methano-2H-cyclobuta [c,d] pentalene) and Kepone®(decachloroocta hydro-1,3,4-metheno-2H-cyclobuta [c,d] pentalene-2-one) have proved particularly useful in baits for ants, and Kepone® has also found similar usage against cockroaches.

ORGANOPHOSPHORUS (OP) COMPOUNDS

More organophosphorus compounds have been synthesized as insecticides and acaricides than any other group of compounds. They are characterized as nerve poisons, some members having extremely high mammalian toxicity whereas others are quite nontoxic; residual activity is shorter as a group than is characteristic of chlorinated hydrocarbons, and buildup in food chains is less likely; vapor toxicity is a useful characteristic in some cases; some members are excellent animal systemics.

ALIPHATIC DERIVATIVES OF PHOSPHORUS COMPOUNDS

The best-known compound in this group is *malathion* (diethylmercaptosuccinate, S-ester with 0,0-dimethyl phosphorodithioate). Mammalian toxicity of this compound is low, there is short residual activity, and it has proved effective for a number of medically important arthropods. Resistance has become a problem in many cases.

$$\text{(CH}_3\text{O)}_2\overset{\underset{\displaystyle \text{S}}{\|}}{\text{P}}-\text{S}-\overset{\underset{\displaystyle}{|}}{\underset{\displaystyle}{\text{CH}}}\text{CH}_2\text{C}-\text{CO}_2\text{H}_5$$

malathion

The compound *trichlorfon* (dimethyl [2,2,2-trichloro-1-hydroxyethyl] phosphate; Dipterex®, Dylox®, Neguvon®) has rather low mammalian toxicity and is highly water soluble, making it ideal for use in sugar baits to control flies. Rather low mammalian toxicity is also a characteristic of *naled* (1,2-dibromo-2,2-dichloroethyl dimethyl phosphate; Dibrom®), though this compound appears to be irritating to man and animals.

High vapor toxicity for arthropods makes *dichlorvos* (2,2-dichlorovinyl dimethyl phosphate; Vapona®, DDVP) extremely useful in reaching otherwise inaccessible areas. This compound can be formulated in a plastic resin that delays vaporization and thereby provides long-lasting control.

$$\text{(CH}_3\text{O)}_2\overset{\underset{\displaystyle \text{O}}{\|}}{\text{P}}-\text{O}-\text{CH}\!=\!\text{CCl}_2$$

dichlorvos

Animal systemic qualities are found in *dimethoate* (0,0-dimethyl S-[methylcarbamoylmethyl] phosphorodithioate; Cygon®, Perfekthion®, Rogor®), which can also be used as a direct contact insecticide with good residual properties and moderate mammalian toxicity.

ARYL (PHENYL) DERIVATIVES OF PHOSPHORUS COMPOUNDS

The compound *parathion* (0,0-diethyl 0-*p*-nitrophenyl phosphorothioate) has wide activity against many arthropods but its use is limited due to very high mammalian toxicity, requiring skill and caution in application.

Similar precautions are advised in using EPN (0-ethyl 0-*p*-nitrophenyl phenylphosphonothioate) and compound 4072 (2-chloro-1-[2,4-dichlorophenyl] vinyl diethyl phosphate). Moderate mammalian toxicity is characteristic of Ciodrin® (*a*-methylbenzyl 3-hydroxycrotonate dimethylphos phate) and *fenthion* (0,0-dimethyl 0-[4-(methylthio)-*m*-tolyl] phosphorothioate; Baytex®), the latter having notably low fish toxicity. Very low mammalian and fish toxicity are characteristics of Abate® (0,0,0',0'-tetramethyl 0-0'-thiodi-*p*-phenylene phosphorothioate). Important animal systemics in this group of compounds include *ronnel* (0,0-dimethyl 0-2,4,5-trichlorophenyl phosphorothioate; Trolene®) and Ruelene® (0-4-*tert*-butyl-2-chlorophenyl 0-methyl methylphosphoramidate).

$$\text{(C}_2\text{H}_5\text{O)}_2\overset{\underset{\displaystyle \text{S}}{\|}}{\text{P}}-\text{O}-\!\!\!\bigcirc\!\!\!-\text{NO}_2$$

parathion

HETEROCYCLIC DERIVATIVES OF PHOSPHORUS COMPOUNDS

Among the heterocyclic derivatives of phosphorus compounds the best known is *diazinon* (0,0-diethyl 0-[2-isopropyl-6-methyl-4-pyrimidinyl]phosphorothioate), characterized by moderately high mammalian toxicity and somewhat longer residual activity than most organophosphorus compounds.

$$\text{(C}_2\text{H}_5\text{O)}_2\overset{\underset{\displaystyle \text{S}}{\|}}{\text{P}}-\text{O}-\!\!\!\bigcirc\!\!\!-\text{CH(CH}_3)_2$$
$$\text{CH}_3$$

diazinon

The compound Dursban® (0,0-diethyl 0-[3,5,6-trichloro-2-pyridyl] phosphorothioate) has moderate mammalian toxicity, and dioxathion (S,S'-p-dioxane-2,3-diyl 0,0-diethyl phosphorodithioate cis and trans isomers; Delnav®) has high toxicity. The product *coumaphos* (0-[3-chloro-4-methyl-2-oxo-2H-1-benzopyran-7-yl] 0,0-diethyl phosphorothioate; CO-RAL® is an animal systemic.

Three aziridinyl compounds, *tepa* (tris [1-aziridinyl] phosphine oxide), its methyl derivative *metepa* (tris [2 methyl-1-aziridinyl] phosphine oxide) and *apholate* (2,2,4,4,6,6-hexakis-[1-aziridinyl]-2,2,4,4,6,6-hexahydro-1,3,5,2,4,6-triazatriphosphorine) have found extensive experimental use as chemosterilants.

metepa

CARBAMATES

Carbamates have been developed for arthropod control more recently than have the organophosphorus compounds. Some have extremely high mammalian toxicity; however, *carbaryl* (1-naphthyl methylcarbamate; Sevin®), the carbamate most used in controlling medically important arthropods, is noted for very low mammalian toxicity.

carbaryl

SULFONATES, SULFIDES, SULFONES, SULFONAMIDES, SULFITES

The sulfonate group contains several specific acaricides with very low mammalian toxicity. Because their use for ectoparasite control is mostly experimental, they are simply listed here as *ovex* (Ovotran®, chlorfenson), Genite 923®, *tetrasul* (ANIMERT V-101), and *chlorbenside* (Chlorocide®, Mitox®).

MICROBIAL INSECTICIDES

A number of bacteria, fungi, Protozoa, and viruses have been tested as arthropod-controlling agents and for possibilities of commercial development. Of these only *Bacillus thuringiensis* Berliner has had extensive development and has received adequate testing against medically important arthropods. This is an aerobic spore former that occurs in many strains of varying effectiveness, and is nontoxic to mammals. The resistant spores are formulated and marketed under specific trade names. For many insects toxicity is attributed to a crystalline structure in the spore, but such does not appear to be the case when the spores are fed as additives in livestock feed; rather house fly larvae developing in cattle feces are affected by an extracrystal toxin, which is not especially toxic, so large amounts must be fed. Though other microbial agents effective against medically important arthropods have not been developed commercially, their widespread occurrence in nature suggests that such possibilities will be explored.

INORGANIC COMPOUNDS

Some inorganic compounds have found limited use in controlling medically important arthropods. Powdered *sulfur*, added to an inert carrier such as talcum, helps to control ectoparasites of poultry when placed in dusting boxes. Various arsenicals find use; notably *Paris green* for controlling mosquito larvae, and *lead arsenate* as a livestock dip to control ectoparasites.

One group of inorganics has useful properties as desiccating agents, causing death of arthropods by water loss. Various formulations of *silica gel* have this characteristic, and have proved useful under some conditions for ectoparasite and household pest control because they are virtually nontoxic to warm-blooded animals.

INSECTICIDE RESISTANCE

The high degree of selective pressure placed by modern organic insecticides upon arthropod populations has caused the development of many cases of marked resistance. In 1968, on a worldwide basis, it was reported that ninety-seven species of insects and acarines of public health and veterinary importance had developed resistance to one or more insecticides (Brown, 1968). Ultimately, resistance reaches so high a level that a toxicant can no longer be used in an area where it was formerly effective. The appearance of resistance is so dramatic, and such a threat to adequate control, that the underlying mechanisms are being thoroughly studied. To cite all examples and mechanisms of resistance is impossible here; the interested student should review articles such as Brown, 1958; WHO Technical Report Series No. 265 (1963) and 268 (1964), and particularly the exhaustive treatment in Brown (1967). It will suffice here to cite factors governing resistance, and to use a few examples as illustrations.

The term *resistance* requires clarification. In the context of this discussion the term resistance will be applied only to arthropods no longer controlled by a formerly effective pesticide, for our purposes meaning at least two to ten times (and often as much as 100 times) as much toxicant as was initially used is required to achieve the same degree of control. Prior to the actual development of resistance there may be some slight increase in required dosage, but this condition is due to a more vigorous population rather than a specific mechanism and is termed *vigor tolerance* (Hoskins and Gordon, 1956).

The underlying process controlling the appearance of resistance is genetic selection. With that basic knowledge it has been possible to analyze factors governing the degree of resistance and rapidity of its development. Factors favoring the development of resistance in a natural population of arthropods include: (1) The selection pressure; resistance to a given pesticide develops with maximum rapidity the more effective the control has been, and exposure of all stages of an arthropod causes resistance to develop more rapidly than if the pesticide is applied against a single stage only. (2) The generation time of an arthropod; more rapid development of resistance is likely in an arthropod having several generations per year than one having only a single generation. (3) Complexity of the gene pool governing resistance; rapid development of resistance is most likely where a single gene governs the resistance mechanism, and slow where several genes along with associated genes must be selected out.

Several mechanisms of resistance have been distinguished. *Physiological resistance* refers to (1) the presence of detoxifying enzyme systems, best known for DDT and its analogs (see Lipke and Kearns, 1960); (2) absorption of toxicant by lipids, thought to occur in some cases of cyclodiene (dieldrin and so forth) resistance; (3) impermeability, in which in some instances resistant strains apparently do not absorb a toxicant through the integument or through membranes surrounding target sites as readily as do susceptible strains. *Behavioral resistance* refers to avoidance of treated surfaces by arthropods; a number of examples are known where mosquitoes change their resting habits, no longer resting on the walls of treated houses and thereby avoiding a fatal exposure to pesticide. Physiological mechanisms may very well underlie such behavioral changes; behaviorally resistant insects have been demonstrated to be more readily irritated by insecticide deposits, a phenomenon explainable by increased sensory sensitivity.

To actually verify the presence of resistance it is necessary to conduct exposure tests comparing known susceptible strains of a species with suspected resistant strains. Standardized resistance tests have been pioneered by the World Health Organization. Such standardized tests have been reviewed by Quarterman (1960) and Hamon and Mouchet (1962), and additional references to tests may be found in the *Bulletin of the World Health Organization*.

COMMON INSECTICIDE FORMULATIONS

Most organic insecticides have high solubility in appropriate organic solvents and low solubility in water. For proper application they are formulated in a number of ways, each with its own specific use characteristics.

1. *Technical grade* (tech.) insecticide is the greatest purification of toxicant that can be practically manufactured on a bulk scale; it generally consists of 90 per cent or more pure toxicant plus other side products of synthesis. Technical grade may be purchased for addition to oil carrier in larviciding mosquitoes, or for dilution with oil for use in fogging against adult flying insects, or in some cases for direct application at ultra low volume (ULV).

2. *Solutions* (s) are composed of technical toxicant diluted directly with suitable solvents. Oil solutions applied to water stay on the surface, where most mosquito larvae breathe; but they are likely to damage plants.

3. *Emulsifiable concentrates* (ec) are formulated with technical grade toxicant in suitable organic solvents, plus emulsifier. The latter makes it possible to mix the concentrate with water to make a relatively stable emulsion suitable for spraying.

4. *Wettable powders* (wp) are inert carriers impregnated with insecticide. There is generally a wetting agent added, and this formulation can be kept in suspension in water by agitation. When sprayed on objects, wettable powders stay on the surface, are less harmful to plants than are emulsions or oil solutions, and frequently have longer residual effectiveness. They may leave clearly visible powdery deposits.

5. *Dusts* (d) are finely ground inert carriers impregnated or mixed with insecticide. They are applied in dry form. The dust form of Paris green floats on the water surface where *Anopheles* larvae do most of their feeding.

6. *Granules* (g) are much like impregnated dusts, but the particles are larger and therefore settle rapidly when broadcast, resting on the ground or sinking in water. Formulation on sand has been a convenient means of distribution, being particularly good for treating culicine mosquito larvae.

7. *Baits* (b) are comprised of toxicant incorporated into a material upon which insects like to feed; for example sugar syrup or granules for flies, peanut meal granules for ants and cockroaches.

APPLICATION EQUIPMENT

Equipment for application of insecticides has been developed to handle the various formulations listed above. It may consist of devices that can readily be carried and operated by one man, often a necessity in remote and inaccessible areas. On a worldwide basis the type of sprayer shown in Figure 6-5 is probably used more than any other one piece of equipment for insecticide application to control vectors. Heavy motorized application devices are more characteristic where large areas are being covered. For general information on spray equipment Potts (1958) may be consulted. The World Health Organization has prepared a publication on the subject of application equipment for vector control (World Health Organization, *Equipment for Vector Control. Guide to major items—specifications—use descriptions—field tests*, Geneva, 1964, 200 pp.).

Vehicles used during application depend on the type of terrain and the amount of area to be covered. For general distribution onto a terrestrial environment conventional vehicles such as bicycles, motorcycles, or light trucks are used. In marshy environments four-wheel-drive or tracked vehicles prove necessary, and amphibious vehicles can operate in deep water also. On water, boats with conventional propeller propulsion find use, though in very shallow water choked with vegetation a shallow-draft, flat-bottomed craft with aerial propeller is ideal. Aircraft, either rotor or conventional fixed wing, can provide rapid coverage of terrestrial or aquatic environments (Fig. 6-6). One drawback has been the relatively small amount of territory that could be covered when insecticides were diluted, necessitating frequent returns for refills. Ultra low volume spraying (often only a few ounces of technical insecticide per acre)

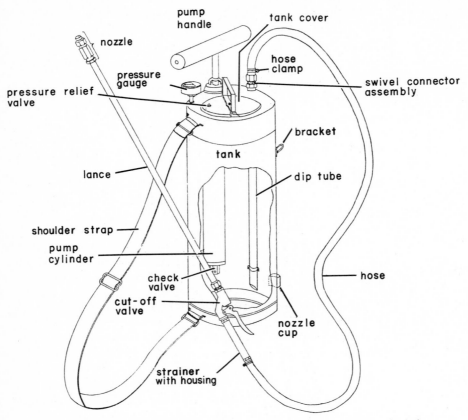

Fig. 6-5 Hand pump compression sprayer. This item of equipment is particularly useful because it is readily carried and can be used to apply a residue to walls or vegetation to control adult vectors, or it readily treats waters that breed mosquito larvae. (Courtesy of World Health Organization.)

promises to change this situation whenever it can be used, making returns to base more a necessity for refuelling than for reloading.

In addition to the equipment traditionally used to control agricultural pests, means of applying *aerosols* composed of very fine droplets have been highly developed to control adult flying insects of medical importance. For use indoors aerosols are available in the form of *pressurized cans*, the released compressed propellant gas forcing insecticide and solvent through a fine orifice causing it to break up into very fine droplets. Rapid breakup of the propellant at reduced pressure also reduces the droplet size. For outdoor application a common aerosol dispersing device is a *thermal fogger* (Fig. 6-7); any of a number of devices that heat diesel oil to the vapor point and release it along with insecticide so that a dense smokelike or foggy cloud of very fine particles of oil and insecticide is released. An interesting recent development for outdoor use is the dissolving of insecticide in $SiCl_4$ and reacting this with ammonia water, to produce a dense and penetrating fog at less expense than diesel oil thermal fogs (Stokes, 1967). This type of fog may not enter into general use because it could be hazardous to humans.

REPRODUCTIVE MANIPULATION

Manipulating the natural reproduction of arthropods is an innovation showing exceptional promise. For medically important arthropods this has generally meant the use of methods to sterilize insects, but the utilization of sex attractants has also been investigated. Sterility methods have been conceived mostly for use on a large-area basis, generally with eradication in mind. Although reproductive manipulation shows much promise, at this time it is still largely restricted to laboratory experimentation.

The most notably successful instance of control by sterilization concerned eradication of the primary screw-worm fly, *Cochliomyia hominivorax* (Coquerell). In this program sterilization was achieved by exposing male flies to gamma irradiation and overwhelming native populations by releasing sterilized flies in numbers much greater than the wild populations. It was first successfully utilized on the island of Curaçao, thereafter progressing from the southern tip of Florida north and westward along the southeastern tier of states. An excellent appraisal of this program has been prepared by Baumhover (1966).

The impact of the remarkably successful screw-worm eradication scheme has inspired numerous studies on sterilization procedures for arthropod control. These studies have included population models to determine the amount of overflooding needed in releases (Knipling, 1964; Knipling, 1966), the investigation of various chemicals as chemosterilants (Bořkovec, 1966; La Brecque and Smith, 1967), genetic manipulation to develop predominantly male-producing strains (Craig, *et al.*, 1960) or to take advantage of cytoplasmic sterility factors (Laven, 1953), and the discovery of naturally occurring factors in male insects that are transferred to the female during mating to result in single fertilization even though additional matings may occur (Craig, 1967). This latter investigation suggests that natural or synthetic compounds could be applied to induce sterility of specific arthropods without harmful side effects to vertebrates. Insect sex attractants have also received much attention as another possible means of reproductive manipulation (Jacobson, 1965), though they have not been recognized as an important factor with most medically important arthropods.

At this point of development two pilot projects should be mentioned. A preliminary survey for the island of Ceylon suggests that bancroftian filariasis might be controlled there by eradicating the primary vector, *Culex pipiens quinquefasciatus* Say, through a sterile release program (Rai, 1966). This same vector has been shown to be made up of a number of strains that are not interfertile because of cytoplasmic incompatibility (Laven, 1967a). In a pilot scheme in Burma complete eradication of the indigenous population of this mosquito in a village was achieved by overflooding with males of an incompatible strain (Laven, 1967b).

CONTROL OF SPECIFIC GROUPS OF INSECTS

Using the principles and specific methods outlined above, mention will now be made of control procedures usually employed against specific groups of arthropods. Biological control agents are mentioned in many instances to alert the student to the possibilities of such methods, rather than to suggest that biocontrol is usually effective. Also one should be aware that use of insecticides may destroy natural biocontrol agents. The succession of arthropods is listed in the same order as is used in the chapters that follow. For the most part, whenever pesticides are mentioned, actual dosages are not included. *Therefore, before any pesticides are used, the proper dosages and precaution information should be obtained from appropriate public health agencies and manufacturers.* Particular precautions to avoid contamination of foodstuffs and cooking or eating utensils must be observed when pesticides are applied within the home. The user should also bear in mind that resistance is a likely consequence of pesticide use, and for this reason specific pesticide recommendations are modified frequently. Furthermore, resistance often is rather local in nature, requiring adequate testing to determine the status of arthropods in any given region. Specific controls are mentioned here, listing a number of insecticides when possible. The potential user should be aware that more modern compounds may have been developed, or some compounds listed may have been withdrawn from the use recommended at the time the user is seeking information.

COCKROACHES

Good sanitation is important for controlling cockroaches. In humid semitropical regions cockroaches occur both outdoors and indoors, making sanitation a more comprehensive task. They are omnivorous feeders, living especially well on kitchen scraps and table food in homes. Simply cleaning up all traces of food and storing food in tight or screened containers will go a long way toward reducing their numbers. The suggestions of Twomey (1966), although mainly for control of the German cockroach, are also applicable to other species.

Specific survey methods can include the use of baited baffle-entrance traps, and searching in dark places or at night with a light. At least for the American cockroach, *Periplaneta americana* (Linnaeus), a potent sex attractant is present (Jacobson and Beroza, 1963). It seems likely that this attractant will be utilized for control, either simply as a tool for surveying the presence of this species of cockroach, or in combination with insecticide or chemosterilant. Hymenopteran egg parasites appear to be the most effective of known biocontrol agents. A prime example is the encyrtid wasp, *Comperia merceti*, which nearly eliminated the brownbanded cockroach *Supella supellectilium* (Serville) in parts of Hawaii (Jenkins, 1964).

Toxicants are generally applied as residual deposits or as baits. Sprays or dusts can be applied near and behind baseboards, and where pipes go through walls or floors, using the chlorinated hydrocarbons chlordane, dieldrin, heptachlor, and lindane, and the organophosphorus compounds diazinon, dichlorvos, malathion, and ronnel. Resistance is known, particularly for the chlorinated hydrocarbons. A bait of kepone in peanut meal granules has been very effective against some species. The silica gel desiccants have been successful when dusted into wall spaces and other enclosed areas that cockroaches frequent.

TRUE BUGS

The bloodsucking bugs are generally nocturnal in habit, hiding in cracks and crevices during daytime. Some relief can be obtained through eliminating such hiding places, particularly for bed bugs (*Cimex* species). Improved home construction eliminating hiding places would do much to control conenose bugs in tropical America. Screening of houses is useful in reducing bites of conenose bugs. Survey procedures for true bugs are not standardized, but their presence is indicated through the occurrence of typical welts caused by their bites.

Pathogens for bugs have been described, but do not usually appear to be effective. Ants are predaceous on bed bugs, having been used to free clothing and furniture of these pests (Negi, 1933); and a spider was introduced into Germany to provide control of these same insects (Hase, 1934). Ants have also been known to destroy large numbers of blood-filled triatomids in Uruguay and Venezuela (Jenkins, 1964).

Residual insecticides applied to crevices and other hiding places are useful. These are generally applied as sprays, using DDT, lindane, malathion, ronnel, or dichlorvos. Silica gel desiccants show promise against bed bugs.

LICE

For humans, frequent bathing and laundering of clothes are largely effective against lice, though if once well established they may be hard to eliminate. The presence of lice is likely wherever personal hygiene is poor, and is associated with crowded conditions and poor nutrition. On livestock and poultry, sucking and chewing lice are suspected when excessive scratching is seen, and louse eggs may be found attached to hairs and to feathers. A number of louse pathogens are known, but these seldom achieve significant control. Ants are predaceous on lice in clothing, and an old practice in Germany was to use this method for removing the body louse (Hase, 1942). Clothing may also be fumigated or heated with steam or hot water.

Delousing of humans or livestock is readily effected with insecticides. For *human* lice dusts of DDT and malathion were used, but resistance has become widespread. Rotenone remains useful. On *dairy cattle* control can be achieved with a thorough spraying with Ciodrin®, pyrethrins plus synergist, or rotenone, or dusting with the latter; a second treatment one to three weeks later is advised. On *beef cattle* many compounds are available, but particular attention must be paid to dosage and interval between treatment and slaughter; materials are usually applied as a spray or dip and include carbaryl, Ciodrin®, coumaphos, dioxathion, diazinon, lindane, malathion, methoxychlor, ronnel, toxaphene, and Ruelene®. The pour-on treatment of Ruelene® to control cattle grubs also affects but does not completely control lice. To control lice on *sheep* and *goats* the same materials as used for beef cattle, excepting Ruelene®, are satisfactory; DDT and rotenone are additional insecticides that may be used. Compounds recommended for lice on *swine* include carbaryl, ciodrin®, coumaphos, DDT, dioxathion, lindane, malathion, methoxychlor, ronnel, rotenone and toxaphene. To control biting lice on *poultry* the materials coumaphos,

malathion, naled, and carbaryl are used to treat directly; or roosts and cracks are treated with coumaphos, malathion, carbaryl, nicotine sulfate, or rotenone. On *dogs* and *cats* louse infestation can be treated with topical applications of ronnel, or, in dogs, with oral administration of the same insecticide.

GNATS: SIMULIIDS, *PHLEBOTOMUS*, *CULICOIDES* AND *LEPTOCONOPS*

Survey methods include the use of light traps, black lights being especially attractive in certain cases. Some species, particularly of simuliids, are attracted to the carbon dioxide released from dry ice. For ceratopogonids a vehicle-mounted net driven through problem areas at times of peak flight activity has been an effective means of maintaining an estimate of adult population activity (Bidlingmayer, 1961). Human biting rate estimates are also valuable, though minute species are hard to sample by this means.

Surveys of aquatic forms of simuliids are accomplished by examining rocks and other objects in running water. One useful method consists of anchoring standard-sized artificial objects, such as plastic cones, in streams and examining the attached larvae at intervals.

Personal protection is generally achieved with repellents, particularly deet. It is doubtful that repellents can adequately protect live stock against massive flights of black flies. Screening of houses may require the use of very fine mesh screen, or application of deodorized kerosene solutions of DDT, lindane or malathion to regular window screening. Current experiments suggest that repellents applied to screens or fabrics will greatly increase their effectiveness.

BLACK FLIES

Environmental modification is difficult to practice with Simuliidae, as it may require extensive changes in watercourses that are considered desirable as they are. In building irrigation systems it is helpful to avoid regions of swiftly rushing water, and reduction of vegetation in flowing watercourses will reduce attachment sites for larvae, though algal mats have been noted to eliminate larval habitat. Unintentional changes in habitat include modification of the river environment with the increase of agriculture around Mt. Elgon, Uganda; and reduced populations of the buffalo gnat *Cnephia pecuarum* (Riley) in the Mississippi river are thought to be caused by factors such as increased silting and pollution.

A number of pathogens have been described, and undoubtedly this is an area where further attempts toward utilization are needed. Particularly noteworthy are Protozoa in the genus *Thelohania* as well as various gregarines. Nematodes may be important, having been effective against black flies in irrigation systems of Saskatchewan and Alberta (Fredeen and Shemanchuk, 1960), in Wisconsin (Phelps and DeFoliart, 1964), and in the Leningrad region of the Soviet Union (Welch and Rubtsov, 1965). Water mites may parasitize black fly adults, weakening them greatly (Davies, 1959). Effective predators include a great variety of insects, and various fish, which suggests caution should be used in treating waters with insecticides. Near Mt. Elgon, Uganda, *Potamon* crabs that harbor larvae of *Simulium neavei* were rare in two rivers due to predation by introduced rainbow trout (Hynes, *et al.*, 1961).

Insecticidal treatments have largely been directed toward aquatic stages. For this purpose the long-lasting toxicant DDT has been most frequently applied, often by drip methods or impregnated plaster blocks that provide long-term application in streams. Treatment of small jungle streams has proved to be impractical in Central America and Africa. In Kenya virtual eradication of *Simulium neavei* Roubaud from the Kodera focus was achieved by treating rivers nine times at intervals of ten days with DDT at 0.5 parts per million (ppm), and streams with 1.0 ppm or more at each application (McMahon, *et al.*, 1958). Treatments of this sort can be damaging to aquatic fauna, but in New York State there appeared to be no real change in total numbers of arthropods (Jamnback and Eabry, 1962). More specific control of simuliids was achieved in Britain by applying insecticide on particles of the size range on which larvae feed (Kershaw, *et al.*, 1965).

PHLEBOTOMUS

Developmental sites are generally too inaccessible or unknown to use environmental modification as a means of controlling *Phlebotomus*. Pathogens, parasites, and predators have been described, but are not known to have much effect in nature. *Phlebotomus* are extremely sensitive to many residual insecticides and are also rather weak flyers, making frequent stops on vegetation and other surfaces. In many areas where DDT was used for malaria control there was a virtual disappearance of *Phlebotomus* adults. Even local and limited control procedures are of value because of the slow recovery rate and slow dispersion of sandfly populations.

CULICOIDES AND LEPTOCONOPS

Environmental modification is a distinct possibility for this group. Diking and continuous flooding with water for several months, or filling with a mixture of sand, shell, and clay, is a lasting means of controlling *Culicoides furens* Poèy in Florida (Rogers, 1962). *Leptoconops torrens* Townsend, the valley black gnat of California, can be controlled by soil manipulation and by various insecticidal treatments (Whitsel and Schoeppner, 1966).

Salt marsh *Culicoides* have been effectively reduced by aerial application of dieldrin granules on their developmental sites. Treating window screens or bed netting with DDT can provide protection within the home. Fogging as practiced for mosquitoes will control adults for temporary relief. In Florida mermithid nematodes can apparently cause perceptible natural control of salt marsh *Culicoides* (Smith and Perry, 1967).

CHIRONOMIDAE

Considerable emphasis has been directed in California toward preventing huge swarms of chironomid midges. The studies of Anderson, *et al.*, 1964, provide a comprehensive analysis of several procedures. They state that pond rotation, letting settling basins dry 5 to ten days, is very effective. Carp (fish) at 200–400 pounds per acre were particularly useful in test basins. Bay and Anderson (1965) subsequently concluded that carp are less valuable for large lakes and temporarily disrupted habitats than for smaller sources of chironomid midge nuisance. Granular preparations of dieldrin, DDT, or TDE (1,1-dichloro-2,2-bis (*p*-chlorophenyl) ethane; Rhothane®) gave good control of larvae for two to four weeks.

CHAOBORIDAE (PHANTOM MIDGES)

The Clear Lake gnat, *Chaoborus astictopus* Dyar and Shannon, continues to be a difficult problem. Recent efforts are directed especially toward biological control, concentrating on pathogens and on fish predators. A protozoan in the genus *Thelohania* appears to be particularly damaging at times, being transovarially maintained and thereby continuing to take its toll in succeeding generations (Sikorowski and Madison, 1968).

MOSQUITOES

Undoubtedly more information has been developed for control of mosquitoes than for any other group of medically important arthropods. By and large this is a comprehensive communitywide task, requiring technical supervision usually provided by public health agencies, or on the local level by mosquito abatement districts.

A multitude of methods have been developed for assessing mosquito populations, the ones used depending on objectives of the survey, peculiarities of the species involved, availability of types of survey equipment, and technical training of personnel. Some survey methods are mentioned in Chapter 4 and additional procedures will be listed.

Surveys of eggs and oviposition sites can be a useful technique. Looking for egg rafts of *Culex* and *Culiseta*, and single floating eggs of *Anopheles* has potential value. Surveying for eggs of floodwater species holds real promise in helping to determine the potential population in the next active season and in planning an efficient pre-hatch treatment. A specific attractive oviposition container made up of a dark jar, wooden paddle as oviposition site, and ethyl acetate as attractant, has proved valuable in sampling the presence of *Aedes aegypti* (Linnaeus), particularly when populations are low and natural breeding sites scarce (Fay and Eliason, 1966).

Larval surveys are made to decide when control measures should be applied. A dipper provided with a long handle is the collecting utensil most used; more quantitative information can be gained by pushing a walled metal cylinder into the mud and removing and examining all the water enclosed. In dipping procedures it is important to not overlook potential larval sites, such as cattle hoofprints filled with water (Fig. 6–8). For examining treeholes and similarly inaccessible containers a large-capacity rubber suction bulb and rubber extension tube can be used to draw out the water. Determining the presence of *Mansonia* larvae requires uprooting aquatic plants, to which the larvae attach, and vigorously agitating the root system in a container of water. As the resulting water is usually muddy, it should be strained through fine screen.

Adult survey procedures, further described in Chapter 4, consist of incandescent light traps, resting sites, attraction to man or animal hosts or carbon dioxide or moving visual patterns, Malaise traps, and moving net devices.

Environmental modification has been a common procedure for mosquito control. Draining or filling of marshy areas is a normal practice in many abatement districts. In salt marsh areas diking and flooding with sea water can destroy mosquitoes, as most salt marsh species cannot withstand so intense a salinity. It is also good procedure to see that irrigation canals and drainage ditches are kept free of vegetation at their margins, thus permitting complete access of fish and insect predators. Concrete lining of such canals provides mosquito control and reduces water loss. Dropping reservoir water levels in quick steps will prevent the growth of emergent vegetation, and has been very effective in controlling *Anopheles* (Anon., 1947), but requires careful management to minimize the development of *Aedes* (Snow, 1958). Some effective control schemes have employed a schedule of rapid water flushing to periodically clear sluggish channels. Various other simple means are employed; for example emptying or removing cans, tires, and other water receptacles, and cementing in treeholes. Merely adding 10 per cent raw salt to water in containers has controlled *Aedes aegypti* and *Ae. albopictus* (Skuse) in the Philippines, though dilution by rainwater can be a problem (Banez, 1964). In the Naaman Swamps, Acre District, Israel, a suitably dense population of the aquatic rodent called nutria or coypu, *Myocastor coypus*, kept river and adjacent ponds free of algal mats and other vegetation that provided food and cover for *Anopheles sacharovi* Favre. This also permitted more accurate spraying with insecticides (Ehrlich and Spielberg, 1960). In Czechoslovakia carp and ducks in rice fields removed water weeds and provided some control of *Anopheles maculipennis* (Trpiš, 1960). In Kerala, India, the vector of brugian filariasis, *Mansonia annulifera* (Theobald), breeds in abundance on roots of the aquatic plant *Pistia stratiotes*. An introduced water fern, *Salvinia auriculata*, crowded out *Pistia* and formed an impervious growth that increased larval mortality. The incidence of *M. annulifera* dropped where *Pistia* was replaced by *Salvinia* (Joseph, *et al.*, 1963).

More pathological microorganisms are known for mosquitoes than for any other group of medically important arthropods. Laird (1960) has reviewed their possible use in control. Particularly well known are several species of pathogenic fungi in the genus *Coelomomyces*. One of these has been used in an interesting biological control experiment in the Tokelau Islands (Laird, 1966). Laird (1959) has listed the fungal parasites of mosquito larvae from Oriental and Australian regions and provided keys to *Coelomomyces*. Couch and Umphlett (1963) also discuss this fungus genus. The fungus genus *Entomophthora* is likewise frequently effective. Among Protozoa, microsporidia in the genera *Stempellia* and *Thelohania* are widespread, and are under consideration as control agents.

Effective parasites of mosquitoes include mermithid nematodes and water mites. Mermithids in the genus *Agamomermis* have been reported throughout the world, with as high as 80 per cent incidence found in natural mosquito populations. Water mites that commonly attach to the thorax or abdomen of adult mosquitoes have little effect when infestations are light, but when abundant they may kill the host.

Predation of larval and pupual mosquitoes by insects is commonplace. More research needs to be done on manipulation of predatory insect populations. Present practice consists of keeping aquatic vegetation in control to permit predators access to their prey. The nymphs of dragonflies and damselflies readily eat mosquito larvae. Aquatic Hemiptera that feed on mosquitoes include Belostomatidae, Nepidae, Corixidae, and Notonectidae. Bugs of the latter family are particularly voracious and are credited with substantial *Anopheles gambiae* Giles control in Tanzania (Christie, 1958) as well as mosquito control in California (E. C. Bay, personal communication). Aquatic Coleoptera in the families Dytiscidae, Gyrinidae, and Hydrophilidae destroy large numbers of larvae. Diptera in the family Culicidae, members of the predaceous genus *Toxorhynchites*, have been extensively studied for biocontrol. They have great potential use against mosquito larvae developing in treeholes. However, introduction of three species to

Hawaii to control *Aedes albopictus* (Skuse) was not very successful (Nakagawa, 1963).

The most effective larval and pupal predators found thus far are various fishes. A very comprehensive annotated bibliography on the use of fish in mosquito control, covering more than 200 species, has been provided by Gerberich and Laird, 1966. Best known is a South American top minnow that produces live young rather than eggs, the mosquitofish *Gambusia affinis*. It has been introduced to all continents and is now present as cold-resistant strains as far north as Utah and Oregon in the United States. A strain of *Gambusia* from areas in Mississippi that have been treated with insecticides appears to be somewhat insecticide resistant (Boyd and Ferguson, 1964). The common guppy, *Lebistes reticulatus*, also a live bearer, has been found capable of breeding in very polluted waters in Thailand (Sasa, *et al.*, 1964). A cold-resistant strain of guppy has been reported from Japan. Both mosquitofish and guppies are voracious feeders with very high reproductive potential. They can readily be transported and introduced into mosquito breeding waters. A more recent possibility concerns species of South American egglaying fish whose eggs resist desiccation, making them ideal for control in temporary waters such as the breeding sites of *Aedes* and *Psorophora* mosquitoes. The Argentine pearlfish, *Cynolebias bellottii*, belonging to this group, is under investigation in California (Bay, 1966).

Many predators of adult mosquitoes are known though their effectiveness is uncertain. Commonly included as effective are spiders, dragonflies and damselflies, frogs and toads, lizards, many birds such as fly catchers, swallows, and warblers, and bats. In the United States purple martins have been promoted as efficient mosquito predators, and special bird-houses have been offered for sale to encourage this species. However, recent studies indicate that though these birds eat large numbers of insects, mosquitoes constitute only an insignificant fraction of their diet.

Various plants have been associated with reduced mosquito populations, though aquatic plants usually encourage mosquitoes by blocking efficient predation. Algae in the Characeae are sometimes noted to affect mosquito larvae, but reports on this subject are somewhat conflicting. Some observers suggest that certain species of *Chara* release toxic substances that inhibit larval growth. In California certain bluegreen algae, Cyanophyta, have prevented mosquito development in rice fields (Gerhardt, 1956). Carnivorous plants, especially in the genus *Utricularia*, capture mosquito larvae. Other plants such as the duckweed *Lemna* can cause such a heavy surface covering as to prevent oviposition and larval development.

Most repellents developed have been initially tested against mosquitoes. The materials deet and 6–12® are commonly used in the United States for personal protection. Some experimental compounds provide exceptionally lasting repellency when applied to fabrics (Gouck, *et al.*, 1967; McGovern, *et al.*, 1967).

Control with insecticides is directed toward larvae and adults. The American Mosquito Control Association has sponsored bulletins that comprehensively cover equipment for mosquito control. One revised in 1968 is concerned with ground equipment, entitled *Ground Equipment and Insecticides for Mosquito Control*, AMCA Bull. No. 2; another covers the use of aircraft, but its publication is being delayed because technical advances, particularly on the techniques of ultra low volume sprays, are being developed so rapidly.

Materials for egg control, particularly of *Aedes* and *Psorophora*, should be further sought, as Judson, *et al.* (1962), found organophosphorus compounds will kill emerging embryos, and certain lachrymatory compounds caused rupture of *Aedes aegypti* eggs. Preflooding treatments of floodwater mosquito egg sites with granular formulations of dieldrin, DDT, or various organophosphorus compounds has proved useful. A duck-hunting area in California achieved excellent

Fig. 6-6 Use of airplane in spraying operations. (Courtesy of Mosquito Abatement District, Kern County, California.)

control of *Aedes melanimon* Dyar by large-scale preflood application of granular parathion from aircraft (Whitesell, 1965).

Direct treatment of larval waters is often practiced. Sprays of emulsifiable or oil base malathion, Abate®, DDT, TDE, fenthion, and lindane have been used. With resistance to more recent pesticides, dusting with Paris green has been reemployed to control surface feeding *Anopheles* larvae. The same toxicant formulated with adhesive and emulsifier on vermiculite granules has effectively controlled culicine larvae.

Problems peculiar to control of specific aquatic environments may be encountered. Control in waters of high organic content can be particularly difficult, perhaps because toxicants absorb readily to organic substances, as noted when treating log storage ponds and sewage effluent. Rice fields require lengthy flooding and may encourage large mosquito populations. To overcome the brief period of control that usually follows larviciding, a longlasting effect has been accomplished by placing dieldrin-cement briquettes in larval waters (Laird, 1966).

Adult mosquitoes are treated with aerosols, ultra low volume sprays, residual deposits, or an organophosphorus compound with fumi-

gant action. Aerosols for home mosquito control are generally in the form of pressurized cans releasing DDT or malathion, and pyrethrins plus synergist. Aerosols outdoors are in the form of fogs, usually using malathion, Lethane 384®, or DDT. A particularly promising current procedure involves ultra low volume spraying of malathion, usually from aircraft, using special spraying apparatus (Glancey, *et al.*, 1966). Undoubtedly other insecticides will also prove satisfactory when applied by this method. A number of residual treatments are satisfactory, such as vegetation coverage with carbaryl, DDT, lindane, or ronnel; wall spraying in dwellings with malathion, methoxychlor, DDT, dichlorvos, lindane, and ronnel. The World Health Organization has used wall spraying with DDT or dieldrin to reduce *Anopheles* vector populations, though the exceptionally open type of shelter found in some tropical regions greatly reduces the effectiveness of this method. Fumigant action is a characteristic of dichlorvos, and resin strips impregnated with this toxicant and hung indoors or in sewer catch basins have been exceptionally effective.

Reproductive manipulation still remains largely experimental in mosquito control. Laboratory strains of *Aedes aegypti* producing

Fig. 6-7 Aerosol equipment in adulticiding operations. (Photograph by E. A. Smith.)

Fig. 6-8 Hoofprints around puddles, ponds, and streams are good breeding places. The water in the hoofprints shown here produced 60 to 80 larvae, mostly *Culex tarsalis,* per pint; much greater productivity often occurs in similar breeding areas. (Photograph by Harry G. Davis.)

as high as 82 per cent males have been selected (Craig, *et al.*, 1960). A volatile female substance stimulating the male sexual response has been found in *Culiseta inornata* (Williston) (Kliewer, *et al.*, 1966), and a naturally occurring material termed matrone, found in male accessory glands of *Aedes aegypti*, prevents fertilization (Craig, 1967). A pilot experiment in Burma eradicated a native population of *Culex pipiens quinquefasciatus* by overflooding with cytoplasmic incompatible strain males (Laven, 1967). Radiation sterilization and chemosterilants have been tested extensively in laboratory experiments, the latter showing indications of also controlling malaria parasites (Jamnback, 1967) and filarial worms (Bertman, 1964). Unfortunately, laboratory studies indicate mosquitoes can develop a certain degree of resistance to chemosterilants (Hazard, *et al.*, 1964; Patterson, *et al.*, 1967).

HORSE FLIES, DEER FLIES, AND SNIPE FLIES

Control of biting flies can be very difficult because their developmental sites may include extensive marshy or aquatic zones, as well as relatively dry soil environments, and frequently are not adequately identified. They are not usually associated closely with the dwellings of man or his domestic animals.

Surveys of Tabanidae usually consist of counting adults attacking cattle, horses, or other large animals. Many tabanids are attracted to large and dark objects, and Thorsteinson (1958) has used this plus residual solar heat to develop the so-called "heliothermal" trap. In California, Anderson, *et al.,* (1967, and next paper), found Malaise traps in combination with dry ice to be an effective means for sampling populations of some species of tabanids and for the biting snipe flies, *Symphoromyia.*

Jones and Anthony (1964) have presented a comprehensive review of natural enemies of tabanids. These include hymenopterous egg parasites, dipterous (tachinid) larval parasites, hymenopterous pupal parasites, and predators including insects, spiders, lizards, birds, and fish. Egg masses are often heavily parasitized, the wasp *Telenomus emersoni* being most effective according to Jones and Anthony. A wasp predator mentioned frequently in the literature is the horse guard, *Bembix carolina* Fabricius (often referred to the genus *Strictia*).

For all of these insects personal protection seems to be most applicable; the repellent deet on humans, and a number of repellents on livestock (see Kenaga, 1966). Control on range animals is difficult because treatments must be renewed once or twice a day. Dairy cattle or horses handled daily may be hand sprayed; cattle in enclosures causing them to go through a chute at least once a day in search of food or water can be automatically treated, using a treadle-step on switch, or electric eye-operated sprayer (Bruce, 1952; Cheng, *et al.*, 1957; Berry and Hoffman, 1963) to apply pyrethrins plus synergist, or Lethane 384®.

Chemical control away from the host is difficult. Benzene hexachloride applied to vegetation where tabanids congregate can produce complete, though temporary, control (Brown and Morrison, 1955). Larvae of *Chrysops discalis* were killed by the application of DDT to breeding sites, and *Tabanus* larvae were controlled in salt marshes by applying granular dieldrin at levels causing no immediate serious effect on desirable animal life (Hansens, 1956; Jamnback and Wall, 1957).

EYE GNATS (*HIPPELATES*)

Hippelates flies are readily sampled by using attractive baits. Simple traps having bait covered by a cone leading into a collecting chamber, and rather coarse screen preventing access by large flies, are effective. A number of decaying materials are suitable attractants, ranging from putrefied liver to a putrefied dried egg and water suspension (Mulla, *et al.*, 1960).

Immature forms develop in soil, and freshly turned soil is especially attractive for oviposition; therefore, it would seem cultural practices could be applied to reduce populations, though more research is needed along these lines. Though it was originally believed uncultivated land did not breed eye gnats, more recent observations have revealed that development continues if small grass rootlets are present (Bay and Legner, 1963). Precultivation treatment of weeds or cover crops with herbicidal petroleum oils has proved very effective, denying the larvae organic vegetable matter to feed on and also repelling gnats attracted to the area for oviposition (Mulla, 1965).

Methods of finding natural parasites of *Hippelates* have included exposing larvae and pupae, protected from predators by screening, in natural environments. By this means Legner and Bay (1964) discovered two species of cynipid wasps in the West Indies; of these *Spalangia drosophilae* Ashmead later proved to be the most efficient species in seeking *Hippelates* pupae.

Insecticides worked into soil may adequately control *Hippelates* (Mulla, *et al.*, 1960), but the expense rarely justifies such a procedure. Perhaps this is worthwhile when agricultural practice requires soil to be treated for other insects attacking the root system of crops.

LOUSE FLIES (*HIPPOBOSCIDAE*)

This discussion is limited to the sheep ked, *Melophagus ovinus* (Linnaeus). Close examination is required to find adult keds or puparia in fleece when infestations are low. High infestations are indicated by vigorous rubbing, biting of wool, and scratching. Sheep infested by keds for a considerable time develop a certain degree of resistance (Nelson, 1962), suggesting that some form of immunization or breeding of resistant strains of sheep might be possible. Power dusting with dieldrin, or rubbing a dust of coumaphos into wool over the entire body will provide control. Thorough sprays or dips of DDT, coumaphos, dioxathion, lindane, malathion, pyrethrins plus synergist, ronnel, rotenone, toxaphene, or diazinon are also effective.

BLOODSUCKING MUSCOID FLIES: TSETSE (*GLOSSINA*), STABLE (*STOMOXYS*), AND HORN (*HAEMATOBIA*) FLIES

A reasonable degree of personal protection can be achieved against these bloodsucking flies by using repellents or fast-acting insecticides. Such methods are not practiced against tsetse because conditions would require nearly continuous application for nomadic or village human populations, and for cattle herds in unfenced grazing conditions.

Tsetse Flies (*Glossina*). Surveying tsetse populations is largely accomplished by human capture and by traps. In Kenya an attractant serum has been used to assess activity of *Glossina longipennis* Corti. (Langridge, 1961). The procedure most used, particularly in eradication and control schemes, is to have personnel acting as catchers with nets patrol a standard prescribed route for a standard period of time—the so-called *fly-round* (Ford, *et al.*, 1959). Quite effective traps have been developed also, the Morris trap being notably useful with some species of tsetse (Morris, 1961; Glasgow, 1967).

Environmental manipulation has been an important control practice, often in conjunction with other procedures. *Glossina* adults are restricted to high humidity zones, and adults seldom fly over cleared areas, particularly in drier savannah zones; pupariae are found in moist soil conditions, especially associated with rivers and streams. In heavy jungle areas reduction of tsetse attack is achieved by clearing a wide strip of vegetation around villages. In savannah conditions blocks of land are laid out for control, with natural isolation where brushy vegetation ends, or with cleared zones at boundaries. Bushy vegetation may also be reduced in such zones to provide fewer resting sites for adults. Within control blocks wild mammalian hosts, such as antelopes and pigs, may be destroyed to reduce adult food sources. Host destruction is especially applicable because adult tsetse do not feed on nectar or other sugar sources. Destruction of animals also prevents adult tsetse from being carried across cleared boundaries. Traffic control points are necessary to prevent spread of tsetse on vehicles, and where visual inspection is impossible, as with large vehicles, treatment with BHC from a fog machine can be used (Cockbill, 1960).

Biological control agents of several types have been noted for tsetse (see Buxton, 1955) with some occasionally causing quite high natural mortality but none having been effectively utilized. Insect parasites and predators are perhaps most noteworthy. *Syntomosphyrum albiclavus* Kerrich (Hymenoptera, Eulophidae), a pupal parasite recorded only from *Glossina* in nature, can be cultured on a variety of cyclorraphous Diptera in the laboratory (Saunders, 1961). It appears to be a good candidate for mass culture and release. *S. glossinae* has been noted to parasitize as high as 84 per cent of *G. morsitans* pupae in the dry season (Chorley, 1929). As predators various ants and shrews occasionally exert considerable control, and adult tsetses may be preyed on extensively by spiders and robber flies (Asilidae). All these findings suggest that widespread application of insecticides in control would drastically affect natural biocontrol agents.

Insecticides have been very satisfactory in some control schemes. Along 300 miles of river system in Kenya, DDT, and later dieldrin, was applied to vegetation. Within three years *Glossina palpalis fuscipes* Newstead became exceedingly difficult to find and human cases of gambian sleeping sickness were reduced from a previous level of 107–157 cases per year to sixteen (Glover, *et al.*, 1960). Because many species of *Glossina* wait for prey on vegetation along paths and game trails, spraying of resting surfaces has provided exceptional control.

Reproductive manipulation is receiving considerable attention as a means of controlling tsetse, but until mass rearing procedures are mastered any such techniques require some means of self treatment such as uptake of chemosterilant from specific resting site

surfaces. Dipping mature pupae, or exposing adults to surfaces treated with tepa sterilizes *Glossina morsitans* Westwood, and yields males that are favorably competitive with untreated males (Dame and Ford, 1966).

Stable Flies (*Stomoxys*). Survey methods consist largely of observing stable flies on animals or on favored resting sites. A great deal can be done to reduce populations by controlling the amount of wet and rotting straw and manure around premises. Where development is occurring in such media as beach seaweed, this debris may be hauled away, spread out to dry, or burned.

Biological control agents are generally identical or similar to those attacking house flies, though with the exception of some hymenopterous parasites they seem to exert minimal control.

Insecticides and repellents, as listed for horse flies, are effective for direct treatment of cattle. In addition, residual insecticides applied to resting surfaces around farm premises provide good control.

Reproductive manipulation may have distinct possibilities, the more so because stable fly populations tend to be focal in nature and this insect can be readily reared. Chemosterilant treatment in the field would have to rely on general contact since sweet baits are not eaten. One factor favoring sterile male techniques is the observation that *Stomyxs calcitrans* (Linnaeus) females apparently mate but once (Harris, *et al.*, 1966).

Horn Fly (*Haematobia*). Horn fly populations are readily estimated by direct counting of adults, particularly along the back, flanks, and legs of cattle.

Control may be effected by modifying the cattle droppings in which larvae develop. For example pigs in pastures scatter cattle dung so it dries rapidly, preventing larval development—hardly practical for range animals. Feeding of insecticides, or *Bacillus thuringiensis*, to make feces unsuitable for larval development has been one experimental approach. Species of coprophagous insects, such as dung beetles, that compete with horn fly larvae also help. No doubt some of the same egg and larval predators that affect house flies and face flies, such as mites and staphylinid beetles, exert an influence.

Insecticides may be applied to cattle in conjunction with repellents. The automatic sprayer systems discussed for horse flies are useful in dairy herds; more applicable for range cattle are back rubbers consisting of insecticide-treated burlap fastened to a chain or wire cable between two posts, such as that proposed by Rogoff and Moxon (1952). For dairy animals oil solutions, water sprays, or dusts are applied directly according to directions, using dichlorvos, methoxychlor, Ciodrin®, pyrethrins plus synergist, or Lethane 384®. Again, for cattle, back rubbers with coumaphos or Ciodrin® in oil solution are used. On beef cattle, additional direct treatments include carbaryl, dioxathion, and malathion; back rubbers may be additionally prepared with dioxathion, DDT, toxaphene, ronnel, and malathion; thorough spraying, or pouring along the back line of animals (pour-on treatment) of the animal systemics ronnel and ruelene also provides control.

THE HOUSE FLY AND RELATIVES (*MUSCIDAE, CALLIPHORIDAE, SARCOPHAGIDAE*)

Population estimates are based upon observing the numbers of adults on resting sites, or caught by baited traps, or by examining larval developmental sites. See Chapter 4 for further details.

Environmental modification consists of preventing the accumulation of larval developmental media; feces in the case of the house fly, face fly, lesser house fly, and some sarcophagids, and carcasses for calliphorids and other sarcophagids. Methods for municipalities are covered in *Municipal Refuse Disposal*, 1966. One type of environmental modification results from larvae of the stratiomyid fly *Hermetia illucens*, which cause feces in privies to be too liquid for optimal house fly

development (Furman, *et al.*, 1959). A dung beetle, *Copris incertus* Say, of Mexican origin, was introduced to Samoa where it plays a significant part in fly control by removing animal droppings; its introduction to New Zealand is not as likely to be successful because it does not multiply fast enough there (Thomas, 1960). Waste disposal in the tropics is often difficult because of poor disposal facilities. However, a three-inch layer of green vegetation above and below night soil buried in trenches resulted in only a fifth as many *Musca vicina* Macquart as emerged from soil buried without vegetation (Thevasagayam and Tharumarajah, 1962).

In regions with better sanitary control procedures, the use of sanitary land fill to keep garbage covered with earth greatly reduces fly populations (Fig. 6–9). Composting of manure in well-constructed, concrete-lined pits having a drain and sump, combined with frequent turning over of the top three inches or so, will prevent fly breeding. Composting for sanitary disposal is discussed by Gotaas (1956) (Fig. 6–10). A method of rapid composting (Fig. 6–11), employing a rotary drum to accelerate mechanical and microbial reduction, economically yields an odor-free product that does not breed flies and has desirable fertilizer characteristics (Scovel, 1958). Fly breeding may also be prevented in pits of organic matter, such as cannery wastes, by applying a tight cover such as polyethylene tarpaulin.

In the absence of modern plumbing, attention should be paid to the location and construction of a box privy with receptacle or dug pit. The requirements are (1) a type of construction that prevents flies from gaining access to excreta and insures privacy, and (2) a location that avoids pollution of wells or other water supply. A sanitary privy (Fig. 6–12) must meet the following requirements, according to Stiles and Lumsden (1911):

(1) The excreta must not touch the ground; hence, some kind of watertight receptacle (box, pail, tub, barrel, tank, or vault) for the excreta must be used under the seat. (2)

Fig. 6-9 An excellently operated sanitary landfill. (Photograph by Arthur C. Smith; courtesy of California Bureau of Vector Control.)

Domesticated animals must not have access to the night soil; therefore the privy should have a trapdoor in the back to exclude them. (3) Flies and other insects must not have access to the excreta; therefore the entire privy must be made rigidly flyproof, or some substance must be used in the receptacle to protect the contents from insects.

Screening, an effective means of excluding flies from homes and food, is widely used.

A vast variety of biological control agents have been reported to affect the house fly and related species. Further research is required to indicate the practicality of most of them. The bacterium *Bacillus thuringiensis* Berliner contains a filterable principle that interferes with development (Briggs, 1960), and when the spores are fed to caged chickens (Burns, *et al.*, 1961) or to cattle a variable degree of fly control is achieved in their droppings. Three grams of spores per day fed to laying hens resulted in 99 per cent reduction of adult fly emergence from feces (Briggs, 1960). Pathogenic fungi, notably *Beauveria bassiana*,

Fig. 6-10 Properly composted manure may be piled without producing any fly breeding. This "manure mountain" in southern California bred no flies except in one small seepage area along its edge. (Photograph by Arthur C. Smith; courtesy of California Bureau of Vector Control.)

Fig. 6-11 The Dano plant at Sacramento, California. (Courtesy of Dano of America, Inc.)

Fig. 6-12 A sanitary privy: front view to *left*, rear and side view to *right*. (After Stiles and Lumsden.)

Entomophthora americana, and *E. muscae* (Dresner, 1949), also cause mortality and should be further exploited.

A number of quite effective predators of flies are known. Among acarina, members of the genus *Macrocheles* are widely distributed and have received particular attention. Fly eggs and small larvae are eaten by *M. muscae-domesticae*, which is credited with considerable control in field tests (Axtell, 1963; Wade and Rodriguez, 1961). Beetles may also be efficient predators. The histerid *Platylister chinensis* feeds on fly larvae, and upon its introduction to Fiji and Samoa it helped to control house

flies (Simmonds, 1958). Staphylinid beetles of the genus *Aleochara* eat fly eggs and larvae; in the United States these are under investigation for controlling the face fly and other dung-breeding flies. In Japan *Trichopria commoda* Muesebeck (Hymenoptera: Diapriidae) was mass produced in a campaign to control house flies (Muesebeck, 1961). Poultry readily eat fly larvae and pupae; the presence of cockerel chicks under battery raised chickens in a one to ten ratio exerts considerable fly control by keeping the feces scattered to dry, and developing flies consumed (Rodriguez, 1959).

Insecticides should be used as a last measure in fly control, not only because sanitation is more permanently effective but also because resistance develops so readily. Sprays are applied as residual deposits, with particular attention being paid to favored resting sites such as sunny surfaces of barns, shelters, and fences. Emulsifiable concentrate or wettable powder sprays for use inside barns are prepared from Ciodrin®, compound 4072, diazinon, dichlorvos, dimethoate, fenthion, lindane, malathion, methoxychlor, naled; outside barns chlordane, DDT, toxaphene, and dichlorvos may also be applied. As space sprays within barns dichlorvos, naled, and pyrethrins plus synergist may be used. Dry sugar or syrup baits are very effective. These can be broadcast, sprayed, or painted onto surfaces within barns using diazinon, dichlorvos, malathion, and trichlorfon.

A number of chemicals can sterilize both sexes of house flies and their relatives. Use of some of these may be practical in the future, particularly because their incorporation into baits would permit self treatment in field use, and limited careful application of such baits should not endanger other forms of life. Of several chemosterilants tested on Grand Turk Island (B.W.I.) 1 per cent metepa in liquid bait yielded a 90 per cent reduction of the house fly population in eighteen months (Meifert, *et al.*, 1967). Female sex attractant is present in house flies (Rogoff, *et al.*, 1964; Mayer and Thaggard, 1966), but is not as effective as with many other insects because visual factors are also strongly involved in mating behavior. There is considerable interest in the biochemical factor present in the reproductive tract of males that, when transferred to females, prevents second matings (Adams and Nelson, 1968).

FACE FLY (*MUSCA AUTUMNALIS*)

The face fly has become particularly bothersome to cattle and horses in the United States, where it has been introduced and apparently is not held in check by natural enemies to the same extent as in Europe. The same biocontrol agents mentioned for the house fly are under investigation. In addition a native nematode parasite, *Heterotylenchus* spp. that has been found in New York state (Stoffolano and Nickle, 1966) seems to be rather effective and is widespread.

Insecticide measures are similar to those used for the house fly, but in addition applications directed specifically toward the face of livestock and the dung of cattle are most effective. Automatic spray procedures, as mentioned for horse flies but more specifically directed toward the head region, can provide good control. Treatment of range cattle is very difficult. One practical method has been to use dusting bags containing a dust of malathion or methoxychlor and suspended at head height, or more effectively to attach such dusting bags to covered mineral salt boxes (Turner, 1965). Control on horses is a great problem, and these animals seem particularly bothered by face flies. Making cattle feces unsuitable for face fly development is experimentally promising, using ronnel in mineral salt mixture (Wallace and Turner, 1964), or various insecticides in a polymer-insecticide feed additive that will provide toxicant sufficiently undegraded in feces to control larvae (Lloyd and Matthysse, 1966).

MYIASIS-CAUSING FLIES

Specific controls for myiasis-causing flies are restricted here to species having the obligatory myiasis habit. Facultative species are kept reduced in numbers by the methods suggested for house flies and their relatives.

Cattle Grubs, *Hypoderma* **Species.** Spectacular success has been realized in the use of animal systemics for controlling cattle grubs in beef cattle. The same materials cannot be applied to producing dairy cattle because milk becomes contaminated. For dairy animals, wettable powder-water suspensions of rotenone must be thoroughly sprayed, sponged, or brushed, or a dust formulation thoroughly rubbed into the back. On beef cattle ronnel can be added to feed or to mineral salt blocks, or coumaphos, Ruelene®, or trichlorfon can be applied to the skin by thorough spraying or pouring evenly along the animal's back line. Time of year of application is important to achieve good control.

The Tórsalo, *Dermatobia hominis* (Linnaeus). Control of the tórsalo, most serious pest of cattle in the tropics of Mexico and Central and South America, is difficult. Sprays as used for direct application on cattle for horse fly control can be effective if used continuously, killing newly hatched tórsalo larvae and repelling the egg vectors. Systemic insecticides used against cattle grubs provide control, but cannot be expected to be as effective as against those insects because the tórsalo has a number of animal hosts, and development is more continuous. Guimarães and Papavero (1966) have reviewed methods for controlling this insect.

The Primary Screw-Worm, *Callitroga hominivorax* (Coquerell). The spectacularly successful control of the screw-worm by overflooding natural populations with irradiation-sterilized males is discussed earlier in this chapter under the heading of reproductive manipulation. An excellent review has been provided by Baumhover (1966). Chemosterilization of prepupae or adults with apholate, and probably other chemosterilants, is also possible (Chamberlain, 1962).

Sheep Nose Bot. *Oestrus ovis* is controlled by using a drench of ruelene.

Fleas. Flea populations are generally analyzed by examining living or freshly killed hosts. Their presence may be suspected by the host's scratching or by typical welts resulting from bites.

Because flea larvae feed in debris found at ground level, beneath old carpets, or in floor cracks, keeping such debris to a minimum indoors will at least help to reduce their numbers. Rat fleas are controlled, particularly when plague or murine typhus threaten, by controlling their rodent hosts. Personal protection may be achieved by applying repellents;

deet to the skin, or the same material or benzyl benzoate to clothing (Gouck, 1966). Flea pathogens include the protozoan *Nosema pulicis*, taken up by larvae and causing very high mortality on occasion (Weiser, 1959). The pteromalid hymenopteran, *Bairamlia fuscipes* Waterston, may cause heavy parasitization of flea cocoons (Jurgenson and Teplyh, 1960). Ant predation on fleas in rat nests is suggested as an important factor in the reduction of murine typhus incidence in Puerto Rico (Fox and Garcia-Moll, 1961).

Insecticides are effective against fleas. Flea powders containing rotenone, pyrethrins plus synergist, malathion, or methoxychlor are safe for use on pets. Topical or oral treatment of dogs and cats with ronnel will control fleas. DDT dust also can be used but must be avoided on small puppies and on cats because the latter lick themselves. DDT dust along rodent runs and around garbage areas and warehouses will control fleas on rats, and is carried back to larval developmental sites. Kartman (1958) placed DDT dust on the floor of boxes baited with rolled oats, resulting in immediate control of all fleas on *Microtus* and other small native rodents; analysis of *Microtus* nests showed considerable amounts of DDT had been transferred and fleas in such nests were controlled for at least 132 days after the treated boxes were removed. Tarshis (1961) found silica aerogel sorptive dusts control fleas in homes, and are desirable because they are nontoxic to man.

Some suggestions on rodent control are pertinent here. A successful program should include: (1) elimination of rat harborages; (2) elimination of available food supply; (3) rodentproofing of buildings; (4) destruction of rodents.

The commensal rodents usually concerned are the house mouse *Mus musculus* Linnaeus, the brown or Norway rat *Rattus norvegicus* (Erxleben), the black rat *Rattus rattus* (Linnaeus), and the Alexandrine or roof rat *Rattus alexandrinus* (Geoffrey-Saint Hilaire and Audouin). If poison baits are used special precautions are required to keep them away from children, pets, and farm animals. Because rats are quite suspicious, prebaiting with unpoisoned bait is commonly practiced. As baits, various cereals, bread, raw meat, or fish are satisfactory. Rodenticides in current usage are the anticoagulants *warfarin*, *Pival*, or *Fumarin*; *red squill* is safe but far less effective; ANTU is effective against the Norway rat only; *sodium fluoroacetate* (called 1080) is highly effective, but is extraordinarily toxic and has no antidotes. Use of 1080 is therefore discouraged and should be employed only by licensed operators. Control of wild rodents is difficult and is generally not practiced, though dieldrin (Wolfe and Durham, 1963) or toxaphene may be applied to ground cover as a barrier against field mice (*Microtus*).

Ticks. Tick surveys consist of close observation of hosts, premises, or other habitat. Dragging a white flannel cloth over ground and vegetation, termed *flagging*, and examining it frequently for attached ticks, will provide an index of ixodid ticks in range and pasture areas and along game trails. Most argasid ticks are infrequently found on the host; the fowl tick *Argas persicus* is observed in cracks around roosts in chicken houses, and other argasids are found in hiding places around the habitations of their hosts. Brush piles, stumps, or other harborages of wild rodents should be removed from around dwellings to deplete hosts for populations of argasids associated with transmission of relapsing fever.

Biological control of ticks has been attempted, and though pathogens, parasites, and predators are known, they have not been utilized very successfully. Various fungi destroy ticks, and *Beauveria cinerea* has been considered for control of *Ixodes ricinus* in pastures (Bočiev and Rizvanov, 1960). The encyrtid wasp, *Hunterellus hookeri* Howard, parasitizes many species of ixodid ticks. Originating from France, this parasite was unsuccessfully introduced into Montana in 1927–32. It was introduced to Massachusetts and adjacent islands in 1926 to control *Dermacentor variabilis*, and the tick population of Naushon Island was significantly reduced the year after release (Larousse, *et al.*, 1928). African tick birds, *Buphagus* spp., feed heavily on ticks on large mammalian hosts.

Protection against ticks can be achieved for humans by the use of repellents. Repellents such as deet may be applied to skin, but impregnated clothing provides best control, using deet, Indalone® (2,3 butyl 3,4-dihydro-2, 2 dimethyl-4-oxo-2-pyran-6-carboxylate), dimethyl carbate, dimethyl phthalate, and benzyl benzoate. Butyl, propyl, and isopropyl acetanilide are most effective but have not been accepted for general civilian use in the United States (Gouck, 1966). Tick repellents have not been thought practical for livestock.

Controlling ticks on livestock has long been a problem. A comprehensive review of methods is available in Barnett (1961). For one host species of ticks on cattle, keeping the host off pasture, termed pasture spelling, for a period sufficient to cause high mortality of larval ticks, can be very effective if conducted properly. Such a method has been practical against *Boophilus microplus* in Australia. In Queensland, alternating pasture every two to three months minimizes the amount of insecticidal control necessary, yet leaves a low level of ticks so that cattle do not lose immunity to piroplasmosis (Wilkinson, 1957). In that country innate and acquired resistance of cattle to ticks has been studied (Riek, 1962); progress has been made in breeding resistant strains of shorthorn cattle (Wilkinson, 1962). Consult New South Wales, Sci. Bull. No. 78, 1961, *The Cattle Tick Problem in New South Wales*, for an overall discussion.

Sprays, dusts, or dips for cattle can contain the insecticides carbaryl, Ciodrin®, coumaphos, diazinon, dioxathion, lindane, malathion, ronnel, trichlorfon, or toxaphene. Sodium arsenite is also used in dips. The spinose ear tick, *Otobius megnini* (Dugès), is controlled by dusting coumaphos or spraying malathion lightly into ears and adjacent head area, or various organophosphates in combination with silica aerogel can be used (Tarshis and Ommert, 1961). Treating vegetation with insecticides provides rather temporary control of ticks, is too expensive for widespread application, and is not applicable around dairy animals or livestock being finished for slaughter. Materials recommended include chlordane, DDT, lindane, and toxaphene. The fowl tick, *Argas persicus*, is controlled by spray coverage of walls, ceiling, and floors, and forcing into cracks, with malathion, carbaryl, or naled. Dogs may be freed of ticks by topical or oral applications of ronnel.

Mites. Ectoparasitic mites are found by careful combing or washing of live or dead vertebrate hosts, and subsequent microscopic examination. Discovering those forms that live within the skin or respiratory passages is usually very difficult. On domestic mammals mites can be suspected when scratching and skin irritation is accompanied by hair loss; on birds by feather loss or raised leg scales.

Attack of trombiculid or chigger mites can be almost completely prevented by using repellents. Best control is achieved by application to clothing, though skin may also be treated. The repellents listed for ticks, and in addition ethyl hexanediol, are satisfactory. Benzyl benzoate treatment of clothing is particularly useful as it can withstand some washing and rinsing in water. Controlling habitat and hosts of trombiculid mites will also reduce numbers. Sprays or dusts of chlordane, lindane or toxaphene, when applied to vegetation around premises will control chiggers. Chigger vectors of scrub typhus in Malaya were controlled for a minimum period of two years by a treatment of dieldrin (Traub and Dowling, 1961). Malathion spray applied the day before putting turkeys on range is beneficial against chiggers but requires repetition in two to three weeks.

Mites on poultry are treated with sprays or dusts of coumaphos, malathion, naled, or carbaryl; or thoroughly painting roosts with malathion, carbaryl, or nicotine sulfate. The depluming mite *Knemidokoptes gallinae* (Raillet) can be treated by a thorough dusting or water dip in sulfur. Sulphaquinoxaline, used in low doses for common poultry diseases, prevents infestation with northern fowl mite *Ornithonyssus sylviarum* (Canestrini and Fanzago). When given in higher doses in feed this compound will completely free heavily infested hens within five weeks (Furman and Stratton, 1963). Malathion in dust bath boxes controls this same mite in community wire cages (Rodriguez and Riehl, 1960).

Dogs and cats may be treated for mange and ear mites by topical applications of ronnel, or oral treatments of the same toxicant may be used on dogs. Scabies of cattle can be controlled with dips using lime-sulphur, or toxaphene. Such treated cattle must not be slaughtered for food purposes until an adequate period has elapsed after treatment.

When man is annoyed in his home by fowl mites or rodent mites, control of the normal vertebrate hosts is recommended. This consists of destroying bird nests under eaves and cleaning out rodent harborage. The northern fowl mite and tropical rat mite can be controlled in homes by silica aerogel preparations (Ebeling, 1960; Tarshis, 1964).

VENOMOUS AND ALLERGENIC ARTHROPODS

Arthropods that merely cause allergies by their presence may be controlled by the same means employed for agricultural pests. No mention of specific control procedures will be made here.

Wasps and Hornets. Control of wasps and hornets is best achieved by destroying nests or by treating nests with insecticides. Destruction or spraying at night lessens the likelihood of being stung. Direct spraying or dusting of nests with DDT, chlordane, dieldrin, dichlorvos, or heptachlor will achieve control. Specific attractants for yellow jacket wasps, which do not affect honeybees or other beneficial insects, have been found (Davis, *et al.*, 1968). These attractants, composed of 2,4-hexadienyl butyrate and esters of other α, β-unsaturated acids, will probably be combined with insecticide or pathogens, or used to bait traps, to control yellow jackets around households, parks, and resort areas.

Ants. Within the home ants may be controlled by painting or spraying baseboards and cracks, or dusting behind baseboards and in out-of-sight areas. Insecticides used include chlordane, diazinon, dichlorvos, dieldrin, heptachlor, lindane, and malathion. Baits of peanut meal granules, incorporating the insecticide Kepone® are placed in nest openings and around foundations.

Control outdoors has been largely directed toward the imported fire ant and mound building harvester ants. Granules of heptachlor, dieldrin, Kepone®, or Mirex® may be broadcast, but can cause residue problems on forage and will likely affect desirable wildlife. A better procedure is to place these materials into the mound openings. Peanut meal granules with Mirex® can be effective when broadcast in imported fire ant infested areas.

Spiders. Indoors, webs and corners frequented by spiders may be treated with sprays or dusts, using chlordane, dichlorvos, dieldrin, malathion, or ronnel. Care must be taken not to contaminate food, water, dishes, or utensils. Control outdoors is not considered practical, though areas around house foundations and in sheds can be treated additionally with DDT to control the black widow spider.

Scorpions. Scorpion hazard around premises can be greatly reduced by removing favored hiding places such as boards, rubbish, dry cattle droppings, loose rocks, bricks, and lumber. Cracks and recesses should also be eliminated as they are favored hiding places. Man may be stung by scorpions that crawl into the shoes of a sleeping person to hide; shoes, therefore, should be turned over and shaken before wearing. Effective predators include cats, ducks, and chickens. Old crankcase oil, fuel oil, or kerosene, especially with creosote added, will make hiding places unattractive. The insecticides DDT, chlordane, lindane, and dieldrin can be selectively applied to scorpion hideouts to provide lasting control.

7

COCKROACHES AND BEETLES

COCKROACHES

ORDER BLATTARIA

Present day cockroaches have changed but little in general structure since upper Carboniferous times, some 250,000,000 years ago, when, as indicated by the coal beds of that period, they occurred abundantly in swamps. Cockroaches are usually flattened dorsoventrally with smooth (sometimes pilose) tough integument, varying in color from chestnut-brown to black in the more pestiferous house-invading species, but frequently green or orange, and other colors in tropical species. The head is decidedly flexed backward and downward when at rest. The prominent antennae are filiform and many segmented. There are two pairs of wings in most species; in some the wings are vestigial; in others, e.g., *Blatta orientalis* Linnaeus, they are well developed in the males and short in the females. The outer pair of wings (tegmina) is narrow, thick, and leathery; the inner pair is membranous and folds fanlike. Though most cockroaches possess the power of flight, they are typically runners (cursorial) and can move swiftly by means of their long, well-developed legs. They are highly gregarious and primarily nocturnal, but a few species are diurnal. Metamorphosis is simple.

The name cockroach, supposedly derived from the Spanish name for the insect (cucaracha), is preferable to the commonly used "roach," which properly should be applied to certain species of cyprinid fishes.

Feeding Habits. The mouth parts of cockroaches are of the generalized biting-chewing type (orthopteran). (see Chapter 3). These insects are omnivorous, feeding on a great variety of foods, with preferences for starchy and sugary materials. They will sip milk, nibble at cheese, meats, pastry, grain products, sugar, sweet chocolate—in fact, virtually no edible material available for human consumption is exempt from contamination by these insects, which feed just as freely on book bindings, the sized inner lining of soles, dead insects, their own cast-off skins, and dead and crippled kin, fresh and dried blood, excrement, sputum, and the finger and toe nails of sleeping or comatose human beings. They feed principally at night; hence, many people live in ignorance of their disgusting and dangerous feeding habits.

Cockroaches habitually disgorge portions of their partly digested food at intervals and drop feces wherever they go. They also discharge a nauseous secretion both from the mouth and from glands opening on the body, imparting a persistent and typical "cockroach" odor to food and dishes with which they come in contact.

Identification of Cockroaches. The scope of this work requires only that the student have a means of identifying the common pest species of cockroaches; the vast number of nondomestic forms does not concern us. Rehn (1950) has presented a key to the North American genera that, together with the study of Hebard (1917), will form a basis for a more serious study of the Nearctic forms. Mackerras (1965–1967) has treated the Australian Blattidae, which family includes all species that probably would be of the nature of a pest on that continent. The following key is designed to separate the species that occur as pets, actual or potential, or as possible vectors of disease in temperate North America. Inasmuch as pest cockroaches tend to become cosmopolitan, this key should serve to a limited extent for many other parts of the world, especially the temperate regions.

KEY TO THE COMMON PEST SPECIES OF COCKROACHES*

1. Middle and hind femora both with numerous strong spines along the ventral margins 2

* This key has been prepared for this work with the aid of Dr. Ashley B. Gurney.

Middle and hind femora without strong spines along the ventral margins, except for a few distal spines 11

2. Front femur, on its ventral anterior margin, with a row of strong spines on its basal half or more with two or three similar ones near the apex, the intervening ones being suddenly and distinctly much shorter and weaker, closely set, and dentate rather than spinelike 3
Front femur, on its ventral anterior margin, with a row of strong spines that are either of the same length and strength throughout or (except for a few near the apex) gradually decrease in length toward the apex 4

3. Ventroanterior margin of front femur with three long apical spines (the basal one much the shortest of the three); body length at least 11 mm, often much more; tegmina fully developed or lobate . . . .
. . . . *Parcoblatta* spp.
Ventroanterior margin of front femur with two long apical spines; body length about nine mm or less; tegmina fully developed, not lobate, but sometimes not covering all of abdomen (tegmina with numerous small spots on the veins) . . . .
. . . . *Ectobius pallidus* (Olivier)

4. Comparatively large species, 18 mm or more in length; subgenital plate of female divided longitudinally, valvular 6
Species smaller, less than 18 mm long; subgenital plate of the female simple 5

5. Pronotum with two conspicuous longitudinal dark bars on a pale background
. . . . *Blattella germanica* (Linnaeus)
Pronotum with disk dark brown, that color extending to both anterior and posterior margins, the lateral margins contrastingly pale; closed tegmina of both sexes appearing to have two transverse brown bars, some pale specimens showing the bars poorly . . . .
. . . . *Supella supellectilium* (Serville)

6. Tegmina of both sexes short, transversely truncate, touching or but narrowly separated (deep southeastern states) . . . .
. . . . *Eurycotis floridana* (Walker)
Tegmina fully developed or, if not, subtriangular, widely separated 7

7. Tegmina shortened, subtriangular and

basal only in female, usually exposing about three to five abdominal segments in males; length normally not exceeding 27 mm; general color rather uniform, ranging from rich chestnut brown to blackish; arolium between claws very small (male) to vestigial (female).......
............*Blatta orientalis* (Linnaeus)
Tegmina fully developed, covering abdomen in both sexes; length usually exceeding 27 mm; color variable, either uniform or in a distinctive pattern; arolium well developed...............8

8. Tegmen with a rather broad, long yellow vitta along the anterior margin at its base; pronotum with a complete yellow ring sharply contrasting in color with the dark central part and equally dark margin.....
......*Periplaneta australasiae* (Fabricius)
Anterior margin of base of tegmen without a pale vitta and pronotum not so colored, its color pattern less definite....9

9. Pronotum and tegmina a deep mahogany brown, the pronotum darker than the tegmina and without pale markings; posterior margin of supra-anal plate of the male almost transverse, with a slight indentation at the middle...............
..........*Periplaneta fuliginosa* (Serville)
Pronotum and tegmina reddish brown, the former with pale (though sometimes indefinitely limited) markings........10

10. Last segment of cercus twice as long as wide; supra-anal plate of male with a deep, narrow, acute median emargination.....
......*Periplaneta americana* (Linnaeus)
Last segment of cercus not twice as wide; supra-anal plate convex in male.........
........*Periplaneta brunnea* Burmeister

11. Very large cockroaches, usually 50 mm or more in length; arolia absent; pronotum subelliptical. Several species that are commonly introduced into the eastern United States; a common pest species of Cuba that also occurs in southern Florida is....
..........*Blaberus craniifer* Burmeister
Medium-sized to large species; arolia present; pronotum more nearly transverse posteriorly or produced angularly in the middle of its posterior margin, not subelliptical 12

12. Large species, about 40 mm or more in length...*Leucophaea maderae* (Fabricius)
Medium sized species, less than 30 mm in length 13

13. Pronotum uniformly blackish except for narrow yellow band along anterior and lateral margins (which may be indistinctly interrupted anteriorly) ....
.....*Pycnoscelus surinamensis* (Linnaeus)
Pronotum pale with a narrow dark longitudinal submarginal band on each side and irregular brown blotches on the disc
..............*Nauphoeta cinerea* (Olivier)

Species of Sanitary Importance. There are about 4,000 species of cockroaches. The taxonomic position of these insects has been the subject of dispute. They have been placed in a single family, the Blattidae, of the order Orthoptera, but they are now generally considered as forming a separate order, the Blattaria (sometimes called Blattodea), and are divided into several families, one of which is the Blattidae. Considerable light has been thrown on the relationships of the cockroaches by the studies of McKittrick (1964) and of Roth (1967, 1968) and the student who is interested in the taxonomic and phylogenetic aspects of the subject is referred to those publications.

Cockroaches occur throughout the warmer parts of the world but are largely tropical. Worldwide distribution of certain species has been effected by maritime trading; holds of vessels, the galleys, and crew's sleeping quarters are often overrun with cockroaches. Only a very few (less than 1 per cent of the known species) are troublesome to man. Among the better-known species invading the household, restaurants, hotel kitchens, grocery stores, and so forth are the following.

Blattella germanica (Linnaeus), the German cockroach (also known as the "water bug" or "croton bug") (Fig. 7-1), is the best known and probably the most widely distributed species. It is a small species, native to Europe, measuring from 12 to 16 mm in length, and is pale yellowish-brown in color with two dark brown longitudinal stripes on the pronotum. Both sexes are fully winged. The female carries

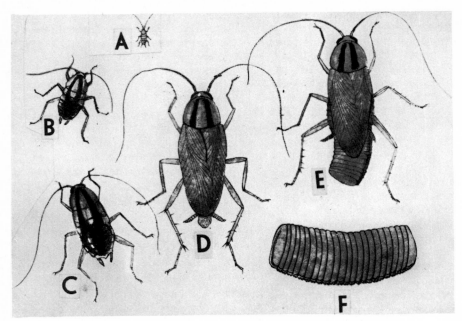

Fig. 7-1 The German cockroach, *Blattella germanica. A.* First nymphal instar. *B.* Third instar. *C.* Fourth instar. *D.* Adult female. *E.* Female with egg case. *F.* Egg case. Egg case, × 3; others, × 4. (U.S.D.A. photograph.)

the egg capsule partly protruding from the tip of the abdomen until hatching time.

Blatta orientalis (Linneaus), the Oriental cockroach (also known as the "black beetle") (Fig. 7-2), is very much darker than the German cockroach. It is dark brown to black in color and is about 22 to 27 mm in length; the wings of the female are rudimentary, and those of the male do not quite reach the tip of the abdomen. Enormous numbers of the Oriental cockroach are often found in damp basements where food is available.

Periplaneta americana (Linnaeus), the American cockroach (Fig. 7-3), is a very large (30–40 mm in length) chestnut-brown species, native probably to Africa (Rehn, 1945) (despite its common and scientific names), but now widely distributed over the earth. Both sexes have long wings that are frequently used in flying short distances. A related household pest in the eastern and southeastern states is *Periplaneta fuliginosa* (Serville), the smoky-brown cockroach. This species is smaller than

americana and is dark brown to mahogany black in color.

Periplaneta australasiae (Fabricius), the Australian cockroach, is, despite its common

Fig. 7-2 The Oriental cockroach, *Blatta orientalis,* female. × 1.3.

Fig. 7-3 The American cockroach, *Periplaneta americana.* × 1.3.

on the dorsum. The wings are well developed in both sexes.

Supella supellectilium (Serville), the brown-banded (or tropical) cockroach (Fig. 7-4), resembles the German cockroach in appearance but has two brown cross bands, one at the base of the wings and the other about $\frac{1}{16}$ of an inch farther back. The tegmina do not quite reach the tip of the abdomen in the female; the male has longer tegmina and is more slender. This difference in the appearance of the two sexes may delude the housewife into thinking that two species may be involved in an infestation. Adults fly readily when disturbed. The species is decidedly a gregarious one. Unlike the German cockroach, which confines its activities to the kitchen or around water or heat pipes, the brown-banded cockroach hides in cupboards and pantries, invades all rooms of the house, and frequently occurs in high locations such as on shelves in closets or behind pictures and picture molding. The egg capsule is fairly regularly stuck with an adhesive to surfaces, often in furniture, such as radio cabinets; consequently, the insect is sometimes called the "TV roach" or "the furniture cockroach." The insect is therefore

name, probably not indigenous to Australia; like *americana* it is a cosmopolitan species. It is reddish-brown in color, resembling *americana*, but has a strong straw-colored streak extending about one-third of the way down the outer margin of the wing covers (tegmina), as well as a yellow area around the margin of the pronotum, forming a double dark area

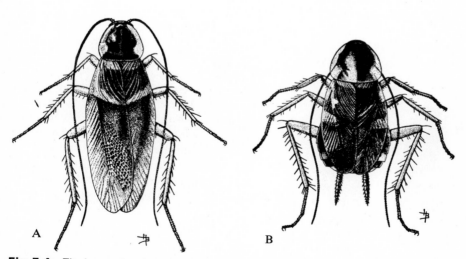

Fig. 7-4 The brown-banded cockroach, *Supella supellectilium. A.* Male. *B.* Female. (After Back.)

carried around easily and is rapidly becoming cosmopolitan.

Pycnoscelus surinamensis (Linnaeus), the Surinam cockroach, is a dark brown to black circumtropical species measuring from 18 to 24 mm in length. It is a burrowing species, burrowing under piles of debris, leaves, and other materials. It has become established in parts of the southeastern United States.

Other pest species and potentially dangerous cockroaches have been discussed by Gould and Deay (1940), Gurney (1953), and Roth and Willis (1957). Among the harmless species that attract attention, *Panchlora nivea* (Linnaeus) is the green Cuban cockroach frequently transported in bunches of bananas.

Life History. The eggs of cockroaches are lined up vertically, two by two, in the vestibule or oothecal chamber (Fig. 7-5), and the leathery, bean-shaped ootheca is then extruded to the outside. Some species, such as *Blattella germanica,* may carry the ootheca for several weeks, but most cockroaches will drop or deposit it within a day or two. In the so-called ovoviviparous species this structure is retracted into the uterus or blood sac for incubation until the young are born. In some species facultative parthenogenesis may occur. A valuable account of the reproduction of cockroaches and an analysis of oviparity and viviparity in this group have been given by Roth and Willis (1954, 1958).

The number of eggs within each capsule varies with the species. For *Periplaneta americana* the number is usually sixteen, occasionally eighteen to twenty-four. The normal number for *Blatta orientalis* is also sixteen, whereas that for *Blattela germanica* varies between thirty and forty with a maximum number of forty-eight; for *Supella supellectilium* the average is eighteen. Many egg capsules are produced during the lifetime of the female cockroach; e.g., as many as ninety by the American cockroach, eighteen by the Oriental, and but four to six by the German.

The length of the incubation period varies with the temperature and humidity. At a constant temperature of about 86° F and a relative humidity of about 70 per cent, Gould and Deay (1940) found the incubation period for the American cockroach to be 31.8 days; at room temperature it averaged 52.9 days. For the Oriental cockroach the same authors found the incubation period at room temperatures to vary from forty-two to eighty-one days; for the German cockroach under similar conditions (room temperature averaging 76° F), it was 28.4 days. The eggs of the latter species hatched in sixteen days at a temperature of 88° F or higher. The brown-banded cockroach required ninety days to hatch at room temperature of 73° F, and forty-nine days at 82° F.

On hatching, the young cockroaches are almost all white and quite wingless; the skin is cast on emergence, with a second molt in three or four weeks, followed by other molts at intervals of several weeks until maturity is reached. The American cockroach may have as many as thirteen molts, with wing pads appearing in the third or fourth molt, maturity being attained in from 285 to 642 days; however, Gould and Deay report as high as 971 days under similar conditions for one individual. Rau (1924) reports the development period for the Oriental cockroach as one year. For the smaller species, such as the German cockroach, the developmental period is much shorter, an average of about two months

Fig. 7-5 Egg cases (oothecae) of cockroaches. *A.* Oriental cockroach. *B.* German cockroach.

(fifty to sixty days according to Seamans and Woodruff (1939), and ninety to ninety-five days at room temperature according to Gould and Deay. This permits the development of two or more generations a year for the German cockroach. There are normally six molts, but there may be seven under adverse conditions.

The longevity of the American cockroach is reported by Gould and Deay to range from 102 to 588 days under room conditions, and the *complete* life span of three females of this species is reported to have been 783, 793, and 913, respectively. The mean length of life of female German cockroaches is reported by these authors to be 200 days, with a maximum of 303 days.

Cockroaches as Vectors. To date, cockroaches have never been positively incriminated in the natural transmission of pathogenic organisms to man. However, that they potentially and, under, proper circumstances, actually act in this capacity is virtually undeniable, in the light of studies by Roth and Willis (1957). The evidence, though circumstantial, is as strong as much of that generally accepted in other instances of mechanical transmission. A particularly convincing bit of such evidence is cited by Roth and Willis. In a pediatric hospital in Brussels, Belgium, an epidemic of *Salmonella typhimurium* in human infants persisted in spite of quick isolation of patients, the absence of healthy carriers, and the suppression of direct or indirect contact, other than through cockroaches. It was discovered, however, that the cockroaches were running over clothing, covers, and bodies of the babies by night, and the bacterium was isolated in considerable numbers from the bodies of the insects. The epidemic ceased immediately after the nursery was disinfected with DDT.

Herms and Nelson (1913), by means of a simple bacteriological experiment, showed that *Blattella germanica* can acquire specific bacteria by crawling over cultures and then depositing the bacteria on food; e.g., by crawling over sugar. They found a minimum

of 13,470 bacteria per cockroach. According to Roth and Willis, the parts of the insect that normally come in contact with the substrate are the euplantulae and terminal structures that would be most apt to pick up the pathogens and, by the same token, to deposit them on food, though obviously much contamination occurs through fecal deposition.

Roth and Willis list eighteen species of domiciliary cockroaches, including most of the common pest species, which have been incriminated by experimental evidence or by the recovery from their bodies of organisms pathogenic to man, or which have been known to bite man. A major consideration relating to the actual role of cockroaches in the transmission of disease concerns the likelihood of those insects passing from contaminated areas and media to homes. Though largely confined to buildings in cooler climates, domestic cockroaches may freely leave such structures under tropical and warm temperate conditions; they may frequently migrate to buildings from sewers, cesspools, septic tanks, privies and dumps. Most domesticated species readily feed both on human feces and human food. It is well established that cockroaches may nibble at the skin or toenails of sleeping or sick persons, helpless babies, or corpses. The abundance of cockroaches in some areas where poor hygienic conditions prevail is beyond the imagination of persons who live in civilized, highly sanitary areas. The true nature of the problem of cockroaches in relation to vectorship of pathogens cannot be judged, therefore, from the United States but, rather, from those areas where these insects afford the greatest threat to human health.

Natural isolations from wild-caught cockroaches include four strains of poliomyelitis virus, about forty species of pathogenic bacteria, largely Enterobacteriaceae but including what is probably the leprosy bacterium, two pathogenic fungi (*Aspergillus*), and the protozoon *Entamoeba histolytica* Schaudinn. Other pathogenic organisms cockroaches have been shown to harbor under experimental conditions include the Coxsackie, mouse encephalitis, and yellow fever viruses; the bacterial agents of Asiatic cholera, cerebrospinal fever, pneumonia, diphtheria, undulant fever, anthrax, tetanus, tuberculosis, and others; and the Protozoa *Trichomonas hominis* (Davaine), *Giardia intestinalis* (Lambl) and *Balantidium coli* (Malmsen), all suspected or proven agents of diarrhea or dysentry.

Cockroaches as Intermediate Hosts of Parasites. It was very early known that cockroaches may become infected with the nematode *Spirura gastrophila* Muller of the rat by feeding on rat feces, and that other rats may become infected in turn by feeding on infected cockroaches. As early as 1878, Galeb reported the discovery of nematodes in the adipose tissue of *Blatta orientalis* that were considered identical with nematodes found in the Norway rat.

Fibiger (1913) presented evidence to support the theory that the nematode *Gongylonema neoplasticum* (Fibiger and Ditlevsen), a parasite of the rat, produced malignant tumors in the rat. At least four species of cockroaches serve as intermediate hosts of this parasite. Fibiger's argument was convincing enough that he was awarded the Nobel Prize in 1926 for these discoveries; but Hitchcock and Bell (1952), in a series of carefully controlled experiments, failed to substantiate his findings and produced the same results with a diet deficient in vitamin A. The present evidence indicates that cancer must join beriberi, pellagra, scurvy, and several other diseases wrongly attributed to the vectorship of cockroaches.

Roth and Willis (1957) summarize the association of cockroaches with helminths as follows:

The eggs of 7 species of pathogenic helminths have been found naturally in cockroaches 11 times. The eggs of 4 of these species and of 5 additional species have been fed experimentally to cockroaches 19 times. Cockroaches have been found to serve naturally as the intermediate hosts of 12 species of helminths in about 43 observations. Cockroaches were used successfully as intermediate hosts for 11 of these species and also for 11 other species in about 44 experiments.

Though of no medical importance, it is of interest to note that a pentastomid, tentatively identified as *Raillietiella hemidactyli* Hett, was found to use *Periplaneta americana* as an intermediate host (Lavoipierre and Lavoipierre, 1966). The definitive hosts of the pentastomid were geckoes.

Cockroaches and Allergy. The subject of allergy is discussed in Chapter 20.

BEETLES

ORDER COLEOPTERA

The Coleoptera constitute the largest insect order, comprising over 270,000 described species of insects. Very few of the families of beetles concern the medical entomologist, but, because of their abundance and successful invasion of all sorts of environments, it is certain that contact will be made with members of this order of insects sooner or later. Familiarity with the order is important.

Characteristics. Beetles are readily distinguishable from all other insects. Their integument is horny or leathery; their mouth parts are strongly mandibulated, i.e., biting-chewing. Although wings are absent in some species, usually at least the fore-pair is present; these, which are called elytra, are not used in flight, are horny, and when at rest meet in a straight line down the dorsum; the hind wings are membranous and functional, often folded both horizontally and vertically. Metamorphosis is complete (eggs, larva, pupa, imago). The larvae are of various forms. Most of them have three pairs of well-developed legs, although those of the weevils and some other groups are legless.

Scavenger Beetles. All scavenger beetles, of which there are several families, are potentially of some public health importance because their habits of feeding as larvae or adults on dead animals, hides, or other animal matter may accidentally bring them into contact with pathogenic organisms. They may carry pathogens in at least two ways, either mechanically on their legs, mouth parts, or body, or in their excreta after feeding on infectious material.

Nuttall (1899) reports that, as early as 1894, Proust in examining goatskins taken from anthracic animals, found quantities of living *Dermestes vulpinus* Fabr. [= *D. maculatus* De Geer] upon them. He found virulent anthrax bacilli in their excrements, as also in the eggs and in the larvae. It is evident from this that these insects which feed on the skins permit the anthrax spores to pass uninjured through the alimentary tract. Heim (1894) also had occasion to examine some skins which were suspected of having caused anthrax in three persons engaged in handling the leather. He found larvae of *Attagenus pellio* Linn., *Anthrenus museorum* Linn. (both Dermestidae), and *Ptinus*; also fully developed insects of the latter species on the skins. All these insects had virulent anthrax bacilli (spores) on their surface and in their excreta, from which Heim concludes they might spread the disease. He says the excreta are very light and easily scattered by the slightest current of air. Heim does not believe the bacilli multiply in the bodies of these insects, but that the latter may be dangerous through their scattering the spores about.

Among the families of scavenger beetles are the following:

1. *Family Staphylinidae*, commonly known as rove beetles, includes many species that feed on carrion, dung, and decaying animal matter; they are characterized by the abbreviated elytra, which leave much of the abdomen exposed and gives the beetles a "larval" appearance; the abdomen is flexible and is often curled up and thrown forward dorsally; the long functional wings are folded up or concealed beneath the short wing covers when not in use. The scavenger species are commonly seen when one turns carrion, hides, heaps of bones, and so forth (Fig. 7-6).

2. *Family Silphidae*. These insects, commonly known as carrion beetles, burying

Fig. 7-6 Rove beetles (Staphylinidae). ×1.5.

Fig. 7-7 Sexton beetles (Silphidae). × 1.5.

beetles, or sexton beetles, are as a rule attracted to dead animals, which they undermine and, in the case of small ones, may even bury. They deposit their eggs on the dead animals and the larvae feed on the decomposing flesh (Fig. 7-7).

3. *Family Dermestidae*, which includes hide beetles, larder beetles, museum pests, and dermestids. These are small oval or elongated beetles, often mottled, grayish or brownish in color. The hairy larvae as well as the adults feed on dead animals, museum specimens, wool, cured meats, cheese, and many other animal as well as vegetable products (cereals). *Dermestes lardarius* Linnaeus is known as the larder beetle; *Dermestes maculatus* De Geer is commonly used to clean dried flesh from bones for museum use; *Anthrenus scrophulariae* (Linnaeus) is a carpet beetle and museum pest. Larvae of the carpet beetle may enter the ears of persons and cause much discomfort (Fig. 7-8).

Beetles as Intermediate Hosts of Helminths. Many species of beetles serve as intermediate hosts of helminthic parasites of man and of wild and domesticated animals. The common relationship is no doubt due to the variety of

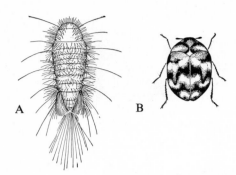

Fig. 7-8 The varied carpet beetle, *Anthrenus verbasci*. *A*. Larva. *B*. Adult.

feeding habits of beetles that enables them to ingest fecal matter in which eggs of intestinal parasites of animals commonly occur; thus, many cereal and omnivorous feeders, as well as coprophagous beetles, may readily lend themselves as intermediate hosts. The infective stage of nematode worms of the genus *Gongylonema* commonly occur in dung beetles belonging to the family Scarabaeidae, such as members of the genus *Aphodius*; also in meal worms belonging to the family Tenebrionidae such as *Tenebrio molitor* Linnaeus. *Gongylonema pulchrum* Molin parasitizes many species of mammals, such as goats, swine, and occasionally man. It invades tissues of the oral cavity and esophagus, causing *gongylonemiasis*.

Many beetles or cockchafers (family Scarabaeidae) are known to be intermediate hosts both in the larval and adult stages of the thornheaded worm, *Macracanthorhynchus hirudinaceus* (Pallas) (=*Gigantorhynchus gigas* [Bloch]), a parasite of swine said also to occur in man in rare instances. This acanthocephalan worm in its adult stage measures 200 to 300 mm in length and about 3 to 5 mm in thickness and inhabits the small intestine of the host. The eggs pass out with the feces, which may be ingested by the larvae of cockchafers. These are often extremely abundant among the rootlets of grass in heavily sodded pastures, and swine with free range are fond of these grubs, in search of which they diligently root

up the soil with their snouts. Thus every opportunity is given for the grubs, and in turn the swine, to become infected. In Europe the intermediate host is commonly *Melolontha melolontha* (Linnaeus) or *Cetonia aurata* (Linnaeus). Many beetles of the genus *Phyllophaga*, as well as soil inhabiting scarabaeids of other genera, are probably more or less involved.

Numerous species of beetles have been proved to be intermediate hosts of the fowl tapeworm, *Raillietina cesticillus* (Molin). The species listed by Reid, Ackert, and Case (1938) belong to the following families: Scarabaeidae, two species; Tenebrionidae, one species; Carabidae, subfamily Harpalinae, twenty-six species, to which they add twelve not previously reported, giving a total of thirty-eight species in this family. The species of *Amara* proved to be particularly favorable hosts, although the largest number of cysticercoids were produced by a species of *Pterostichus*, a total of 626 by one beetle that had been fed on four proglottids.

Canthariasis is a term used to designate the rare accidental beetle (larva or adult) infestation of organs of the body; e.g., infestations of the alimentary canal by larvae of the churchyard beetle, *Blaps mortisaga* (Linnaeus), as the result of superstitiously drinking foul graveyard water in which these beetles may occur. The ingestion of meal- and flour-infesting insects such as the meal worm, *Tenebrio molitor* Linnaeus, has also been known to result in infestation.

Vesicating and Poisonous Beetles. Vesicating and poisonous beetles are dealt with in Chapter 20.

Miscellaneous Annoying Beetles. Aside from any economic or other injury for which the beetles may be responsible, the sheer abundance of certain species at times causes annoyance. Herms reported considerable annoyance caused by the copra "bug," or red-legged ham beetle, *Necrobia rufipes* (De Geer), in the Philippine Islands, as these insects swarmed over him while he was trying to do desk work. These small greenish-blue beetles originated in vast numbers in copra stored in neighboring sheds. The larvae of this species may also enter the ears of persons.

Tiny (3 mm long) saw-toothed grain beetles, *Oryzaephilus surinamensis* (Linnaeus), belonging to the family Cucujidae, may invade bed chambers in great numbers, crawl over the bodies of occupants, and nibble the skin. One infestation of this kind was traced to the bathroom and thence out of the house through the yard and into an old barn where, under the stalls, grain from the manger had collected, affording a breeding ground for the beetles. Extreme dryness had apparently driven the insects to the bathroom for moisture, and the annoyance of occupants of the adjoining bedchamber was merely accidental.

Minute species of Staphylinidae, such as *Atheta occidentalis* Bernhaeur, a blackish species 3 mm long, are often encountered on the wing in the late autumn, and may accidentally enter the eyes, causing a severe burning sensation and temporarily blinding the victim. Such a mishap to a person driving a motor car might lead to a serious accident. These minute species breed in cow dung and decomposing plant refuse.

Many species of the family Carabidae possess vile odors. One of these, the so-called tule beetle or stink beetle, *Agonum maculicolle* (Dejean), of California, is normally a beneficial predator, but when its natural habitat in the marshes becomes dry in summer it commonly leaves in search of moisture and may invade homes in the neighborhood. Heavy early winter rains and cold weather may likewise cause invasions. The nauseous odor of this beetle is almost intolerable.

Beetles as Parasites. Belonging to the family Platypsyllidae of some authors (here considered part of the Leptinidae), is the coleopterous parasite of the beaver, *Platypsyllus castoris* Ritsema. This is a permanent, obligate parasite in all its stages. The eggs are deposited on the skin of the beaver among dense hairs. It occurs in both Europe and North America.

The Leptinidae also includes other beetles that are parasitic on beavers and certain other rodents. The three known species are *Leptinus testaceus* Muller, parasitic on mice and shrews in Europe and North America; *Lepinillus validus* (Horn), found on North American beavers; and *Leptinillus aplodontiae* Rowan, taken on *Aplodontia*, the mountain beaver of the Pacific coast states.

8

THE BUGS

(Bed Bugs, Assassin Bugs, and Others)

Aphidae (plant lice or aphids), Cicadidae (cicadas or harvest flies), Cicadellidae (leaf-hoppers, sharpshooters), Membracidae (tree-hoppers) and many others of great agricultural importance, including many vectors of plant pathogens. These insects have piercing-sucking mouth parts, and though plant-feeders, many of them have been reported as biting or sucking blood from human beings. Usinger (1934) attributes this uncommon phenomenon of bloodsucking in the normally phytophagous groups of the Hemiptera to three influences, namely, "the stimulus of artificial light or other unusual conditions of the environment, the attractive qualities of exposed liquids, mainly perspiration, and hunger." He further remarks that this change

... from plant feeding to bloodsucking, is not such a profound one as would at first be supposed. This is evidenced by a comparison of the composition of plant juices and blood and by the various plant-feeding groups, some members of which have adapted themselves to a predaceous habit or have shown their ability occasionally to suck the blood of mammals.

ORDER HEMIPTERA

The order Hemiptera contains about 55,000 described species and is divided into two sub-orders: (1) Heteroptera, in which the fore wing (hemelytron) is usually divided into a coriaceous or leathery basal part and a mem-branous apical portion, the latter overlapping the membranous part of the opposite fore wing; and (2) Homoptera, in which the fore wing is usually of the same texture throughout.

The suborder Homoptera includes such important phytophagous families as the

The Heteroptera or true bugs are character-ized by a segmented suctorial proboscis, attached anteriorly and, when not in use, flexed under the head. The true bugs are separated into two divisions: (1) the **Gymnocerata,** in which the antennae are conspicuous and capable of being moved freely in front, of the head, e.g., *Cimex lectularius* Linnaeus the bed bug, *Anasa tristis* (De Geer), the squash bug, and *Triatoma protracta* (Uhler), a conenose; and (2) the **Cryptocerata,** in which the antennae are concealed in small cavities (foveae) and are closely pressed to the under side of the head, e.g., *Lethocerus americanus* (Leidy), the giant water bug. Metamorphosis is simple.

THE BED BUGS

FAMILY CIMICIDAE

The family Cimicidae, which includes the bed bugs, swallow bugs, poultry bug, bat bug, and others, is characterized by a very short, broad head, broadly attached to the prothorax, an oval body, well-developed compound eyes, absence of ocelli, four-segmented conspicuous antennae, a three-segmented proboscis lying in a groove beneath the head and thorax, and very short padlike hemelytra. The bodies are broad and flat, enabling the bugs to creep into narrow crevices. A disagreeable pungent odor is present in the group as a whole, with few exceptions. They are night-prowling and bloodsucking in habit, mostly feeding on birds and bats, but some either regularly or occasionally attack human beings. Peculiar to these bugs is the organ of Ribaga located in the fourth and fifth abdominal segments. The presence or absence of this organ and its particular location when present provide characters useful in the identification of species.

Seventy-four species, representing twenty-two genera and six subfamilies, are known (Usinger, 1966). Many are local in distribution and are of little or no medical importance, but two species have followed their unusual host, man, over a large part of the world. These are *Cimex lectularius* Linnaeus, the common human bed bug, a cosmopolitan species of both hemispheres but particularly occurring in the temperate regions, and *C. hemipterus* Fabricius, also found widespread in both hemispheres but essentially a species of the tropics. A third human parasite is *Leptocimex boueti* (Brumpt), which is restricted to tropical Africa where it infests native huts. Only two species of bed bugs, namely *C. lectularius* and *C. hemipterus*, are common to both hemispheres, although the swallow bugs, genus *Oeciacus*, are represented by one species, *O. hirundinis* (Lamarck), in the Old World and by another, *O. vicarius* Horvath, in the New.

Usinger (1966) has published an extensive and very valuable monograph dealing not only with the taxonomy of the Cimicidae of the World but also with an extensive treatment of their ecology, external and internal morphology, reproduction, cytology and cytogenetics, medical importance, and methods of control.

The Bed Bug. The adult of the bed bug, *Cimex lectularius* Linnaeus (Fig. 8-1) measures 4 to 5 mm in length and 3 mm in breadth; it is obovate and much flattened. The adult is reddish brown in color, whereas the young are yellowish white. Among the local names applied to bed bugs are "chinches," "chintzes," "red coats," "mahogany flats," "wall louse," "common bed bugs," or simply "bugs." Usinger has given an interesting list of more than fifty names in various languages that have been used for this insect.

Bed bugs, like lice, have been the constant companions of man for centuries; the earliest writings on natural history (Pliny and Aristotle) mention them. Bed bugs occasionally gain a foothold among animals, such as white rats and guinea pigs, upon which they feed readily. They are nocturnal in their feeding habits, hiding in crevices during the day. At night they are active, crawling out of their hiding places, often traveling considerable distances to attack their victims. This is especially true where iron bedsteads are used, as these do not provide convenient

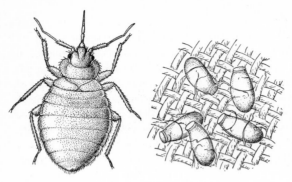

Fig. 8-1 The bed bug, *Cimex lectularius*. Eggs shown at right.

hiding places for the bugs. Ordinarily, where wooden bedsteads are used, the bugs stay closer to their point of attack. Mattresses in any case may afford harborage. Bed bugs are gregarious; hence, great assemblages often may be found in some convenient crevice or beneath some nearby loose wallpaper, where the eggs are deposited and the tarry-black excrement collects.

The female deposits eggs in batches of ten to fifty, totaling 200 to 500, spread out in a yellowish patch. The eggs are large and yellowish white in color. The young hatch in four to twenty-one (usually about ten) days, according to temperature, which also affects their later growth. The time required for development from egg to maturity is given by Omori (cited by Usinger) as 37 to 128 days, depending upon temperature; this, however, is under favorable laboratory conditions, which are seldom, if ever, realized in nature. All instars, particularly the later ones, can endure prolonged starvation (80 to 140 days, depending on the instar and sex, the higher figure being for the adult male); this, of course, lengthens the life cycle. Temperature and humidity also have an effect on the length of the life cycle.

Bed bugs are evidently sensitive to high temperatures. The termal death point for *C. lectularius* is 44 to 45° C (about 112° F), but even a temperature of 36 to 37° C (about 100° F) with fairly high humidity will kill many of them. Activity ceases below about 13 to 15° C

(56 to 59° F). Conditions of temperature and humidity that deviate from the optimum, consequently, also have the effect of prolonging the life cycle. Johnson, cited by Usinger, calculates that in an unheated bedroom in London, where conditions for development are limited to a period extending from the second week of May to the second or third week of October, only one complete generation and a partial second could be produced in one year. Bed bugs molt five times, and the minute wing pads characteristic of the adult insect make their appearance with the last molt. Ordinarily but one meal is taken between each molt and one before egg deposition; an average period of eight days is required between moltings.

Method of Distribution. Bed bugs, lice, or other organisms cannot originate spontaneously in filth as some uninformed persons still believe; infestations are traceable to introduced eggs, young, or adults. Thus, the introduction of one impregnated female might furnish the nucleus for a well-developed colony in a few months. The best-regulated household is not exempt from invasion, though cleanliness is the best preventive against the multiplication of any household pest.

Public conveyances and public gathering places are common avenues for the dissemination of bed bugs. Furthermore, migration from house to house by way of water pipes, walls, and the like is not at all unlikely when infested houses are vacated and the food supply is cut off. The insects are also easily carried in clothing, traveling bags, suitcases, laundry and so forth, and they may be introduced with secondhand beds, bedding, and furniture.

Bed Bug Bites. Persons bitten by bed bugs are affected differently; in some the bite produces marked swellings and considerable irritation; in others not the slightest inconvenience is caused. The bite of the bed bug is produced by piercing organs of the hemipteron type already described. It is probable that puncture by these stylets, unattended by contamination or specific poisons, would produce little pain. The welts and local inflammation are caused by allergic reaction to the saliva that is introduced early in the act of feeding. The bed bug is able to engorge itself completely with blood in from three to ten minutes. Although persons are usually bitten at night while in bed, because of the nocturnal habits of the bed bugs the insects will bite freely in subdued light by day.

Pathogen Transmission. The fact that bed bugs are obliged to feed at least five times, either upon the same or a different host, to reach maturity has placed these insects under grave suspicion as potential vectors of disease-causing organisms. Though many workers have tried to incriminate the bed bug in the role of a vector (see most recently the review of Burton, 1963), virtually all evidence has been negative or inconclusive. The bed bug would, therefore, appear to be relatively unimportant in this respect. In spite of the fact that it can transmit experimentally the pathogens of Oriental sore, relapsing fever, leprosy, kala-azar, Chagas' disease, and other diseases, there is no convincing evidence that it is a vector of any human or animal pathogen.

Other Species that Attack Man. The bed bug of the tropics, *Cimex hemipterus*, is similar in its biology to *C. lectularius* but is adapted to a warmer climate. It is widespread in tropical parts of America, Africa, and Asia, in the East Indies, and in some islands of the Pacific. Like *C. lectularius* it is essentially a human parasite; also, like that species, *C. hemipterus* will attack the domestic fowl and certain bats. It is difficult to differentiate from *C. lectularius*, but its pronotum is but little more than twice as wide as long, whereas that of *lectularius* is about two and a half times as broad as long. The short hairs on the sides of the pronotum will distinguish both *C. lectularius* and *C. hemipterus* from such bat-infesting species as *C. pilosellus* (Horvath) and from the swallow-infesting *Oeciacus* species.

Leptocimex boueti (Brumpt) has a narrow thorax, not much wider than the head, short, flaplike hemelytral pads, and a greatly elongated third antennal segment, which is twice as long as the fourth and almost four times as long as the second. It is found in native huts in Africa, where it feeds on the natives but will apparently not attack Europeans. It will also feed on bats, the normal host for other members of the genus.

The genus *Cimex* includes two species of bat parasites, namely, *C. pillosellus* (Horvath) of America and *C. pipistrelli* Jenyns, of Europe. These bugs, as well as the *Oeciacus* species, will bite man if he disturbs them, but will not become established on him as a regular host. Poultry bugs may also bite man, but only incidentally. These belong to two genera of the subfamily Haematosiphoninae. The Mexican chicken bug, *Haematosiphon inodorus* (Dugès), has an interesting host range as it feeds on the California condor, owls, eagles, and chickens. Lee (1955), who studied the biology of this species, reports heavy infestations of birds; for example, two barn owl nests harbored 1,425 and 1,778 bugs respectively. Reports of this species infesting houses, however, are rare. *Ornithocoris toledo* Pinto, the Brazilian chicken bug, once a pest of considerable importance, has been brought under control by the use of residual insecticides. Another species of this genus *O. pallidus* Usinger, feeds on swallows and poultry in Brazil and also in the southeastern United States, where it probably was introduced.

THE ASSASSIN BUGS

FAMILY REDUVIIDAE

The Reduviidae are typical examples of the Heteroptera. As a family they are commonly known as assassin bugs. There are more than 2,500 species divided among twenty subfamilies. A very large percentage of the reduviids are predaceous and feed on insects, many of which are harmful; hence, the family is to an extent useful. A number of these species, when handled carelessly, defend themselves by biting; a relatively small, but important group of them, constituting the sub-family Triatominae, feed exclusively on the blood of vertebrates. Comprehensive treatments of this subfamily have been published by Neiva and Lent (1941), by Usinger (1944) for North and Middle America, by Abalos and Wygodzinsky (1951) for Argentina, and by Cova Garcia and Suarez (1959) for Venezuela.

Various names have been applied to members of this subfamily. The designations conenoses or "kissing bugs" are used in the United States; in Central and South America some of the names that are employed are vinchuca, pito, chupon, chirimacha, chinche; the last term is often used in combination with a modifier, for example chinche de monte, chinche tigre, and chinchev oladora.

In the Triatominae, the head is more or less elongated or cone-shaped and has a remarkably free movement; the ocelli are located behind the compound eyes; the sturdy, three-segmented proboscis can be thrust forward, but when in repose it lies beneath the head; the piercing stylets can be extended far beyond the tip of the proboscis; the long, slender, four- or five-segmented antennae are situated in front of the eyes or on the border of the head; the prothorax is strongly developed. Most species are able to fly well.

Life History. The rather large, more or less barrel-shaped eggs of reduviids (often with stellate or fringed caps) are generally deposited in situations where the adults occur; i.e., the ground-inhabiting forms deposit their eggs on the ground, arboreal forms lay their eggs on leaves and stems, and house-inhabiting forms oviposit in dusty corners. Much information has been given by Miller (1956), mostly in the form of illustrations, on the eggs, and Readio (1926) has illustrated the eggs of many species and has published an excellent account of the bionomics of the family (Readio, 1927).

The eggs are commonly deposited singly, but sometimes in small clusters, the total number per female varying considerably from a few dozen to more than 600. The incubation period varies from eight or ten days to nearly a month, depending upon the species and temperature. The newly hatched nymphs are wingless. The usual number of nymphal instars is five, although Readio states that *Melanolestes picipes* (Herrich-Schaeffer) passes through only four. Some species overwinter in the egg stage, others as adults, and still others as nymphs. In most cases there appears to be but one generation a year. The length of the life cycle of *Triatoma rubrofasciata* (De Geer) was found by Neiva to cover 210 days, and for *Panstrongylus megistus* (Burmeister) it was 260 days. Usinger (1944) reports a two-year life cycle for *Triatoma recurva* Stål (=*longipes* Barber).

Assassin Bug Bites. Many of the species of assassin bugs inflict a painful bite when handled carelessly. The masked hunter, *Reduvius personatus* (Linnaeus), a European species that has been introduced into the United States, where it is now widespread, is one of these. Its popular name is derived from the habit of the nymph of "masking" itself under debris, which accumulates upon it. Occasionally a person receives a painful bite from one of these bugs, but the general alarm caused by newspaper stories in 1899 about the bite of the "kissing bug," and to an extent perpetuated since, was greatly exaggerated.

Another reduviid that has a bad reputation as a biter is the wheel bug, *Arilus cristatus* (Linnaeus). Reporting on the bite of this species, Hall (1924) says

The finger became reddened and felt hot to the touch. In the course of a few days, growths resembling papillomas developed at the site of the punctures, the largest of these projecting as a small hornlike structure. Both of these growths persisted for months, the largest slowly disappearing between six and nine months after the infliction of the bite. The injured finger remained warmer than the other fingers during this period, and, according to the patient's statement, still feels warmer than the other fingers, a year later. The development of pronounced cutaneous growths after a bite appears indicative of the action of some toxin as a stimulant irritant.

The feeding bites of *Triatoma* and *Panstrongylus* are in themselves benign; they are hardly, if at all, felt by their hosts. If this were not so, xenodiagnosis would be impractical. The painless bite is an adaptation to the habitual bloodsucking habit in contrast to the painful bite of the occasional bloodsucker (Usinger, 1944). On the other hand, the thrust produced in self-defense (but not the feeding bite) of *Triatoma rubrofasciata* (De Geer) in Hawaii is sharp and painful and is accompanied by the emission of an offensive musk (Zimmerman, 1948).

In some individuals however, serious complications may result from anaphylactic reactions. For example, such reactions may result from the bite of *Triatoma protracta* (Uhler) (Fig. 8-2), a widely distributed Pacific coast species commonly known as the China bed bug or cross bug. Normally, this species occurs in *Neotoma* (wood rat) nests, and feeding on man is an aberrant, though unfortunately not uncommon, part of its behavior. Walsh and Jones (1962) and Mortensen and Walsh (1963), through an analysis of 110 case histories, note two distinct types of sensitivity reactions: (1) a localized reaction at the site of the bite, accompanied by an intense itching and the formation of a large wheal that persists for about a week; and (2) a systemic response to the foreign protein injected into the bite. Apparently, one can acquire hypersensitivity as the result of having been bitten repeatedly. Patients may develop nausea and diarrhea; welts and rash may appear on various parts of the body, and marked edema, especially around the eyes, tongue, and upper respiratory tract may be observed; fainting spells may occur; and there may be intense itching, especially on the scalp, palms, and soles.

The bite of the bloodsucking conenose or "Mexican bed bug," *Triatoma sanguisuga* (LeConte), (Fig. 8-3*B*) is said to result in sensitive individuals, in a "burning pain, intense itching, and much swelling ... with red blotches and welts all over the body and limbs." The effect of the bite may last for months;

A   B

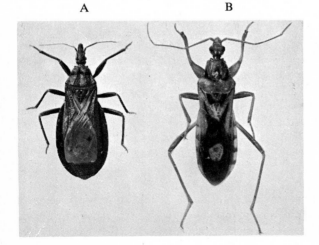

Fig. 8-2 Members of the family Reduviidae. *A. Triatoma protracta. B. Rasahus thoracicus.*

A   B   C   D

Fig. 8-3 Examples of Reduviidae. *A. Triatoma protracta. B. Triatoma sanguisuga. C. Panstrongylus geniculatus. D. Rhodnius pallescens.*

however, it usually disappears within a few days. In Hawaii, *Triatoma rubrofasciata* produces similar symptoms and the anaphylactic reactions of the feeding bites result in intensely itching welts that may become swollen and painful (Zimmerman, 1948).

The "two spotted corsairs," *Rasahus biguttatus* (Say) and *R. thoracicus* Stål (Fig. 8-2*B*), belong to the subfamily Piratinae, the former common in the southern United States, Cuba, and South America, and giving way to the latter in the Northwest and California. Bites of these species are often mistakenly considered as "spider bites."

Relief from bites may be obtained by using lotions containing 0.25 per cent or more of menthol; 1 per cent phenol or 2 per cent camphor may give temporary relief (Keh, 1956).

Chagas' disease (American trypanosomiasis) was first described by Chagas from Brazil. Chagas named the causative organism *Schizotrypanum cruzi* (now more generally known as *Trypanosoma cruzi*), a spindle-shaped trypanosome with a single flagellum and a characteristic undulating membrane. The trypanosomes occur sparsely in human blood; hence, diagnosis of the infection by recovery of the organism from the blood is very difficult. The diagnostic method of Brumpt (1914), xenodiagnosis, is now widely used. Essentially, this method involves the use of appropriate noninfected (clean) *Triatoma* bugs, and after incubation in the body of the insect the try-

panosomes, if present may be recovered very easily from the digestive tract either by dissection or by microscopic sampling of feces taken from the rectum by means of a slender pipette. In Panama, this parasite often occurs in mixture with another species, *T. rangeli*, which is considered nonpathogenic to man. The discovery that *Rhodnius prolixus* Stål will not harbor *T. rangeli* successfully adds another diagnostic tool, since this bug can be used as a filter in mixed cultures, only *T. cruzi* being recovered when both parasites are fed to the bug (Galloway, 1967).

The most apparent symptoms of Chagas' disease in most cases is the unilateral swelling of the eyelid and face known as the sign of Romaña. This swelling marks the site of the initial infection. The acute form of this disease is prevalent in children, in whom it causes a high, long-continued fever, facial edema, adenitis, and anemia. In the chronic form, infection may last many years. Symptoms are commonly cardiac because of the cardiotropism of the causal organism; death is frequently due to chronic myocarditis and is usually sudden. The trypanosome invades and destroys endothelial and other cells, notably those of the cardiac and skeletal muscles. Dysfunction of the esophagus, manifested by prolonged transit time and dilation, often occurs in cases in South America; this has been attributed to loss of nervous control resulting from destruction of parasympathetic ganglia (Galloway, 1967). Romaña (1947) reemphasizes the nervous forms of Chagas' disease, based on a study of cases of chronic encephalopathy; the patients presented a "syndrome of psychic states and of spastic paralysis," which agrees with the classical descriptions of Chagas and Villela.

The disease occurs in man throughout most of South and Central America from Argentina to Mexico. According to World Health Organization estimates made in 1960, about 7,000,000 cases occurred in American south of the United States at that time (Ryckmann, 1967). It has been recorded in Texas (Woody and Woody, 1955; Ryckmann, 1967) and it has probably occurred, though unreported or not diagnosed, in areas of the Southwest near the Mexican border. In reservoir animals the infection occurs rather widely in the southern United States, particularly in the Southwest, but extending at least as far east as Alabama.

Transmission. Chagas reported successful transmission through the agency of *Panstrongylus megistus* but believed it was effected through the bite of the insect. Brumpt (1912), using *Rhodnius prolixus* disproved the salivary theory of transmission by demonstrating that the infectious stage of the trypanosome resides in the hind gut of the insect and that infection reaches the victim through the feces of the bug, which almost invariably defecates on the skin of its victim while in the act of sucking blood. From the soiled skin the trypanosomes are readily transferred by the fingers or otherwise to the highly receptive conjunctiva of the eye or the mucosa of the mouth or nose, where entry of the infectious agent takes place. Inoculation may also be effected by rubbing in the organism through the excoriated skin, e.g., by scratching. The incubation period in man is said to be ten to twelve days.

Although bugs may receive the parasite from man, it is no doubt usually received from reservoir animals. Bugs may become infected through so-called "cannibalism," or the feeding of nymphs on engorged nymphs, apparently without any detriment to the latter (Ryckman, 1951). The percentage of *Triatoma*

found infected in nature is startling; thus, studies of this nature by various workers in widely separated areas cited by Usinger (1944) showed that 43 per cent of 4,181 bugs were infected. Aside from transmission associated with the bite of triatomines, the possibility of congenital transmission of Chagas' disease must be considered; three such cases were recorded by Howard, *et al.* (1957).

Panstrongylus megistus (Burmeister), a bug with distinctly domestic habits, is the chief vector of *T. cruzi* in Brazil. This is a rather large bug, 21 to 34 mm in length, blackish in color, with four reddish spots on the pronotum and a series of six reddish spots on each side of the abdomen. In southern Brazil and in Uruguay, Paraguay, Argentina, Chile, and southern Bolivia, this species is replaced in importance by *Triatoma infestans* (Klug), also a highly domestic species. *T. infestans* is a little smaller, its head is longer, and the red spots on the pronotum are lacking. In Venezuela, *Rhodnius prolixus* Stål (Fig. 2-4) becomes the most important vector, with *Triatoma maculata* (Erichson) also of considerable importance (Cova Garcia and Suarez, 1959). From Panama through Central America into Mexico *Triatoma dimidiata* (Latreille) is the most important vector, and *T. barberi* Usinger also promises to be of importance in Mexico.

At least eleven additional Triatominae in Argentina (Abalos and Wygodzinsky, 1951) and an equal number in Brazil have been found infected with *T. cruzi*. Of twenty-six species and subspecies of the subfamily known to occur in Mexico, sixteen have been found to be infected with this parasite (Biagi and Navarrete, 1961). Some of the conenoses that have been found infected naturally in the area extending from northern South America into the United States, in addition to those mentioned above, are *Panstrongylus geniculatus* (Latreille) in Brazil and Panama; *Nesotriatoma flavida* (Neiva) in Cuba; *Dipetalogaster maximus* (Uhler), *Triatoma rubida* (Uhler), *T. hegneri* Mazzotti, *T. phyllosoma* (Burmeister), all in Mexico; *T. sanguisuga sanguisuga* (Le Conte), *T. sanguisuga ambigua* Neiva, *T. gerstaeckeri* (Stål), and *T. protracta woodi* Usinger in Texas; *T. recurva* (Stål), *T. protracta* (Uhler), and *T. rubida uhleri* Neiva in Arizona. In California S. F. Wood (1942) found a high natural infection in *Triatoma protracta* (Uhler), namely, 25 per cent of 816 bugs examined.

Domesticity on the part of the triatomine bug is, of course, necessary if it is to be an efficient vector of *T. cruzi*, although undoubtedly species such as those of the *Triatoma protracta* complex, though they do not frequent human habitats, are of possible importance in maintaining the parasitemia in non-human reservoirs. It is certainly conceivable that *T. protracta*, in its occasional attacks on man, may bring him into the transmission picture. Another factor of importance in the epizootology and consequently epidemiology of Chagas' disease is the fact, demonstrated by Ryckman, *et al.* (1965), and by Little, Tay, and Biagi (1966) that the North American *T. barberi* and *T. protracta* respectively are much more susceptible to Mexican strains of *T. cruzi* than is the Argentine *T. infestans*, although the latter is the most important vector of the parasite in its own area.

The infection occurs in natural reservoirs such as armadillos, opossums, house mice, Norway rats, spiny rats, several species of bats, cats, dogs, squirrels, and wood rats.

Ryckman, *et al.* (1965), have shown that the Southern Aligator Lizard, *Gerrhonotus multicarinatus* (Blanville), and the Whiptail Lizard, *Cnemidophorus tessellatus multiscutatus* Cope, can become infected with *T. cruzzi* and can in turn infect triatomine bugs for at least a period of several weeks; moreover, there is evidence that a given strain of *T. cruzi* may increase in virulence as the result of passing through these hosts. Wood (1934), working with *T. protracta*, was able experimentally to infect the following animals with the trypanosome: albino rats, albino mice, rhesus monkeys, a puppy, an opossum, the dusky-footed wood rat, and five species of white-footed mice. The reservoir host range of *T. cruzi*, therefore, is quite broad. Animals may become infected either in the same way as man does or by eating bugs infected by the trypanosome or their feces.

Several species of bed bugs are capable of transmitting the parasite experimentally, as well as many species of ticks, among them *Amblyomma cajennense* (Fabricius), *Rhipicephalus sanguineus* (Latreille), *Ornithodoros moubata* (Murray), and *O. savignyi* (Audouin). *Ornithodoros turicata* (Dugès) has been proven by Wheeler (1938) to be an experimental vector of the Brazilian strain. A number of other reported vectors, including a dipteron, the sheep ked, *Melophagus ovinus* (L.), and a caterpillar, the wax moth, *Galleria mellonella* L., are listed by Usinger (1944).

9

THE LICE

General Characteristics and Classification of Lice. The sucking lice comprise the order Anoplura. The common practice is to consider that group as separate from the so-called biting lice, or Mallophaga, but this classification is rejected by some for two reasons. First, the genus *Haematomyzus* Piaget, which includes the curious elephant louse and another species that parasitizes wart hogs, does not fit well into either order; in fact, it has been suggested that this genus should constitute a separate order of insects. Second, some specialists (for example Königsmann, 1960;

see also Hopkins, 1949) consider the Mallophaga to be diphyletic, one section of it, the Ischnocera, being more closely related to the Anoplura than either is to the other section of Mallophaga, the Amblycera. Königsmann refers all lice to one order, the Phthiraptera, which he divides into four suborders, Rhynchophthirina (genus *Haematomyzus*), Amblycera, Ischnocera, and Anoplura. Inasmuch as his views have not had general acceptance, however, the purposes of the present work are best served if the lice are classified as members of two orders, Anoplura and Mallophaga.

The Anoplura are blood-sucking ecto-parasites of mammals. For a discussion of their mouth parts see Chapter 3. Feeding habits of the Mallophaga vary. Most Amblycera, which infest birds, marsupials, and Neotropical rodents, feed on blood, which is caused to flow by the rasping action of the mandibles or even by puncture made by the mandibles in the skin or the quills of feathers; some species take solid food and one genus, *Ricinus*, found on song birds, is bloodsucking. The Ischnocera take only solid food, hairs and feathers. In both the Anoplura and the Mallophaga wings are absent, the body is flattened in a dorsoventral axis, and the legs are in part adapted for clinging to hairs and feathers. Metamorphosis is simple.

The literature on lice is very extensive. For a bibliography on human lice prior to 1943 (961 entries), see Grinnell and Hawes (1943). An extremely valuable work on Anoplura and Mallophaga, with a summary of host records and extensive information on the phylogeny and biology of lice, is that of Hopkins (1949).

ORDER ANOPLURA

THE SUCKING LICE

Classification. Students technically concerned with the sucking lice will need to consult the monograph of the species of the world by Ferris (1951). One must keep in mind, however, that this is merely a foundation work; it was incomplete even at the time when it was written, as Ferris did not include work that was currently being done in eastern Europe and China. Recent and current work, particularly the publications of P. T. Johnson, Kuhn and Ludwig, and Ke Chung Kim, need to be taken into consideration. Ferris listed 225 species; this number has been increased to 415 at the time of this writing (Kim, personal communication). These are arranged in six families, four of which include species of medical or veterinary importance. They are as follows.

(1) The Haematopinidae, in which definite eyes or pronounced ocular projections are present and in which the abdomen bears irregular plates on the dorsum and venter as well as strongly sclerotized paratergal plates, consist of two genera, the common *Haematopinus* and the peculiar peccary parasite *Pecaroecus*. (2) The Linognathidae, considered by many authors a part of the Haematopinidae, lack paratergal plates and all external evidence of eyes, except for one species that parasitizes camels; this family includes two genera of veterinary importance, namely *Linognathus* (Fig. 9-1) and *Solenopotes*. (3) The Pediculidae,

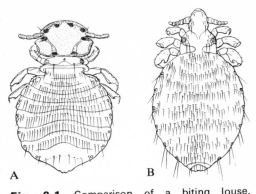

A   B

Fig. 9-1 Comparison of a biting louse, *Trichodectes canis* (*A*) *and* a sucking louse, *Linognathus setosus* (*B*). Both are parasites of the domestic dog. (Courtesy of U.S. Public Health Service.)

the one family that contains parasites of man and other anthropoids, have distinctly developed eyes; *Pediculus* and *Pthirus* are referred to this family, although some authorities place the latter in a separate family. (4) The Hoplopleuridae, the largest family, consist of heterogenous groups of lice, mostly rodent parasites, of which at least two genera, *Polyplax* and *Hoplopleura*, may be involved in the transfer from rodent of such human and animal parasites as the tularemia bacillus, the murine typhus pathogen, and *Trypanosoma lewisi*.

The genus *Pediculus*, according to Ferris, includes only three or four species: (1) *Pediculus humanus* Linnaeus, the head louse and body louse of man; (2) *Pediculus mjoebergi* Ferris on New World monkeys; *Pediculus shaeffi* Fahrenholz, on the chimpanzee; and *Pediculus pseudohumanus* Ewing, which, Ferris thinks may not be valid, described from a monkey, *Pithecia monachus*, and subsequently recorded by Ewing from aboriginal man in tropical Africa and Polynesia. The nomenclature affecting the species considered here as *Pediculus humanus* has been confused in the literature. Ferris (1951) has discussed this subject in detail. The names adopted here, in accordance with current usage, are *Pediculus humanus humanus* Linnaeus for the body louse (=*P. humanus corporis* and *P. vestimenti* of much of the earlier literature) and *Pediculus humanus capitis* De Geer (=*P. capitis*) for the head louse.

The genus *Pthirus* (also incorrectly spelled *Phthirus* and *Phthirius*) includes the crab louse, *Pthirus pubis* (Linnaeus), of man, and *Pthirus gorillae* Ewing, of the gorilla.

The crab louse, *Pthirus pubis* (Linnaeus) (Fig. 9-2), also called the pubic louse, is easily recognized by its crablike appearance. It is 1.5 to 2.0 mm long, nearly as broad as long, and grayish white. Its middle and hind legs are much stouter than those of the head louse and body louse. It infests the pubic regions particularly but also the armpits and more rarely other parts of the body, such as the mustache, beard, eyelashes, and eyebrows. Heavily parasitized persons have been reported to be infested with this louse over the whole body. These lice are remarkably stationary in their habits, often remaining attached for days at one point with mouth parts inserted into the skin. Continued defecation during this time results in accumulation of excrementous materials around the insect. The pruritus caused by the bites is very intense, and a discoloration of the skin usually results if the infestation continues for some time. The term *pthiriasis* may be employed to designate infestations of pubic lice, although the term pubic pediculosis is also used.

The female louse deposits her eggs on the coarser hair of the body where the parasites

occur. The number of eggs per female is apparently quite small, usually not more than thirty. The life cycle requires not more than a month under usual conditions; Nuttall (1918) determined the egg-to-egg period as twenty-two to twenty-seven days. Pubic louse infestations are characteristic of adults, children under the age of puberty usually not being infested. Spread is by physical contact with infested individuals or by the use of infested toilet seats, blankets and so forth.

The head louse, *Pediculus humanus capitis* De Geer (Fig. 9-3) is gray in color but tends to resemble the color of the hair of the host. The male averages 2 mm in length and the female 3 mm. This form occurs on the head, about the ears and occiput, but from reliable statements made by a number of observers, in heavy infestations it may establish itself on other hairy parts of the body. In severe infestations the hair may become matted with eggs (nits), parasites, and exudate from the pustules that originate from the louse bite; a fungous infection may develop in the whole fetid mass, forming sort of a carapace under which large numbers of lice may be found.

The number of eggs deposited by the female ranges from 50 to 150. These are glued to the

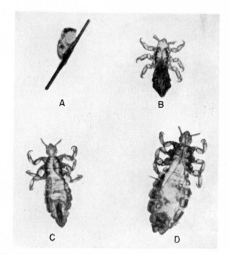

Fig. 9-3 Life cycle of the head louse, *Pediculus humanus capitis*. *A*. Egg attached to hair. *B*. Nymph. *C*. Adult male. *D*. Adult female.

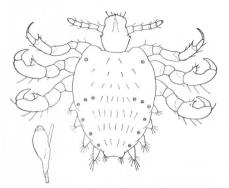

Fig. 9-2 The pubic louse, *Pthirus pubis*. Egg attached to hair, lower left.

hair and hatch in five to ten days, an average being seven days. Development is very rapid. There are three molts and three weeks usually covers the entire life cycle from egg to egg. Lice are easily disseminated by physical contact, stray hairs, and so forth, hence slight infestations may occur under the best of sanitary conditions, particularly among school children. As in the case of the body louse, crowding under unsanitary conditions aids in the development of massive infestations. The continued presence of lice on head or body is inexcusable, however, since eradication is simple if the proper lousicides are used. The mere use of soap and water in washing the hair and head is ineffective in destroying lice present in the hair.

The body louse, *Pediculus humanus humanus* Linnaeus (Fig. 9-4) is the common clothing louse, which during World War I became known as the "cootie," also called the "grayback." During World War II it was popularly termed "mechanized dandruff."

Body lice are most common where the clothing comes in close contact with the body, rather continuously, for example underwear,

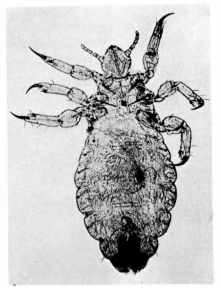

Fig. 9-4 Human body louse, *Pediculus humanus humanus.* × 15.

the fork of the trousers, the armpits, the waistline, neck, and shoulders. In heavy infestations some lice may remain on the body after all clothing is removed. Eggs are deposited by preference in the seams of clothing. Sometimes the louse may attach its eggs to the coarser hairs of the body.

Nuttall (1917) states that a female body louse may lay 275 to 300 eggs, the average number laid per day being about ten for twenty to thirty days. The incubation period varies from five to seven days when eggs are near the body at 35–38° C. Hatching according to Leeson (1941) does not occur when the temperature drops to 23° C nor when it reaches 38° C or higher. At 24° C the incubation period is seventeen to twenty-one days; at 29° it is nine to eleven days. The effective zone for the egg stage is 23–38° C.

Suitable temperatures are essential for the continued existence of louse populations (Hopkins, 1949). The optimum for the body louse is approximately the temperature of the normal human body. A rise of four to five degrees is fatal to them within a few hours. Temperatures below the optimum are much less critical, although prolonged exposure to 20° C or lower may result in death.

After hatching, the young lice begin to suck blood at once and throughout their development feed frequently both day and night, particularly when the host is quiet. Maturity is reached sixteen to eighteen days after oviposition. There are three molts. Females begin to lay eggs a day or two after reaching maturity. The egg-to-egg cycle averages about three weeks. Unfed lice soon die; probably ten days would cover the longest period of survival without food. However, if fed, lice may live thirty to forty days. Moist fecal matter in masses or spiral threads is extruded as the louse feeds; the feces dry quickly in the air.

Dissemination of Body Lice. Lice normally live on the surface of the body or in clothing being worn. They thrive best in temperate regions where at least moderately heavy clothing is worn, thus producing an area near or next to the body where the conditions of temperature and relative humidity are close to the optimum. They do not voluntarily leave unless the body grows cold in death or becomes hot with high fever. Even then they cannot travel far, but are easily dislodged. They will quickly invade a new host if there is one close enough. Louse infestation is mainly the result of contact with lousy persons or their infested clothing. More than 10,000 lice and 10,000 additional nits have been reported from one shirt; Eichler (1940) has estimated that 25,000–30,000 lice occurred on the clothing of one lousy individual. In heavily infested populations one may readily collect 400 to 500 lice from one person.

Pediculosis. The presence of lice on any part of the body is called *pediculosis*. That louse bites may produce certain systemic disturbances seems to be indicated in a report made by Moore (1918):

I started feeding about 700 to 800 twice a day. Almost immediately a general tired feeling was noticed in the calf of the legs and along the shin bones, while on the soles of the feet and underneath the toes this tired feeling was so intense as often to prevent sleep until late in the night. An irritable and pessimistic state of mind developed. An illness resulted with symptoms very similar to grip and rash similar to German measles was present, particularly over the shoulders and abdomen.

The intense discomfort some persons feel when lice are biting may persist for several days. Typically a red papule will develop at the site of each feeding puncture. The skin may "weep," and swellings may occur. In time sensitization may develop. The skin of persons who continuously harbor lice becomes hardened and deeply pigmented, a condition designated as *vagabond's disease* or *morbus errorum*.

Epidemic Relapsing Fever. Epidemic relapsing fever is one of three important diseases of man that are associated with lice. It has occurred in many parts of the world and was probably once cosmopolitan. Great epidemics

have occurred as recently as the period of World War I and its aftermath in Russia, Central Europe, and North Africa; in French Western and Equatorial Africa in 1920–30; and during and after World War II, in 1943–46 (Sparrow, 1958). There were frequent epidemics of the disease in Europe during the eighteenth and nineteenth centuries. It was in an 1868 epidemic in Berlin that Obermeier observed "myriads of living and activity motile spirilla in the blood of relapsing fever patients during the febrile attacks." In 1873 during another epidemic Obermeier applied Ehrenberg's nomenclature and called these organisms "*Spirochaeta*." To honor the discoverer of the organism in the blood of relapsing fever patients, Cohn proposed the name *Spirochaeta obermeieri*. The name currently accepted by microbiologists is *Borellia recurrentis* (Lebert), although the combination *Spirochaeta recurrentis* (Lebert) has been widely used in the literature.

Although lice had long previously been under suspicion, it was Mackie (1907) in India who secured evidence associating them with the relapsing fevers. The relationship is now clearly established. Not only *Borellia recurrentis*, but also most species of *Borellia* (see Chapter 18), will survive and multiply in the human body louse. The insect can acquire the pathogen by a single feeding on an infected person or animal, but cannot pass it on to a second human being in this way. Man acquires the parasite by crushing the louse, usually in the act of scratching to alleviate the irritation caused by the bite, and in this way releases the spirochaete, which then enters the excoriated skin.

After being ingested by the louse, the spirochaetes pass through the stomach wall into the haemolymph. The digestive tract of the insect seems to be a hostile environment, but the ability of a sufficient number of spirochaetes to survive there and to pass into the haemolymph, where they will multiply without being affected themselves and without damaging the host, indicates a highly successful adaptation of the parasite to its host (Weyer, 1960). Once infected, the louse remains so for life. Multiplication of the spirochaetes in the haemolymph, by simple fission, is rapid, becoming even more so after five to seven days and reaching a maximum after ten to twelve days. The spirochaetes do not invade the gonads, salivary glands, or Malpighian tubes and are not found in the feces (Chung and Feng, 1936). Consequently transovarian transmission and transmission by fecal contamination are not possible.

Whereas in tick-borne or endemic relapsing fever endemicity is maintained in nonhuman reservoirs, such as rodents, man is the usual reservoir of the louse-associated disease. Ticks can serve as reservoirs; see Chapter 18. A single infective louse crushed upon the excoriated skin can produce relapsing fever. The incubation period in the human is three to ten days. The onset of the disease is sudden, with headaches, chills, and fever, and generalized pains. The fever remains high for several days (an average of four) and subsides abruptly, with an afebrile period of three to ten days followed by one or more relapses. Mortality is usually low but may vary from 2 to 50 per cent, or even higher in crowded poverty-stricken and louse-infested populations. Microscopic (darkfield) examination of blood smears taken during the febrile periods will reveal *Borellia*. Mouse inoculation with the patient's blood will produce the organisms in the blood of the mouse in twenty-four to forty-eight hours. (For tick-borne endemic relapsing fever, consult Chapter 19).

Epidemic Typhus, Typhus Fever. Classical or epidemic typhus, known also by such names as tabardillo (Mexico), Brill's or Brill-Zinnser disease (United States), jail fever, war fever, and European typhus, is a disease of ancient origin and wide distribution, chiefly in Europe, North Africa, Asia, and higher altitudes of Mexico and Central and South America. The causative organism is *Rickettsia prowazeki* Da Rocha-Lima. Whenever human beings are concentrated in close quarters,

especially in times of war and famine, the disease may become rampant. It is chiefly a disease of winter and spring. Mortality varies; it is low in children under fifteen years of age, but usually ranges from 10 to 100 per cent in adults, the incidence increasing with age. The disease is characterized by a high fever continuing about two weeks, backache, intense headache, bronchial disturbances, mental confusion, stupor, a congested face (designated also as a "besotted expression"), and on the fifth or sixth day by a brick-red macular eruption on chest and abdomen, later spreading to other parts of the body, even to hands, feet, and face. The mottling led to the belief that the tabardillo of Mexico was identical with spotted fever of Montana, a supposition that was proven erroneous by Ricketts and Wilder (1910b). Ricketts contracted typhus during the course of this investigation and died of the disease.

Prior to 1870, louse-borne typhus was widespread and endemic, or in some cases prevalent, throughout much of Europe, but since that date, except during times of major emergencies, there has been a gradual decline to the point that no lives were sacrificed to the disease during most of the period between World War I and World War II. During World War I, severe epidemics occurred in Russia, Poland, and the Balkan States. According to the *Statistical Bulletin* of the Metropolitan Life Insurance Company issued in November, 1941, Russia alone is said to have lost 2,500,000 to 3,000,000 of her people. Typhus fever was again threatening in the early years of World War II. During 1942 there were some 3,000 cases in Egypt and about 80,000 in the rest of North Africa. When Allied forces landed in Italy in September, 1943, a typhus epidemic was threatening Naples, a city of nearly a million persons, where there was congestion, unsanitary living conditions, food scarcity, and undernourishment. The bombproof shelters were converted into "human warrens," in which bodies of dead and living were piled together with lice crawling over the bedclothes. In the course of the epidemic as high as 81 per cent of the victims died, and the city would have been virtually wiped out, except for the effectiveness of the delousing campaign largely employing DDT that followed the Allied invasion. An excellent account of the Naples epidemic and its control has been given by Cushing (1951). A similar epidemic threatened in Cologne, Germany, but prompt action arrested it.

Transmission by Lice. That the louse, *Pediculus humanus humanus*, is probably the sole agent in the transmission of the typhus organism from man to man was shown by Nicolle, *et al.* (1909), working in Tunisia, and Ricketts and Wilder (1910a), working in Mexico. Experimental and epidemiological evidence has confirmed their observations. There is a tendency to disregard the head louse, *P. humanus capitis*, as a possible vector; however, it must be remembered that Goldberger and Anderson (1912) did succeed in transmitting typhus to a monkey by cutaneous injection of a saline suspension of crushed head lice. The crab louse, *Pthirus pubis*, also, cannot be dismissed as a possibility; *Rickettsia prowazeki* is capable of multiplying in it (Weyer, 1960). However, there is no doubt that *Pediculus humanus humanus* is by far the most important, if not the sole, vector.

The typhus patient is infectious for the louse during the febrile period. The louse acquires the parasite by way of the blood meal. The rickettsiae multiply enormously in the epithelial cells of the midgut of the louse; these cells become so distended after a few days that they rupture and release enormous numbers of rickettsiae into the lumen of the digestive tract; these then appear in the louse's feces. The rickettsiae are pathogenic to the louse; most infected lice die in eight to twelve days because of the damage to the gut epithelial cells. If a louse survives the infection it remains infective for life.

The usual route by which man becomes infected is through fecal contamination, though it may be brought about through the crushed body contents of the louse. The bite of the louse is not directly involved; the rickettsiae do not occur in its salivary glands. The parasites may remain alive and virulent in the louse's feces kept at room temperatures for more than sixty days; thus, infection may be acquired through the respiratory passages by inhalation of minute particles of louse excrement. The normal means of transmission is through scratches and through contact with the conjunctivae or mucous membranes by fingers contaminated with louse feces.

Man is generally considered to be the reservoir of the pathogen. Asymptomatic human carriers may be capable of infecting lice for many years; latent periods may follow the first attack, followed by recrudescences which may occur as long as forty years after the initial attack (Wilcocks, 1959). These could lead to infection of the louse population and the beginning of an epidemic. A mild form of the disease, known as Brill's disease or the Brill-Zinnser syndrome, may maintain the pathogen and introduce it, through asymptomatic carriers, into a susceptible human population. Animal reservoirs have been investigated, but these are not considered to be of much, if any, importance. However, Reiss-Gutfreund (1956), working in Ethiopia, demonstrated a higher titer by agglutinization tests in domestic sheep, goats, and zebu, than in the human population, and she has infected lice from strains of the parasite isolated from ticks that were feeding on zebu.

Epidemic typhus is a poverty-associated disease. Unsanitary conditions, in cooler climates, with infrequent bathing and ineffective laundering, lead to multiplication of lice, and consequently opportunity for transmission. Likewise, susceptibility and pathogenicity increase with malnutrition, particularly protein deficiency.

Murine (Flea-Borne) Typhus Fever. Murine fever is a much milder disease, maintained in nature in rats and transmitted to man by rat fleas. The use of the terms "endemic" to distinguish the "flea-borne" from the "louse-borne" strains of typhus is open to criticism, since both must have an endemicity to survive and both may be epidemic at times. The relation of fleas to murine typhus is discussed in Chapter 17.

Trench Fever. Trench fever, also known as five-day fever, Wolhynian fever, shank fever, and His-Wernerische Krankheit, is a nonfatal disease characterized by sudden onset of fever, headache, dizziness, pains in the muscles and bones, particularly in the legs, with especial tenderness of the shins, and lasting twenty-four to forty-eight hours or longer, followed at intervals of about five days by other attacks of fever of diminishing severity. This disease was first noticed during World War I when, under conditions of trench warfare, it became of considerable importance, involving at least a million men. It reappeared in Yugoslavia and the Ukraine during World War II.

The causative organism of trench fever is *Rickettsia quintana* Schminke. Unlike *R. prowazeki*, this organism is found in the lumen of the digestive tract, not in the epithelial cells, and it is not pathogenic to the louse. However, it multiplies freely there. An infected louse may live a normal life span and is infective for life. As in the case of epidemic typhus, the louse acquires the rickettsia in its blood meal and passes it on to man through the feces or through the body contents of a crushed louse. Man is the only known reservoir; he may be an asymptomatic carrier for a period of five years or more. Human epidemics, as in the case of typhus, depend upon heavy louse infestations, in a susceptible human population.

Other Louse-Related Infections. The only known microbial agents pathogenic to man that are adapted biologically to lice and, consequently, effectively transmitted by them, are rickettsiae and spirochaetes. Lice have been suspected, however, in the transmission of other human and animal pathogens, and their feces are frequently contaminated with such. Weyer (1960) has concluded that natural transmission of other pathogens by lice is probably

insignificant, although an extensive louse infestation may play some role in spreading *Salmonella* infections under certain circumstances. Such a situation may have occurred, for example, in Russia in 1920–22, in association with the epidemics of typhus and relapsing fevers.

Microorganisms other than rickettsiae and spirochaetes that are most likely to be louse-transmitted are bacteria. Milner, Jellison, and Smith (1957) produced infections of *Salmonella enteritidis* (Gaertner) by feeding lice on infected rabbits. The bacillus multiplied in the midgut of the louse and attacked the epithelium, producing 90 per cent mortality in the lice; the *Salmonella* remained infective in the feces of the lice for more than one year, in an extreme case for more than four years. Similar results have been obtained by other workers with typhoid, paratyphoid, and colon bacilli.

There is some evidence, though it is far from conclusive that lice can transmit leprosy and plague bacilli. Experimental infection of the body louse with the tularemia bacillus, with multiplication in the louse, was reported by Price (1956). Also, experimental transmission of this bacillus from rabbits has been obtained, but there is no evidence that this occurs in nature. In general, however, louse feces have proved to be a good medium for the preservation of several pathogenic bacteria. Experiments with other microorganisms give less conclusive results, but the following facts are pertinent: (1) Certain bartonellae of rats have been transmitted from rat to rat by lice of the genus *Polyplax*; (2) intracoelomic injections of *Bartonella baciliformis* Noguchi resulted in multiplication in the haemolymph of the louse; (3) the protozoon, *Toxoplasma gondii* Nicolle and Manceau, similarly injected, remained infective and capable of reproduction up to thirteen days, but did not multiply; and (4) some experimental success has been had with transmission of viruses.

Anoplura Affecting Domesticated Mammals. The important sucking lice of domestic ungulate mammals belong to three genera,

Haematopinus, in the family Haematopinidae, and *Linognathus* and *Solenopotes*, in the family Linognathidae. Swine have one species of louse, *Haematopinus suis* (Linnaeus) (Fig. 9-5). This is the largest species of the entire group, measuring as much as 5 to 6 mm in length; it is cosmopolitan in distribution. According to Florence (1921), hog lice feed readily on man but will not feed on guinea pigs. Other neotropical rodents, notably mice, may be fed on under experimental conditions (Lavoipierre, 1967).

Cattle lice belonging to the Anoplura number five species, namely: (1) *Linognathus vituli* (Linnaeus), commonly known as the long-nosed ox louse or blue louse, measuring about 2 mm in length and distinguished from the next species by its long nose and slender body; cosmopolitan in distribution; (2) *Haematopinus eurysternus* (Nitzsch), the cosmopolitan short-nosed ox louse, somewhat larger (3.50–4.75 mm in length) than the former and much broader in proportion; (3)

A

B

Fig. 9-5 *A.* Hog louse, *Haematopinus suis.* × 7. *B.* Nits (eggs) of the hog louse attached to the hairs of the host. One of the eggs has hatched. × 10.

H. quadripertusus Fahrenholz, the cattle tail louse or tail switch louse, very similar to the preceding but found in the long hair about the tail and on the neck and around the eyes; this was considered to be the same as *euryternus* by Ferris, but its distinctness is now generally recognized; (4) *H. tuberculatus* (Burmeister), the buffalo louse, infests cattle in parts of Australia; common on cattle and caraboa (water buffalo) in Asia, absent in North America; measures 3.5–5.5 mm; resembles *H. eurysternus* closely but differs in that the number of setae at the margin of the abdominal segments caudal of the paratergal plates is usually eight or more (may be only five or six); (5) *Solenopotes capillatus* Enderlein, redescribed by Bishopp (1921) and shown to have a wide distribution in the United States as well as in other parts of the world. It is known in the United States as the little blue cattle louse and in Australia as the tuberclebearing louse. It measures 1.2–1.5 mm in length and in general resembles the short-nosed ox louse.

Horses, mules, and asses are frequently infested with one species of sucking louse, *Haematopinus asini* (Linnaeus), which measures 2.5–3.5 mm in length. It resembles the hog louse except that the head is relatively longer and more robust. Sheep may be affected by the foot louse, *Linognathus pedalis* (Osborn). This species occurs not only in the United States but also in parts of South America, New Zealand, Australia, and South Africa. Dogs are commonly heavily infested with *L. setosus* (Olfers) (Fig. 9-1*B*) and domestic rabbits in many parts of the world harbor *Haemodipsus ventricosus* (Denny).

ORDER MALLOPHAGA

THE BITING LICE

The Mallophaga, in the sense accepted here, are divided into three suborders. (1) The Rhynchophthirina consists of one family, the Haematomyzidae, which in turn includes but two species, *Haematomyzus elephantis* Piaget, a parasite of elephants, and *H. hopkinsi* Clay, a parasite of wart hogs (Clay, 1963). (2) The Amblycera includes several families, of which one, the Menoponidae, is of importance because of the genera *Menacanthus* and *Menopon*, which attack domestic birds. Some Amblycera, notably the Gyropidae, attack mammals; at least two of these infest guinea pigs. *Heterodoxus spiniger* (Enderlein), family Boopidae, a parasite of coyotes and wolves in the New World, may infest dogs. Amblycera are body lice. (3) The Ischnocera also contain both avian and mammalian parasites, but unlike the Amblycera they are all found fixed to fur or feathers. Such genera as *Columbicola*, which feeds on the domestic pigeon, and *Chelopistes*, *Cuclotogaster*, *Goniocotes*, *Goniodes*, *Lipeurus*, and *Oxylipeurus*, which parasitize domestic fowls, belong to the family Philopteridae, and three genera of mammalian lice of the family Trichodectidae, namely *Bovicola*, *Felicola*, and *Trichodectes*, infest domestic mammals.

The biting or chewing lice, of which there are about 3,000 described species in the world, are much more numerous than the Anoplura but are of relatively little medical and veterinary importance. The injury done by them is restricted largely to poultry, although some trouble may result when mammals are badly infested. Man is attacked only by accident, if at all. Poultry become irritated by the creeping insect and its incessant gnawing at the skin. Some species, such as the chicken body louse, *Menacanthus stramineus*, frequently obtain blood by gnawing through the skin and rupturing the quills of pinfeathers. Parts of feathers, particularly the barbs and barbules, constitute a major part of the food of this and certain other species. The irritation from the feeding of the louse causes the host to become exceedingly restless, thereby affecting its feeding habits and digestion; young birds are particularly vulnerable. Egg production in fowls is greatly reduced and development retarded. When lice are abundant, uncleanliness and overcrowded conditions usually exist.

Important literature on biting lice includes the work of Hopkins (1949), the useful checklists of Emerson (1962b, 1962c, 1964), and that same author's reviews of Mallophaga occurring on the domestic chicken (Emerson, 1956) and turkey (Emerson, 1962a).

Lice of Domestic Fowls. More than forty species of lice are said to occur on domestic fowls. The most common lice of chickens (Fig. 9-6) are the following. (1) The chicken body louse, *Menacanthus stramineus* (Nitzsch), is a very active species occurring on all parts of the fowl; it is probably the most damaging species to its host because it frequently occurs in large numbers (up to 35,000 lice or perhaps more on one bird). (2) The shaft louse, *Menopon gallinae* (Linnaeus), resembles the chicken body louse very closely but is smaller in size and occurs mainly on the shaft of the feathers. The shaft louse may infest turkeys, ducks, and guinea fowl, especially when they are housed with chickens, and it sometimes infests horses that are stabled nearby. Other species of major importance on chickens are the fluff louse, *Goniocotes gallinae* (De Geer); the brown chicken louse, *Goniodes dissimilis* Denny; the wing louse, *Lipeurus caponis* (Linnaeus); and the chicken head louse, *Cuclotogaster heterographa* (Nitzsch). All these species are worldwide in distribution, wherever their hosts occur.

Turkeys may likewise be attacked by the chicken body louse, but they have their host-specific parasites as well, as would be expected in consideration of the New World origin of the turkey. Chief among these are the turkey louse, *Chelopistes meleagridis* (Linnaeus) and the slender turkey louse, *Oxylipeurus polytrapezius* (Burmeister).

Pigeons are often abundantly infested with the slender pigeon louse, *Columbicola columbae* (Linnaeus) (=*Lipeurus baculus* Nitzsch), a very slender species measuring about 2 mm in length, and with the small pigeon louse, *Campanulotes bidentatus* (Scopoli), about 1 mm in length, whitish in color with the head rounded in front. A number of additional

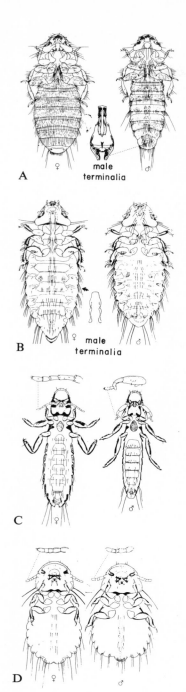

Fig. 9-6 Common biting lice of poultry. *A. Menacanthus stramineus. B. Menopon gallinae. C. Cuclotogaster heterographa. D. Goniocotes gallinae.* (Courtesy of U.S. Public Health Service.)

species infest domestic birds, but these are of lesser importance.

Biting Lice of Domesticated Mammals. The biting lice of domesticated mammals are for the most part rather easily identified by their presence on a given host, since commonly not more than one species of Mallophaga is found on each species of mammalian host. Cattle are often heavily infested on the withers, root of tail, neck, and shoulders with the biting cattle louse, *Bovicola bovis* (Linnaeus) (Fig. 9-7), a little red louse about 1.5 mm in length, definitely marked with transverse bars (ladder-like) on the abdominal segments. Horses, mules, and asses, but horses more particularly, when poorly or irregularly groomed, may suffer from the horse biting louse, *Bovicola equi* (Linnaeus). Sheep may at times show severe infestation of the sheep louse, *Bovicola ovis* (Linnaeus). Goats are commonly very heavily infested with biting lice. Several species from goats have been described, about which there is still some confusion, but the common species is *Bovicola caprae* (Gurlt). Dogs, particularly puppies, may suffer much irritation from the dog biting louse, *Trichodectes canis* De Geer (Fig. 9-7*A*), a broad, short species, measuring about 1 mm in length, and by *Heterodoxus spiniger* (Enderlein). Cats may become heavily infested with the cat louse, *Felicola subrostratus* (Nitzsch). *Tricholipeurus lipeuroides* (Megnin) and *T. parallelus* (Osborn) infest American deer (*Odocoileus*) and other genera are found

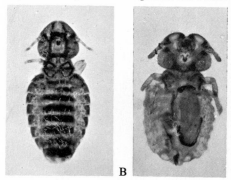

Fig. 9-7 *A.* The biting ox louse, *Bovicola bovis.* × 26. *B.* The biting dog louse, *Trichodectes canis.* × 35.

on other wild mammals. *Tricholipeurus* and *Bovicola* are considered by some to be only subgenera of *Damalinia*, so that generic name is used in some of the literature for the species referred to *Tricholipeurus* and *Bovicola*.

Lice and Taeniasis. *Dipylidium caninum* (Linnaeus), the double-pored dog tapeworm, is a common parasite of the dog and is occasionally found in humans, especially children. It measures 25–35 cm (10–14 inches) in length, has long seedlike proglottids and an armored scolex; as its larval host it has the dog biting louse, *Trichodectes canis*, the dog flea, *Ctenocephalides canis* (Curtis), the cat flea, *C. felis* (Bouché), or the human flea, *Pulex irritans* Linnaeus. The cysticercoid stage has been experimentally produced in the louse by placing ripe crushed proglottids of the tapeworm on the skin of the dog infested with lice.

As has already been explained, many biting lice subsist on epidermal scales, skin exudations, and other matter on the skin of the animals. This habit makes it comparatively easy for the louse to become infected by swallowing egg capsules. The dog, on the other hand, readily infects itself by devouring the lice (or fleas) that irritate its skin.

Persons, particularly children, while fondling louse-infested (or flea-infested) dogs, may easily become infected by accidentally swallowing lice (or fleas) that contain bladder worms (larval tapeworms). This is more apt to occur if the person is eating while fondling dogs.

10

BITING GNATS AND RELATED FORMS

(Families Simuliidae, Psychodidae, Ceratopogonidae, and Others)

ORDER DIPTERA

The several families of gnats discussed in this chapter, as well as those insects discussed in the following six chapters, are members of the order Diptera, the two-winged or true flies. About 80,000 species have been described in approximately 140 families, and new ones are being added at a rapid rate. Members of this order are involved in the transmission of more pathogens of diseases of man and animals than any other group of arthropods; hence, the medical entomologist must be extensively familiar with the Diptera.

As the name implies, all winged members of the order have only one pair of wings; the posterior pair is represented in nearly all species by a pair of short knobbed organs known as halteres. In certain families, e.g., muscoid flies, there are membranous structures at the juncture of the wings with the body; these are known as squamae, calypters, or alulae. The squamae are two pairs in number, one, the thoracic, being more closely associated with the thorax, and the other, the alar, being close to the wing. The latter should not be confused with the anal lobe of the wing. Conspicuous compound eyes are present, and most species possess three simple eyes (ocelli). The metamorphosis is complete, consisting of four stages—egg, larva, pupa, and adult (imago). Most flies are oviparous, but all gradations occur between ovipary and pupipary, that is, the larva may hatch before it is deposited, or it may be retained by the female, before deposition, until it is partly or even completely developed, as in the tsetse flies and the Pupipara. The mouth parts, as previously described, are subject to great variation although all are suctorial; many species are provided with very effective piercing stylets that enable them to "bite" fiercely and to suck blood.

Much attention must be given to the larval stages because the larvae, especially those of the higher Diptera, frequently invade the tissues and organs of the body of man and animals, causing myiasis (see Chapter 15); also a wider knowledge of aquatic larvae (of which there are many species) is important in pursuing work with mosquitoes and other gnats, as well as in the study of the biology of water supplies (see Johannsen, 1933–1937).

The Diptera have a wide range of breeding habits. There are few habitats suitable for animal life which have not been invaded by flies. The petroleum fly, *Psilopa petrolei* Coquillett, as the name implies, actually passes its larval life in crude oil, and several species of the same family (Ephydridae) inhabit the Great Salt Lake and salt evaporation beds.

Classification of the Diptera. In the classification of the Diptera, knowledge of wing venation is important (Fig. 10-1). The great diversity of antennal structure provides a useful series of characters (Fig. 10-2), as does the arrangement of bristles (chaetotaxy) on the body of certain species such as the blow flies (see Chapter 13). The terminalia are important taxonomic structures in many Diptera. Structures of special importance in the various groups will be discussed under the individual group involved.

In respect to the suborders, several classifications of the Diptera are in common use, but many students of the Diptera now recognize the three suborders used here, namely the Nematocera, Brachycera, and Cyclorrhapha. In the Nematocera and Brachycera the adult escapes from the pupal case through a

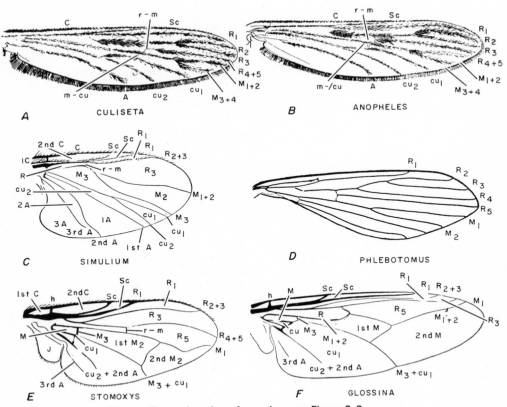

Fig. 10-1 Wings of Diptera. For explanation of venation, see Figure 2-2.

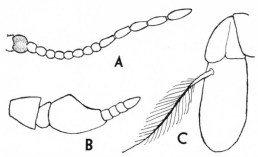

Fig. 10-2   Three antennal types in the Diptera; in outline, setation and hairs omitted. *A.* The many-segmented type, *Culicoides (after Irving Fox). B.* The stylate type, *Tabanus. C.* The aristate type, Sarcophaga.

T- or Y-shaped suture, whereas in the Cyclorrhapha the emerging adult pushes off the anterior end of the puparium as a circular cap by means of a bladder-like structure known as the ptilinum. On this basis, a two suborder classification has been used extensively, with the Nematocera and Brachycera, as defined here, being united and called the Orthorrhapha.

SUBORDER I. NEMATOCERA

Larvae with well-developed, exserted head and horizontally biting mandibles; pupae exarate. Antenna of adult often longer than the head and thorax combined, but sometimes much shorter, its flagellum composed of six or more divisions (flagellomeres), the majority of them usually alike; no differentiation of any flagellomeres into a style or arista. Palpi usually four- or five-segmented. Anal (second anal) cell when present widely open.

SUBORDER II. BRACHYCERA

Larvae with incomplete, usually retractile head, and with vertically biting mandibles; pupae usually exarate. Antenna of adult shorter than thorax, the flagellum usually incompletely or obscurely subdivided, but often with the apical flagellomeres forming a style or arista; arista, when present, terminal or nearly so. Palpi two- or three-segmented. Anal cell contracted before the apex or closed.

SUBORDER III. CYCLORRHAPHA

Larvae with no apparent heads and with mouth hooks that operate side by side vertically, or with only one such hook; pupa coarctate (enclosed in a puparium). Antenna of adult usually aristate, the flagellum without evidence of its composite nature except for the arista, which is dorsal in position (rarely, a style instead of the arista is present in some forms of no medical importance). Palpi one-segmented. Anal cell contracted or closed.

The manuals of Curran (1934) and of Lindner (1949), the latter being the introductory volume to the monumental *Die Fliegen der Palaearktichen Region*, will aid in the identification of the families and genera of the Holarctic Region. The families of Nematocera of medical importance may be separated by the following key.

KEY TO MEDICALLY IMPORTANT FAMILIES OF NEMATOCERA

1. Mesonotum with an entire V-shaped suture. Of no medical importance, but likely to be confused with mosquitoes, though proboscis not elongated . . . .
. . . . .Superfamily Tipuloidea
Mesonotal suture transverse or wanting, not V-shaped 2
2. Costa continuing around margin of wing, though weaker beyond apex 3
Costa ending at or near the apex of the wing 6
3. Wing short and broad, folded roof-like over the body when at rest, usually pointed; small, hairy mothlike flies . . . .
. . . . .Family Psychodidae
Wings long, or if broad the apex is very broadly rounded, always lying flat over the back when at rest 4
4. Apical wing veins strongly arched, without scales. Of no medical importance, but likely to be confused with mosquitoes . . . .
. . . . .Family Dixidae
Wing veins straight or nearly so, with scales, or at least scales on the wing margins 5

5. Proboscis not elongated, extruding but little beyond the clypeus; wings with scales confined mostly to the fringe......
............Family Chaoboridae
Proboscis elongated, extending far beyond the clypeus; wings with scales on the margin and on the veins.............
............Family Culicidae

6. Wing very broad, the posterior veins weak and poorly developed; antennae shorter than thorax, never plumose............
............Family Simuliidae
Wing narrow and long, the posterior veins not noticeably weakened; antenna usually longer than the thorax, often plumose...7

7. Mesonotum and metanotum without a median longitudinal groove; wings lying flat over the body when at rest; femora sometimes swollen; mouth parts fitted for sucking blood........................
............Family Ceratopogonidae
Mesonotum anteriorly and metanotum with a median longitudinal groove; mouth parts not fitted for sucking blood. Of medical importance only as a source of annoyance, but likely to be confused with mosquitoes.......Family Chironomidae

FAMILY SIMULIIDAE
(Buffalo Gnats—Black Flies; Turkey Gnats)

Characteristics. The family Simuliidae, consists of over 1,200 species. They are small (1 to 5 mm long) bloodsucking flies, with mouth parts bladelike and piercing in the female but more or less rudimentary in the male. They are stout-bodied and variable in color; the term "black fly" is somewhat of a misnomer as certain species may be gray or even predominantly yellow. The thorax presents a strong development of the scutum and reduction of the prescutum resulting in a prominent hump (Fig. 10-3). The antennal flagellum is usually nine-, sometimes eight- or seven-, segmented; the eyes of the female are distinctly separated (in the male they are usually close together and prominent, that is, holoptic); ocelli are absent; the palpi are five-segmented; the wings are broad and

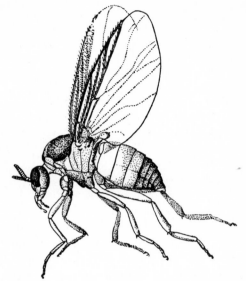

Fig. 10-3 A buffalo gnat, *Cnephia pecuarum.* (After Garman.)

irridescent with distinct alulae, the venation being characterized by a strong development of the anterior veins (Fig. 10-1*C*).

Biology. Buffalo gnats often occur in enormous swarms during late spring and early summer where swiftly flowing streams provide well-aerated water for larval development. They are particularly abundant in the north temperate and subarctic zones, but many species occur in the tropics, and considerable medical importance is attached to some of these.

Larvae are found only in running water, shallow mountain torrents being favored breeding places. Some species, including certain notable pests, breed in larger rivers; others live in temporary or semipermanent streams. Larvae attach themselves to rocks and other solid objects in the stream; sometimes they cling to aquatic or emergent vegetation. The sides and concrete drop structures in irrigation canals may produce large numbers of larvae. Some attach to aquatic animals, such as bivalve mollusca and such aquatic insects as the naiads of Odonata and Ephemeroptera. The African *Simulium neavei* Roubaud and at least two other closely related species regularly attach to the carapace and legs of river crabs of the genus *Potamon*.

Adults may fly from seven to ten miles from their breeding sites (Dalmat, 1955), but migrating wind-borne swarms may go much farther. *Simulium arcticum* Malloch may travel ninety miles or more in this way in the Saskatchewan Valley of Canada, and other species may travel 150 miles or more. *Simulium colombaschense* Fabricius, according to Dinulescu (1966), may travel 200 to 450 kilometers with wind currents in the Danube Valley.

Nectar from flowers provides both males and females with carbohydrates for flight energy, and females, in addition, usually require blood for ovarian development. Males, as in the other Nematocera, never suck blood. Most females are bloodsuckers, often vicious ones, but in some species the mouth parts are so feeble that they cannot penetrate the skin of vertebrates. Nonbloodsucking species are autogenous, but autogeny may occur in certain bloodsucking species as well. Of the hematophagous species, only certain ones attack man. A number of birds and mammals, however, have been reported as hosts.

Males may form hovering swarms, and mating may occur when females fly into or near such swarms. At other times, however, mating occurs, apparently by accidental contacts, on the ground or elsewhere, without the formation of swarms. Parthenogenetic reproduction is known to occur, but apparently as an extreme rarity.

Life History. Eggs, usually to the number of 200 to 500 per female, but sometimes as many as 800, are deposited on the water surface, on aquatic plants, or on logs, water-splashed rocks, or other solid surfaces in or at the edge of the water. Sometimes they are scattered loosely on stream bottoms. The shiny eggs are at first creamy white, changing to almost black. Methods of oviposition vary from species to species and even within a species (Davies and Peterson, 1956). A common method is for the female to drop eggs while flying over the water surface; some species will hover and oviposit through a thin film of water that covers sand, rock, or vegetation; others will settle and oviposit on water-lapped surfaces or on surfaces at the waters edge.

In the multivoltine species the time required for hatching is from four to thirty days, depending on temperature and motion of the water. When diapause takes place in the egg stage, as is usually the case in univoltine species in temperate regions, the time from egg deposition to hatching is, of course, much greater. *Simulium venustum* Say requires four days at 24° C, five days at 18° C, and twenty-seven days at 7° C (Davies, Peterson, and Wood, 1962).

The newly emerged larva attaches itself by means of a caudal sucker (Fig. 10-4) to the submerged object that is to form its support and resting place; it is kept from being washed away by a silken thread. Movement from place to place is achieved by shifting anchorage. In some favorable locations, such as riffles on the downstream side of an old log partially damming a stream, there may be thousands of these tiny, black, spindleshaped larvae. The larvae, as well as the pupae, are provided with gill filaments and usually remain submerged or partially so. The food of the larvae consists of small crustacea, protozoa, algae, bacteria, parts of animals and plants, and decaying organic matter. Some may graze in the silt, scrape organic material from submerged

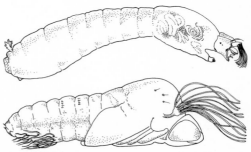

Fig. 10-4 Black fly larva (*above*) and pupa (*below*). (After Dinulescu.)

surfaces, or even resort to cannibalism. The larval period may require twelve days or fewer under optimum conditions; that for *Simulium ornatum* Meigen is given by Smart (1934) as seven to ten weeks when temperatures in the stream ranged between 9° and 15.5° C. The time required varies with the species and with water temperatures. Some species overwinter as larvae. There are apparently four to seven larval moults. At the end of the larval period, the organism spins a basketlike cocoon in which pupation takes place. These cocoons are firmly attached to shallowly covered objects such as rocks.

The pupal period is quite short in some species, requiring not over two to six days; in others it may last three to four weeks. Temperature influences this stage, that is, cooler weather retards the emergence of adults. Smart gives the pupal period for *S. ornatum* as 3.75 days at a constant temperature of 21° C. When the adult is ready to emerge, it can be seen through the translucent pupal integument. In about a minute's time the fly breaks through the T-shaped emergence slit and rises to the surface quickly in a bubble of gas. In some species, the multivoltine ones, there is continual breeding from early spring to late autumn with overlapping generations; in others that are univoltine, there is evidently one sudden brood coming fairly early in the spring with stragglers following. The life cycle, egg to adult, ranges from sixty days to fifteen weeks or over, and the number of generations a year, in temperate regions, from one to five or six, depending on the species and climatic conditions.

An excellent regional study containing a wealth of information concerning the individual habits of the species involved is that of Sommerman, Sailer, and Esselbaugh (1955) on the biology of the black flies of Alaska. The student is also referred to the biological study of Davies and Peterson (1956).

Larvae. The light brown to black larvae are cylindrical, twelve-segmented, slightly thinner in the mid region, and when fully grown, from 10 to 15 mm in length (Fig. 10-4). Fan-shaped filamentous structures located on the head are for the purpose of creating a current by means of which food is drawn into the mouth. The posterior end of the body is provided with a toothed disklike sucker, composed of two modified parapodia. The anterior pseudopod is also modified into a prehensile toothed disk. By means of these organs, and aided by silken threads, the larvae move from place to place with a looping motion. They attach themselves to supports in the water by means of the posterior sucker, the hooks of which they insert into the network of silken threads, produced by secretions from the salivary glands, with which they cover the substratum.

Although the larvae are provided with a well-developed tracheal system, and nine pairs of spiracles may be observed, these are, at least usually, not open. The exact means of respiration in larvae is an undecided question. It may be carried through the entire integument, or it may, at least in part, be through the anal papillae. These are branched, retractile structures located dorsally on the last abdominal segment.

Pupae. When the larva is ready to pupate, it spins a crude pocketlike cocoon that is open at the upper, or anterior, end. The form of the cocoon, as well as the pupal site, varies with the species. The pupa is provided with respiratory filaments attached anteriorly to the dorsal portion of the thorax. The filaments are often quite numerous and because of their constancy in number in a given species may be of value in identification (Fig. 10-4).

Natural Enemies. Black flies have numerous parasites and predators, and those may act at times as important natural controls of black fly populations. The systematic utilization of this information for control purposes, however, is quite a different matter.

Dinulescu (1966) gives account of the natural enemies of Simuliidae. Invertebrate predators on immature stages include hydras, planarians, hydractinoids, crustaceans (*Rivulo-*

gammarus), and insects, the latter including the larvae and naiads of Plecoptera, Trichoptera, Ephemeroptera, and Diptera (Chironomidae and Ceratopogonidae). Vertebrate predators include numerous fish as well as three species of birds, genus *Cinclus*. Predators on adults include Odonata, Diptera, Hymenoptera, and various birds, as well as the insectivorous plant *Pinguicula vulgaris*. Parasites, either on simuliid larvae or adults, including fungi, trypanosomes, infusoria, sporozoa, spirochaetes, and nematodes (Mermithidae).

Other authors, for example Peterson (1960) and Peterson and Davies (1960), have added other natural enemies to this list —mites, spiders, Coleoptera, and possibly leeches. Barnley and Prentice (1958) conclude that certain muscoid flies (Coenosiinae) may exercise considerable control when black fly populations are depleted by other control measures.

Mermithid parasitism may be of especial importance. Phelps and De Foliart (1964), in an excellent study of nematode-simuliid relationships, have pointed out that, in Wisconsin, parasitism resulting in castration or death of adults amounted to 37 to 63 per cent, with an additional conservative estimate of 50 per cent larval mortality. The effect of such high parasitism on black fly populations is evident. Mermithid parasitism cannot be expected to eliminate a species from any given area, but it can certainly hold down the numbers.

Classification. The classification of the Simuliidae is at present in an unsettled condition, particularly on the generic level. Smart (1945) used a conservative system and recognized only six genera, namely *Parasimulium, Prosimulium, Cnephia, Simulium, Gigantodax*, and *Austrosimulium*. Stone *et al.* (1965), in the Nearctic catalog, recognizes two additional genera, namely *Gymnopais* and *Twinnia*. The student will find additional generic names in the literature, some of them generally accepted, some not. In this family of insects, as in most others, the idea of the genus varies from one authority to another. If the student will keep this in mind, he will not be confused by contradictory or inconsistent terminology.

A recent contribution to Lindner's Palaearctic Diptera series, by Rubtsov (1964), contains very extensive material on the morphology, taxonomy, biology, and medical and veterinary importance of these flies. Some good regional works of more limited geographic scope are available, among them Dinulescu's (1966) very informative work on the Romanian species (in Romanian), Davies, Peterson and Wood's (1962) and Wood, Peterson, Davies, and Gyorkos (1963) on the Ontario species, Peterson's studies of the Utah Fauna, Stone's (1964) contribution to the Diptera of Connecticut series, and Dalmat's (1955) monograph of the Guatemala species.

Important Species. *Prosimulium hirtipes* (Fries) is a European species that has, in the past, been confused with several American species, at least two of which, *P. fuscum* Syme and Davies and *P. mixtum* Syme and Davies, may be seriously annoying to man and animals in wooded areas. *Cnephia pecuarum* (Riley), the southern buffalo gnat, has been known as a great scourge of livestock as well as of man in the Mississippi Valley, although ecological changes such as increased siltage and organic pollution that have taken place in that area in recent years have somewhat modified the situation.

Most important species of black flies belong to the genus *Simulium*. *S. vittatum* Zetterstedt is widespread throughout North America. It may be annoying because of its crawling over the skin and probing. It attacks livestock freely, but usually does not bite man. Some puzzling discrepancies occur in accounts of the biology of this fly, and it is likely that more than one species is involved in the complex that currently goes under that name.

Simulium meridionale Riley, the turkey gnat, is also common and widespread in North America, particularly in the Mississippi Valley and the southern states, where the gnats appear in late spring following the buffalo gnat. They attack poultry, biting the combs and wattles, and are said to cause symptoms similar to "cholera," hence the name "cholera" gnat. *Simulium venustum* Say is one of the most annoying and widespread species. It torments fishermen and campers in the northern United States, Canada, and Alaska. The gnats occur in the greatest numbers during June and July but may persist throughout the summer. *Simulium arcticum* Malloch is a plague to livestock in western Canada where vast numbers of this gnat frequently attack and kill livestock. In 1944, 1945, and 1946, 800 domestic animals, 80 per cent of which were cattle, were killed by this fly in Saskatchewan.

Simulium colombaschense Fabricius is the infamous goloubatz fly of middle and southern Europe. In 1923 two immense swarms of this fly invaded southern Romania in May, June, and July, causing the death of 16,474 domestic animals, including cattle, horses, pigs, sheep, and goats. Large numbers of deer, foxes, and hares, as well as other wild animals, were reported to have been killed at the same time. Other European livestock pests include *S. kurenze* Rubtsov and Diafarov, in the Soviet Union, and *S. erythrocephala* De Geer, in western Europe (Rubtsov, 1964).

In Africa, *S. damnosum* Theobald and *S. neavei* Roubaud are both known for their annoyance as well as for their role as vectors of *Onchocerca*. In Central America, *S. ochraceum* Walker, a highly anthrophilic species, also plays this double role.

The Bite. Simuliids are daytime biters and are rarely found indoors. The mouth parts are similar to those of the horse fly but differing in details; the mandibles and maxillae are flattened, usually serrate or armed with teeth.

Human beings as well as domestic animals are viciously attacked. The eyes, ears, nostrils, wrists, and all exposed parts of the body of man are subject to attack. The extreme pain, intense itching, and the resultant local swellings, together with occasional severe complications, indicate the presence of an active allergin. In some individuals the face, arms, and other exposed parts may be greatly swollen as a result of the bites; in others, effects other than blood loss may scarcely be noticeable. Deaths seems in most cases to be the consequence of a toxemia caused by the bites or the result of an anaphylactic shock, although debility resulting from blood loss and suffocation brought about by inhalation of the flies is apparently a contributing cause. A similar picture is presented by livestock; a very good discussion of this is given by Rubtsov (1964).

There is some correlation between the habit of larval breeding in large rivers and adult viciousness, particularly where attacks on livestock are concerned. *Cnephia pecuarum* has, in past time, killed horses, mules, and cattle, in numbers and within a few hours, in the Mississippi Valley. Apparently, modifications of the river environment, involving extensive elimination of the large river type of breeding grounds, has changed this situation. *S. arcticum* is an outstanding pest where it is associated with large-river breeding conditions, as in the Saskatchewan, and outbreaks of *S. colombaschense* have been associated with breebing in the Danube. On the other hand, mountain stream species are often seriously annoying to man. *S. ochraceum* is an example of such; this and other smaller stream-produced species become so annoying in the coffee plantations in Guatemala that workmen at times refuse to continue their work (Dalmat, 1955).

Relation to Disease. Owing to the vicious intermittent bloodsucking habits of simuliids, it has long been suspected that they might play a role in the transmission of the causative organisms of disease. Though Sambon's (1910) theory of the relationship of black flies to the cause of pellagra was erroneous, his startling report at least initiated thought in this direction.

The most important human pathogen transmitted by simuliid flies is a filarial worm, *Onchocerca volvulus* (Leuckart). It causes human onchocerciasis, also known as Robles' disease or blinding filarial disease, which affects natives in certain parts of Africa, Mexico, and Central and South America. The female worm measures from 350 to 700 mm in length, the male 20 to 40 mm. These worms occur in the human body in conspicuous subcutaneous nodular tumors located primarily on the trunk, shoulders, and head of infected persons. Several adult worms and numerous larvae (produced viviparously) usually occur in each tumor. Serious involvements of the eye, caused by migration of the larvae often result in complete blindness.

Robles, in Guatemala, was the first to suggest, in 1955, that *Onchocerca volvulus* was transmitted by simuliids (Aguilar, 1958). Blacklock (1926), working in Sierra Leone, showed that when the microfilariae were taken up with the bite of *Simulium damnosum*, they migrate from the fly's stomach and find lodgment in the thoracic muscles, where further development takes place. Blacklock thought that the metacyclic microfilariae migrated to the labium and escaped while the fly was biting, but the research of De Leon (1961) indicates otherwise, at least in the Guatemala vector. Dissection of 1,000 flies failed to reveal any microfilariae in the mouth parts; the parasites were present, however, in the abdomen. De Leon believes that the microfilariae escape from the anus while the fly is biting its host. The time required for development in man from inoculation by the bite to maturity of the worm in the skin nodule has not been definitely determined, but it is probably about six months.

Onchocerciasis and its relation to black flies in Guatemala have been studied in detail by Dalmat (1955) whose monograph on the subject contains a wealth of information. About 35 per cent of the population in the *Onchocerca* areas of that nation is infected; ocular involvement is manifest in more than half of the persons infected; and blindness occurs in about 5 per cent. The most important vector in the light of host preference, feeding habits, and epidemiological information is *Simulium ochraeum*, but *S. metallicum* Bel-lardi and *S. callidum* Dyar and Shannon readily bite man and occupy the highly endemic areas of the disease zone. Three additional species in Guatemala attack man readily and should be placed on the list of potential vectors; also, actual or potential transmission has been demonstrated in additional Mexican species.

The most important vector of human onchocerciasis in Africa is *S. damnosum*: *S. neavei* is also of considerable importance in this respect and in some areas is apparently entirely responsible for the transmission of *Onchocerca*.

Bovine Onchocerciasis. Other species of *Onchocerca* and related genera have been shown to be transmitted by black flies. Simuliid-transmitted *Onchocerca* in cattle has been recorded in Russia by Rubtsov (1964). Steward (1937) pointed out that onchocerciasis of cattle is of considerable importance in Australia, that the "worm nodules" due to *Onchocerca gibsoni* Cleland and Johnson at that time were causing losses to the state of Queensland estimated at £500,000 per annum. The work done by Steward in England with *Onchocerca gutturosa* Neumann proved that this parasite is transmitted by *Simulium ornatum* Meigen.

Leucocytozoon Infections of Poultry. The name *Leucocytozoon* was given to certain sporozoa found in the blood of birds by Danilewsky in 1890, and in 1895 Theobald Smith discovered a *Leucocytozoon* in the blood of turkeys. Skidmore (1932), in Nebraska, reported the successful transmission of this parasite by *Simulium occidentale* Townsend. An important infection of both domestic and wild ducks, caused by *Leucocytozoon simondi* Mathis and Leger, occurs in the northern United States and Canada. *Simulium ruggIesi* Nicholson and Mickel is the chief vector (Shewell, 1955; Anderson, Trainer and De Foliart, 1962). *Leucocytozoon* parasites are known to occur in twenty-four species of Anatidae, but larger ducks, such as mallards or black ducks, harbor them more commonly than do the smaller species. Anderson, Trainer, and De Foliart believe that the incidence of infection is related to host preference by *S. rugglesi*, which in turn is related to the size of the host.

FAMILY PSYCHODIDAE

(Moth Flies—Phlebotomus Flies)

Family Psychodidae. The family Psychodidae consists of several hundred species and includes the tiny gnats known as owl midges, moth flies, and phlebotomine sand flies. The ovate, usually pointed wings and the body are densely covered with hairs, and in *Psychoda* and related genera the wings when held at rest lie rooflike over the abdomen. The appearance of a tiny, rather robust moth has suggested the name "moth fly." Only the longitudinal veins are prominent, the cross veins, when present, being restricted to the base of the wing. The antennae are fairly long with usually ten to fourteen flagellomeres. The Nearctic species have been monographed by Quate (1955).

Psychodidae of medical importance belong to one of two subfamilies; (1) the Psychodinae, the moth flies or owl midges, whose females are not bloodsuckers, whose wings are held rooflike over the body, and whose larvae are commonly aquatic; and (2) the Phlebotominae, whose females are bloodsuckers, whose wings are not held rooflike over the body, and whose larvae are never truly aquatic. Two other subfamilies may be recognized, but these are uncommon and of no medical importance.

Psychoda Flies. Several species of *Psychoda* and *Telmatoscopus* are commonly found in great numbers around sewage disposal plants, cesspools, and washbasins in bathrooms where larvae may develop in sink drains in spite of hot water and soap. Although the flies of these genera are not bloodsuckers, they may breed in such numbers in the filter beds of sewage disposal plants as to constitute a real annoyance to neighboring households. *Psychoda alternata* Say, a widespread species occurring in most of the United States, is known as the "trickling filter fly." These gnats may become annoying in the house, either when they enter from outside or when they breed in the surface of the gelatinous material in sink and bathroom drain traps. The life cycle is short, ranging from twenty-one to twenty-seven days at room temperature at Berkeley, California, according to Quate.

Phlebotomus Flies. The genus *Phlebotomus* (*Flebotomus*) comprises many species of small-sized hairy gnats or midges measuring from 1.5 to about 4 mm in length. They are commonly known as sand flies. They differ from *Psychoda* and *Telmatoscopus* in that the wings are held upward and outward so that the costal margins form angles of about sixty degrees with each other and with the body. The body is less hairy than in the Psychodinae. The venation is peculiar; the radial sector branches in a pectinate fashion with the result that the apparent second vein (actually the true second vein, R_{2+3}, plus the anterior branch of the third, R_4, is three branched (Fig. 10-5). The females alone have piercing mouth parts and are bloodsuckers. Many species feed on cold-blooded animals such as lizards, snakes, and amphibians; others feed on a variety of warm-blooded animals, including man. There is evidence that some females take plant juices (Adler and Theodor, 1957); this fact is of importance, since the capacity of one species known to transmit *Leichmania donovani* is enhanced by feeding on raisins. The males suck moisture from any available source and are said even to suck sweat from humans. These gnats are active only at night and when there is little or no wind, seeking protection by day in shelters both out of doors in crevices, caves, and among vegetation, and within buildings where they hide in dark corners. Their weak, noiseless flight is usually in short so-called "hops" when they are disturbed; however, in longer flights their progress is slow and steady and can be followed with the eye.

Life History of Sand Flies. Hertig (1942), who has had wide experience with *Phlebotomus*

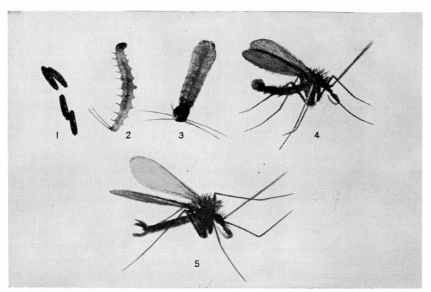

Fig. 10-5 Life cycle of *Phlebotomus verrucarum. 1.* Eggs. *2.* Larva. *3.* Pupa (*P. noguchii*). *4.* Adult female. *5.* Adult male. (After Hertig.)

flies, points out that the breeding places of sand flies are "typically under stones, in masonry cracks, in stables, poultry houses, etc., in situations combining darkness, humidity, and a supply of organic matter which serves as food for the larvae. In no case is the breeding place aquatic." To situations mentioned might be added surfaces under dead leaves on the forest floor, hollow trees, tree buttresses, and animal burrows (Hanson, 1961). Rodent burrows, which fulfill very well the three requirements stipulated by Hertig, have been shown to be an extensive habitat for these larvae in various parts of the Old World (Adler and Theodor, 1957) and North America (Harwood, 1965). This habit has some epidemiological significance since certain species of rodents are reservoirs of *Leishmania tropica*, which is propagated among them by flies in their burrows.

The eggs are deposited in small batches (Fig. 10-5). The incubation period is from six to seventeen days. The minute whitish larvae have long anal spines; the mouth parts are strongly mandibulate. The larvae feed on organic debris, such as moist excrement of lizards and mammals, insect debris, decaying plant material, and fungi. There are four instars; the duration of the larval stage is usually four to six weeks, with extremes ranging from about two to ten weeks (Barretto, 1943). The pupa, which is naked, requires about ten days for development. The female usually lays eggs in five to seven days under micro-climatic conditions of virtually 100 per cent relative humidity. Refeeding habits of females in relation to oviposition vary greatly with the different species, and this fact has considerable significance in respect to transmission of pathogenic organisms. The egg-to-egg cycle requires from seven to ten weeks; however, where there are cold winters *Phlebotomus* flies are subject to diapause in the fourth larval stage which may last from several weeks to nearly a year. Tropical species may undergo diapause during the dry season in certain areas.

Adult phlebotomine sand flies are weak fliers and are deterred from activity by air currents, even slight ones. They commonly rest in protected places, such as the rodent and armadillo burrows and termite mounds. Feeding habits vary from species to species. Mice and other rodents, armadillos, and reptiles serve as hosts for many species. Only certain species can be classed as anthropophagous.

Phlebotomine sand flies are of medical importance because of their role in transmitting the pathogens of Carrión's disease, sand fly fever, and leishmaniasis.

Carrión's Disease (Bartonellosis). Carrión's disease is known also under the names of its two chief clinical forms, namely, *Oroya fever*, a severe anemia that is frequently fatal, and *verruga peruana*, a benign form recognized by characteristic cutaneous nodular eruptions. The disease was named after Daniel Carrión, a medical student at Lima, Peru, who gave his life by infecting himself in a successful attempt to prove that the two clinical forms were one and the same disease. The etiological agent is *Bartonella bacilliformis* (Strong, *et al.*), a minute rodlike or coccoid organism "which occurs in or on the red cells and intracellularly in a number of organs, notably in the endothelial cells of lymph glands" (Hertig, 1948).

The disease occurs in mountain areas of Peru, Colombia, and Ecuador at elevations between 800 and 3,000 meters (2,600 to 9,700 ft.). This range is apparently determined by the breeding habits of its vector, the night temperatures above this zone being too cold and the rainfall below it being insufficient for successful development. The disease is not known to occur in lower animals. However, the pathogen can be recovered from patients who no longer show any symptoms of the disease and even from individuals who have no clinical history. Consequently, man himself appears to be the only source of infection.

The transmission of verruga was attributed to *Phlebotomus* flies by Townsend (1913), who described *Phlebotomus verrucarum* and attributed a human infection to this species. Based on careful field studies in the "Verruga zone," Noguchi, *et al.* (1929), substantially confirmed Townsend's contention that *P. verrucarum* is a

vector of verruga and added another species, *P. noguchii* Shannon as a probable vector (now known to be in error). In 1939 Hertig discovered a clue to the mechanism of infection when the verruga organism was recovered in pure culture from the extreme tip of the proboscis, the piercing stylets themselves being thoroughly contaminated.

Subsequent work has substantiated the case against *P. verrucarum* as the chief, and perhaps the sole, vector of Carrión's disease in its area (Adler and Theodor, 1957). *P. noguchii*, which restricts its feeding to field mice, must be eliminated so far as transmission to man is concerned. In epidemic areas of Colombia, where *P. verrucarum* is not known to occur, the vector is probably the closely related *P. columbianus* Ristorcelli and Van Ty. Considerable further work will be necessary to clarify the vector-pathogen relationships and the ecology of the disease, particularly in areas where it is known to be endemic and that lie outside the geographical range of its known vector (Barnett, 1962).

Sand Fly Fever. Sand fly fever, also known as pappataci fever, three-day fever, and Phlebotomus fever, is a seasonal (May to October) febrile, viral disease of short duration occurring in the *Phlebotomus*-infested regions of the Mediterranean, South China, parts of India, Ceylon, the Near and Middle East, and Central Asia. It is a nonfatal infection that may, because of its clinical similarities, especially in sporadic cases, be confused with dengue and other febrile infections. At least two, and probably more, strains of the virus are capable of producing sand fly fever. The epidemic form may occur either when a large number of susceptible individuals enter an endemic area or when the disease becomes extended into a previously uninfected area where there are large numbers of susceptible individuals (Barnett, 1962). As an example of the latter, when the disease was introduced into Serbia in 1948, three fourths of the population of the new area, or 1,200,000 persons, acquired the disease.

Epidemiological evidence and the fact that the virus has been isolated from *Phlebotomus* males, which of course do not suck blood, strongly indicate that the infection may be transmitted transovarially. If this is so, the insect itself is probably the reservoir. *Phlebotomus papataci* Scopoli in the Mediterranean region becomes infective seven to ten days after an infecting blood meal; the virus is present in man's blood for twenty-four hours prior to onset and for the first twenty-four hours of the disease, hence the infective period for the sand fly is limited to that length of time. After a person has been bitten by an infected fly the incubation period is usually three or four days, but this period may range from 2.5 to nine days. *Phlebotomus papatasi* Scopoli is the only proven vector, and the geographic distribution of the disease corresponds, with some exceptions, with that of this vector. *P. perniciosus* Newstead has been suggested as a vector, but the case against it is quite inconclusive. Other species may serve as vectors in China where *P. papatasi* is not known to occur.

There is need for further study of vector-pathogen relationships. Not only species of *Phlebotomus*, but also of *Sergentomyia*, should be considered as possible vectors (Barnett, 1962), because strains that are antigenically related to one known sand fly fever strain have been recovered from flies of that genus.

Leishmaniases. The leishmaniases are caused by parasitic Protozoa belonging to the genus *Leishmania*, round or oval intracellular bodies that develop flagellate leptomonadal stages in the digestive tract of insects. Several types of human leishmaniases result from a pathogen or pathogens transmitted by *Phlebotomus*. For successful transmission, a vector must fulfill certain requirements that may be rigid; but in general, as pointed out by Adler and Theodor (1957), it must have a sterile alimentary tract, because human leishmanias do not tolerate bacterial contamination. In some instances, a definite dependence upon plant juices as a partial diet is also essential.

Kala-azar, dumdum fever, or tropical splenomegaly is a visceral leishmaniasis caused by *Leishmania donovani* (Laveran and Mesnil), which localizes in the reticuloendothelial cells. It is a widespread disease, occurring in all countries on the shores of the Mediterranean, south Russia, India, China, Manchuria, equatorial Africa, Brazil, and other parts of tropical America, from Argentina to Mexico (Biagi, Lopes and Biagi, 1965). In man there is progressive enlargement of the spleen and later of the liver. As the disease progresses, the skin becomes grayish in color, whence the name "black disease." In untreated cases it is usually fatal, death resulting within a few weeks in acute infections and in from two to three years in chronic cases. Medication, however, has reduced fatality to a very low level.

Visceral leishmaniasis exists in three epidemiological types: (1) in India it occurs in both endemic and epidemic forms; all age groups, but mostly young adults, are attacked. No animal reservoir is known, but the epidemiological picture can be explained by assuming that man himself constitutes the chief reservoir (Adler and Theodor, 1957). (2) In the Sudan, and probably other parts of tropical Africa, cases are sporadic, but epidemics occur in which cases may be unevenly distributed. Again, all age groups, but principally young men, are the victims. Murine rodents, including *Rattus rattus* Linnaeus, the black rat, have been found to be infected in nature, and these rodents are probably the reservoir host (Hoogstral and Dietlein, 1963). (3) In the Mediterranean and some other areas within its range, the disease attacks to a high degree children under the age of five years. Here dogs are highly susceptible, in fact, the incidence among dogs usually far surpasses that among human beings. A separate pathogen, *Leishmania infantum* (Nicolle), was at one time considered responsible for this form of the disease, though *infantum* is now considered a synonym of *donovani*. This form of the disease is more widespread than has previously been suspected in tropical America, also occurring in forest environments, especially in Brazil, where the wild dog *Lycalopex vetulus* (Lund) seems to be its chief reservoir; though domestic dogs are also involved in this respect, the usual cycle seems to be between *Lycalopex* and man.

Various species of bloodsucking arthropods have been suspected as being vectors. The low susceptibility of laboratory animals made progress difficult, but with the discovery that hamsters were highly susceptible to the infection rapid progress was made. Shortt and his co-workers in India recorded, in 1926, a massive infection of the pharynx and buccal cavity of *Phlebotomus argentipes* Annandale and Brunetti, and subsequently, in 1931, reported successful transmission by the bite of the fly. The vectorship of *P. argentipes* was not proven, however, until Swaminath, Shortt and Anderson (1942) succeeded in transmitting the disease to five out of six volunteers, but only after the infected *Phlebotomus* had previously been fed on raisins. In the case of *P. argentipes*, there seems to be a necessary relationship between the intake of plant juices and the ability to infect the mammalian host. Some have considered this relationship one of blocking the digestive tract, analogous to that of the blocked flea, but Adler and Theodor believe that the ingestion of fruit juices stimulates a descent of the flagellates to the tip of the proboscis where they can readily enter the wound.

Phlebotomus orientalis Parrot is the proven vector of *Leishmania donovani* in the Sudan. It is a distinctly anthropophilous species, characteristic of the *Acacia* forest islands in the savannah. In China, where dogs form the reservoir of the pathogen, *P. chinensis* Newstead is the incriminated vector. *P. perniciosus* is the chief vector in the Mediterranean region, although *P. major* Annandale is of local importance, and *P. longicuspis* Nitzulescu and *P. sergenti* Parrot are probable vectors. In Brazil, *P. longipalpis* Lutz and Neiva has been found naturally infected and has been used to produce experimental infections. Other vectors occur in kala-azar zones in other parts of the world.

A very concise discussion of kala-azar as a zoonosis has been given by Biagi, Lopes, and Biagi (1965). A series of articles by Hoogstraal and his associates (1961–1963) has added important information on pathogen transmission, general epidemiology of the disease, reservoirs, sand fly biology, and other aspects of *Phlebotomus-Leishmania* relationships.

Oriental Sore. Oriental sore, also known as Bagdad or Delhi boil, is a cutaneous leishmaniasis caused by *Leishmania tropica* (Wright); it has a wide distribution in Mediterranean areas, Asia Minor, Arabia, Iraq, India, the Congo, and other parts of the world. Unlike kala-azar, in Oriental sore the leishmanias inhabit the skin and do not invade the viscera. Adler and Theodor succeeded in incriminating *P. papataci* to the extent that *L. tropica* was passed successfully from a natural infected sand fly to the human host and back to the sand fly. Attempts to obtain infection by the bite of the insect were unsuccessful, however, but suspensions of the infective material in saline were successful. These workers found that the developmental cycle of the *Leishmania* in the fly required eight to twenty-one days. They report that in India *P. sergenti* Parrott is the most effective vector. The infection is apparently perpetuated by sand flies inhabiting burrows of various species of gerbils, and this explains outbreaks among groups of human beings passing through un-inhabited regions. Dogs also become naturally infected.

American mucocutaneous leishmaniasis (nasooral), also known as papalomoyo, espundia, or uta, is widely distributed in tropical and subtropical America. The causal agent is *Leishmania brasiliensis* Vianna. The horribly disfiguring effects of this infection are shown by Goldman (1947), who points out that it is the mucosal involvement that is so characteristic of this type of leishmaniasis. Once the infection gets into the mucocutaneous junction, it destroys all types of tissue including cartilage and bone.

Leishmaniasis Mexicana. A form of cutaneous leishmaniasis, which does not involve the mucosa, is found in Central America and Mexico. The pathogenicity involves the ears in the majority of cases. The pathogen is *Leishmania mexicana* Biagi, a species that has been shown to be immunologically distinct from related forms. *Phlebotomus flaviscutellatus* Mangabeira is according to the investigations of Biagi, Biagi, and Beltrán (1965), at least an important vector; this fly was found infected significantly (6 per cent) in nature, and two cases of leishmaniasis among the experimental workers apparently were transmitted by this fly.

Although the four leishmaniases discussed here are clinically different and immunologically distinct, the theory that but one species is involved has its adherents. Barnett (1962) suggests that the ability of leishmanias to cause different clinical syndromes may be conferred upon them by the different *Phlebotomus* species involved in their transmission. The theory is based on the geographical correspondence of the leishmaniases and their phlebotomine vectors and on the fact that cultured *Leishmania* rapidly lose their pathogenicity and also rapidly regain it when passed through sand flies again.

The Species of Phlebotomus. Although the genus is now known to occur as far north as southern Canada, species of medical importance are confined, in the New World, to the tropical and subtropical regions. A similar distribution prevails in the Old World. The most important species have been dealt with in the preceding discussion. Many species of *Phlebotomus* never attack man or domestic animals and consequently are of no medical importance. Many of these feed on reptiles.

The catalog of the New World species by Barretto (1947) will serve as a useful starting point for students of the taxonomy of this group, although it must be kept in mind that much taxonomic investigation has been done since that time.

FAMILY CERATOPOGONIDAE (HELEIDAE)
(Biting Midges, Punkies)

Characteristics. The Ceratopogonidae are very small (0.6–5.0 mm in length), slender gnats resembling some of the smaller non-biting midges of the family Chironomidae. In their biting habits, the anthropophagous species resemble the black flies (Simuliidae) and are frequently mistaken for them. Among the fifty or more genera comprising the family, three, namely *Culicoides* (Fig. 10-6), *Lasiohelea*, and *Leptoconops*, attack man and other warm blooded animals. These are popularly known by a variety of names, including "punkies," "no-see-ums," and "sand flies" (not to be confused with the phlebotomine sand flies). The wings, which are narrow, with few veins and usually no scales, may be clear or hairy, and are folded flat over the abdomen when at rest; the alulae are slender. The larvae (Fig. 10-7) are aquatic or semiaquatic, or else they live in moist soil; habitats include fresh or salt water, tree holes, decaying plant

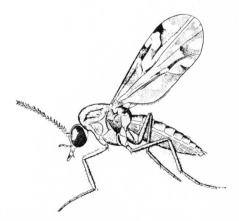

Fig. 10-6 *Culicoides* sp., female. (After Dampf.)

Fig. 10-7 *Culicoides variipennis,* larva. (Drawing by James in W. T. Edmondson, 1959. Ward and Whipple's *Fresh Water Biology.* New York: John Wiley & Sons, Inc. Fig. 41.14, p. 1068.)

materials such as cactus, banana stems, or plantain, and moist adobe, sandy, and alkaline soils.

A catalog of the blood-sucking midges of the Americas, with keys to the Nearctic species, has been published by Fox (1955), and a monograph of the Neotropical *Culicoides* has been presented by Forattini (1957). Taxonomic work on this group of insects is currently progressing at a rapid rate; consequently, it is not practical to attempt to list all the more important literature. Some studies of particular significance, however, are those of Wirth and Blanton (1959) on the fauna of Panama, of Gutsevich (1960) for the U.S.S.R., of Tokinaga (1962, 1963) for New Guinea, and Arnaud (1956), for Japan.

Ceratopogonid Bites. Many species of *Culicoides* never attack man. However, certain ones constitute a serious economic problem, for example in coastal summer resort areas, particularly about fresh-water inlets and tidewater pools, and in mountain areas, where they may be so annoying as to drive out campers and fishermen. The bites of these minute flies, which are often blamed on the larger and more conspicuous black flies or mosquitoes, cause itching and, in sensitive individuals, welts and lesions that may persist for several days. These are sometimes complicated by secondary infections resulting from scratching to relieve the itch.

Culicoides furens (Poey) may be taken as an example of a vicious biter that occurs over a broad geographical area. This species breeds in salt marshes and similar habitats along the Atlantic and Gulf coasts from Massachusetts to Brazil, throughout the West Indies, and along the Pacific coast from Mexico to Ecuador. It has been recorded repeatedly as biting

man furiously, especially in the Caribbean areas. Little is known concerning its feeding preferences in other animals. Jamnback (1965) summarizes our knowledge of the biology of the species.

Lasiohelea, now considered a subgenus of *Forcipomyia,* feeds on vertebrates. Pechuman and Wirth (1961) have reviewed the role of two species, the European *Forcipomyia (Lasiohelea) velox* (Winnertz), and the eastern North American *F. (L.) fairfaxensis* Wirth as frog parasites; the former is known to transmit a filarial parasite of the frog. Some species of this subgenus, according to Pechuman and Wirth, are vicious biters of man and other warm-blooded animals in the tropics; their role as possible vectors of filarial worms needs investigation. *F. (L.) taiwana* Shiraki bites man in Taiwan and Japan.

Leptoconops torrens (Townsend) and *L. kerteszi* (Kieffer) severely attack man in many parts of the United States, particularly in the south and west. In California, where they constitute a major pest, the former is known as the "valley black gnat" and the latter as the "Bodega black gnat." Both species feed on man, domestic animals, and birds. The bite usually produces a transient swelling that may become vesicular, rupture and produce an open lesion that may exude moisture for weeks. Itching resulting from the bite is intense.

L. torrens is an American species; *L. kerteszi* also extends over Northern (Mediterranean) Africa. Smith and Lowe (1948) have ably treated the biologies of these species in California. Adults of *L. kerteszi* occur from mid-April until early October, continuously emerging from the soil. Females may feed as many as four times. Males form large swarms, dancing in the lee of windbreaks. Eggs are laid on the surface of damp sand where the salt concentration is about 650 p.p.m. The larval stage lasts for eight to ten months. Pupation occurs in the sand; pupae wriggle to the surface, orienting themselves vertically, before the adult emerges. The pupal period is eight days. Adult females captured in the field lived a maximum of eleven days, with blood meals. The details of the biology of *L. torrens* are somewhat different. The larvae occur in clay-adobe soils at a depth of fifteen to thirty inches. Egress and entrance are dependent on the cracking and drying of the soil. The larval period is at least two years in length. Other *Leptoconops* species known to attack man are *L. camelorum* Kieffer and *L. caucasicus* Gutzevich, both Asiatic in distribution.

Relationship to Disease. The known role of bloodsucking ceratopogonids in the transmission of human and animal pathogens is perhaps more important than has previously been realized. A concise account of their role in this regard has been given by Kettle (1965). Five helminths are involved. The night-biting *Culicoides austeni* Carter, Ingram, and Macfie is an intermediate host of the filarial worm *Acanthocheilonema perstans* (Manson). The microfilariae of this worm are found in the peripheral circulation both by day and by night; diurnal periodicity is the more common. In the vast majority of the cases it is said to be nonpathogenic. It is primarily equatorial and African in distribution, although it occurs also in Guyana and in New Guinea. The microfilariae undergo metamorphosis in the body of *Culicoides austeni*, increasing to three times their original length before they appear in the proboscis of the insect. The cycle in the fly requires seven to nine days. *Culicoides grahami* Austen is a natural, though less efficient, carrier of this helminth, and both *Culicoides* species are involved in the transmission of *Dipetalonema streptocera* Macfie and Corson. Buckley (1933) found that *Culicoides furens* (Poey) transmits the filarial worm *Mansonella ozzardi* (Manson). *Onchocera reticulata* Diesing, the causative organism of fistulous withers of horses, is transmitted by *C. nubeculosus* Meigen and *C. obsoletus* Meigen, and *Onchocerca gibsoni* Cleland and Johnson, which infests cattle in Australia, South Africa, and southeastern Asia, has *C. pungens* de Meijere as an important vector;

other known vectors of this latter species are *C. oxystoma* Kieffer, *C. shortti* Smith and Swaminath, and *C. orientalis* Macfie.

Several protozoan and viral diseases of domestic and wild animals, poultry, and waterfowl, and possibly man are related to ceratopogonid transmission. *Hepatocystis*, a genus of *Plasmodium*-like sporozoans, but belonging to a different family (Haemoproteidae), parasitize Old World monkeys and other mammals, mostly arboreal. Vectors are either known or presumed to be species of *Culicoides* (Garnham, 1966). *Haematocystis kochi* (Laveran), a parasite of African monkeys, is transmitted by *C. adersi* Carter, Ingram and Macfie and probably by *C. fulvithorax* (Austen). There is little pathogenicity resulting from this parasite and, so far as is known, other species of the genus. Another genus of this family, *Parahaemaproteus*, which includes several known avian parasites, is also *Culicoides*-transmitted (Fallis and Bennett, 1961). One member of this genus, *P. nettionis* (Johnson and Cleland), parasitizes domestic and wild ducks and geese and other wild waterfowl. Wild birds probably serve as the reservoir in epizootics among domestic birds (Garnham, 1966).

Though *Leucocytozoon* parasites of poultry are simuliid-transmitted, a member of the same family (Leucocytozoidae), *Akiba caulleryi* (Mathis and Leger), is *Culicoides*-transmitted. This parasite produces a very important poultry disease in Japan and southeast Asia. Known vectors are *Culicoides arakawae* Arakawa, *C. circumscriptus* Kieffer, and *C. shultzei* (Enderlein). Garnham (1966) points out that *Culicoides* may replace *Simulium* as a vector of the Leucocytozoidae in areas where the latter genus is absent; for example, *C. adersi*, which feeds avidly on chickens, may transmit a *Leucocytozoon* of poultry in Africa.

The virus of bluetongue, an important disease of sheep, is transmitted by *C. pallidipennis* Carter, Ingram, and Macfie in Africa and by *C. variipennis* (Coquillett) in the United States (Fig. 10-8). Jones (1961) has recently added to the evidence incriminating the latter

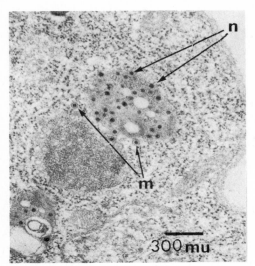

Fig. 10-8 Salivary gland of infected *Culicoides variipennis* 10 days after infection, showing mature (*m*) and nonencapsulated (*n*) virus particles. (Courtesy of Bowne and Jones, 1966, *Virology, 30*:127-33.)

flies bear little resemblance to them on closer examination. In the midges the proboscis is short and not adapted for piercing, the palpi are three- or four-semented, and the wings are bare or haired. The metanotum is longitudinally grooved in most species; this will aid in separating the midges from similarly appearing Nematocera. The antennae are plumose in the males (Fig. 10–9) and sparsely haired in the females. Midges are widely distributed and may be extremely abundant in the vicinity of standing water, since the larvae (Fig. 10-10) of most species are aquatic. Massive adult emergence frequently occurs. The general adult behavior pattern is to rest by day and fly in the evening, night, and early morning hours. Occasionally great swarms of these insects hover in the air toward evening and produce a distinct humming noise, They are attracted to light in great numbers.

Medical Importance. Chironomids can not bite, but they may and frequently do constitute a major nuisance. Grodhaus (1963) has given an excellent summary of this subject. Comfort

species by his observation that it feeds on sheep under natural conditions. Undetermined species of *Culicoides* are probably involved in transmitting the virus of African horse sickness, a disease that within recent years has extended into Pakistan and other parts of the Middle East, where it has taken a heavy toll of horses and mules. The viruses of eastern equine encephalitis, in Georgia, U.S., and of Venezuelan equine encephalitis, in Ecuador, have been isolated from undetermined species of *Culicoides*, but this is probably of little epidemiologic significance. The first incrimination of *Forcipomyia* as a possible vector of a human pathogen came with the recovery of the Japanese B encephalitis virus from *Forcipomyia* (*Lasiohelea*) *taiwana* Shiraki.

FAMILY CHIRONOMIDAE (TENDIPEDIDAE)

(*Midges*)

The family Chironomidae is a large one, comprising more than 2,000 species. Though commonly mistaken for mosquitoes, these

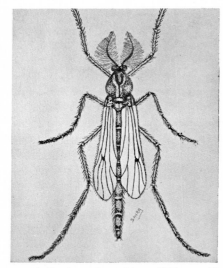

Fig. 10-9 A male midge (Chironomidae), commonly mistaken for a mosquito. × 12. (After Osborn.)

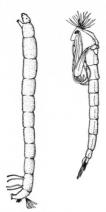

Fig. 10-10 Larva (*left*) and pupa (*right*) of a chironomid gnat (midge). (Larva redrawn after Needham, and pupa redrawn after Grünberg.)

and activities of persons may be interfered with near areas of heavy midge emergence, and even livestock may be bothered. When one encounters swarms of midges, it may be difficult to keep them out of one's eyes or avoid inhaling them. The latter may result in an allergic reaction. Swarms crossing highways may produce a traffic hazard. The aquatic forms may be troublesome when, as occasionally happens, they enter water distribution systems and occur in tap water.

So far as known, mechanical transmission of pathogens by midges is not a probability, though the possibility of such transmission by species whose larval stages are spent in sewage-contaminated water has been mentioned. But, even aside from the health and accident hazard, the discomfort and offense to personal tastes can not be tolerated in a sanitation-conscious community.

FAMILY DIXIDAE

(*Dixa Midges*)

Dixa midges, sometimes considered as constituting a subfamily (Dixinae) of mosquitoes, have a characteristically different venation and have the wings almost devoid of hairs and scales; the proboscis, although somewhat projecting, is not fitted for piercing. The family is mentioned here particularly because the larvae are frequently mistaken for those of *Anopheles*, being commonly found in similar situations, and also because the adults resemble and are related to the true mosquitoe. Dixa larva are usually seen at the surface of water among vegetation and debris, moving in a horizontal U-shaped pattern.

FAMILY CHAOBORIDAE

(*Chaoborid Gnats*)

The Chaoboridae, sometimes considered a subfamily (Chaoborinae) of mosquitoes, constitute a group of nonbloodsucking flies that have some importance as predators on mosquitoes; on the other hand, they may at times be nuisances. Though in most cases chaoborids do not develop under conditions proper to develop the pest potential, at least one species, the Clear Lake gnat of California, *Chaoborus astictopus* Dyar and Shannon (Fig. 10-11),

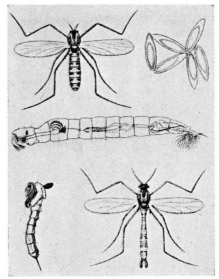

Fig. 10-11 A chaoborid, the Clear Lake gnat, *Chaoborus astictopus*, showing life cycle. (*Top left*) female gnat; (*top right*) eggs; (*lower left*) pupa; (*lower right*) male gnat; (*middle figure*) larva.

becomes such a nuisance that thousands of these flies may swarm around a patio light bulb. Their gillbreathing larvae, which live in deep water, are almost transparent and are seen with some difficulty, except when in motion, even in fairly clear water; hence they are called "phantom larvae." The tiny lead-colored, cigar-shaped eggs are deposited in great numbers on the surface of still water, such as ponds, lagoons, lakes, and so forth. The eggs soon sink to the bottom. The incubation period is less than twenty-four hours. The larvae grow slowly during the summer, reaching approximately full growth by winter, remaining thus through the winter, and pupating in the early spring. The pupal stage requires about two weeks. The pupae quickly come to the surface, where the gnats literally "pop" out of the pupal skins, balance on the water momentarily, and then fly shoreward.

Though associated historically with Clear Lake, in northern California, *Chaoborus astictopus* is becoming more widespread as the result of the development of impounded waters and other habitats that provide conditions suitable for its breeding (Cook, 1967).

11

MOSQUITOES

ORDER DIPTERA, FAMILY CULICIDAE

CLASSIFICATION AND BIOLOGY

Importance. Mosquitoes are the most prominent of the numerous species of blood-sucking arthropods that annoy man and other warm-blooded animals. Their number is legion, and they are an almost constant annoyance. Great swarms may be produced even in small quantities of water. They breed in practically all sorts of still water, fresh and salt, foul or potable; water in tin cans, car and airplane tires, hoofprints, tree holes, deposits in leaf cups, water impoundments, and salt marsh. Great areas of seacoast are at times made uninhabitable by salt-marsh mosquitoes, and agriculture and real estate development may be retarded. They may make potential recreational areas unsuitable and interfere with normal living in and outside the home. Losses resulting from lowered industrial efficiency are frequently considerable because of mosquito annoyance. Economic losses caused by mosquitoes would alone amply justify great sums spent on mosquito abatement, yet these losses are minor compared with prodigious losses caused by mosquitoes as vectors of disease.

Mosquitoes are the sole vectors of the pathogens causing malaria, yellow fever, and dengue, and they are of prime importance in filariasis and the encephalitides. It is reported that in an ordinary year in India alone, before the nationwide antimalaria campaign went into effect, at least a hundred million persons suffered from, and a million succumbed to, the direct ravages of malaria. The indirect effect in lowered vitality and susceptibility to other diseases accounted for another million deaths.

Family Culicidae. Although some authors, Edwards (1932) and others, include the dixa midges and the chaoborid gnats (see Chapter 10) as well as the true mosquitoes in the family Culicidae, only the latter are so classified for the purpose of this book. Excepting the large sturdily built American gallinippers, *Psorophora ciliata* (Fabricius) and *P. howardii* Coquillett (body length 9 mm and wingspread 13 mm), and a few other species, mosquitoes are small and fragile, ranging in body length from 3 to 6 mm. The most obvious characteristics separating adult mosquitoes from all other Diptera are a combination of wings with scales on the wing veins and posterior margin, and an elongate proboscis.

Additional characteristics include their wing venation (Fig. 10-1) as follows: subcosta (Sc) long, reaching the costa; radius (R) four-branched; R_{2+3} forked; R_{4+5} simple; no cross-vein connections of R_1 and R_2; media (M) two-branched; cross veins r-m and m-cu both present; cubitus (Cu) forked; anal vein (A) long and reaching wing margin; characteristic scales clothing the wings, and more or less abundant on the head and body (often scant or wanting). The antennae are long and filamentous with fourteen or fifteen segments, hairs in whorls, plumose in the males of most species; males of *Opifex* and *Deinocerites* do not have plumose antennae.

Larvae of mosquitoes are without exception aquatic. They are separable from all other aquatic insects by an absence of legs, and by the bulbous thorax being wider than the head or abdomen. They differ from other dipterous larvae by a complete head capsule plus only one pair of functional spiracles, situated dorsally on the eighth abdominal segment. Larval anatomic structures most used in taxonomy are shown in Figure 11-1. Larvae of mosquitoes are collected for several reasons: (1) a positive record in the absence of adult specimens; (2) in some cases more positive identification than adults; (3) an aid to or a check on the determination of adults; (4) per-

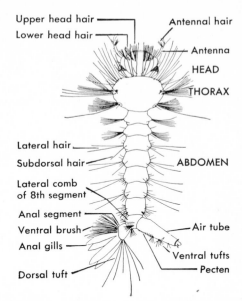

Fig. 11-1 Larval characters used in identifying mosquitoes. (After Stage, Gjullin, and Yates; U.S.D.A. photograph.)

fect adult specimens for identification of both sexes may often be obtained through rearing; (5) infection-free stock from reared sources.

There are about 2,500 described species of mosquitoes in the world; about 150 occur in temperate North America (Stone, *et al.*, 1959, Stone 1961, 1963, 1967). These ubiquitous insects occur at elevations of 14,000 feet in Kashmir and as low as 3,760 feet below sea level in gold mines of South India (Russell, *et al.*, 1943), they are abundant in species in the tropics, and almost unbelievably large swarms of them occur in Arctic regions. Mosquitoes may be divided into three subfamilies: (1) **Toxorhynchitinae** (=Megarhininae) adults large, with metallic scales, proboscis strongly curved downward, flower-feeding, and larvae predaceous, e.g., *Toxorhynchites rutilus* (Coquillett); (2) **Culicinae** with palpi of the female less than half as long as proboscis, scutellum trilobed, and females hematophagous, e.g., *Culex pipiens* Linnaeus and *Aedes aegypti* (Linnaeus); (3) **Anophelinae** with palpi of both sexes as long as or nearly as long as proboscis, scutellum straplike, and females likewise hematophagous, e.g., *Anopheles maculipennis* Meigen.

The literature dealing with the taxonomy of mosquitoes is extensive. Carpenter and LaCasse (1955) monographed the Nearctic species; state and regional studies are available for most parts of the United States. Larval and adult characters are described, keyed, and figured by Carpenter and LaCasse and in at least most of the regional works. Characters of the other immature stages have not proven of as much value in identification, but some use has been made of pupal characters. Falleroni (1926) differentiated the species of the *Anopheles maculipennis* complex on the basis of surface features of eggs, and Horsfall and his associates (1952, 1956) have shown that the eggs of *Psorophora* and *Aedes* can similarly be differentiated.

Male Terminalia. Most critical differences used in the identification of adult mosquitoes are found in the male terminalia (Fig. 11-2). The terminal portion of the abdomen of the adult male begins to rotate on its axis within a few hours after emergence from the pupa, and a rotation of 180 degrees is completed in twelve to twenty-four hours, depending on temperature; this portion of the abdomen remains rotated thereafter. The terminalia are prepared for microscopic study by clipping off the tip of the abdomen, treating with potassium hydroxide to partially clear and relax if dry, appropriate dehydration, and positioning in properly supported microscopic thick mount for comparison with drawings of the terminalia of various species in such publications as the *Mosquito Atlas* by Ross and Roberts (1943). A more complete description of the technique for dissecting male terminalia of mosquitoes is given by Komp (1942).

THE ECOLOGY OF MOSQUITOES

Important books dealing with the biology and physiology of mosquitoes are by Bates (1949) and Horsfall (1955); more recent

discussions are included in Christophers (1960) and Clements (1963). The serious student of the subject will need to be familiar with these works.

Life History of Mosquitoes. All mosquitoes undergo complex metamorphosis—egg, larva, pupa, and adult (Fig. 11-4). The larvae are commonly known as *wigglers*, and the pupae as *tumblers*. Water in which to pass the larval and pupal stages is essential, although a moist substrate may permit development of the pupa. Eggs, on the contrary, in some species may survive long periods out of water, though preferably under humid conditions. Gjullin, *et al.* (1950), found eggs of *Aedes vexans* (Meigen) and *Aedes sticticus* (Meigen) to survive in numbers for three years when kept moist, and Breeland and Pickard (1967) observed hatching of eggs of nine common *Aedes* and *Psorophora* to occur after four years of intermittent flooding. According to Dyar (1928), the eggs of *Psorophora*, with their spinose protecting coat, withstand desiccation on dry ground for months or years, hatching with the advent of water.

Mosquito eggs are deposited singly, e.g., *Anopheles*, or in rafts, e.g., *Culex* and *Culiseta*, (Fig. 11-3) on the surface of quiet pools of water, and by some species along the margins; floodwater and salt marsh species, as well as many treehole breeders, e.g., *Aedes* and *Psorophora*, however, oviposit in sites subject to inundation by tidal water, seepage, overflow, or rain water. One feature that all sites have in common is protection of the ovipositing female from action of wind and wave. It has been shown by a number of authors that substances attractive to ovipositing females may aid in the selection of specific sites for oviposition (Hudson and McLintock, 1967; Perry and Fay, 1967). The egg incubates for several days and may hatch as soon as this period is completed; on the other hand, in eggs deposited out of water or subject to desiccation, the embryo may remain quiescent for extended periods of time, so that the egg will hatch only under the proper conditions. Such conditions vary from one group of mosquitoes

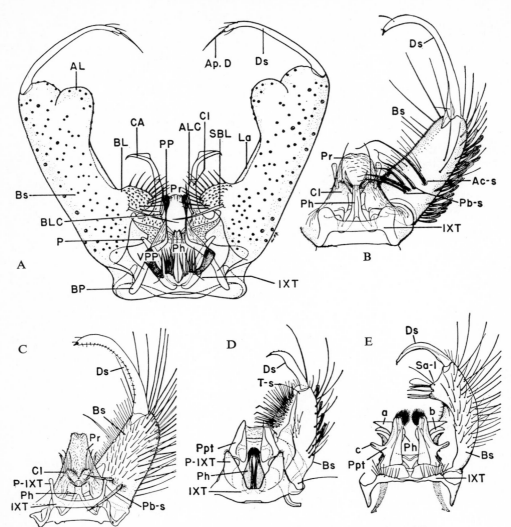

Fig. 11-2 Male terminalia of (*A*) *Aedes squamiger*, (*B*) *Anopheles gambiae*, (*C*) *Anopheles freeborni*, (*D*) *Aedes aegypti*, and (*E*) *Culex pipiens quinquefasciatus*. *AL*, apical lobe; *ALC*, apical lobe of claspette; *Ap.D*, appendage of dististyle; *Bs*, basistyle; *BL*, basal lobe; *BLC*, basal lobe of claspette; *Cl*, claspette; *CA*, claspette appendage; *Ds*, dististyle; *La*, lacuna; IXT, lobe of 9th tergite (=process of 9th tergite); *P*, paramere; *Ph*, phallosome; *Ppt*, paraproct; *Pr*, proctiger; *SBL*, spine of basal lobe; *VPP*, ventral arm of paraproct; *IXT*, 9th tergite. (*B* to *E* after Ross and Roberts.)

to another. In the case of the snow pool mosquitoes, eggs laid during the summer and autumn remain buried under the snow through the winter and hatch with the melting snow in spring; thus one brood is produced annually. Eggs of floodwater mosquitoes do not all hatch at one time; most of the eggs of one laying will hatch after the first flooding, but some remain for the second and subsequent floodings. In all cases of floodwater mosquitoes studied thus far, essentially *Aedes* and *Psorophora* species, there must be reduction of dissolved oxygen in the water that covers eggs for significant hatching to occur; caused

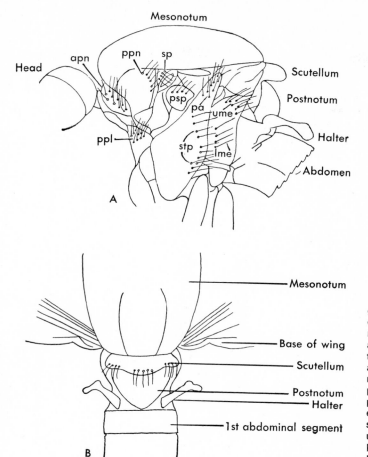

Fig. 11-3 Composite diagram of (*A*) lateral and (*B*) dorsal view of thorax of adult mosquito showing structures and pleural bristles. Explanation of abbreviations: *apn*, anterior pronotal; *lme*, lower mesepimeral; *pa*, prealar; *ppl*, propleural (prosternal); *ppn*, posterior pronotal (proepimeral); *psp*, postspiracular; *sp*, spiracular; *stp*, sternopleural; upper mesepimeral. (After King, Bradley, and McNeel; U.S.D.A. photograph.)

naturally by microorganisms growing on freshly flooded nutrients (see discussion in Clements, 1963).

The larvae of most Culicinae hang suspended diagonally from the water surface by means of a prominent breathing siphon. Exceptions occur in species that remain most of the time under water respiring by cutaneous diffusion, and in the genus *Mansonia* where the air tube is modified to form a short and sharp structure that pierces the roots of aquatic plants. The larvae of Anophelinae lie horizontally just beneath the surface of the water, suspended particularly by means of palmate hairs (Fig. 11-3).

The larvae of most species filter out suspended microorganisms, both plants and animals, or browse microorganisms present on solid surfaces. The food is carried to the mouth by currents produced by the action of oral brushes, two dense tufts of long curved hairs borne by the maxillae; it is then made to flow into the water through suction of the pharynx (Horsfall, 1955). Within the pharynx fine comblike structures remove microorganisms and other fine suspended particles (see Chapter 3).

The larvae molt four times, the last molt resulting in the pupa. About seven days, depending on temperature, are required for the larval stage of commoner Culicinae under optimum food conditions. The larval stage of the Anophelinae generally requires a somewhat longer time.

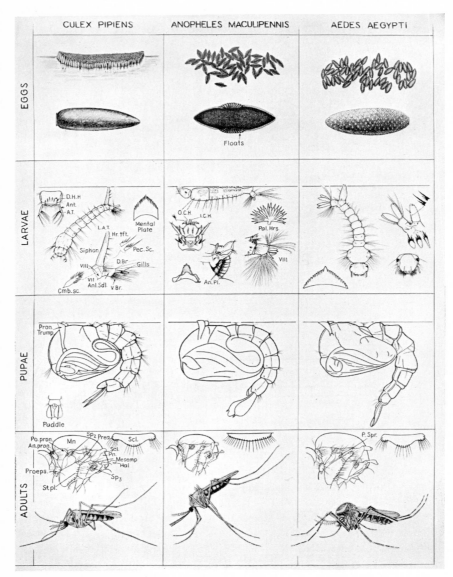

Fig. 11-4 Anatomic details and life history of three genera of mosquitoes, *Culex,* *Anopheles,* and *Aedes.* Explanation of abbreviations: *An.Pl.,* anal plate; *An.pron.,* anterior pronotal setae; *Anl.Sdl.,* anal saddle (dorsal plate); *Ant.,* antenna; *A.T.,* antennal tuft; *Cmb.Sc.,* comb scale; D.Br., dorsal brush; *D.H.H.,* dorsal head hair; *Hal.,* halter; *Hr.tft.,* siphon hair tuft; *I.C.H.,* inner clypeal hair; *L.A.T.,* lateral abdominal tuft; *Mesemp,* mesepimeral setae; *Mn.,* mesonotum (tergum₂); *O.C.H.,* outer clypeal hairs; *Pal.Hrs.,* palmate or float hairs (tuft); *Pec.Sc.,* pecten scale; *Pn.,* postnotum; *Po.pron.,* posterior pronotal setae; *Prea.,* prealar setae; *Pron.Trump.,* pronotal trumpet; *Proeps.,* proepisternal setae; *P.Spr.,* postspiracular setae; *Scl.,* scutellum; *Sp.,* spiracle; *St.pl.,* sternopleural setae; *V.Br.,* ventral brush. (Adapted after various authors.)

172

With the fourth molt the pupa or "tumbler" appears. In this nonfeeding stage there is a pair of breathing "trumpets" situated dorsally on the cephalothorax (Fig. 11-3). The pupa is remarkably active and sensitive to disturbances of the water, suddenly darting with a tumbling motion to deeper water and after a few moments rising with little motion to the surface. The pupal stage is quite short, usually two to three days.

Food Habits of Adult Mosquitoes. The mouth parts of male mosquitoes are not suited to piercing, hence they are not bloodsuckers. Their nourishment is normally derived from nectar and plant juices and other liquids. With the exception of a few species, such as the plantfeeding Toxorhynchitinae, and *Harpagomyia*, which feeds on regurgitated stomach contents offered by ants (*Crematogaster*), female mosquitoes pierce the skin of many kinds of animals and feed on blood. The great majority of species are *zoophilous*, i.e., feed in nature on animals other than man; some will feed on coldblooded vertebrates. Species that feed on man by preference are said to be *anthropophilous*.

Normally, females of bloodsucking species require a blood meal before oviposition. However, Rowland has applied the term "autogeny" to cases where reproduction occurs without a blood meal. Autogeny was once regarded as something of a rarity, but now many species in at least nine genera are known to have autogenous strains or to be totally autogenous (Clements, 1963, and more recent authors).

Consult Chapter 4 concerning the flight habits of mosquitoes.

Mating Habits of Mosquitoes. There is great variation in the requirements for mating of mosquitoes, making some species notably easy to rear and others nearly impossible. *Aedes aegypti* (Linnaeus) mates readily in a small space, the males responding to female flight sounds (Roth, 1948). The majority of mos-

quitoes, however, form crepuscular swarms of males in which females can be observed to enter and to mate. Apparently such swarms are not exclusively for mating, as pointed out by Nielsen and Haeger (1960).

A brief review of the principal subfamilies of Culicidae, with discussion of important representative genera and vector species, follows. A general listing of mosquitoes known as vector species has been prepared by Foote and Cook (1959), but this work needs modernization, particularly in light of much greater recent information on arboviruses.

Longevity of Mosquitoes. Male mosquitoes usually remain alive for but six or seven days, although careful laboratory maintenance with adequate carbohydrate and high humidity may yield survival beyond a month. Females with ample food may live for four or five months, particularly under hibernating conditions. During their period of greatest activity, where summers are hot, female survival may average closer to two weeks. The staining experiment by Stage, *et al.* (1937), produced important data relative to longevity. Thus, six *Aedes sticticus* (Meigen) females were taken fifty-two days after staining, one female of the same species eighty-five days after staining, one *Aedes vexans* (Meigen) female after fifty-five days; also, under especially favorable conditions, one 94-day *A. sticticus* male was taken, and females of both *Aedes sticticus* and *A. vexans* were collected from 104 to 113 days after staining. The latter species appears to have the greater maximum longevity by approximately fifteen to twenty days. The importance of longevity for vector effectiveness has been mentioned in Chapter 4.

Internal Anatomy of Mosquitoes. To be prepared to study the relation of mosquitoes to such diseases as malaria and filariasis, the student must be familiar with their internal anatomy. The student is referred to Figure 2-6C and to the excellent treatment of mosquito anatomy by Snodgrass (1959).

SUBFAMILY TOXORHYNCHITINAE

Characteristics. The members of the subfamily Toxorhynchitinae occur in tropical as well as temperate climates and are usually highly colored; they are day fliers; both sexes are flower-feeders and do not suck blood. The basal half of the proboscis is stout and rigid and the distal portion is flexible, which accounts for the curious hooklike position of the proboscis when at rest. The palpi vary in length from one-fourth the length of the proboscis to nearly the same length. The larvae are large, predaceous, and cannibalistic. Their appetites are prodigious; one larva during its last stage was reported by Garnham, *et al.* (1946), to have devoured 195 mature larvae of *Aedes aegypti* (Linnaeus) during twelve days. On the other hand, they resist starvation for considerable periods.

The eggs are deposited singly. The larvae breed in small confined collections of water, such as in bamboo stems, tree holes, pitcher plants, and the like.

Stone, *et al.* (1959), list fifty-nine species of the "tropicopolitan" genus *Toxorhynchites* (*Megarhinus*), the only one in the subfamily. One species represented by two subspecies occurs in the United States. *Toxorhynchites rutilus rutilus* (Coquillett), the typical form, occurs only in the extreme southwest, but *T. rutilus septentrionalis* (Dyar and Knab) is much more widely distributed. The giant species *T. inornatus* (Walker) was introduced from New Britain into the Hawaiian Islands (Williams, 1931) for purposes of mosquito control, without practical result, although two other species, *T. brevipalpis* Theobald from Africa and *T. splendens* (Wiedemann) of the oriental region appear to have become established there more recently.

SUBFAMILY CULICINAE

Characteristics. All members of the subfamily Culicinae have the scutellum trilobed with each lobe bearing bristles, but with bristleless areas between lobes. The abdomen is completely clothed with broad scales, which nearly always lie flat; the larvae have a prominent siphon usually with a well-developed pecten (Figs. 11-1, 11-4), and one to several hair tufts on the siphon. The eggs are deposited in tight raftlike masses on the surface of the water, singly on the surface of the water, on ground, or just above the waterline in containers; they lack the floats characteristic of anopheline eggs.

The subfamily Culicinae includes about 1,500 species distributed among more than twenty genera; roughly two-thirds of the described species belong to the genera *Culex* and *Aedes*.

The Genus Culex. The genus *Culex* includes a number of species known as vectors of arboviruses and of avian malaria. In general they are typically bird feeders, though narrow host specificity is uncommon. Adults lack both postspiracular and spiracular bristles, abdomens of females blunt, pulvilli present, and the first flagellar segment of the antenna no longer than each succeeding segment. Larvae typically possess a long and slender air tube bearing numerous hair tufts.

The Culex pipiens Complex. The northern house mosquito, or rainbarrel mosquito *Culex pipiens* Linnaeus, and the southern house mosquito, *Culex pipiens quinquefasciatus* Say (=*C. p. fatigans* Wiedemann of European authors) are best considered subspecies of the same polytypic species (Mattingly, *et al.*, 1951). Barr (1957) has shown that, in North America, *C. pipiens* occurs only north of the thirty-sixth parallel and *C. p. quinquefasciatus* (except in coastal California) only south of the thirty-ninth; in the area of overlap, identification is difficult because of the frequent occurrence of intergrades and hybrids. The two subspecies can be best distinguished anatomically on the basis of male genitalia. Both these mosquitoes occur widely in the Old World. Autogeny, deposition of the first batch of eggs without a prior blood meal, is of widespread occurrence in this species complex. Autogenous forms occurring throughout the range of *pipiens* have been designated as *C. p. molestus* Forskål, but appear to be biotypes of uncertain taxonomic status. Barr gives evidence to support his belief that *"Culex molestus"* represents merely local populations of *C. pipiens* that have developed autogeny. The thorax, abdomen, and proboscis of *Culex pipiens* are brown; the latter is darker toward the tip. The basal white bands on the abdomen join lateral basal triangular patches. This mosquito, a domestic species, lays its eggs in rafts on water, in rain barrels, tanks, cisterns, catch basins, and other small collections of water; favoring waters with high organic pollution. Where breeding places are favorable, it may occur in enormous numbers. It invades houses freely. Because of its persistence and high-pitched, tantalizing hum continued late into the night, it may be a considerable pest. Although greatly influenced by temperature, the life cycle requires but ten to fourteen days under warm summer conditions, egg stage twenty-four to thirty-six hours, larva seven to ten days, and the pupa about two days.

Although a number of vertebrates can be used as a blood source, with many *Culex* birds appear to be most suitable. Woke (1937) found that *Culex pipiens* that had fed on a canary yielded over twice as many eggs per volume of blood as compared with those fed on man.

There is growing evidence that *C. p. quinquefasciatus* is increasing in Africa and Asia in response to favorable habitats accompanying urbanization, and the disregard of sanitary measures as a consequence of increased use of persistent insecticides (Mattingly, 1962). In northern Nigeria this species replaced *C. nebulosus* Theobald in many locations because it is more tolerant to DDT than the latter (Service, 1966).

Culex pipiens and *C. p. quinquefasciatus* may serve as intermediate hosts of the human filarial worm, *Wuchereria bancrofti*. They are also involved in transmitting the pathogens of bird malaria, heartworm of dogs (*Dirofilaria immitis*), and avian pox virus. In the eastern United States, from Texas to New Jersey, members of the *C. pipiens* complex are considered important vectors of St. Louis encephalitis, and have repeatedly been found infected with this virus in nature. Western encephalitis virus is also frequently isolated from this mosquito complex.

Culex tarsalis Coquillett (Fig. 11-5) is an abundant and widespread species of the semiarid regions of North America; however, it occurs throughout the southern United States and as far northeast as Indiana. Its latitudinal range includes southwestern Canada and Mexico. It has been taken at elevations of 9,000 feet. It is an important vector of the viruses of western and St. Louis encephalitis. It is a fairly large and robust species for *Culex*, generally dark brown to black in color; the black abdomen has broad, segmental basal bands of yellowish-white scales; each segment of the venter with V-shaped markings of black scales, the apex of the V directed anteriorly; femora are black with a dotted white line along both sides, knees white; tibiae black, also with white line, bases and apices white; tarsi black; hind tarsi with apical and basal white bands on all segments, last tarsal

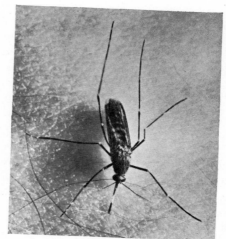

Fig. 11-5 *Culex tarsalis,* an important vector of the virus of western encephalitis. (Photograph by R. Craig.)

segment white; proboscis black, with a sharply outlined white ring just before the middle.

Culex tarsalis breeds in all sorts of waters, both clear and with high organic pollution, but especially in sunny ground pools, roadside ditches, in and around corrals, artificial containers, and so forth. It is generally considered a summer-active mosquito, but winter adult activity is known for part of its southern range, as reported for the Lower Rio Grande Valley of Texas (Eads, 1965). In cold regions inseminated females hibernate in natural sites, for example rock piles in the state of Washington (Rush, *et al.*, 1958). Preparation for hibernation, as evidenced by carbohydrate feeding and fat body development, is in response to short day length and is enhanced by low temperature (Harwood and Halfhill, 1964). Although in California it has been experimentally shown that blood feeding can precede successful overwintering, observations of field populations indicate this is not common (Bellamy and Reeves, 1963). Autogenous strains are known to occur in this species, as in *C. pipiens*. Domestic and wild birds are the preferred hosts, although this mosquito readily bites man, horses, and cattle, and will feed on reptiles. The mosquito bites chiefly at night.

Culex tritaeniorhynchus Giles is considered the most important vector of Japanese encephalitis in the Oriental region. Its distribution includes the Far East, Near East, and several locations in Africa. It is a small species, with brown scaling on the scutum and accessory pale scaling on the lower surface of the proboscis, resembling other species in the *vishnui* subgroup, but with distinctive long filamentous teeth of the buccopharyngeal armature (Bram, 1967). In Japan its biology includes overwintering as adult females, mainly in brush and wood piles, fat body development on short day length (Newson and Blakeslee, 1957); about fourteen days from adult to adult in summer, larvae in temporary and semipermanent ground water as hyacinth ponds, streams, swamps; females prefer to feed on cattle and pigs, but also bite birds and man.

The Genus Culiseta (= *Theobaldia*). *Culiseta* includes nine North American species. The postspiracular bristles (Fig. 11-4) are absent, and in the females of most species the anterior and posterior cross veins tend to lie in one line. In *Culiseta incidens* (Thomson), a species west of the Rocky Mountains, the wings are spotted. It breeds throughout the year, where temperature permits, in all sorts of permanent pools, and is a common domestic species. *Culiseta inornata* (Williston) is found throughout the United States and southern Canada. Its wings are broad and clear, the cross veins are scaled, and the very short black palpi have white scales at the tip. Precipitin tests indicate that it feeds chiefly on large mammals, such as horses and cattle. Both *C. incidens* and *C. inornata* may have some importance in relation to transmission of the encephalitides and other arboviruses. *Culiseta melanura* (Coquillett) of the eastern and central United States is predominantly a swamp-inhabiting bird feeder that rarely bites man, and is implicated in the maintenance of eastern equine encephalitis. In this species there is a winter larval diapause.

The Genus Aedes. Nearly half of all the species of mosquitoes in North America belong to the genus *Aedes*. In most of the species, the claws are toothed in the female, postspiracular bristles are present, the pulvilli are absent or hairlike, and the female abdomen tends to be more pointed and the cerci longer than in other groups. The larvae have siphons bearing one pair of posteroventral hair tufts, and nearly always a distinct pecten (Figs. 11-1, 11-3). The eggs are deposited singly on the surface of the water, on mud, just above water line in container-breeding species, or even in situations where there may be little moisture but where submergence is likely to follow. The females of all species bite, many of them viciously. Many species are diurnal in biting habits, most of them biting toward evening.

Salt-Marsh Mosquitoes. *Aedes dorsalis* (Meigen), a fierce day biter, has a holarctic distribution that includes Mexico, Formosa, and North Africa. In general the body is straw colored (tan), readily confused with *A. campestris* Dyar and Knab, varying from almost white to dark brown; the thorax has three longitudinal bright brown stripes; the hind tarsi have white bands at bases and apices of all segments, the last one wholly white. Although the species breeds freely and abundantly in fresh water, such as flood water, rice fields, and drainage from irrigation, it is nevertheless the commonest salt-marsh mosquito of the Pacific coast north of Monterey, California. It is here a distinctly brackish-water breeder, generally breeding in pools reached only by the monthly "rip" tides. There are thus several monthly broods, the first appearing as early as March. The eggs are deposited singly, most of them in mud along the edge of receding pools; they may remain unhatched for many months in situations from which water is excluded. Development after hatching is rapid, and emergence of the adult mosquitoes may be within eight days.

Aedes taeniorhynchus (Wiedemann) is a typical species of the American coasts and inland saline areas from Massachusetts to Brazil and California to Peru, the Antilles, and Galapagos Islands. It is the black salt-marsh mosquito; its proboscis is distinctly white-banded. It is a fierce day biter, and large migratory flights are well documented (see Chapter 4). There are monthly broods throughout the summer. Development is exceedingly rapid; the larval stage may require but four days, the adults emerge in eight to ten days.

Aedes sollicitans (Walker), of the Nearctic region and Greater Antilles, is a pestiferous salt-marsh mosquito of the Atlantic coast from Maine to Florida and thence west along the Gulf of Mexico to Texas. There are many broods, and in its southern range breeding may be continuous. As with *A. taeniorhynchus*, there may be nearly unbelievably large numbers of larvae developing in pools.

Flood-Water Aedes. *Aedes vexans* (Meigen) is a typical flood-water mosquito of Holarctic and Oriental regions, Pacific Islands, and South Africa. It is one of the fiercest day biters and exceedingly abundant; it is truly a vexatious mosquito. It breeds in greatest numbers along the flood plains of rivers and like other *Aedes* species lays its eggs along the muddy edges of receding pools, where they may hatch the same season when water due to intermittent flooding or freshets reaches them, or they may carry over (Fig. 11-6). There may thus be several broods where flooding occurs as a result of melting mountain snows or thunderstorms, or there may be only one brood where there is a single spring flood. The species is a rapid breeder and migrates many miles, though generally along wooded river valleys. It varies in color from brown to gray; tarsi are basally narrowly banded; the wings uniformly brown. *Aedes dorsalis* (Meigen), already referred to as a salt-marsh breeder, is frequently in association with this species in the western United States.

Aedes nigromaculis (Ludlow), of the western and central plains of the United States, is an important irrigated pasture mosquito in the western United States, especially in California. Development is extremely rapid; adults may appear as early as four days after the eggs have been flooded by irrigation. Swarms of these fierce daytime biters may bring normal activities of livestock to a virtual standstill.

Tree-Hole Mosquitoes. Although the habit of breeding in water-holding tree holes (Fig. 11-7) occurs in various species belonging to other genera, e.g., *Anopheles barberi* Coquillett, there are a number of typical tree-hole breeders in *Aedes*, notably *A. sierrensis* Ludlow, a Pacific Coast species; *A. triseriatus* (Say) of the eastern United States; *A. luteocephalus* Newstead, Ethiopian; *A. simpsoni* Theobald, Ethiopian; *A. seoulensis* Yamada, Chinese; and others.

Aedes sierrensis (Ludlow) has bright white markings on the legs at bases and apices of the tarsal segments, and many white or silvery scales distributed over the body so as to give the vestiture a silver-mottled appearance. It is a small mosquito but a fierce biter. This Pacific Coast species deposits its eggs on the sides of tree holes, notably various species of

A

B

Fig. 11-6 *A.* Willow flat along the lower Columbia River offers shelter and breeding places for floodwater mosquitoes. *B.* Same willow flat cleared of shade and other protection and thus freed of mosquitoes. Regular maintenance is necessary to prevent their return. (After Stage, Gjullin, and Yates; U.S.D.A. photographs.)

oaks. Freeborn (1926) noted that there is an extremely long larval period of one to seven months, with intermingled broods having a pronounced early summer and fall peak; it overwinters as larvae.

Aedes triseriatus (Say) lacks the white rings on the tarsal segments. It is a widespread tree-hole breeder east of the Rocky Mountains. Overwintering may occur in the egg or larval stage, due to a diapause caused by short day length (Love and Whelchel, 1955; Kappus and Venard, 1967). Both *A. triseriatus* and *A.*

sierrensis may be very annoying pests, and their special larval habitat may be overlooked unless one realizes that they are tree-hole breeders.

Aedes hendersoni Cockerell, first thought to be a subspecies of *A. triseriatus*, occurs in western Kansas, Nebraska, and South Dakota; Texas, Wyoming, and Colorado. Hibernation occurs in the egg stage.

Boreal Aedes or Snow Pool Mosquitoes. An interesting group of *Aedes* consists of the so-called snow pool mosquitoes that appear in

Fig. 11-7 Tree hole where *Aedes* larvae are found. (After Stage, Gjullin and Yates; U.S.D.A. photograph.)

early spring in the high mountains and northern ranges of distribution, breeding in the pools left by melting snow (Fig. 11-8). A low temperature adaptation is evident; the northern species *Aedes nigripes* (Zetterstedt) and *Aedes impiger* (Walker) at Fort Churchill, Manitoba

having a very low developmental threshold of 34° F (Haufe and Burgess, 1956). Furthermore, warming by the sun is utilized by larvae in muskeg pools aggregating in the warmest sector and changing daily in response to sun movement (Haufe, 1957); or in the case of *Aedes nigripes* (Zetterstedt) by oviposition at sites facing the sun (Corbet, 1964a) (Fig. 11-9). These snow pool *Aedes* have but one generation yearly and appear in enormous swarms in the higher elevations and northern ranges much to the dismay of the alpine traveler. Dyar (1916), speaking of the occurrence of alpine mosquitoes in the Sierra Nevada, says:

At an altitude of 6,000 feet, pupae were abundant May 25 and by the first week in June the breeding was complete; even the pools that still contained water or had only just thawed out were empty. Adults appeared by the first of June, and by the 15th the woods were filled with them in all directions....

The seasonal appearance of these mosquitoes varies with the altitude in the ratio of about a month in time to 1,000 feet of elevation. At Yosemite, at about 5,000 feet, all the species were about a month earlier than at Lake Tahoe, at 6,000 feet, while at Summit, at 7,000 feet, they were still another month later, larvae and pupae of *tahoensis* and *hexodontus* being taken there on July 2, 1916,

Fig. 11-8 Typical breeding place for snow pool mosquitoes on floor of Yosemite Valley, California. (Photograph by H. F. Gray.)

Fig. 11-9 Eggs of *Aedes nigripes* massed as a dark line, indicated by arrow, in muskeg. (Photograph by P. S. Corbet.)

about the same stage that they were taken at Fallen Leaf [vicinity of Lake Tahoe] on June 1, 1916.

Hocking, in his review on northern biting flies (1960), has pointed out that Arctic populations of snow pool mosquitoes are a direct hazard to life for man and animals. Fortunately in these areas the risk of disease transmission is small.

In northern Alaska the spring thaw is followed by a sudden emergence of swarms of mosquitoes. Like other boreal mosquitoes, they overwinter in the egg stage and hatch as soon as the ice thaws from around the eggs in the spring. Jachowski and Schultz (1948), who studied *Aedes punctor* (Kirby), *A. communis* (De Geer), and *A. impiger* (Walker) (=*nearcticus* Dyar), classify the sites from which they collected larvae as grassy sloughs, mossy pools ("tundra pools"), frost ditches, and willow-alder pools. The eggs hatch al-

most immediately after the spring thaw, and if a freeze occurs after this, the larvae will freeze into the ice and thaw out again when the ice melts. The larval period was observed to be about twenty-eight days and the pupal period three to five days. During chilly night hours mosquitoes were observed to gather in large numbers about the open doors of heated quarters or hover in the warm draft from chimneys. Blood meals, if necessary, are readily available from herds of caribou, large populations of rodents, and nesting ducks, geese, and other birds. Facultative autogeny is characteristic of several arctic *Aedes* (Corbet, 1964b).

Mosquitoes of the tundra may occur in almost unbelievably large swarms. In a transition area between tundra and forest in Quebec, Jenkins and Knight (1950) sampled, with a few sweeps of the net, a swarm that surrounded them; the sample contained 194 *Aedes*, and the swarm was estimated at 1,500 individuals. Grazing animals may be driven into restless running by these annoyers. *Aedes nigripes* (Zetterstedt), strictly a species of the tundra, together with *A. impiger* (Walker) (=*nearcticus* Dyar) are the most abundant species of the far north; both are circumpolar in distribution (Vockeroth, 1954).

Aedes aegypti (Linnaeus), the yellow fever mosquito, is the most important vector of the viruses of yellow fever, dengue, and chikungunya. This mosquito is widely distributed within the limits of forty degrees north and forty degrees south latitude, but it is highly susceptible to temperature variations. According to Hindle (1914), it soon dies in the open air at a temperature of 7 to 8° C, succumbing in a few seconds to an exposure of 0° C, and 37° C is rapidly fatal. Furthermore, it does not thrive in dry hot climates. The adult insect (Fig. 11-10) is beautifully marked with silvery-white or yellowish-white bands and stripes on a nearly black background, whence the name "tiger mosquito." It has a "lyrelike"

pattern dorsally on its thorax, i.e., two outer-curved yellowish-white lines and two median parallel lines. The legs are conspicuously banded, and the last segment of the hind leg is entirely white. The head is covered with broad flat scales with only a single row of upright forked scales.

A very comprehensive account of the yellow fever mosquito has been provided by Christophers (1960). There are three forms or varieties recognized (Mattingly, 1957, 1958). The type form *aegypti* is brownish or blackish, widely distributed, but absent from inland Africa south of the Sahara. Form *queenslandensis* (Theobald) is a pale variety from northern Australia with distribution similar to the type form. Form *formosus* (Walker) is a black variety from Sierra Leone and confined to Africa south of the Sahara where it is the only form except in coastal areas. Outside of Africa the distribution of *Aedes aegypti* is often mainly coastal. The form *queenslandensis* is entirely domestic; the type form is mainly domestic in Africa but may be semi-wild in places; and the form *formosus* can exist as a fully wild mosquito.

Differences in the various forms of *Aedes aegypti*, and differences in the areas in which they exist, promise to create special problems in the worldwide effort to eradicate this species. Success in eradicating this mosquito from various South American countries where it had been relatively recently established, and where it was still dependent on artificial breeding sites of man, may not be duplicated in Africa where the form *formosus* is able to breed far from man. LeBrun (1964) discusses these difficulties in analyzing an eradication failure at Leopoldville in the Congo.

The eggs of the yellow fever mosquito are deposited singly in containers at or near the waterline; they are near black in color. Comparatively few eggs are deposited at one laying, and although there may be two layings, possibly more, the total number of eggs produced averages about 140 (144 according to Woke) when *A. aegypti* has fed on man.

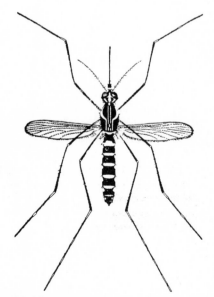

Fig. 11-10 *Aedes aegypti*, an important vector of the viruses of yellow fever and dengue. (After Soper, Wilson, *et al.*)

The eggs can withstand desiccation to a very marked degree, even up to a year's time. Ordinarily the eggs have completed embryonic development and can hatch when flooded after four days. The larvae are quite robust, the breathing siphon is comparatively short and heavy and black (Fig. 11-3), and the position of the larva in the water is almost vertical, considerably more so than that of other culicine species. The larval stage is ordinarily passed in about nine days under average conditions and in four to seven days under warmer conditions. The pupae have broadly triangular breathing trumpets. Normally one to five days are spent in the pupal stage.

The yellow fever mosquito breeds by preference in artificial containers of rain water. It is known, however, to occasionally breed in brackish water. Rainwater barrels, tanks, cisterns, tin cans, urns, and so forth provide suitable breeding places, with wooden containers preferred; water collected among the leaves of certain members of the agave family, and in banana palms, may contain many *aegypti* larvae.

Other Genera of Culicinae. The genus *Psorophora* is a totally American genus that includes only twelve Nearctic species. It is distinguished by the presence of both prespiracular and postspiracular bristles and by the second marginal cell of the wing, which is more than half as long as its petiole. The larvae of very large species are predaceous, feeding on other mosquito larvae and small aquatic animals in temporary ground pools.

Psorophora confinnis (Lynch-Arribálzaga) is widely distributed in the eastern United States, but ranges from parts of South America through Cuba and Mexico to Canada. It is strikingly speckled in appearance and is a fierce biter. It commonly breeds in rice fields. In 1932 this species is reported to have caused a great loss of livestock in the Everglades section of Florida. The *United States Insect Pest Survey Bulletin* (vol. 12, no. 10, p. 428) describes the plague:

... by evening of that day the buzzing was as loud as that of a swarm of bees. During the night livestock could be heard running and thrashing in the underbrush, and on the morning of September 6, dead animals were found throughout the section. The recorded mortality was 80 head of cattle, 3 horses, 1 mule, 67 hogs, 20 chickens, and 2 dogs. Postmortem examinations showed no mosquitoes in the respiratory apparatus, indicating that the animals died either from loss of blood, nervous exhaustion, or the effects of some toxin.

The milk supply was also greatly reduced during the four days of the infestation.

The genus *Mansonia* is characterized in large measure by the scales of the wings, which are very broad by comparison with those of other species of mosquitoes. The larvae have the air tube pointed, enabling them to pierce the stem or roots of aquatic plants from which they obtain air and to which they remain attached (submerged) throughout larval development. Several Asiatic species are vectors of brugian filariasis.

Mansonia perturbans (Walker) is widely distributed throughout North America from southern Canada to the Gulf of Mexico; Europe from Sweden and Britain to Palestine. It has severe biting habits and evidently travels some distance from its breeding place. The larvae hibernate in the mud.

The genus *Orthopodomyia* includes four species from North America. The adults are described by Matheson as "rather gaily ornamented and easily recognized by their coloring." The larvae are found in tree holes, also in broken bamboo and leaf axils of certain plants. *Orthopodomyia signifera* (Coquillett) extends along the eastern seaboard of the United States and westerly from Florida into southern California, thence northerly to near Sacramento.

SUBFAMILY ANOPHELINAE

Characteristics. The following features are generally employed to characterize the subfamily Anophelinae: palpi of both sexes are usually about as long as the proboscis (except in *Bironella*), male palpi club-shaped at tip; the scutellum (Figs. 11-3, 11-11) is evenly rounded or straplike (except in *Chagasia* where a slightly trilobed condition occurs); legs are very long and slender (Fig. 11-12) with no distinct tibial bristles and no pulvilli; the abdomen is without scales, or at least with sternites largely bare; the wings usually have distinct markings.

The subfamily Anophelinae has been

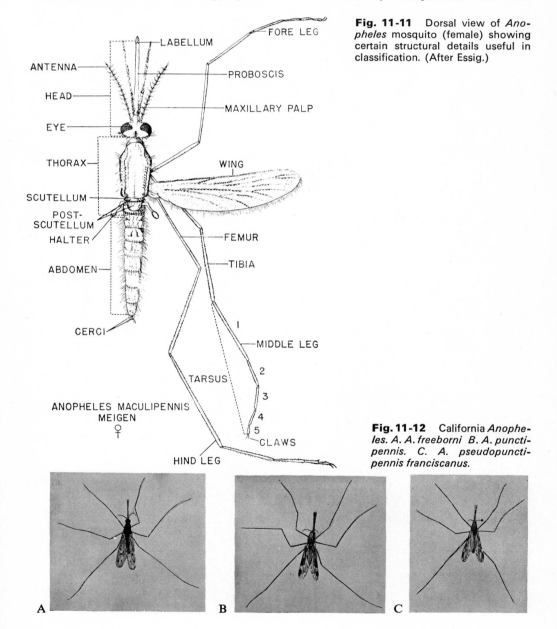

LABELLUM
FORE LEG
ANTENNA
PROBOSCIS
HEAD
MAXILLARY PALP
EYE
THORAX
WING
SCUTELLUM
POST-SCUTELLUM
HALTER
FEMUR
ABDOMEN
TIBIA
CERCI
MIDDLE LEG
1
2
TARSUS
3
ANOPHELES MACULIPENNIS
MEIGEN
♀
4
5
CLAWS
HIND LEG

Fig. 11-11 Dorsal view of *Anopheles* mosquito (female) showing certain structural details useful in classification. (After Essig.)

Fig. 11-12 California *Anopheles. A. A. freeborni B. A. punctipennis. C. A. pseudopunctipennis franciscanus.*

A   B   C

divided into numerous genera such as *Myzor-hynchus, Arribalzagia, Neomyzomyia, Cellia*, and more than thirty others. Edwards, as well as other culicidologists, reduced the number of genera to three: *Chagasia*, with the scutellum slightly trilobed; *Bironella*, with scutellum evenly rounded, wing with stem of median (M) fork wavy; and *Anopheles*, with scutellum evenly rounded, wing with stem of median (M) fork straight. There are four species of *Chagasia*, all of tropical America. The genus *Bironella* includes five species, all of New Guinea and Melanesia. The genus *Anopheles* includes over 300 species and subspecies, of which about ninety occur in the Americas, fifteen in North America.

The common species rest with the proboscis, head, and abdomen nearly in a straight line and when feeding hold the body at an angle from a given surface (Fig. 11-13). In exceptional cases, as in *Anopheles culicifacies* Giles of India, the resting position is *Culex*-like. Hoffman (1926) states that *A. grabhamii* Theobald rests with its body almost at a right angle to the vertical surface. *Anopheles hyrcanus sinensis* Wiedemann takes a similar position. The hum of anophelines is distinctly low pitched and almost inaudible unless they are close to the ear or in a bottle. Most of the common anophelines are not strong fliers and usually take to cover even in a moderate breeze. Dispersal is usually the result of creeping low movements in the vegetation, though high altitude flights may take place. In California, *Anopheles freeborni* engages in an annual dispersal flight of overwintering females about mid-February, during which time the mosquitoes may invade much territory, traveling more than twenty-five miles. During this flight the first eggs are deposited. In the main this flight favors the spread of the species. Bailey and Baerg (1967) have provided a very detailed account of the flight habits of this mosquito.

The usual method of overwintering is as the adult female. The eggs of tropical species may survive as long as two weeks on moist surfaces, and tree hole infesting species may overwinter as larvae.

Mating and Oviposition. Fertilization of the females takes place soon after emergence. The males emerge first and may be seen dancing over or near the breeding places in small swarms apparently awaiting the appearance of the females; when these dart into the dancing swarm, mating occurs. Species requiring wide spaces for mating are known as *eurygamous*, whereas those forms such as *Anopheles sacharovi* Favre that mate in confinement in a small space are known as *stenogamous*. At

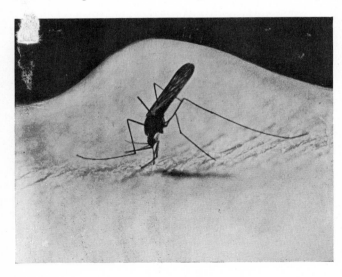

Fig. 11-13 *Anopheles freeborni* in the act of sucking blood. Note characteristic position assumed by *Anopheles* mosquitoes.

northern latitudes overwintering females are fertilized by the last brood of males during autumn, and the eggs are deposited soon after the spring dispersal flight. In certain localities at least, there is a period in spring when the species exists only in the larval stage, all the adults having died after egg deposition. There is probably only a single laying at this time.

Oviposition takes place on the surface of water that is free from wave action (Figs. 11-14, 11-15), the female either resting on the water or dropping the eggs while hovering a short distance above it. Eggs are laid singly. Herms and Freeborn, 1920, and Herms and Frost, 1932, found the average number of eggs deposited per batch for *A. freeborni* Aitken, *A. punctipennis* (Say), and *A. pseudopunctipennis franciscanus* McCracken to be respectively 200, 203, and 151. At least three batches of eggs may be laid during the lifetime of a female, with a total deposition of more than a thousand eggs recorded. Herms reports a

Fig. 11-15 Breeding place for *Anopheles freeborni* in overflow from river. Larvae particularly along margins and in hoofprints at edge. (Photograph by L. L. Williams, Jr.)

Fig. 11-14 Typical breeding place of *Anopheles freeborni* in sunlit weed-grown ditch with slowly moving water.

female of *A. freeborni* as depositing 174 eggs in nineteen minutes, an egg every six to seven seconds with intervening periods of rest. During the entire operation the female rested on the surface of the water and remained motionless except for the monotonous jerking of the abdomen when the egg was released. The eggs were pearly white in color, becoming deep brownish black in about forty-five minutes.

Egg Characteristics. The characteristics of anopheline eggs used in classification are presence or absence of floats, position and length of the float, presence or absence of frill, and pattern (Fig. 11-16). Christophers and Barraud (1931) classify anopheline eggs as of four types:

1. Eggs probably of primitive type, with full-float surrounding egg.

2. Eggs with terminal frill (*pseudopunctipennis franciscanus* of Herms and Freeborn).

3. Whale-back eggs with floats separated from dorsal surface.

4. Various types of boatlike eggs with floats touching margin of dorsal surface.

The egg of the Californian *A. freeborni* Aitken (Fig. 11-16) is fusiform, slightly rounded at each end and tapering to the extent that one is slightly broader than the other (Herms and Frost, 1932). The upper surface is flattened with a slightly longitudinal concavity, while the lower surface is broadly convex, the convexity becoming more pronounced at the broad end of the egg.

Species Complexes. Many *Anopheles* occur in closely related groups with rather obvious morphological relationships. In other cases separation of species may be extremely difficult, and only dependably so by characters of the immature forms, even of eggs. In such cases close analysis generally shows there are also distinct behavioral differences. More recently certain complexes have come to light during intensive control programs, being noted as greater resistance to insecticides or apparently changed habitat. Three of the better known complexes are discussed herewith.

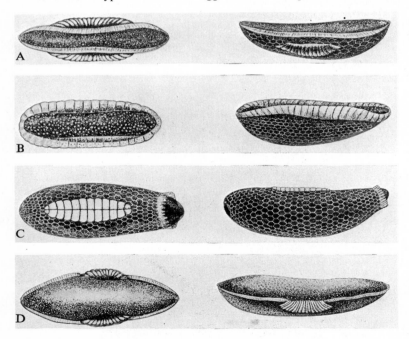

Fig. 11-16 Eggs of certain *Anopheles* mosquitoes. *A. A. punctipennis. B. A. pseudopunctipennis franciscanus,* usual form. *C.* Same, rare form. *D. A. freeborni.*

The *Anopheles maculipennis* complex was one of early interest. Hackett and Missiroli (1935) have discussed the relationship of different habits to the occurrence of malaria in Europe, and Horsfall (1955) gives a comprehensive account of the problem. The complex in Europe was initially divided into seven subspecies, most reliably separable by egg characters, and by the fact that some strains were zoophilous and exophilous in contrast to others that preferred to feed on man and readily entered houses. Presently *Anopheles maculipennis* Meigen is recognized as occurring in continental Europe and southwest Asia to the Persian Gulf. The subspecies *messeae* Falleroni is from the northern Palaearctic region, and the subspecies *melanoon* Hackett and its variant *subalpinus* Hackett and Lewis are from southern Europe, the Caucasian region of the U.S.S.R., and Iran. *Anopheles labranchiae* Falleroni of Italy, Spain, and North Africa, and its variant *atroparvus* Van Thiel occurring somewhat more north in Europe, were both formerly considered subspecies of *A. maculipennis*. *Anopheles sacharovi* Favre is found in the U.S.S.R., Italy, Austria, Greece, Syria, Israel, and Jordan. American representatives of the *maculipennis* complex are *Anopheles quadrimaculatus* Say, *A. earlei* Vargas, *A. freeborni* Aitken, *A. occidentalis* Dyar and Knab, and *A. aztecus* Hoffmann.

The intensive control programs against *Anopheles gambiae* Giles in Africa have revealed a species complex. Crosses of dieldrin-resistant and -susceptible strains yielded sterile male progeny with atrophied testes (Davidson and Jackson, 1962). Differences were also noted in house resting or outdoor forms, as well as fresh water and brackish water forms (Iyengar, 1962). By combining behavioral differences with crossing experiments, as reviewed by Mattingly (1964) and others, it has been possible to distinguish five members of the complex. A west African salt-water form is designated as *Anopheles melas* Theobald and an East African salt-water form as *Anopheles merus* Dönitz. Three fresh-water forms are as yet designated only as A, B, and C. Forms A and B are the most effective vectors of malaria, the salt-water forms somewhat less effective, and form C primarily zoophilous and exophilous and of little importance as a vector. Form C seems confined to southeast Africa, A and B are widespread with B possibly more confined to savannah type environment.

Anopheles hyrcanus (Pallas) apparently forms a complex across central and southern Asia, the northern Mediterranean and Libya. The taxonomy of this complex, with many of the forms found in mainland China, is by no means clear. Published information suggests varieties with widely divergent habits, and therefore probably very different in their capacity to serve as vectors of malaria.

Breeding Habits. The breeding habits of anophelines differ considerably for even very closely related species. The American *Anopheles freeborni* Aitken and *A. quadrimaculatus* Say, both four-spotted anophelines separable with accuracy as adults only on differences in male terminalia, have widely different breeding requirements, the former, breeding largely in open sunlit shallow seepage water (Figs. 11-14, 11-15) and the latter in impounded water with floating debris and aquatic vegetation. The European races of *A. maculipennis* Meigen have characteristic larval sites that, within certain limits, differ from one race to another.

The following example illustrates the very great importance of knowing the breeding habits in the conduct of malaria control operations. Williams, 1937, points out that in Malaya *Anopheles umbrosus* (Theobald) is the vector of malaria in the coastal plain, breeding in practically stagnant water densely shaded by mangrove. Its production is controlled, as Williams points out, by clearing the swamps and letting in the brilliant sunshine, or by cutting ditches and confining the water to definite channels. The same type of work when practiced on high inland plateaus increases the malaria rate, because here the vector is *Anopheles maculatus* Theobald, which prefers the quiet edges of trickling streams in the open sunshine. *Anopheles minimus* Theobald, the principal vector of malaria in the Philippines, breeds in small flowing streams in the foothills (Russel, 1932). Several species of *Anopheles* (though unimportant as vectors) are tree-hole breeders, viz.: *A. plumbeus* Stephens (European) and *A. barberi* Coquillett (American). *Anopheles bellator* Dyar and Knab, an important Caribbean vector, breeds in collections of water among bromeliad epiphytes.

An unusual situation is reported for *Anopheles sergentii* (Theobald), a North African and Palestinian species, the larvae of which inhabit small pools and springs among stones at the edge of the lake (Tiberias). The larvae are often under the stones and not easily found (Buxton, 1924).

Life History of Anophelines. Although there is much variation in the life histories of the species of *Anopheles* mosquitoes as well as considerable variation within the species due to temperature and other factors, the length of time required for development from egg to adult is generally longer than in other genera, except in genera where the egg stage may be greatly prolonged, as in *Aedes*.

The usual incubation period for *Anopheles* is about two days. Apparently, the only stimulus needed for the hatching of the embryo is that the egg be floating in water suitable for the development of the larva. The egg shows very little resistance to desiccation. Some tropical species may survive two weeks or even more on a moist surface, but severe drying always kills or injures the embryo or retards its development (Horsfall, 1955).

Herms (1929), testing 20,000 eggs of *Anopheles freeborni* Aitken, determined the duration of the egg stage at room temperature as seventy-two hours. Under field conditions, the egg stage lasted two to four (average, 2.5) days for *A. freeborni* and two to six (average, 3.2) days for *A. punctipennis* (Say).

The eggs of *A. freeborni* removed from the water and dried at temperatures of 74° F and 65° F remained viable after a period of desiccation not over seventy-two hours. No hatching was obtained from eggs of *A. punctipennis* after twenty-four hours' desiccation. Hatching generally took place during the evening and night in the experiments cited.

With yeast as food, the larvae of *A. freeborni* reached the pupal stage in fifteen to sixteen days. The pupal stage requires about three days. Thus the entire life history from egg to adult in *A. freeborni* under experimental conditions requires about twenty-one to twenty-two days; the same is true for *A. punctipennis* and *A. pseudopunctipennis franciscanus* McCracken. Under field conditions this period may be considerably prolonged. Adult mosquitoes reared in the laboratory did not begin oviposition until thirteen to fifteen days after a blood meal.

The life cycle of *Anopheles albimanus* Wiedemann, the important vector of malaria of the Panama Canal Zone, has been carefully studied by Rozeboom (1936). With room temperature between 27° and 32° C and water temperature for larvae 21–27° C, and eggs and pupae at 27–30° C, the entire cycle (egg to adult) required from eighteen to twenty-four days, an average of three weeks. A period of seven days, or a little over, was necessary for the development of the ovaries, an average of 435 eggs being deposited; the incubation period was forty to forty-eight hours; the larval stage required six to twenty-two days, usually eight to thirteen days in hay infusion water; the pupal stage took thirty to thirty-three hours; the longest observed adult life of a female was thirty-one days and of a male twenty-seven days.

Anopheles quadrimaculatus Say is the chief vector of malaria in the eastern, central, and southern United States. According to Williams (1937):

It breeds almost wholly in still water that is relatively clean. It requires some sunshine, never being found in dense shade. However, it requires some darkness, never being found in waters which are wholly unshaded, unless they have a type of flotage which casts narrow strips of shade where the mosquito larvae may lie during a portion of the daylight hours....

An ideal breeding place for *quadrimaculatus*

is in freshly impounded water which floods a basin containing some underbrush and which is sparsely covered with trees. Such a body of water quickly gathers flotage of dead and dying land vegetation, twigs and leaves, among which algae soon appear. Such flotage not only offers the requisite amount of shade, but an abundant food supply. Such an impounding will not acquire a large quantity of natural enemies, such as top minnows and aquatic insects, for a number of years and seldom acquires enough to prevent production of the mosquito.

The normal detritus passing down a narrow stream will clog the interstices of a fallen tree or branch and create a dam. These natural impounded waters are excellent breeding places for *quadrimaculatus*. Swamps covered by a growth of virgin timber, on the other hand, are not good breeding places. Such swamps are almost invariably covered with such a dense timber growth that sunlight can reach the surface of the water only in those small areas where an opening has been made by the fall of a dead tree. Swamps of this description have a small seeding of *quadrimaculatus*, but not enough to propagate malaria. When the lumberman enters, cutting out large trees, leaving the small ones, the branches and tree tops, he changes a safe water surface into one almost ideal for *quadrimaculatus* production. He has let in the sunshine without removing all of the shade, and he has left behind waste which not only creates fine flotage, but large portions of which tend to clog the channel which traverses the average swamp, thus making a series of ponds.

The brood peaks of this species in southwestern Georgia, according to Boyd (1941), are twenty to thirty days apart, with eight to ten annual broods; the first appears twenty to thirty days after the last frost, and the last brood, the tenth, if there is favorable weather, in December. January and February, he states, are the only months when no broods emerge.

MOSQUITOES AS VECTORS OF PATHOGENS

From the standpoint of disease, mosquitoes are potent vectors of three types of organisms

pathogenic to man. These are: (1) the plasmodia, causal organisms of the human malarias, belonging to the phylum Protozoa; (2) arboviruses causing yellow fever, dengue, the encephalitides, and other diseases of man; (3) filarial worms of the genera *Wuchereria* and *Brugia*, the causal organisms of bancroftian and brugian filariasis. Transmission of the bacterium causing tularemia has also been reported. The publication *Mosquitoes of Medical Importance*, by Foote and Cook (1959) has worldwide coverage, presents pictorial keys that include only medically important species, and summarizes their bionomics and relation to disease. This treatise is inclusive through its date of publication, but much more has been learned, particularly in mosquito transmission of arboviruses.

THE MALARIAS

HUMAN MALARIA

Malaria is a widely distributed disease, at one time prevalent to a greater or lesser degree on every inhabited continent and on many islands. Though the general public associates malaria with tropical or subtropical climates, such is not the case; Sweden, Finland, and northern Russia have, in the past, been subject to serious epidemics. Whether or not malaria existed in North America prior to the discovery of the continent has not been definitely established; however, this disease was evidently recognized as a factor in colonization on the Massachusetts coast and the Georgia-Carolina coast as early as the middle of the seventeenth century (Boyd, 1941). As recently as the 1930's there were six to seven million cases annually in the continental United States (Russell, 1959). For the past seventy-five years, however, the disease has been declining in many parts of the world. Europe, once widely malarious, is now in large part free from the disease, and South America can entertain hopes of its eradication. In the United States each year there have been only two or three proven cases of natural malarial transmission by mosquitoes since 1953 (Pratt, *et al.*, 1967). In 1967 a trend in resurgence, primarily due to military personnel returning from Vietnam, was accentuated by the reporting of some 2,600 cases. A number of such cases were definitely attributed to autochthonous transmission. Malaria was considered at one time the most important disease of mankind, but in many previously malarious areas it is now a rarity. Malariologists talk in terms of area eradication, as well as overall control, but in many regions final eradication has not been achieved because of a number of complicating factors.

The presence of endemic malaria is dependent upon a complex of environmental factors favoring the development of large numbers of vector (anthropophilous) mosquitoes, as well as the plasmodia causing the disease. Temperature, particularly as it affects the development of the plasmodium in the mosquito, and temperature combined with humidity as it affects the life of the vector, are critical factors; a mean summer isotherm of 15–16° C in general limits the geographic distribution of malaria fairly well. The distribution of malaria is dependent upon the availability of water for mosquito breeding, not necessarily heavy rainfall; naturally arid regions may be seriously affected through imperfections in irrigation. Although lowlands are more likely to be affected, this does not hold as a general rule, because if one or more important factors are lacking in a lowland region the area is non-malarious. A high degree of endemicity, and great difficulties in control, are found in many foothill and low mountain areas of the Orient. The disease has occurred at high elevations (9,000 feet in Quito, Ecuador) under favorable circumstances. Herms found endemic malaria in California at an elevation of about 5,500 feet; it can occur in Mexico at an elevation of near 7,500 feet.

High levels of malaria transmission are usually associated with endophilic vectors that enter dwellings to effect transmission. As superior control is achieved, particularly when applied to endophilic vectors, more transmission by exophilic vectors is noted. This is particularly true among nomadic peoples, but can also be the case where a large number of humans remain outdoors as in military campaigns. In Vietnam, where the total number of cases in United States Forces exceeded 10,000 in less than two years, exophilic vectors have been thought responsible for very high attack rates in the foothills and highlands (Holway, *et al.*, 1967).

Few diseases have so large a list of synonyms; among these are ague, chills and fever, jungle fever, paludism, marsh fever, remittent fever, intermittent fever, *Wechselfieber, Kaltesfieber*, and so forth. The symptoms are commonly characterized by more or less regularly occurring febrile paroxysms. In most cases there are three fairly well-defined stages: the *cold stage* (the chill) in which the skin becomes pale and has the appearance of "gooseflesh," the patient's teeth may chatter, and he may shiver more or less violently; the next stage is the *hot stage*, or fever, the temperature rising during the chill, the skin hot and flushed; the third stage is marked by a general *perspiration*, the fever falls, and the temperature approaches normal. The entire paroxysm may last but a few hours. In many cases the stages are not well marked, neither do the paroxysms recur at the same intervals. The intervals depend largely on the type of infection. When the paroxysms recur at intervals of twenty-four hours, as is often true in the early stages of infection or in multiple infections, it is *quotidian*; when the interval is forty-eight hours or every third day it is *tertian*; and when the interval is seventy-two hours or every fourth day, it is *quartan*.

The disease in man is caused by an infection with one or more of four species of blood-inhabiting protozoa (Class Sporozoa) belonging to the genus *Plasmodium*. These closely related parasites have a common means of transmission, nevertheless they possess individual characteristics.

The plasmodial parasites attack the red

blood corpuscles, destroying them while undergoing asexual reproduction; this asexual reproduction or sporulation occurs at more or less regular intervals, i.e., forty-eight or seventy-two hours, depending upon the species of *Plasmodium*. The infection, according to Reed (1937) results in: (1) changes in organs, such as enlargement of the spleen and liver, and heart involvement; in fatal cases of sub-tertian malaria capillaries in the brain and pia are found congested or blocked by schizonts and sporulating forms of plasmodia, with punctiform hemorrhages in the white matter of the cerebral cortex; (2) leucopenia with in-crease of mononuclears and varying degrees of anemia as the result of direct destruction of red cells by plasmodia and indirect degen-eration of others; (3) the production of malarial pigment in macrophages in the splenic sinuses and liver. Two pigments are apparently in-volved, originally mistakenly termed *melanin*, both pigments are derived from hemoglobin and are properly called *hemozoin* and *hemo-siderin*. The same pigments are found in the red cells infected by the plasmodia and released with the rupture of infected red cells; (4) changes in physiology, such as periodic febrile paroxysms; these are quite regular in benign tertian malaria, but because of irregular maturing of plasmodia the periodicity is often concealed in subtertian (*Plasmodium falci-parum* [Welch]) malaria; focal symptomatology is due to localization arising from the "sticky tendency" of parasitized red cells that causes agglutination and blockage; (5) malaria cachexia, a chronic condition characterized briefly as inability to concentrate and tendency to depression following repeated malarial attacks.

Persons concerned technically with malaria should consult: *Practical Malariology*, 1963, by Russell, West, Manwell, and MacDonald; *Malariology*, 1950, by Boyd; and *The Epidemi-ology and Control of Malaria*, 1957, by Mac-Donald. A most comprehensive review of malaria parasites and other Haemosporidia

has been prepared by Garnham (1966), and this source should be consulted for further details of life history and characterization of various plasmodia.

Life Cycle of Plasmodia. For purposes of simplicity the cycle in man will serve to illus-trate the generalized condition found in all species of plasmodia and related blood para-sites. The principal point is that two quite different cycles are found, one in the vertebrate host and the other in the arthropod vector, both of which are necessary for completing the life cycle. The processes discussed here-with are illustrated in Figure 11-17.

Microgametocytes and *macrogametocytes* are ingested by an *Anopheles* mosquito in the act of biting. Asexual parasites ingested are destroyed by digestion but the gametocytes shed their erythrocyte covering and undergo maturation to form male and female gametes.

Formation of male gametes takes place in a matter of minutes, and is characterized by the formation of a number of nuclei accompanied by exflagellation, one flagellum being associ-ated with each nucleus. The product in human malaria is generally eight or fewer *micro-gametes* that break away and actively swim about like spermatozoa seeking a macro-gamete.

The macrogametocyte undergoes less ob-vious changes, principally an increase in size to form a *macrogamete*. The nucleus of the macrogamete moves toward the surface where it is entered by a microgamete to form a zygote.

The newly formed zygote is initially quies-cent but then forms a motile vermicule termed the ookinete. The ookinete grows in size, pro-gresses by means of a pseudopod, and intern-ally develops a crystalloid body thought to provide the material that ultimately forms a cyst wall. It was initially believed that the ookinete penetrated the gut between epithelial cells, but more recent studies have revealed its ability to penetrate the brush border to enter an epithelial cell by liquefying its cell membrane.

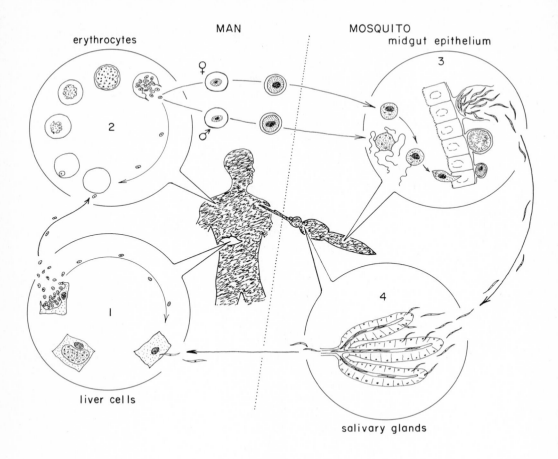

Fig. 11-17 Life cycle of human malaria.

Man Cycle

1. Sporozoites are introduced into man from salivary glands of mosquito in act of biting (arrow from *4* to *1*) and, *1*, sporozoites enter parenchyma cells of liver to establish primary exerythrocytic schizogony. In man there is only this single cycle in *falciparum* malaria; in malaria and various Haemosporidia of man and other animals secondary cycles are characteristic.

2. Merozoites are formed and invade (arrow from *1* to *2*) erythrocytes (red blood cells) where the developing stage is called a trophozoite. The trophozoite grows, destroys its erythrocyte to release merozoites which enter more erythrocytes to continue erythrocytic cycles. Micro (male) and macro (female) gametocytes are also periodically released from erythrocytes and, when ingested by an *Anopheles* mosquito (arrows from *2* to *3*), the microgametocyte divides to form motile microgametes.

Mosquito Cycle

3. A microgamete enters a macrogamete to form a zygote that becomes a motile ookinete. Ookinetes pass through the midgut epithelium to form oocysts that grow, burst, and release sporozoites into the hemocoel (arrow from *3* to *4*).

4. Sporozoites are active, pass freely throughout body cavity, and concentrate in salivary glands where they can be introduced into blood of vertebrate in act of feeding.

After traversing the epithelial layer the ookinete comes to rest between the outer region of the epithelium and a musculo-elastic layer. The ookinete now becomes spherical, secretes a cyst wall, and is then known as an oocyst (Fig. 11-18). It grows from about six microns in diameter to as much as eighty microns at maturity, projecting into the hemocoel. Meiotic and mitotic divisions follow to form a large number of haploid sporozoites, whereupon the oocyst bursts and the sporozoites are released into the hemocoel (Fig. 11-19). A

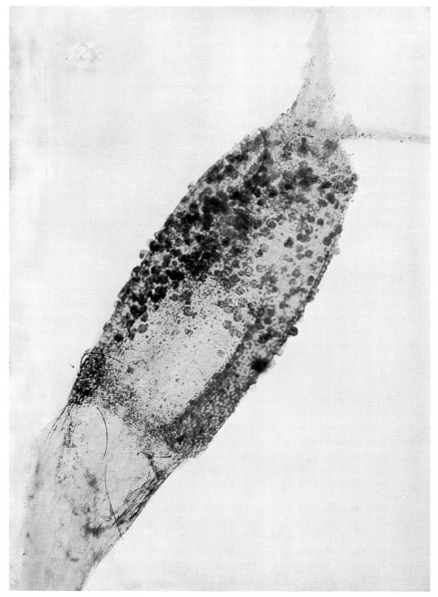

Fig. 11-18 Stomach (midgut) of female *Anopheles* mosquito with numerous oocysts. (Photograph by Mayne.)

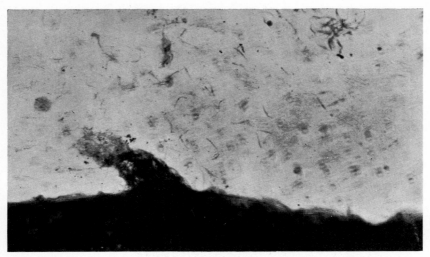

Fig. 11-19 A bursting oocyst on the stomach of a mosquito. Spindle-shaped sporozoites are being liberated. (Greatly magnified.) (Photograph by Mayne.)

probable *Plasmodium falciparum* mature oocyst from *Anopheles funestus* Giles was found to contain 9,555 sporozoites (Pringle, 1965). The number of oocysts on the midgut of a mosquito varies from a few to more than a hundred, and at optimum temperature maturation of the fastest developing species can be completed in four days.

Sporozoites invade all parts of the mosquito's body, but on reaching the salivary glands penetrate and accumulate in the acinal cells. When saliva flows during probing the sporozoites pass into the salivary ducts where they enter with saliva into the blood stream of the vertebrate host. Naturally infected *Anopheles funestus* Giles and *A. gambiae* Giles in Tanzania had an estimated few hundred to nearly 70,000 sporozoites in the salivary glands (Shute, *et al.*, 1965).

Primary *exerythrocytic schizogony* (spore formation) occurs in cells of the reticuloendothelial system of a vertebrate host. One or more cycles termed primary and secondary exerythrocytic schizogony, occur in such cells before the parasite enters the blood stream. A single generation of primary exerythrocytic schizogony suffices in *Plasmodium falciparum*, but in most malarias there is extensive secondary schizogony. The time elapsing from inoculation by the mosquito to appearance of infected erythrocytes varies with the species as well as the strain and other factors. In *falciparum* malaria the incubation period, presumably of primary exerythrocytic schizogony, ranged in the Coker strain from six to twenty-five days, in the Long strain from nine to ten days.

Exerythrocytic schizogony in macrophages and related cells was found in bird malaria parasites by Huff and associates (1948). Garnham (1947) demonstrated the development of *Hepatocystis kochi* Laveran (a near relative of *Plasmodium*) in the liver parenchyma cells of African monkeys, and Shortt and co-workers, in 1948 and 1949, demonstrated the presence of the exerythrocytic stage of *Plasmodium vivax* and *P. falciparum* in liver cells of man. This discovery explained (1) the nature of relapses after blood cell forms had disappeared, (2) the absence of malaria parasites in human blood for several days following the bite of an infective mosquito (the "incubation" period), and (3) the ineffectiveness of most antimalarial drugs during this period.

The sporozoites that enter reticuloendothelial cells develop into *cryptozoites*, assuming a spheroid shape and vastly increasing in numbers through repeated divisions. Finally the parasites, as *trophozoites*, enter the blood to parasitize erythrocytes and thus introduce erythrocytic development.

The blood phase is composed primarily of asexual *erythrocytic schizogony*. Fully developed erythrocytic schizonts cause rupturing of the red blood cells to release *merozoites* to continue the blood cell cycle, and *gametocytes* capable of initiating sexual development if ingested by a mosquito. It is the rupture and release of merozoites with accompanying toxins, occurring at periods typical for the species of *Plasmodium*, that is responsible for chills and fever cycles that typify various human malarias.

The Plasmodia. The causal organisms of malaria are in the genus *Plasmodium*. Garnham (1966) discusses the taxonomic relationships of the genus and its near relatives, placing them in the Phylum Protozoa, Class Telosporidea, Subclass Coccidiomorpha, Order Coccidiida, Suborder Haemosporidiidae, Family Plasmodiidae. They are characterized by the production of limited numbers of microgametes possessing a single flagellum, gametocytes of near equal size in both sexes, oocysts that expand to form numerous sporozoites, and the production of numerous merozoites that lack dimorphism. The presence of malarial pigments formed from breakdown products of hemoglobin is another characteristic.

If parasites are present in the blood, they should be visible, after proper staining, on careful thin-smear microscopic examination, as pigmented intracorpuscular bodies in the form of signet rings, ameboid forms, segmenting forms, or as crescents in aestivo-autumnal fever of ten or more days duration. An excellent manual by Wilcox (1942) is available for the microscopic diagnosis of malaria in man.

Ross (1910) states that the parasites:

... will not generally be numerous enough to cause illness unless there is at least one parasite to 100,000 haematids; that is, 50 parasites in 1 cmm of blood; or 150,000,000 in a man 64 kilograms (142 pounds) in weight.... Such calculations demonstrate the absurdity of supposing that there are no plasmodia present in a person because we fail in finding one after a few minutes' search. As a matter of fact, even if as many as 150,000,000 plasmodia are present in an average man, the chances are that ten to fifteen minutes' search will be required for each plasmodium found; while if we are careless or unfortunate, we may have to look much longer.

◁ *Plasmodium falciparum* (Welch 1897) is the causal organism of *aestivo-autumnal* fever (malignant tertian, subtertian) of the tropics and subtropics, the most severe form of malaria, often fatal. It still rates as the greatest cause of human death by any pathogen over most of Africa and elsewhere in the tropics, though as a result of malaria eradication programs *falciparum* malaria has disappeared from around the Mediterranean, the Balkans, Taiwan, Puerto Rico, and the United States.

Many instances of malignant malaria have been ascribed as being of prime historical importance. It has been related to the decline of Ancient Greek civilization, the termination of Alexander the Great's eastern expansion, and disruption of the Crusades, though likely other contributing factors were present. More recently, during World War II, Raffaele and Coluzzi (1949, as cited in Garnham, 1966) describe a decimating epidemic of malaria around the area of Cassino, Italy. The area had been shattered and deserted, with flooded bomb craters breeding vast populations of *Anopheles* that fed on humans in the absence of animals. In the summer of 1944 the entire human population of more than 43,000 people was infected with malaria, comprising 43 per cent *P. falciparum*, which caused 10 per cent mortality in many villages.

In *tertian fever* there is considerable irregularity in the occurrence and duration of the febrile stage, owing to a corresponding irregularity in the sporulation of the parasites, schizogony usually requiring about forty-eight hours, although often less. The infected red corpuscles are usually normal in size, although some may be slightly shrunken, often crenated, and rather dark green (brassy). The intra-corpuscular parasite in all its stages is small (not over two thirds the size of a corpuscle) and fairly ovoid in outline; the pigment is darker than in other forms; the infected cells agglutinate, and "Maurer's dots" appear in the corpuscles in the later stages. The *signet ring* is thin and small, and the chromatin dot is commonly double and out of line with the ring. There may be two or even four signet rings in one red corpuscle. The segmented state produces from eight to twenty-five merozoites. Characteristic crescent-shaped or kidney-shaped bodies appear in the peripheral blood cells about ten days after infection; these are the sexual forms (*gametocytes*) and occur as crescents in this species of *Plasmodium* only. The *macrogametocyte* or female form, measuring from ten to fifteen microns shows the chromatin granules well concentrated in the mid-region; the *microgametocyte* or male form, measuring from seven to ten microns, has a more hyaline appearance. A remnant of the red blood corpuscle often remains slung from the opposite ends of the crescent and forms the so-called "bib."

There is a decided tendency for schizogony of *falciparum* malaria to occur in deeper tissues of the body, mainly among the endo-thelial cells lining capillaries and sinuses. The assumption is that at a certain stage of growth infected corpuscles become sticky and clump together and to the lining of internal vessels where blood circulation is slow as a result of toxic vasoconstriction.

Man is apparently the only host of *P. falciparum* and, if in an area not previously exposed, the parasites rapidly develop and destroy him. Exposure for generations results in the selection of a human population that survives childhood infection with a consider-able degree of natural immunity that is often restricted to a particular strain. In naturally resistant children spleen enlargement is less evident than with other species of malaria.

The genetic sickle cell trait makes man a poor host for the parasites; the distribution of sickle cell gene in India, Africa, and southern Europe coinciding with areas of high endem-icity of *P. falciparum* (Allison, 1961).

Blackwater fever is a condition practically restricted to *falciparum* malaria inadequately treated with quinine. Administration of this drug to previously treated susceptibles may precipitate hemolysis that causes hemo-globinuria (hence the name blackwater) which is often fatal. This puzzling complication is virtually nonexistent now that quinine is seldom used.

Plasmodium falciparum has been repeatedly shown to be comprised of a number of strains that vary in virulence and in their adaptedness to various species of *Anopheles*. Thus Shute and Maryon (1951b) found the Asiatic *A. stephensi* to be an efficient vector of a Nigerian strain of *P. falciparum*, though the European *A. labranchiae*, which readily supported European strains of the parasite, was a very poor carrier of this African strain. There is much other evidence of strain differences in *P. falciparum*, including development of drug resistance. The appearance of chloroquine resistance has been a feature of the Vietnam conflict, in fact there have been instances of resistance to all the common presently used plasmodicides (Holway, *et al.*, 1967).

Plasmodium vivax (Grassi and Feletti, 1890) is the cause of tertian (benign tertian) fever of temperate climates, which also occurs abun-dantly in the tropics and subtropics. It is characterized by regularly recurrent paroxysms every forty-eight hours. Because malaria eradication has been most successfully applied to temperate regions, *vivax* malaria has prac-tically disappeared from them. The highest incidence of this species of malaria presently occurs in Asia. On the African continent its distribution remains a puzzle, being common in North Africa, but of low significance in much of tropical Africa. Although *P. vivax* is a characteristic temperate zone parasite, it is not normally the species causing epidemics in the cold equatorial highlands (Garnham, 1966). Apparently there is racial resistance to *vivax* malaria in the West African Negro, continuing even after prolonged residence in the United States (Young, *et al.*, 1955).

Generally *P. vivax* infections do not cause death, though fatal infections are found in young children when associated with severe anemia. Chronic bad health is more typical, with *splenomegaly* (enlarged spleen). Spontaneous immunity that is strain specific has been known to arise after infection, and to last at least three years. An experiment by Shortt, *et al.* (1948, cited by Garnham, 1966), showed immunity to be present against erythrocytic forms, but not against exerythrocytic stages.

Parasitized corpuscles are distinctly enlarged, quite pale, and usually contain fine pigment granules known as "Schüffner's dots." The signet ring is large and conspicuous, and the dot is in line with the ring and rarely double. Multiple infection of red blood cells is not as common as with *P. falciparum*. The fully grown *merocytes* or *schizonts* are very irregular and bizarre in form. The number of merozoites developing in the sporulating or segmented stage commonly seen in the peripheral blood is twelve to twenty-four (usually about sixteen), and their arrangement is irregular. Sporulation occurs regularly every forty-eight hours. There are no "crescents" in this species; the gametocytes are round or oval in form, and when fully grown fill virtually the entire red cell. The macrogametocyte has the chromatin arranged in a compact mass; the microgametocyte has the pigment well distributed and presents a more hyaline appearance.

Plasmodium malariae (Laveran, 1881) is the cause of quartan fever, with recurrent paroxysms because of sporulation every seventy-two hours. This form of malaria is much less common than, but coincides in distribution with, aestivo-autumnal fever. It is nearly as common as *P. falciparum* in parts of tropical Africa, particularly East Africa,

and the Congo, and in Burma and parts of India and Ceylon. Further eccentricities in its prevalence remain a mystery. It is long lived so that it tends to become a dominant species during eradication, going from 0.7 per cent of total infections in Rumania during 1953 to 95 per cent by 1962 (Lupascu, *et al.*, 1963).

The pigment in erythrocytic forms is coarse and generally occurs in marginal streaks. The parasitized corpuscles are usually normal in size, and the parasite is small and more or less oval in shape though, when partly grown, it frequently extends across the equator of the corpuscle in the form of a band. The ring-forms have one vacuole and usually one dot. The segmenting stage gives rise to the typical "daisy" form, each sporulated body radiating from the center. The number of bodies is six to twelve, usually eight. The gametocytes resemble those of *Plasmodium vivax*.

It has been difficult to distinguish the primary vectors of *P. malariae*, for in all species of *Anopheles* tested development has been poor. Only a couple of oocysts may be found on mosquito stomachs, in marked contrast to experimental infections with *P. vivax* where hundreds of oocysts may develop. However, though the level is always low, *P. malariae* has been found capable of developing in a wide range of *Anopheles* species, though only some six species have been found naturally infected (Garnham, 1966). One reason for low levels of mosquito infection appears to be the production of few gametocytes in vertebrate blood. Compared to other human malarias, development in the mosquito is slow, with sporozoites not reaching the salivary glands at 25° C until the sixteenth day (Shute and Maryon, 1951a).

Blood parasitemia builds up slowly, often not being detectable until well after quartan fever symptoms have been present for some time. There is also prolonged survival of exerythrocytic stages, and recurrence of natural infections after forty years without the possibility of new transmission suggests that a secondary exerythrocytic cycle has occurred in the liver.

P. malariae is the only human malaria parasite definitely shown to have a wild animal reservoir. Rodhain (1948) succeeded in demonstrating this parasite in chimpanzees, with immunity characteristics identical to the human strain. Thus the chimpanzee parasite formerly known as *P. rodhaini* is synonymous. The disease is present at low levels in chimpanzees along the West African coast and into the interior of the Congolese Republic. Transmission from chimpanzee to man should be possible whenever they are in close association in the forest; this sort of natural transmission has not been verified as the vector to chimpanzees is unknown and might not bite man readily.

The symptoms of *malariae* malaria are rather distinct in humans. Chronicity with low blood parasitemia may leave the disease undiagnosed, but gradual spleen involvement results in greater hypertrophy than is found with other malarias. Involvement of the kidneys, with observable edema is frequently characteristic. The highest incidence of *P. malariae* infection occurs in young children, steadily declines with age accompanied by a reduction in blood parasitemia, and strong immunity is prevalent in hyperendemic areas.

Plasmodium ovale Stephens, 1922 is the cause of a mild form of tertian fever. It is the rarest human malaria, though found throughout the tropics and subtropics and most prevalent on the west coast of Africa. A prolonged latency is common, with the first attack not occurring until several months after feeding of an infectious vector. It may be present in mixed infections, though not apparent until the more virulent species is cured. Immunity in adult humans is commonplace, with evidence of cross strain resistance but no resistance to the other human malaria species.

The name *ovale* indicates the oval shape generally assumed by the parasite as well as the parasitized erythrocyte. The infected corpuscles may become somewhat enlarged.

The pigment is dark and granular and "Schüffner's dots" are present in all stages. The merozoites range from eight to twelve in number.

Natural vectors of *P. ovale* have not been clearly incriminated. *Anopheles gambiae* Giles and *A. funestus* Giles are probable transmitters in tropical Africa, but there is generally poor development in all but African species of *Anopheles*. In mosquitoes the oocyst in early development is characterized by pigment granules being arranged in two rows in the shape of an x. Growth in the mosquito is slow, with sporozoites not reaching the salivary glands before twelve days.

MALARIAS OF HIGHER APES AND MONKEYS

A number of malarias of higher apes, New World monkeys, and Old World monkeys can also develop in man. Garnham (1963) has outlined the possible evolution of primates and their malaria parasites, providing a scheme that accounts for this common susceptibility. Suffice it to say here that intersusceptibility has raised questions concerning the possible natural occurrence of simian malaria in man, undetected as distinct because of clinical and morphological similarities. Even more important is the possible further evolution of simian-infesting species of *Plasmodium* to start virulent strains that can successfully establish a permanent relationship in man and appropriate *Anopheles* vectors. The natural *Anopheles* vectors of wild primate malarias are incompletely known, but there is sufficient evidence to show that some of these also serve as natural vectors of human malaria, and experimentally a number of *Anopheles* are capable of transmitting various monkey and ape plasmodia. A worldwide review of simian malaria vectors has been provided by Warren and Wharton (1963), as well as a tabular summary by Bray and Garnham (1964) of proven and suspected vectors of *Plasmodium* in the wild state and by laboratory transmission.

A complete listing and life history of the known *Plasmodium* and related Haemosporidia can be consulted in Garnham (1966). Here only the some five species of simian malaria known to establish in humans will be mentioned. The human-infesting species, *P. malariae*, which also occurs in chimpanzees has been covered in the discussion of human malaria.

Plasmodium inui (Halberstadter and von Prowazek) is probably the most widely distributed malaria species in Old World monkeys. It naturally occurs in a number of *Macaca* spp. monkeys from Taiwan in the east to possibly India and Pakistan in the west, with island and mainland distribution intervening. Various African monkeys are experimentally susceptible. By intramuscular inoculation of defibrinated highly infected rhesus blood, Dasgupta (1938) obtained a human infection.

Plasmodium brasilianum Gonder and von Berenberg-Gossler occurs widely in Panama and perhaps most of tropical South America, having been found infesting some sixteen species of monkeys in nature. Contacos, *et al.* (1963), easily transmitted this parasite to man by the bite of *Anopheles freeborni*, but no adaptation to the human host was observed in nine serial passages.

Plasmodium cynomolgi Mayer occurs in *Macaca* species of monkeys in Malaya, the East Indies, and India, and has been described from *Presbytis* species of monkeys. Man has proved to be slightly susceptible, with increased virulence after further passage (Coatney, *et al.*, 1961), and though natural infections may occur they could be diagnosed as *P. vivax*. A subspecies designated *P. cynomolgi bastianelli* Garnham may be a laboratory developed aberrant; in any case it readily infects man (Beye, *et al.*, 1961).

Plasmodium simium Fonseca is apparently limited to howler monkeys (*Alouatta* spp.) in the forests of southern Brazil. It caused a case of tertian fever in a human, probably being transmitted naturally by the bite of *Anopheles*

cruzii Dyar and Knab (Deane, *et al.*, cited in Garnham, 1966).

Plasmodium knowlesi Sinton and Mulligan is found in monkeys (particularly *Macaca irus*) in Malayan jungle and swamp forest, extending to the Philippines, and with a subspecies described from Formosa. More widespread natural distribution is suspected. Many species of monkeys can be experimentally infected, and it is generally fatal to the rhesus, *Macaca mulatta*. Humans were found to be susceptible and this parasite has been used for malaria therapy, though continued passage in man increases virulence. A human case of *P. knowlesi* was naturally acquired in Malaya and diagnosed as *falciparum*, then *malariae*, before its true identity was discovered (Chin, *et al.*, 1965).

All members of the genus *Plasmodium* are mosquito-transmitted, but several genera of mosquitoes as well as various vertebrate hosts may be involved. Mammalian hosts include primates, buffaloes, bats, antelopes, and a variety of rodents; a large number of wild and domestic birds serve as vertebrate hosts, as do reptiles, especially lizards. Closely related blood parasites, not in the genus *Plasmodium*, are also found in vertebrates of all kinds. In many cases the characteristics of these other parasites are known only from studying various stages in the vertebrate host. The vectors, when known, have proved to be bloodsucking flies other than mosquitoes. Clearly much remains to be done in studying these interesting parasites. The serious student of this subject should consult Garnham (1966).

Qualities of Good Natural Vectors. Conclusive experimental evidence indicates that the plasmodia of human malaria do not develop within the bodies of culicine mosquitoes even though gametocytes are ingested. In fact all mammalian species of *plasmodium* require *Anopheles* mosquitoes as vectors. The reasons for such a specific vector are by no means clear, all the more so since it has been shown that Malayan *Mansonia uniformis*

Theobald can develop *Plasmodium cynomolgi bastianelli* of monkeys through sporozoite development, but virtually no sporozoites established in the salivary glands and the infection could not be transmitted to uninfected monkeys (Warren, *et al.*, 1962). Whether all anopheline species are infectible is, of course, not known; many malariologists are of the opinion that laboratory tests suggest a matter of degree only, that no anopheline is completely refractory to the plasmodia of human malaria. Only 85 of the approximately 400 known species of *Anopheles* have been definitely incriminated as vectors of human malaria (Foote and Cook, 1959). There is not only a variation in the degree of mosquito species' hospitality to plasmodia but also a variation in strains of the species of plasmodia. For example, *A. quadrimaculatus* is susceptible to both *Plasmodium vivax* and *P. falciparum*; *A. punctipennis*, though equally susceptible to *P. vivax*, seems to be refractory to certain strains but not to others of *P. falciparum* (Boyd and Kitcher, 1936). Likewise within an *Anopheles* species there are strain differences with respect to suitability for plasmodial development, as well as differences in suitability of plasmodial strains. For example, several species of North American *Anopheles* were able to develop native strains of *P. vivax*, but of these, when exotic *vivax* strains were tested, *Anopheles albimanus* was nearly refractory (Young, 1948).

A good natural vector of human malaria is an *Anopheles* species that is freely and abundantly infectible by one or all species of human plasmodia, offers a favorable environment for development to the sporozoite stage, avoids loss of sporozoites in unsuitable places, breeds successfully and abundantly, is a house invader, and lives long enough to take human blood repeatedly. MacDonald (1957) has particularly stressed vector longevity as a highly significant factor. For example *Anopheles culicifacies* Giles of India is short-lived and a poor vector, whereas the long-lived *A. gambiae sensu lato* of Africa is a very important

vector. The maintenance of close and constant contact between an anthropophilous mosquito and its source of food supply is an important factor in endemicity. The concept of species sanitation is based on a knowledge of the factors referred to above. An anopheline may be common, even abundant, yet of little importance as a vector for one or more reasons.

Horsfall (1955) lists four types of reaction of the body of the mosquito unfavorable to the plasmodium. These are: (1) failure of the zygotes to penetrate the epithelium of the gut and, consequently, their degeneration; (2) normal oocyst formation, but rupture into the lumen of the gut instead of into the haemocoele; (3) degeneration, with loss of infectiveness, of both oocysts and sporozoites; (4) the formation of "black spores," sclerotization associated with degenerative oocysts. To this may be added (5) retarded development of oocysts, perhaps never achieving maximum size, and (6) inability of sporozoites to enter the salivary glands.

Epidemiology of Malaria. Hackett (1937) reviewed several theories that attempt to account for "anophelism without malaria," i.e., the presence of the mosquito without the presence of the disease. This phenomenon can probably be explained, however, on the basis of: (1) lack of suitable vectors, as defined previously; (2) vector density below the critical level sufficient to maintain the disease; or (3) climate conditions unfavorable to the maintenance of the parasite at an infective level, although favorable to the development of the mosquito.

The idea of the critical level of vector density below which malaria tends to disappear and above which the incidence of the disease increases, is an important one in the epidemiology of malaria (Russell, 1959). It helps to explain some facts that have been well known but puzzling, e.g., why malaria occurs in explosive outbreaks in some areas, such as Ceylon and northwest India (i.e., is unstable), whereas it occurs in a highly endemic condition, with epidemics only in the fringes of the malarial zone, as in parts of central Africa (i.e., is stable). Refer to succeeding section on malariology.

MacDonald (1957) has attempted a mathematical analysis of the epidemiology of malaria. He traces the thread of malaria through the following successive elements:

(1) Those that determine the stability of the disease, viz. mosquito longevity, man-biting habits, and the mosquito cycle of the parasite.

(2) Those which determine initial transmission, viz. mosquito density and man-biting habits.

(3) Those which determine the normal season, viz. climatic factors.

(4) The inoculation rate, communal immunity expressed in reduced incidence of gametocytes, and reproduction rate of the disease expressed in terms of the critical level of vector density. In areas where the disease is stable, the ruling reproductive rate usually stands just barely above the critical level; where the disease is unstable, this rate vacillates, partly erratically and partly periodically, around it.

"This," says MacDonald, "is the picture of malaria, and the process in reverse is the picture of its control." Of the factors he identified, mosquito longevity is recognized to be critically important, and in many instances accounts for the effectiveness of insecticidal control campaigns (Garrett-Jones and Grab, 1964).

Effects of Temperature on Plasmodia in the Mosquito. In spite of the fact that all conditions appear to be favorable (i.e., presence of numerous anopheline mosquitoes together with ample human population with carriers of plasmodial gametocytes), malaria may be wholly absent in particular localities. An analysis of conditions will usually reveal that the average temperature is low because the nights are cool although the days may be fairly warm, or because of prevailing cool fogs. It is generally agreed that malaria gametocytes cannot develop successfully within the body of the mosquito host when the average tempera-

ture is below about 60° F. It is nevertheless a matter of interest to know that King (1917) observed the survival of the parasite of tertian malaria in the mosquito host (*Anopheles quadrimaculatus*) at a temperature of 30° F for a period of two days; at 31° F for four days; and at 46° F for seventeen days; and the parasite of aestivo-autumnal malaria survived a temperature of 35° F for twenty-four hours.

Knowles and Basu (1943) working with the vector *Anopheles stephensi* Liston, found that the heaviest salivary gland infection of *Plasmodium vivax* was obtained at 80° F and 50 per cent relative humidity. Using the same species of *Anopheles* they found that at a temperature of 100° F and with all percentages of humidity between 59 and 100 no infection with any species of malaria parasite was obtained. From such studies it is apparent that vector species must be able to seek out favorable environments. The sporozoite stage of *Plasmodium vivax* was reached in the salivary glands of *A. stephensi* in eighteen days at 60° F, fifteen days at 70° F, eleven days at 80° F, and nine days at 90° F. For *Plasmodium falciparum*, also at 50 per cent relative humidity, the time was fourteen days at 70° F, ten days at 80° F, and nine days at 90° F.

Hibernation of the anopheline host presents the problem of overwintering of the parasite. Mayne (Mitzmain, 1916) produced evidence, which has subsequently been substantiated, that man, not the mosquito, is the overwintering or reservoir host. Anophelines overwintering in warm stables and homes may nevertheless play an important though highly circumscribed role in the transmission of malaria.

Vectors of Human Malaria. It has been abundantly proved that the causal organisms (plasmodia) of human malaria are nearly always transmitted from man to man only through the agency of mosquitoes belonging to the genus *Anopheles*. Known exceptions include faulty blood transfusions, blood contamination connected with drug addiction, and transplacental infections. Russell,

Rozeboom, and Stone (1943) give identification keys to 240 species and 78 subspecies of anophelines of the world. Russell (1959) later named sixty-three species as the chief malaria vectors. Habitat for these species may be consulted in Horsfall (1955) and more recent authors. These species, with subsequent name changes and additions, are distributed over the world, according to various authorities, as shown in Table 11-1.

TABLE 11-1   Important Anopheline Vectors of Malaria

REGION, SPECIES, AND LOCALITY OF ANOPHELES

United States and Canada
freeborni Aitken—Rocky Mountains, New Mexico, Pacific coast; *quadrimaculatus* Say—eastern, central, and southern United States (Gulf to Ontario).
Mexico, Central America, West Indies
albimanus Wiedemann—Mexico to Colombia and Venezuela, West Indies; *aquasalis* Curry—Central America to Brazil, West Indies; *argyritarsis* Robineau-Desvoidy—Brazil, Guadaloupe; *aztecus* Hoffmann—Mexico; *bellator* Dyar and Knab—West Indies to Brazil; *darlingi* Root—Central America to Argentina; *p. pseudopunctipennis* Theobald—Southern United States to Argentina; *punctimacula* Dyar and Knab—Mexico to Brazil, West Indies.
South America (*see also* Mexico, and so forth)
albitarsus Lynch-Arribalzaga—Argentina; *cruzii* Dyar and Knab—Brazil; *gambiae* Giles—imported into Brazil, now exterminated; *nunez-tovari* Gabaldon—Colombia, Venezuela.
Europe
atroparvus van Thiel—England and Sweden to Spain and northeastern Italy; *l. labranchiae* Falleroni—Mediterranean, Europe, and North Africa; *maculipennis maculipennis* Meigen—E. Europe, Asia Minor; *messeae* Falleroni—Norway, Russia, Siberia, Manchuria; *sacharovi* Favre (=*elutus*)—Balkans, Russia; *superpictus* Grassi—Spain, southern Europe, Greece, Asia Minor.
North Africa and Middle East (*see also* Europe)
claviger Meigen—Ukraine, Asia Minor, North Africa; *multicolor* Cambouliu—North Africa; *pharoensis* Theobald—North Africa, Palestine; *sergenti* Theobald—North Africa, Palestine, Turkey, Syria; *superpictus* Grassi—Asia Minor.
Central and South Africa
d'thali Patton—Ethiopia; *dureni* (Edwards)—Belgian Congo; *funestus* Giles—tropical Africa; *gambiae* Giles (*see also* South America)—tropical Africa, Egypt, Arabia; *hancocki* Edwards—western tropical Africa; *hargreavesi* Evans—Nigeria; *melas*

Theobald—western tropical Africa; *moucheti* Evans—Uganda, Congo, Cameroons; *nili* Theobald—widely distributed in central Africa; *pharoensis* Theobald (*see also* North Africa)—widely distributed in Africa, Palestine; *pretoriensis* Theobald—widely distributed central and south Africa; *rufipes* (Gough)—Sudan, French West Africa.
Philippine Islands
mangyanus Banks—many islands; *minimus flavirostris* Ludlow—many islands, Java, Celebes.
Japan, North China, Korea
pattoni Christophers—northern China; *hyrcanus sinensis* Wiedemann—widely distributed.
South and Central China, Burma, Taiwan
annularis van der Wulp—Burma; *culicifacies* Giles—Burma; *jeyporiensis* var. *candidiensis* Koizumi—Hong Kong area; *leucosphyrus* Dönitz—Burma; *maculatus* Theobald—Burma, southern China; *minimus* Theobald—hilly regions, southern China, Taiwan, Burma; *philippinensis* Ludlow—Burma, Vietnam; *hyrcanus sinensis* Wiedemann—plain of central China, Burma.
India and Ceylon.
culicifacies Giles—India, Ceylon, Thailand; *fluviatilis* James—India, Thailand; *leucosphyrus* Dönitz—India; *maculatus* Theobald—India, Ceylon; *minimus* Theobald—eastern and northern Ceylon; *philippinensis* Ludlow—India; *stephensi* Liston—India; *stephensi mysorensis* Sweet and Rao—India; *tesselatus* Theobald—Maldive Islands; *varuna* Iyengar—India.
Thailand, Malaya, Vietnam (*see also* India and Ceylon)
aconitus Dönitz—East Indies, Malaya, Vietnam; (*baezi* Gater)—Malaya; *b. balabacensis* Baisas—Thailand, Vietnam, Brunei, N. Borneo; *barbirostris* van der Wulp—Indonesia, Malaya, Sarawak; *jeyporiensis candidiensis*—Malaya, Vietnam; (*letifer* Gater)—Malaya, Indonesia; *leucosphyrus* Dönitz—Indonesia, Sarawak; *maculatus* Theobald (*see* South China, etc.)—Thailand, Malaya, Vietnam; *minimus* Theobald—Vietnam; *hyrcanus sinensis* Wiedemann—Vietnam; *subpictus* Grassi—Malaya, East Indies; *sundaicus* (Rodenwaldt)—Thailand, Malaya, East Indies; *umbrosus* Theobald—Malaya, East Indies.
Australia, Melanesia, Polynesia
bancrofti Giles—New Guinea, northern Australia; *farauti* Laveran (=*moluccensis*)—New Guinea, Solomons, New Hebrides; *karwari* (James)—West New Guinea; *koliensis* Owen—West New Guinea; *punctulatus* Dönitz—New Guinea, Solomons.

Malaria Control and Eradication.   Prior to the end of World War II, malariologists were content to keep the disease under control—to hold onto gains and to reduce the incidence of the disease, particularly in highly populated areas, to a low level. The release of DDT for civilian use, along with other potent residual toxicants, new antimalarial drugs such as chloroquine and primaquine, and advances in our knowledge of the bionomics of anophelines, led to a new concept, eradication. This does not necessarily mean eradication of the mosquito vector. If vectors are reduced below the critical level of density, so that all transmission of the human parasite is eliminated for a period of two or three years, the disease will disappear spontaneously from the human host. If reintroduction can be prevented, an extensive area, such as the continental United States, can be freed completely from the disease. Thus, even though we may not be able to eradicate the mosquitoes involved, "anophelism without malaria" may persist over a continent and ultimately, it is hoped, over the world.

This is an amazing concept. It is still far from being realized; in 1955 there were an estimated 200,000,000 cases of malaria in the world, with 2,000,000 deaths (Russell, 1958). Technical difficulties stand in the way of malaria eradication from, in particular, many parts of Asia and Africa. For example, nomadism, isolation of populations, frequent replacement of human dwellings in jungle cultures, inflexibility of monetary and technical resources, disruption of control procedures during times of political instability

and military actions—all present problems for the technically achievable ideal of malaria eradication. The possibility that jungle primates may serve as a reservoir, as they do for yellow fever, must also be considered. Nevertheless, world eradication of malaria is a feasible objective (Soper, 1958).

Malaria control and eradication programs must take into consideration the broad aspects of the ecology of the disease, its vector, and its victim. These are well expressed in the Russell formula,

$$(X + Y + Z)\,b\,e\,p\,t\,i = \text{Malaria incidence},$$

whereby the chain of malaria infection, human carrier (X) to the mosquito vector (Y) to the human victim (Z) is modified by the following factors:

b = bionomics of man and mosquito.
e = environment of man and mosquito.
p = plasmodia, species, and strains.
t = therapy and control measures.
i = the immune factors in man and mosquito.

Russell (1958) sums up very effectively the steps that lead to malaria eradication, symbolically indicated in Figure 11-20. First, there is a *preparatory phase,* including an intitial survey, planning, and preliminary operations. (For modern survey methods, consult

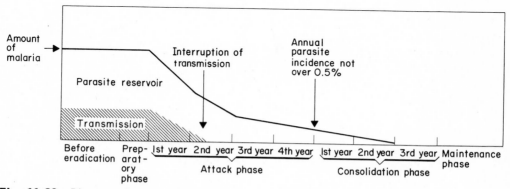

Fig. 11-20 Diagram of malaria eradication. In the attack phase the mosquito population is lowered so that transmission ceases; thereafter annual parasite incidence shows a slow decline. (Courtesy of World Health Organization.)

MacDonald, 1957.) This preparatory phase is followed by the *attack phase* with total spraying coverage, until malaria transmission has ceased and until the parasite has been virtually eliminated from the reservoir host. For *P. vivax* this means three to five years, for *P. falciparum* 2.5 to three years. The *consolidation phase* begins with the wiping out of any residual pockets that may remain. This is the difficult phase; discovery of isolated cases and the application of antimalarial drugs takes first priority. In the *maintenance phase* surveillance must be maintained over the entire area. Local health agencies are on the alert for the reintroduction of malaria, which is becoming an exotic disease in an ever increasing area of the world.

MALARIOLOGY

Malaria has remained the major debilitating disease of the tropics. So much has been done to control, and ultimately to eradicate this disease that a specific vocabulary and epidemiological theories have been developed. All aspects of the study of malaria, including advanced epidemiological theories and simple terminology, may be included under the term *malariology*.

A number of books are available on malariology; those recommended for the interested student are: MacDonald, G. 1957. *The Epidemiology and Control of Malaria*; Pampana, E. 1963. *A Textbook of Malaria Eradication*; Swaroop, S. 1959. *Statistical Considerations and Methodology in Malaria Eradication*. Document WHO/MAL/240, Geneva. In addition the series of World Health Organization publications under the title *World Health Organization, Expert Committee on Malaria,* published as WHO Tech. Rep. Ser. (numbered), is periodically published to provide current viewpoints on the status of malaria. Certain terms recognized by the World Health Organization are included in the discussion that follows to provide a minimal background on malariology.

It is recognized that malaria occurs in relatively *stable* and *unstable* conditions. In stable malaria there is a high rate of transmission to the affected population, no marked fluctuations occur over the years, and a high collective immunity of the population makes epidemics unlikely. In unstable malaria there is marked seasonal or other fluctuations and immunity of the population is often low. Where there is some measurable incidence of the disease continuously present in a given area, that area is said to be *endemic,* and various degrees of endemicity (such as percentage of spleen involvement in children two to nine years of age) are recognized by the prefixes *hypo, meso, hyper,* and *holo* endemic. An *epidemiological investigation* of malaria, then, will in the broad sense study environmental, personal, and other factors determining its incidence. The objectives may be to ascertain the origin and means of aquisition of malaria cases; the existence and nature of malaria foci; the presence or absence of current transmission.

Vectors are studied from the standpoint of their importance as a population. *Principal vectors* have main responsibility for transmitting malaria in a situation, sometimes alternating seasonally. *Secondary vectors* are thought capable of maintaining malaria only at a reduced level in the absence of principal vectors. *Conditional vectors* are presumed incapable of maintaining malaria in the absence of more efficient vectors. Individuals of a vector species are examined for the presence of malaria parasites; those having oocysts being termed *infected* (presence of malaria), and those with sporozoites in the salivary glands are classified *infective* (capable of transmitting at the next blood meal).

In assessing human populations a number of means are employed to determine the status of malaria, and likelihood of change in status. In making surveys of incidence the condition termed *parasitemia* indicates that malaria parasites have been found in the blood even though obvious symptoms such as fever may be absent; palpable enlargement of the spleen, particularly in children two to nine years old, is another indication of the presence and status of malaria. A person that has suffered from a given species and strain of malaria tends to develop a certain degree of immunity, as manifested by lack of fever and low level or absence of parasites in the blood at time of examination. Figure 11-17 diagramatically indicates this course of events and provides the terminology commonly recognized as applicable to describing malaria infections of humans.

In trying to treat individuals, *radical cure* may be attempted to entirely rid the patient of the parasite so no relapses can occur; *clinical cure* may be applied for relief of symptoms without elimination of infection; *suppressive cure* will accomplish elimination from a population by means of a continuous suppressive treatment. If a case is contracted locally it is called *autochthonous*, and if natural to the area it is termed *indigenous*; if brought in from outside it is termed *introduced*.

Vector control and chemotherapy are the means of reducing transmission. Vector control, the more important consideration for the field of medical entomology, is dealt with in Chapter 6; a brief discussion of chemotherapy follows.

MALARIA CHEMOTHERAPY

Antimalarial drugs have been developed for two principal purposes; (1) curing clinical symptoms of the disease, and (2) reduction of malaria transmission. The first medicine known (about 1633) for its curative powers was cinchona, the bark of the cinchona tree indigenous to certain regions of South America. Much later the chief alkaloid of cinchona, *quinine*, was identified and was much used in malaria therapy. Inaccessibility of quinine sources during World Wars I and II led to an intensified search for synthetic antimalarials, candidate compounds being first tested on avian and rodent malarias. Very effective synthetics have been developed; those chiefly used for malaria therapy are *quinacrine* (atabrine), *chloroquine, chloroguanide, pyrimethamine* and *primaquine*. An overall discussion of

malaria chemotherapy may be found in the review by Rollo (1965), and much of what follows is from that source.

The aim of chemotherapy is to disrupt the malaria cycle, primarily in the human host, at any of a number of susceptible stages (refer to Fig. 11-17). (1) *Lethal effects during the exerythrocytic stages* are found with primaquine, chloroguanide, and pyrimethamine; *falciparum* but not *vivax*, malaria is particularly susceptible. (2) *Prevention of erythrocytic infestation* is found with chloroquine, chloroguanide and pyrimethamine; when treatment is stopped relapses are common with *vivax* malaria, *falciparum* is usually cured. (3) *Interruption of erythrocytic schizogony* to terminate a clinical attack can be achieved with the schizontocides chloroquine and amodiaquine; resistant *falciparum* may require quinine. (4) *Elimination of both erythrocytic and exerythrocytic stages* can be accomplished by primaquine; however, Negroes are rather prone to toxicity effects. (5) *Suppressive treatment*, commonly with pyrimethamine, to eliminate parasites for a period longer than the life span of the infection; treatment for ten weeks after leaving a malarious area is used to suppress *vivax* infections. (6) *Gametocytocides* such as chloroguanide and pyrimethamine destroy sexual forms in the blood or prevent development in the mosquito.

Resistance of malaria parasites to drugs is a serious problem. It can be experimentally induced in avian and rodent malarias, but fortunately is mostly limited to *falciparum* malaria of humans. Resistant cases are generally treated with other synthetic compounds or ultimately with quinine. In analyzing the problems of antimalarial drug resistance, Bishop (1962) points out that such resistance occurs particularly at stages where there is rapid nuclear multiplication and in the presence of a drug competing at a single point in biosynthesis; the effectiveness of quinine appears to be due to its general plasmodicidal effects. Continued intensive use of antimalarial drugs in malaria control programs will probably result in further incidence of resistance particularly during military campaigns when drug therapy is increased because control of *Anopheles* becomes more difficult.

MOSQUITO-BORNE
ARBOVIRUSES

Arthropod-borne viruses (abbreviated term is *arboviruses*) are causal agents of some of the most serious and widespread diseases of man and animals. They are by far the most varied and numerous pathogens transmitted by arthropods, with over two hundred entities now known and more being described each year. Mosquitoes are carriers of more of these viruses than any other group of vectors. The description, that follows, in discussing this relationship, adheres to the grouping designations originally developed by Casals and Brown (1954). A summary of these agents is listed in Chapter 4. Basic discussions on each of the arboviruses known to affect man are found in Horsfall and Tamm (1965), and have been relied on heavily to provide this account.

GROUP A ARBOVIRUSES

Group A arboviruses are all mosquito-borne, suggesting a common evolution. There are antigenic similarities, though geographic distribution offers few clues to relatedness. Even within antigenic subgrouping of complexes there may be geographic disparity, providing puzzling questions concerning the evolution of these viruses and their vectors.

Subgroup a: Chikungunya, Mayaro, O'nyong-nyong Fever, Semliki Forest Virus

CHIKUNGUNYA VIRUS

First described from Tanganyika, the disease receives its name from a native term meaning "doubled up," referring to posture resulting from severe joint pains. The virus has been isolated from man or mosquitoes elsewhere in Africa, and has curiously been associated with dengue (a group B virus) in outbreaks of hemorrhagic fevers in south-east Asia, particularly Thailand. The disease is very incapacitating, commencing three to twelve days after incubation with a rapid rise in temperature followed by severe pains in limbs and spine; after two to nine days most patients develop a rash on trunk and limbs. Joint pains can recur intermittently up to four months. The disease does not appear to be dangerous.

Chikungunya virus has been isolated in Africa from *Aedes aegypti* (Linnaeus), *A. africanus* (Theobald), *Culex pipiens quinquefasciatus* Say (=*fatigans*), *Mansonia* spp.; in Thailand from *A. aegypti*, *C. p. quinquefasciatus*, *C. tritaeniorhynchus* Giles, *C. gelidus* Theobald. In vertebrates the virus has been isolated only from man, but *Aedes africanus* being a forest species, and antibodies being demonstrable in various monkeys, it seems likely monkeys and/or apes are part of the reservoir. There may be very high rates of acquisition; during an outbreak in Southern Rhodesia all nine Europeans that did not sleep under mosquito nets in a party spending the night in the open contracted the virus. In this instance *Aedes calceatus* Edwards was suggested as the vector (McIntosh, *et al.*, 1963).

The association of Chikungunya and dengue is demonstrable by isolations of virus, and presence of a high level of specific antibodies in humans during outbreaks. Common occurrence is likely due to transmission by the same vector species, *Aedes aegypti*. In one instance in South India both viruses were isolated from a single patient (Myers and Carey, 1967).

MAYARO VIRUS

First isolated from man in Trinidad in 1954, Mayaro virus has also been associated with human illness in Brazil and Bolivia. Nearly half of 400 Okinawan settlers in the eastern Bolivian rain forest were affected, and fifteen persons died (a close relative termed Uruma was also present). The virus has been isolated from *Mansonia venezuelensis* (Theobald) in Trinidad (Aitken, *et al.*, 1960).

O'NYONG-NYONG VIRUS

Haddow, *et al.* (1960), describe a major epidemic of a nonfatal but very painful disease, called O'nyong-nyong, a native term meaning "joint-breaker," starting in Uganda and spreading into Kenya and the Congo. From 1959–62 an estimated two million persons were affected; in some settlements over 70 per cent of the population. All age groups were affected, indicating the disease was new to the area.

There may be excruciating generalized joint pains, an irritating rash lasting four to seven days, and swelling of the lymph glands in the neck. Other less frequent symptoms include fever, headache, and pain in the eyeballs.

The disease coincides with the distribution of *Anopheles funestus* Giles and *Anopheles gambiae* Giles; the virus has been isolated from both species but Corbet, *et al.*, 1961, concluded the first species was most responsible. This is the first instance wherein an anopheline was known to serve as the vector in an arbovirus-caused epidemic.

SEMLIKI FOREST VIRUS

No disease has been attributed to the Semliki forest virus, though antibodies in man, and inapparent laboratory infections, are known. Because of close relationship to other Group A viruses, reporting of antibodies in man from Africa, India, Malaysia, and South America may in some instances be misidentifications.

Subgroup b: Mucambo, Pixuna, Venezuelan Equine Encephalitis (VEE)

MUCAMBO AND PIXUNA VIRUSES

Mucambo virus has been isolated once from man, and Pixuna caused a mild human infection after accidental laboratory exposure (Casals and Clarke, 1956). Both viruses were isolated in Brazil, and initially were confused with VEE.

VENEZUELAN EQUINE ENCEPHALITIS (VEE, *PESTE LOCA*)

Outbreaks in equines (donkeys, horses, mules) and infections of man have been described from Venezuala (as early as 1938 in horses), Colombia, Panama, and Trinidad. Clinical infection of man may be manifested as a short febrile illness with chills, fever, nausea or vomiting, headache, muscle and bone pains; or in some outbreaks there have been severe cases of encephalitis and death. In Venezuela nearly 7,000 human cases were reported, with 397 involving encephalitis, and forty-two deaths (Casals and Clarke, 1956).

In September 1968, the first reported human case of VEE in North America occurred in Dade County, Florida. The virus had been previously isolated from mosquitoes and from a cotton rat. Serological studies had also demonstrated antibodies in Seminole and Miccosukee Indian residents of southern Florida (*Morbidity and Mortality Weekly Report,* **17**:414, NCDC, U.S. Dept. Health, Education, and Welfare).

The vectors are mosquitoes, though apparently close contact between horses can effect transmission. In late 1962 an outbreak in northwestern Venezuela that caused heavy mortality of children was attributed to exceptionally heavy rainfall resulting in excellent mosquito-breeding conditions, and causing vertebrates to crowd ónto unflooded land areas (Sellers, *et al.*, 1965). In that situation there were isolations from *Aedes taeniorhynchus* (Wiedemann) (most frequent), *Ae. serratus* (Theobald), *Ae. scapularis* (Rondani), *Anopheles aquasalis* Curry, and *Psorophora confinnis* (Lynch Arribalzaga). Isolations have infrequently been made from *Haemagogus* sp., *Psorophora ferox* (Humboldt), *Mansonia titillans* (Walker), and *Culex* species.

The reservoir is apparently quite diffuse. In Trinidad VEE virus has been isolated from wild rodents in the genera *Heteromys, Sygodontomys,* and *Oryzomys* (Downs, *et al.*, 1962), and there has been natural transmission to sentinel mice; experimental symptomless viremia of birds is of uncertain significance. The Trinidad situation is rather puzzling in that antibody studies there have shown man to be extensively exposed during equine outbreaks, yet clinically recognizable illness in man is rare and even doubtful (Tigertt, et al., 1962).

Subgroup c: (Aura), Sindbis, Western (Equine) Encephalitis (WEE, WE)

SINDBIS VIRUS

First isolated from wild mosquitoes in Egypt, further isolations have been made in Uganda, South Africa, India, Malaya, Philippines and northern Australia. Mild human cases have been noted from Uganda; a more severe illness from a South African patient with headache, soreness of tendons and joints, rash, and vesicles on toes.

The virus was isolated in Uganda from *Mansonia fuscopennata* (Theobald) (Woodall, et al., 1964); in India from presumed *Culex vishnui* Theobald, wild birds and domestic fowl, and from the mite *Ornithonyssus bursa* (Berlese) (Shah, et al., 1960); in the Philippines from *Culex bitaeniorhynchus* Giles.

WESTERN ENCEPHALITIS (WEE, WE)

WE virus causes encephalitis, generally not fatal in man and causing high mortality in equines. The infectious agent was isolated in 1930 from horses with encephalitis (Meyer, et al., 1931), and later from wild mosquitoes by Hammon, et al. (1941). Initially thought limited to the western United States, the virus has also been identified on the Eastern seaboard, and from Canada, Brazil, Argentina, and British Guiana. Specific antibodies in man have been reported from Mexico, Poland, and the Soviet Union. An outbreak in 1941 in the north central United States and adjacent Canada involved over 3,000 persons; endemic areas in the western United States, particularly the Central Valley of California, have some human cases nearly every year. Various studies have shown inapparent infections, as indicated by specific antibodies, to be present in up to 11 per cent of individuals in endemic zones. Reeves, et al., 1962, estimated the ratio of human infections to encephalitis is fifty-eight to one in infants and children, and 1,150 to one in persons over fifteen years.

The active disease is virtually impossible to distinguish from other arbovirus-caused encephalitides. Specific antibody tests following recovery are diagnostic, but virus is generally isolated only from the nervous tissues of fatal cases. Fever and drowsiness are usually observed, with restlessness and irritabiilty characteristic in small children who also often have accompanying convulsions. This age group is most likely to have sequelae that are severe, such as convulsions and motor and behavioral aberrations.

In western endemic areas *Culex tarsalis* Coquillett has consistently been the vector found infective during epidemic and interepidemic periods. Thomas (1963) has provided a detailed study of development of the virus in this mosquito, concluding its importance is due to a high degree of susceptibility, short incubation period, prolonged viral persistence, high infectivity of bite, and many ecological and behavioral factors. In eastern areas where *C. tarsalis* is rare, WE virus has frequently been isolated from *Culiseta melanura* (Coquillett). Isolations have also been made from *Culex peus* Speiser, *C. pipiens pipiens* Linnaeus, *C. pipiens quinquefasciatus* Say, *C. salinarius* Coquillett, *Culiseta inornata* (Williston), *Aedes dorsalis* (Meigen), *Ae. flavescens* (Mull.), *Ae. melanimon* Dyar, *Ae. nigromaculis* (Ludlow) and *Anopheles freeborni* Aitken. Isolations from ornithophilous mites are of questionable significance (Reeves, et al., 1947).

The reservoir complex of WE is of great interest. The etiological agent has frequently been isolated from wild birds such as red-winged blackbird, sparrows, prairie chicken, and domestic fowl. Furthermore in birds there is a prolonged viremia of sufficient titer to infect feeding mosquitoes (Hammon, et al., 1951). Mammals, however, develop low titer viremia so that the logical summer maintenance is in *C. tarsalis* (or other mosquitoes) and birds. Winter survival of the virus is more of a puzzle; it has only rarely been isolated from overwintering *C. tarsalis* despite numerous attempts (Rush, et al., 1963), and experimental hibernation studies indicate blood-fed females cannot successfully overwinter. Overwintering in vertebrates appears to be possible as indicated by premunition in birds, occasional isolation in winter from rodents, and more recent demonstrations in Utah and Saskatchewan of virus from cold-blooded vertebrates, namely in the latter area from garter snakes (*Thamnophis* species) and the American leopard frog *Rana pipiens* (Burton, *et al.*, 1966).

There is much speculation as to what conditions make for human and equine epidemics of WE. Apparently drought can be responsible by bringing vectors and vertebrates into close proximity around existing water, or early spring flooding creates large vector populations increasing the likelihood of susceptible vertebrates being bitten. Reeves, *et al.* (1964), attribute the abortion of a potential epidemic in Kern County, California, to the combined effect of low transmission rates in early season (probably due to a prolonged extrinsic incubation period in *C. tarsalis* as a consequence of low temperature), and to successful mosquito control by midsummer in areas with a susceptible human population. Hess, *et al.* (1963), observed that highest transmission rates to sentinel flocks of chickens occurred in those seasons when the April–June period was unusually cold.

Miscellaneous Subgroup c: Includes Eastern (Equine) Encephalitis, (Middelburg), and (Ndumu)

EASTERN ENCEPHALITIS VIRUS (EEE, EE)

Eastern encephalitis virus can cause a severe and frequently fatal encephalitis in man, encephalitis in equines, and epizootics in pheasants. First identified from the brain of horses in 1933, it was identified as the agent causing an epidemic of man in Massachusetts in 1938 (Webster and Wright, 1938). The virus has caused human disease from the eastern seaboard of the United States to Argentina, Dominican Republic, and Jamaica. Isolations reported outside the New World, from the Philippines, Czechoslovakia, Thailand, Poland, and the U.S.S.R. may be different as they have not been associated with human outbreaks or epizootics.

Encephalitis caused by EE virus is seen mainly in infants and children. There is generally a sudden onset with high fever, vomiting, drowsiness or coma, twitching, and severe convulsions. In most severe cases death occurs three to five days from onset, in others death may follow later from complications. Survivors under five often have mental retardation, convulsions, and paralysis; survivors over forty generally recover completely.

The virus is most consistently isolated from *Culiseta melanura* (Coquillett), but has also been found in *Culex nigripalpus* Theobald (Trinidad), *C. taeniopus* Dyar and Knab (Trinidad), *C. restuans* Theobald, *C. salinarius* Coquillett, *Aedes mitchellae* (Dyar), *Ae. sollicitans* (Walker), *Ae. taeniorhynchus* (Wiedemann) (Brazil), *Ae. vexans* (Meigen), *Anopheles crucians* Wiedemann, and *Mansonia perturbans* (Walker). Of uncertain epidemiological significance are infrequent isolations from *Culicoides*, fowl mites and lice, and blackflies (Simuliidae).

Maintenance and transmission of EE virus in nature remain a fascinating problem. Birds of all types frequently have high antibody titers and yield virus, yet curiously the Chinese ring-neck pheasant is very susceptible. This latter bird, when penned, may suffer devastating epizootics, apparently disseminated by feather picking. Antibodies are of low incidence in man, which perhaps accounts for his susceptibility, and which also may incriminate *Culiseta melanura* because it rarely bites man. The virus was isolated from monkeys and mice in a rain-forest area of Brazil (Causey, *et al.*, 1961).

Hayes, *et al.* (1962), associated a 1959 outbreak in New Jersey with heavy rainfall in July and high temperature resulting in exceptionally large mosquito populations. It was suggested there that *Culiseta melanura* was the primary sylvan vector bringing virus to epidemic centers, *Aedes sollicitans* (Walker) was the primary vector in coastal areas where most human cases occurred, and *Aedes vexans* (Meigen) was largely responsible for inland equine outbreaks. A general analysis of climatological conditions for the period 1938–61 associated with EE outbreaks (Hayes and Hess, 1964), found major epidemics in Massachusetts and New Jersey to be associated with excessive rainfall during summer and the preceding autumn, but the same relationship was not found in a 1947 outbreak in Louisiana. Outbreaks in horses coincided in Massachusetts and New Jersey with those in man, were less consistently associated in Delaware and Maryland, and only occasionally noted in southern states.

Middelburg and **Ndumu** viruses are identified from anitibodies in man in southern Africa, but are not known to cause clinical disease.

GROUP B ARBOVIRUSES

In addition to the mosquito-borne agents listed below, a number of tick-borne arboviruses belong in this antigenic grouping. Consult Chapter 18 for further information on the tick-borne group.

Subgroup a: Yellow Fever (YF) Virus

Yellow fever still constitutes a threat to man in the Central and South American and African tropics. This disease occurs mainly as an urban form transmitted by *Aedes aegypti* (Linnaeus), and as a jungle or sylvan form transmitted by forest mosquitoes.

It is generally agreed that the urban vector, *Aedes aegypti*, spread from Africa and was responsible for epidemics, particularly the devastating epidemics of the Americas. Periodic passage along Atlantic trade routes introduced outbreaks into urban North and South America, especially seaports, and parts of Western Europe. As late as 1905 southern ports of the United States had 5,000 cases with 20 per cent mortality.

The jungle type of yellow fever may have existed in the New World in pre-Columbian days before the introduction there of *Aedes aegypti*. Mayan chronicles speak of bloody vomiting (*xekik*) that ravaged populous areas of the Yucatan portion of their empire in 1484 (Soper, 1955), a suggestive but not certain account. Carter (1931) considers the epidemic in Yucatan, Mexico, in 1648 as the first certainly recognizable epidemic of yellow fever. He gives the earliest introduction into Havana as 1649, refers to disappearance of yellow fever from Cuba after 1655, and its reintroduction from Vera Cruz in 1761 with subsequent devastatingly endemic status. The last major American urban epidemic (1928–9) recorded 435 deaths in Rio de Janeiro. The conquest of urban yellow fever, commencing with the work of the United States Yellow Fever Commission in 1900, is documented in Chapter 1. An account of many aspects of the disease may be found in Strode (1951).

Serologic studies have revealed that there may be large numbers of humans acquiring yellow fever virus without apparent symptoms. For example Downs (1957) estimated hundreds of unrecognized cases occurred in Trinidad in 1954.

When clinical manifestations occur the incubation period is usually three to six days, with abrupt onset of illness. In mild cases symptoms lasting less than one week include fever, headache, generalized aches and pains, and nausea. Severe cases frequently are diphasic; the first phase with rapid onset of fever, headache, dizziness, muscular pain, nausea, and vomiting; the second phase (sometimes after brief remission) with high fever, some jaundice, bradycardia, and various hemorrhagic symptoms. In fatal cases there may be profuse vomiting of dark-brown or black material, collapse and death, or termination with a comatose condition or delirium. Fulminating disease without a diphasic course and with early death also occurs.

Prolonged convalescence may be required for severely ill patients, but no lasting complications are known.

The distinctly different factors involved in urban and jungle outbreaks require separate discussions of each. In urban epidemics the proved vector is *Aedes aegypti* (Linnaeus). This mosquito has been shown capable of transmission by bite up to 168 days after an infective meal (Philip, 1962). It is very closely associated with man, except for one variety of *aegypti* in central Africa, generally breeding in small containers near his habitations. On this account the present worldwide emphasis on eradication of *Aedes aegypti* shows promise of permanently removing the threat of urban epidemics.

An account of yellow fever in Middle America from 1948–57, particularly dealing with the sylvatic form, has been prepared by Boshell-Manrique (1959). Permanent epizootics exist in large jungles as the Orinoco and Amazon River Basins, with continual movement among primates. From such permanent foci there is periodic spread by way of mosquitoes and monkeys into adjacent areas. Panama is such an area, Galindo and de Rodaniche (1964) concluding outbreaks there in 1948 and 1956 were due to passage of virus from forested areas in South America. Mosquito vectors for sylvatic yellow fever in the Americas are mainly *Haemagogus* (particularly *H. spegazzinii* Brèthes), *Aedes leucocelaenus* Dyar and Shannon, and *Sabethes chloropterus* (Humboldt). The last species may live long enough to explain survival through the dry season, but its inability to transmit some strains of yellow fever virus, plus an extrinsic incubation period of thirty-four to forty-four days, suggests it is not an efficient vector (Rodaniche, *et al.*, 1959). *Haemagogus equinus* Theobald, a treehole breeder, has been found in the Brownsville area of Texas (Breland, 1958). Primates associated with American foci are howler monkeys (*Alouatta*) and possibly other monkeys (genus *Saimiri*).

In Africa yellow fever occurs south of the Sahara Desert into Zambia (Northern Rhodesia). Taylor (*in* Strode, 1951) points out that the epidemiology of the disease varies in different regions. Along the west coast the man-*aegypti*-man form occurs; in Uganda a modified sylvatic form involves *Aedes africanus* (Theobald), which is a forest canopy species associated with primate hosts, and *Aedes simpsoni* (Theobald), which breeds in vegetation around human dwellings. Other East African vectors implicated are *Ae. vittatus* (Bigot), *Ae. metallicus* (Edwards), and *Ae. taylori* Edwards. Various African primates are apparently involved in the reservoir. The vector-primate relationships are not clear in the Congo, though antibodies have been found in chimpanzees there, and an outbreak in 1958 that resulted in twelve deaths brought *Ae. simpsoni* and *Ae. aegypti* under suspicion (Panthier, *et al.*, 1962).

Vaccines have been developed that are effective in controlling yellow fever, though populations in underdeveloped areas lacking adequate medical services can be seriously threatened as illustrated by the major outbreak that occurred in Ethiopia in 1959–60 (Sérié, *et al.*, 1964). A survey in 1953–55 established that country to be free from yellow fever, but an epidemic spread from the Sudan and penetrated deeply into the southwest portion resulting in no fewer than 15,000 deaths, an estimated 10 per cent of the population in the affected area. An intensive vaccination campaign blocked further advance in Ethiopia. Epidemiological investigations showed river valleys to be mainly involved, especially the Omo river and its tributaries, and *Aedes simpsoni* (Theobald) was undoubtedly the chief vector.

That urban yellow fever still constitutes a threat is evident from an epidemic that occurred in Senegal in 1965, in a region of dry savannah with villages interspersed (Chambon and others, 1967). The population at risk consisted nearly exclusively of 50,000 children under twelve years of age who had not been vaccinated since 1960 because of encephalitic complications possible from the use of vaccine. Up to 20,000 cases of yellow fever were estimated, with a case fatality rate of about 15 per cent. Rigorous *aegypti* control, vaccination, and sanitary measures successfully curtailed the outbreak.

Curiously enough yellow fever is not present in the tropics of the Far East. Part of the reason may lie in the fact that humans show considerable cross immunity to various group B arboviruses, and the widespread presence of antibodies for dengue might deter development of epidemics. The reasons for lack of yellow fever in the asiatic tropics are by no means clear; however, as Philip, *et al.* (1958) have confirmed in experimental transmission studies, at least three species of mosquitoes occurring there are capable vectors. The potential problem emphasizes the need for constant vigilance in preventing introduction of infected animals or humans by rapid means of transportation, and the need for a continued program to eradicate *Aedes aegypti*.

Subgroup b: Dengue (Break-Bone Fever, Asiatic Hemorrhagic Fever)

Dengue is in reality comprised of four (possibly six) distinct strains of virus, infection providing prolonged homologous immunity and rather transient heterologous immunity. Confusion exists because of the variety of nonspecific symptoms, the presence of other arboviruses (particularly Chikungunya) often occurring in the same area and time, and the cross reactivity of other B group arboviruses making serological studies particularly difficult.

Clinical symptoms do not permit clear separation of dengue from some other arboviruses. One characteristic is abnormalities in small blood vessels, with mottling of skin and rash in mild cases, or marked hemorrhagic complications such as hemorrhagic cutaneous petechiae and intestinal bleeding in severe cases. Onset of clinical symptoms occurs after a usual incubation period of five to eight days, with fever and severe headaches, backache, and pains in muscles and joints. Weakness and prostration are common. Hemorrhagic manifestations with significant mortality have been especially characteristic of the disease in children three to six years old during recent times within the Orient. Presumably the involvement of this age group in endemic foci is due to specific immunity acquired by the adult population.

Dengue was first thought of exclusively as a temporarily debilitating but seldom fatal disease. Dengue-like disease was reported in the latter part of the eighteenth century, and in the nineteenth century epidemics were known throughout the tropics and subtropics. Since 1920 very extensive outbreaks involving 500,000 to 2 million cases have occurred in the United States, the Caribbean region, Australia, Greece, and Japan; more recently hemorrhagic manifestations with mortality, especially of children, have been a prominent feature of epidemics in the Philippines, Thailand, and India (Rudnick and Hammon, 1960; Hammon, *et al.*, 1961). In tropical areas outbreaks generally coincide with the rainy season and high mosquito populations; in more temperate areas hot weather is associated, probably because of slow development of the virus in vectors under cooler conditions. The disease is virtually confined to about forty degrees on either side of the equator, closely approximating the distribution of *Aedes aegypti* (Linnaeus) (Wisseman and Sweet *in* May, 1961).

Dengue viruses have been exclusively associated with *Aedes* mosquitoes in the subgenus *Stegomyia*, particularly *Aedes aegypti* (Linnaeus). *Aedes albopictus* (Skuse), *Ae. scutellaris* (Walker), and *Ae. polynesiensis* Marks have also been implicated, the latter species apparently being responsible for an extensive epidemic in the Society Islands in 1944 (Rosen, 1958a). Eradication of *Aedes aegypti* should control the disease in the Western Hemisphere where this mosquito is the sole vector.

The role of vertebrates in the reservoir is not entirely clear; man is the most sensitive experimental host, and most ordinary laboratory animals are refractory except by intracerebral inoculation, particularly in young suckling mice. Inapparent infections, with viremia, have been produced in Old World and New World monkeys (Simmons, *et al.*, 1931, Rosen, 1958b). Suggestions that the reservoir in northern Queensland, Australia, includes flying foxes (*Pteropus*) and migratory shore birds (O'Gower, 1960) have not been substantiated.

Subgroup c: St. Louis Encephalitis, Japanese (B) Encephalitis, Murray Valley Encephalitis, West Nile Virus, Ilheus Virus

ST. LOUIS ENCEPHALITIS (SLE)

St. Louis encephalitis virus basically has an active mosquito-bird cycle, with the possibility of wild rodents entering the picture (Henderson, *et al.*, 1962) and man being an accidental end point. It is the most important mosquito-borne disease remaining in the United States, with up to 1,000 cases in larger epidemics. The largest epidemic of SLE occurred in St. Louis in 1933 with 1,100 cases and more than 200 deaths; one of the largest outbreaks recorded occurred in 1954 in the Lower Rio Grande Valley of Texas, with 373 cases recorded and probably more than 1,000 cases present (Kunin, *et al.*, 1957). Epidemics have occurred in the Midwest (where it was first described in 1932–33), western and central states, and in Florida. A 1964 outbreak in the New Jersey–Pennsylvania region was unprecedented because of its occurrence above forty degrees north latitude, and because of the rarity of this disease east of the Allegheny mountains (except for Florida) in the continental United States (Goldfield, *et al.*, 1966).

Generally SLE virus causes a clinically inapparent infection of man, various serological studies showing prior exposure of 10 to 70 per cent of individuals in endemic areas. Most clinical manifestations are benign, comprised of a few days of fever and severe headache followed by complete recovery. More grave illness, particularly noted in the Florida outbreaks, is characterized by usually abrupt onset of malaise, chills, and nausea; rapid temperature rise with severe headache, con-

fusion, and drowsiness; nausea and vomiting, and convulsions; and commonly tremors, speech problems, and visual difficulties. Recovery is often dramatically sudden, generally without complications, though weakness, dulled mentality, and paralysis may follow. Serological demonstration of increased specific antibodies is required to verify the etiological agent.

Although mosquitoes were early suspected as vectors of SLE virus (in 1933 by Lumsden, Lumsden, 1958), this was not verified until isolations were made from *Culex tarsalis* Coquillett by Hammon, *et al.* (1941), in studying human encephalitis in the Yakima Valley, Washington. The importance of *Culex pipiens* Linnaeus and *C. pipiens quinquefasciatus* Say as vectors of SLE virus has been confirmed in the central states (Chamberlain, *et al.*, 1959), and *C. nigripalpus* Theobald for outbreaks in Florida (Hess, *et al.*, 1963). The last species is a tropical bird- and man-feeder, and was also the source of SLE virus isolations in Jamaica. The virus has also been isolated in Trinidad (from four species of *Culex* and *Psorophora ferox* (Humboldt); Downs, 1963), and Panama (from *Sabethes*, especially *S. chloropterus* (Humboldt), *Trichoprosopon* sp.; Galindo, *et al.*, 1964). In Pará, Brazil, SLE virus was obtained from *Sabethes belisarioi* Neiva, and *Gigantolaelaps* sp. mites from a rice rat, *Oryzomys* sp. (Causey, *et al.*, 1964). Serological investigations suggest its presence also in Colombia, Mexico, and Argentina. Hess, *et al.* (1963), show a temperature dependence of St. Louis encephalitis epidemics in the United States, maximal activity following unusually warm spring temperatures. The means of overwintering of the virus in temperate zones remains uncertain, though it has been isolated from bats in Texas (Sulkin, *et al.*, 1966).

Since there are different vector species, the epidemiology of SLE is distinct in the western United States from the central states. In the far west the disease is mainly rural with a fairly even distribution among human age groups; in the central states the disease is more urban and suburban with a higher morbidity in older age groups. The case fatality of 20 per cent in a large outbreak during 1962 in the Tampa Bay area, Florida, is attributed to the high incidence of elderly people (Bond, *et al.*, 1965). In Kern County, California, Reeves, *et al.* (1962), have shown *Culex tarsalis* Coquillett to be the main vector and *C. pipiens* Linnaeus, *C. peus* Speiser, and *Aedes melanimon* Dyar to be at most only secondary in importance.

Effective areawide control of mosquitoes by ultra low volume application of insecticides from aircraft shows promise in controlling outbreaks of SLE and other arboviruses. Epidemics of SLE in Dallas and Corpus Christi, Texas, in August 1966, were curbed by ultra low volume spraying of malathion at about three ounces per acre, against *Culex pipiens quinquefasciatus* (Kilpatrick and Adams, 1967). Spraying resulted in a radical decline in vector population and in vector infection rate; and rapid decline of human encephalitis approximately fourteen days (one incubation period) after spraying was initiated.

JAPANESE ENCEPHALITIS (JAPANESE B ENCEPHALITIS, JBE, JE)

Japanese encephalitis occurs in eastern Siberia, China, Malaya, Singapore, and India; it has caused major epidemics in Japan, Korea, and Taiwan. The disease has been reported on Okinawa and was apparently introduced to Guam. Rapid means of transportation constitute a threat in that two cases entered the United States from Japan and Korea (Aidem and Garagusi, 1961).

Reports of a disease resembling Japanese encephalitis go back to 1871, and the agent involved was characterized by Japanese workers during a severe epidemic in 1924. Outbreaks of up to 8,000 cases per year can occur; in 1958 there were 5,700 cases with 1,322 deaths reported for Korea, and 1,800 cases with 519 deaths in Japan. A 1961 outbreak in Taiwan involved 704 reported cases. Elsewhere (except perhaps for mainland China)

the disease occurs as small outbreaks or sporadic cases.

Japanese encephalitis resembles St. Louis encephalitis, but with more severe clinical manifestations and higher mortality. Inapparent infection is common, and mild systemic illness without central nervous system complications is too nonspecific to verify its frequency. Commonly cases developing encephalitis have a sudden onset of severe headache, vomiting, and high fever; cerebral and meningeal involvement and transient ocular aberrations are frequent; fatal cases usually undergo coma and die within ten days. Convalescence is usually prolonged, and accompanied by weakness, tremors, nervousness, and incoordination. Permanent damage may involve mental impairment and personality changes. Diagnosis of nonfatal cases is confirmed by a rise in specific antibodies.

The virus of Japanese encephalitis is maintained in mosquitoes and hosts other than man, the latter becoming accidentally involved. In major outbreaks the main vector is *Culex tritaeniorhynchus* Giles, which feeds preferentially on large animals and birds; man is not affected until infective populations of this mosquito are large (Fig. 1-1). The disease occurs in warm weather in temperate regions; in tropical climates it occurs sporadically in any season. In Japan *C. tritaeniorhynchus* is the only mosquito consistently infected; it is a rural species, overwinters as inseminated females, and reaches maximum population size by late June (Scherer, *et al.*, 1959). Virus is frequently found in black-crowned night herons, egrets, and pigs. All these animals increase the virus and serve to infect more of the vectors; horse infection occurring at the time of pig infection is of economic significance but not of epidemiological significance because horses experience a low and transient blood titer. *Culex tritaeniorhynchus* is found wherever Japanese encephalitis occurs, but other vectors are also involved elsewhere; *Culex gelidus* Theobald in Malaya, Gould, *et al.*, 1962; *C. pipiens* Linnaeus in China, Liu, *et al.*, 1959; *C. fuscocephalus* Theobald in Taiwan, Grayston, *et al.*, 1962; *C. pseudo-vishnui* Colless in India, Anderson, 1963; *C. pipiens quinquefasciatus* Say, *C. bitaenior-hynchus* Giles, *Aedes japonicus* (Theobald), and *Ae. togoi* (Theobald) in the Maritime Province of the Soviet Union, Grashchenkov, 1964.

MURRAY VALLEY ENCEPHALITIS (AUSTRALIAN X DISEASE)

Murray Valley encephalitis, first recognized in an epidemic in 1917–18, is very close to Japanese encephalitis. Infection, mostly in-apparent, has occurred in all the states of Australia and in New Guinea. Apparently the virus exists in a bird-mosquito cycle in north-ern tropical Australia and New Guinea. Epidemics have occurred in more closely settled areas of southern Australia and coastal areas in the southern half of Queensland, being brought south in a chain of migratory bird-mosquito cycles. In southern epidemic regions domestic fowl and water birds serve as an important reservoir for vector infection (Miles, 1960). *Culex annulirostris* Skuse is the vector most clearly implicated; the virus has been frequently isolated from this species, and from *Aedes normanensis* (Taylor) and *Anopheles bancrofti* Giles (Doherty, *et al.*, 1963).

WEST NILE VIRUS

West Nile virus has been isolated from South Africa to southeastern India; it also occurs in southern France (Hannoun, *et al.*, 1964); its natural history and disease potential have been studied by Taylor, *et al.* (1956), in Egypt. There can be symptomless infection, and when clinical cases occur they most often resemble dengue.

The severity of illness seems to relate to age of the victim. Infants and young children generally experience a mild, nonspecific illness; adults have typical dengue-like symptoms; in the elderly the central nervous system under-goes complications such as meningoencephali-tis. In most cases infection is relatively benign without permanent aftereffects.

Epidemiology of West Nile virus has been most amply studied in Egypt and Israel. In the former country there is high endemicity and the disease is unrecognized, presumably be-cause infection occurs during childhood; in Israel the virus occurs in sharply defined epidemics from May to October (Goldblum, 1959). In both countries *Culex pipiens* Lin-naeus and *C. univittatus* Theobald are impli-cated in a bird-mosquito cycle, with man and other vertebrates entering rather incidentally into the picture. The virus has been isolated from *Culex pipiens quinquefasciatus* Say (=*fatigans*) and *Culex vishnui* Theobald in India; from *Mansonia metallica* (Theobald) in Uganda; from *Culex modestus* Ficalbi in southern France. Isolation of West Nile virus from the soft tick *Argas reflexus hermanni* Audouin in pigeon cotes of the Nile delta suggests a means of overwintering as well as a more lasting reservoir (Schmidt and Said, 1964).

ILHEUS VIRUS

Ilheus virus has been isolated in continental South and Central America, and in Trinidad. Apparently it is not an important cause of human disease, though fever and occasional involvement of the central nervous system are known. Evidence gained from virus isolation and antibody surveys suggests Ilheus virus to be associated with forest communities. In Colombia this virus has been isolated from *Psorophora ferox* (Humboldt); in Panama from *Haemogogus spegazzinii falco* Kumm, *et al.*, and from *Trichoprosopon* species; in Guatemala from *Sabethes chloropterus* (Hum-boldt); in the Belem area of Brazil from *Aedes* (probably *Ae. serratus* (Theobald)), *Psorophora ferox* (Humboldt), and from monkeys (Causey, *et al.*, 1961).

Subgroup d: Spondweni, Uganda S, and Wesselsbron Viruses

These Subgroup d viruses have been found respectively in South Africa, East Africa, and South Africa. The first two have been isolated from febrile children and mosquitoes; their significance as causal agents of human disease seems slight. Wesselsbron virus was recognized as a new agent of disease in sheep by Weiss, *et al.* (1956), causing abortion and death. Subsequent isolations from man have been associated with a moderately severe, influenza-like illness, at times requiring prolonged convalescence. In South Africa Wesselsbron virus has been isolated from a number of mosquitoes, and two species of *Aedes* have been found capable of transmission.

GROUP C ARBOVIRUSES

(Apeu, Caraparu, Itaqui, Madrid, Marituba, Murutucu, Nepuyo, Oriboca, and Ossa Viruses)

Isolations of Group C agents have been made in Brazil, Panama, and Trinidad; antibody studies suggest their presence in man in Africa, Puerto Rico, and the Soviet Union. Neither epidemics nor serious illness have been associated with these viruses, and though immunologically separable they cause similar clinical symptoms; fever of short duration, headache, backache, and muscular pains sometimes accompanied by dizziness, chills, vertigo, and nausea. Mostly men working in forests are affected. There have been isolations from culicine and sabethine mosquitoes as well as from various rodents.

MISCELLANEOUS ARBOVIRUSES

BUNYAMWERA AND RELATED VIRUSES

Bunyamwera virus was first isolated in Uganda from *Aedes* mosquitoes (Smithburn, *et al.*, 1946) and subsequently from several regions of Africa. This agent has been known to cause a mild fever of man, accompanied by backache and joint pains, as well as a more serious encephalitis. Related viruses placed in this group (Casals and Whitman, 1960) include Wyeomyia virus (United States), Cache valley

virus (United States, Brazil), Kairi virus (Trinidad, Brazil); also included (Kokernot, *et al.*, 1960) is Germiston virus (South Africa). Further viruses included in the Bunyamwera group are Tensaw virus (southeastern United States), and Guaroa virus (Colombia and Brazil). All these viruses have been isolated from various culicine and anopheline mosquitoes.

BWAMBA VIRUS GROUP

Bwamba virus has been found in Uganda, associated with an illness of man having sudden onset of fever, headache, backache, and no lasting complications (Smithburn, *et al.*, 1941). Antibodies for this virus were later found in monkeys, suggesting a flying insect vector though natural isolations from arthropods have not been made. A closely related agent termed Pongola virus has been isolated from *Aedes* and *Mansonia* mosquitoes in South Africa and Uganda, but has not been associated with disease in man.

OROPOUCHE VIRUS

Oropouche virus was first isolated in Trinidad (Anderson, *et al.*, 1961) and has been repeatedly found around Belem, Pará State, Brazil. An epidemic in the latter area involved over 7,000 cases characterized by fever, headache, backache, and generalized joint and muscle discomfort, with no deaths or lasting complications (Theiler and Downs, 1963). The virus has been isolated from *Mansonia* mosquitoes in Trinidad, and from *Aedes serratus* (Theobald) and from a sloth in Brazil; antibodies have been found in wild monkeys in Trinidad.

CALIFORNIA VIRUS GROUP

Viruses in the California group, according to Sather and Hammon (1967), are represented in the United States by at least eight antigenically related though distinct types. These isolations have been termed California encephalitis virus (CEV), snowshoe hare, La Crosse, trivittatus, Keystone, Jerry Slough,

San Angelo, and Jamestown Canyon viruses. Melao virus is also in this group and from the Western hemisphere, whereas Tahyna and Lumbo viruses of this group are from eastern Europe and Africa respectively. These viruses as a group have been isolated from *Aedes* and *Culex* mosquitoes. Hammon and Reeves (1952) believed California virus could cause encephalitis, though Gresikova, *et al.* (1964), showed active transmission of California and Tahyna viruses occurs in Kern County, California, generally without symptoms, and must involve other than the common *Culex* and *Aedes* mosquitoes that have been intensively tested over eighteen years without evidence of infection. Ticks may enter into the cycle of California type viruses, as natural isolations have been made from these vectors, though Newhouse, *et al.* (1963), determined that ticks lose their infection within forty-eight hours.

The first recognized epidemic of California encephalitis occurred in 1964 (Beadle, 1966). This involved cases in children sixteen years old and under in Indiana (Marshall, 1965), as well as additional recognized cases in Ohio, Wisconsin, and North Carolina. This disease now rates second only to St. Louis encephalitis in causing cases of insect-transmitted encephalitis in the United States in the last few years.

VIRUSES PRINCIPALLY OF WILD AND DOMESTIC ANIMALS TRANSMITTED BY MOSQUITOES

Among the mosquito-transmitted viruses of animals are found myxomatosis, avian pox virus, encephalomyocarditis, and Rift Valley fever. These pathogens can cause extensive epizootics among their respective hosts; and though mosquitoes are often the main agents of dissemination, there may be situations where other arthropods fill this function.

Rabbit **myxomatosis** (big head in rabbits) was observed in a devastating epizootic of domestic European rabbits in Uruguay in 1896. This disease, immediately suspected to be caused by a virus, was characterized by numerous mucinous tumors in the skin of infected animals, with further lesions affecting many other body tissues, and death ensuing in a week or two. The disease affected rabbits, but seriously affected only the European wild rabbit, *Oryctolagus cuniculis*, being mild or asymptomatic in the American *Lepus* and *Sylvilagus*. Myxomatosis was long regarded as confined to South America, but in 1930 the disease broke out in commercial rabbit farms of southern California.

Because of its devastating effects on the European rabbit, and because this rabbit was a major threat to agriculture in Australia and parts of Europe, myxomatosis was introduced for rabbit control. Fenner and Ratcliffe (1965) have provided a comprehensive historical and biological account of the disease and its use in rabbit control. Mechanical transmission of myxoma virus is accomplished in the laboratory by a wide variety of arthropods including mosquitoes (Fig. 11-21), blackflies, fleas, sucking lice, mites, and ticks. In Australia natural transmission has typically spread along river valleys, and has primarily involved the vectors *Culex annulirostris* Skuse, *Anopheles annulipes* Walker, and various *Aedes* species, as well as Simuliidae. In France the principal means of spread is thought due to *Anopheles* mosquitoes, but in Great Britain the rabbit flea, *Spilopsyllus cuniculi* Dale is most suspect.

Biological control of rabbits by myxomatosis has at times been spectacularly successful in Australia, and in Europe it threatened the existence of rabbits even where they were considered of value. Continued natural exposure of rabbits to the disease, as well as laboratory studies, has revealed the presence of virulent and attenuated strains of virus, and the development of a certain degree of resistance in rabbit populations.

Avian Pox Virus. Avian pox virus affects many wild and domestic birds, causing lesions much as with myxoma virus of rabbits. Though transmission by mosquitoes is solely by mechanical means, in Stefferud (1956) it is

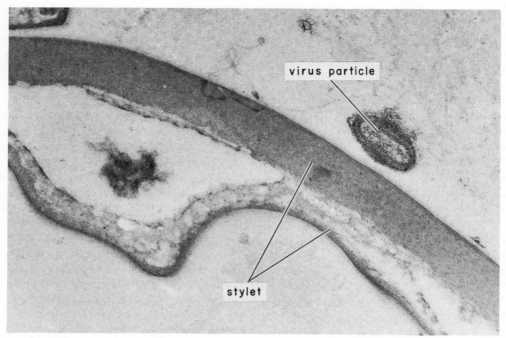

Fig. 11-21 Myxoma virus on maxillary stylet of *Aedes aegypti.* Note that virus particle does not adhere very strongly to stylet. (Courtesy of B. Filshie, C.S.I.R.O. Canberra, Australia.)

stated that these vectors can infect susceptible birds as long as two months after feeding on an infected bird. *Culex pipiens* Linnaeus, and its subspecies *quinquefasciatus* Say (=*fatigans*) are notable bird feeders, the latter being particularly implicated in transmission of avian pox in Australia, though this virus was also isolated there from *Aedes notoscriptus* (Skuse) (Lee, *et al.,* 1958).

Encephalomyocarditis Virus. No deaths have been reported from human patients suffering from encephalomyocarditis virus, of which there are apparently many strains. Human infections range clinically from mild fever to severe encephalitis. It is primarily a zoonosis, affecting the central nervous system and heart of a number of wild and domestic animals. Isolations have been made from many parts of the world from primates, swine, and rodents, the latter frequently being associated with human cases. Encephalomyocarditis virus was isolated in Uganda from *Mansonia* *fuscopennata* (Theobald); study of an epizootic in Pará, Brazil, yielded isolations from wild rodents, opossum, horses, birds, sentinel mice, *Aedes* species, two species of *Mansonia,* and one *Culex* (Causey, *et al.,* 1964).

Rift Valley Fever Virus (Enzootic Hepatitis). The disease caused by Rift Valley fever virus is fairly widespread among domestic animals on the African continent; man may become infected by direct contact with sick animals, and presumably by bite of infective vector. Characteristically this virus causes abortions in pregnant sheep, cows, and goats, and heavy mortality of lambs and calves. In man the disease is serious but almost never fatal; symptoms include fever, headache, muscular pains, liver engorgement, and there may be permanent visual impairment. An epizootic in South Africa in 1950–51 was estimated to cause the deaths of 100,000 sheep and cattle and to have involved 20,000 human cases (Weiss, 1957).

Rift Valley fever virus appears to exist in enzootic forest foci involving mosquitoes and wild animals, particularly rodents (Weinbren and Mason, 1957). From such foci, when vector populations and susceptible vertebrates are plentiful, epizootics can occur. In Africa the mosquitoes *Eretmapodites chrysogaster* Graham, *Aedes caballus* (Theobald), *Ae. circumluteolus* (Theobald), *Ae. deboeri* Edwards, *Ae. tarsalis* (Newstead), and *Culex theileri* Theobald have been found infected.

FILARIASIS

Infection of vertebrates with filarial nematodes and the transmission of the immature forms by biting arthropods raise many evolutionary problems. The range of relationships includes a simple mechanical transfer on the surface of the vector (see *Stephanofilaria*) to a more complex developmental cycle within the vector, and release into the host during the act of feeding. This latter situation is characteristic of filarial transmission by mosquitoes. The subject of filarioid nematode transmission is reviewed by Lavoipierre (1958b), and Hawking and Worms (1961), with epidemiological aspects covered by Edeson and Wilson (1964).

The human filarial parasites transmitted by mosquitoes were originally considered two species in a single genus, but as a consequence of studying the adult worms Buckley (1960) developed the present classification; namely *Wuchereria bancrofti* (Cobbold) known only from man, and *Brugia malayi* (Burg) (=former *Wuchereria malayi*) of man and animals. The vertebrate hosts of various mosquito-transmitted filariae include wild and domestic carnivorous and herbivorous mammals, insectivores, birds, monkeys, frogs, and lizards.

Development of both mosquito-transmitted human-infesting filariae is very similar. The microfilariae, each in a saclike sheath, are ingested from the peripheral blood during the act of feeding, shed their sheaths and migrate through the walls of the stomach, apparently with the aid of an anterior hook (Hawking and Worms, 1961). Migration through the stomach wall can occur in minutes, though live and possibly unsuccessful filariae may be found in the mosquito gut up to four days after ingestion. Practically all microfilariae passing through the gut migrate forward into the thorax within twelve hours. Development of filariae takes place within muscles, particularly those of the thorax, where the larvae become slightly shorter and much thicker developing into a "sausage" form. A number of internal changes and two molts occur during this stage, ultimately resulting in an infective larva about 1.5 mm in length. After completing development the infective larvae migrate with little difficulty toward the proboscis. When the mosquito feeds on a vertebrate these larvae emerge, probably mostly through the tip of the mosquito's labellum, and penetrate the skin of the vertebrate host where it has been broken by the mosquito's mouthparts. In studying *Brugia pahangi* in *Aedes togoi* (Theobald), Lavoipierre and Ho (1966) conclude that bending back of the labium is the most important factor bringing about escape of the infective forms. A study in Ceylon (Samarawickrema, 1962) indicated *C. pipiens quinquefasciatus* Say can transmit *W. bancrofti* by the fourth blood meal. Infective larvae enter the vertebrate host's lymph stream and develop to sexual maturity in the lymphatics to produce new microfilariae in the peripheral blood (Fig. 11-22). Blood stream infection of children less than five years old is rare in bancroftian filariasis (presumably due to a long development period of the worms) and quite common in brugian filariasis.

Filariasis is manifested in humans in a number of ways. In endemic areas a considerable proportion of the population is infected, as confirmed by blood smear examination, but otherwise remains without observable symptoms. An inflammatory, or acute phase, characterized by fever and chills as well as swollen lymphatics may occur months after exposure to infection. Brown (1945) suggests

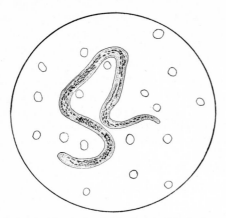

Fig. 11-22 *Wuchereria bancrofti,* in human blood. × 333.

these are allergic phenomena in response to products of the worms or to an accompanying bacterial infection. In obstructive filariasis (*elephantiasis*) there will be gross enlargement of structures (scrotum, vulvae, breasts, legs) due to blockage of lymph drainage, a consequence of years of exposure. In brugian filariasis obstructive symptoms are generally not as extreme, often being only a less obvious swelling of the legs and ankles. Fortunately elephantiasis is the exception rather than the rule in endemic areas.

Manson observed in 1877–78 that microfilariae are particularly prevalent in the peripheral blood at night. Since his observations it has been found that markedly *periodic* forms and forms much less periodic occur. The less-periodic forms are properly termed *subperiodic*, though older literature refers to these as aperiodic. Recognition of periodicity is important, for it is necessary to sample peripheral blood at night in making surveys of filarial infestation where nocturnal periodism is present. In bancroftian filariasis, presence of the subperiodic forms provides a valuable clue indicating the vector is likely a species of *Aedes*. Causality of periodicity, or its lack, is a point of considerable interest relating to the subject of circadian rhythms. Undoubtedly the selective factor dictating periodicity has been

a response to the vector, with incidence of peripheral blood microfilariae coinciding with the natural biting period of the local vector(s). The migrating characteristics of microfilariae may be in response to certain daily physiological changes within the vertebrate host; for example, filariae of *Brugia malayi* that are nocturnally periodic in leaf monkeys became subperiodic when transmitted to cats (Laing, 1961); or consist of a self-propagating internal rhythm as illustrated by the nocturnal form of *B. malayi* in man that retains this periodicity in cats or monkeys (Laing, *et al.*, 1961).

Bancroftian Filariasis. *Wuchereria bancrofti* occurs in periodic and subperiodic forms. The periodic form, with marked nocturnal periodicity, is characteristic of humid tropics of the world and is transmitted by night-biting mosquitoes. This form also occurs around the Mediterranean and in Turkey. The other form is diurnally subperiodic, restricted to Polynesia, and transmitted mainly by day-biting *Aedes* mosquitoes. Various strains within these forms have been shown in experimental vector studies.

Bancroftian filariasis is largely an urban and surburban disease due to the habits of its principal vector, *Culex pipiens quinquefasciatus* Say (=*C. p. fatigans* Wiedemann). Strains of periodic *W. bancrofti* with an *Anopheles* vector have been found in rural areas of Malaya and Borneo. Attempts to find wild vertebrate hosts other than man for this filaria species, as well as laboratory attempts to infect various vertebrates, have all been unsuccessful. Despite the listing of many more mosquito species as being infected, Edeson and Wilson (1964) make the distinction of "infective" (capable of infecting a vertebrate because of the presence of mature infective larvae at time of capture) to derive a listing of vectors of bancroftian filariasis. Their listing is: *Anopheles bancrofti* Giles, *A. sinensis* Wiedemann, *A. whartoni* Reid, *A. darlingi* Root, *A. farauti* Laveran, *A. funestus* Giles, *A. gambiae* Giles, *A. melas* (Theobald), *A. koliensis* Owen, *A. minimus* Theobald; *Mansonia uniformis*

(Theobald); *Aedes kochi* (Dönitz), *Ae. togoi* (Theobald), *Ae. vigilax* (Skuse), *Ae. fijiensis* Marks, *Ae. polynesiensis* Marks, *Ae. pseudoscutellaris* (Theobald); *Culex annulirostris* Skuse, *C. bitaeniorhynchus* Giles, *C. pipiens pallens* Coquillet, and *C. p. quinquefasciatus* Say. To this may be added *C. sinensis* Theobald, *Ae. niveus* (Ludlow), *Ae. samoanus* (Grünberg), *Ae. poicilius* (Theobald).

Brugian Filariasis. *Brugia malayi* is predominantly an infection of rural populations in the Far East between 75–140 degrees east longitudes, occurring in small endemic foci. The periodic form in man is transmitted by night-biting *Mansonia* and some *Anopheles* and is the main form in man with only rare occurrence in other animals. The subperiodic form is transmitted by *Mansonia* of swamp forests that feed at any time, with infections common in a variety of mammals. It may be extremely difficult to separate *B. malayi* in mosquitoes from other species of mammal-infesting *Brugia* where these occur. Edeson and Wilson (1964) list the vectors of *B. malayi* as *Anopheles campestris* Reid, *A. sinensis* Wiedemann, *A. lesteri* Baisas and Hu; *Mansonia annulifera* (Theobald), *M. indiana* Edwards, *M. uniformis* (Theobald), *M. annulata* Leicester, *M. bonneae* Edwards, *M. dives* (Schiner). To these can be added *A. barbirostris* Wulp, *M. longipalpis* Van der Wulp, *M. ochracea* (Theobald), *Aedes togoi* (Theobald).

There are other *Brugia* filariae that may be difficult to distinguish. *Brugia pahangi* (Buckley and Edeson) is found naturally parasitizing a variety of mammals in various locations in Malaya. It has been experimentally transmitted to man (Edeson, *et al.*, 1960). *Brugia patei* (Buckley, *et al.*) occurs as a natural infection of domestic dogs and cats in East Africa; it occurs also in genet cats (*Genetta tigrina*), bush baby (*Galago*), and probably other mammals (Nelson, *et al.*, 1962). *Brugia buckleyi* of hares, and *Brugia ceylonensis* of dogs occur in Ceylon (Jayawardene, 1963).

Control of Human Filariasis. The control of filariasis has been extensively studied under the auspices of the World Health Organization and various regional organizations. Control of the disease may be approached by reducing the vector populations to a low level, and in this endeavor control of *Culex pipiens quinquefasciatus* Say (=*C. p. fatigans* Wiedemann) has received particular attention for bancroftian filariasis. In India Bhatia and Wattal (1958) concluded transmission by *C. p. quinquefasciatus* does not occur where biting density of the mosquito does not exceed 3.4 per man hour in seasons when climate favors development of the parasite. Chemotherapy may also be practiced for radical cure and to reduce the number of microfilariae in peripheral blood to a subinfective level. Reduced numbers of microfilariae also diminish the likelihood of development of obstructive filariasis. The drug commonly used is orally administered diethyl-carbamazine (N, N-diethyl-4methyl-1-piperazinesorboxamine dihydrogen citrate). This compound is much more lethal to microfilariae than to adult worms, and is often used for prophylactic treatment in endemic areas; resistance has not appeared, probably because of its low lethality for adult worms. Kessel (1957) reports that in Tahiti diethylcarbamazine administered for four years reduced acute bancroftian filariasis by 84 per cent, and in a follow-up report (Kessel, 1967), not only were the per cent positives reduced, but the microfilariae level in blood became so low that transmission by vectors seemed much less a possibility; a similar program against brugian filariasis in Malaya (Wharton, *et al.*, 1958) was ineffective, probably because the areas controlled were too small and there was an untreated reservoir in domestic and forest animals.

Dog Heartworm and Other Filariae. Filariae of dogs, caused by *Dirofilaria* species, are a major veterinary problem in much of the world. *Dirofilaria immitis* (Leidy), a cosmopolitan species found in nearly all tropical and subtropical regions of the world, is now quite common in parts of the Great Lakes and New England areas of the United States (Beaver,

1966). This species occurs in dogs, and occasionally in cats and other species of carnivores. The adult worms invade the heart and pulmonary arteries of the host, where they often form tangled knots and may cause death by embolism, asphyxia, and dilation of the heart. *Culex pipiens, Aedes aegypti*, and many other culcines and anophelines are known vectors. *Dirofilaria repens* (Railliet and Henry) also affects dogs and is transmitted by *Aedes* and *Anopheles*. Both nematodes develop in the Malpighian tubes of their insect host, causing damage and even death of the vector if too many microfilariae are ingested.

Other *Dirofilaria* species, all mosquito transmitted, are listed by Hawking and Worms (1961) as *Dirofilaria corynodes* (Linstow) and *D. magnilarvatum* Price of monkeys, *D. scapiceps* (Leidy) of cottontail rabbit, *D. subdermata* (Monnig) of *Erethizon dorsatum* (porcupine), and *D. tenuis* Chandler of raccoon.

Dirofilaria in man can constitute a health problem. Beaver and Orihel (1965) discuss cases where *D. immitis* reached maturity in man, to be discovered at autopsy in heart and adjacent vessels; or dead and folded in a pulmonary artery when lung sections were removed surgically on suspicion of cancer. They also mention the occurrence in the southeastern United States of subcutaneous nodules or abscesses from which *Dirofilaria* (probably *D. tenuis* of raccoon) were removed.

Other filariae of warm- and cold-blooded vertebrates, transmitted by mosquitoes, are included in Hawking and Worms, 1961. Filariae of vertebrates other than man may be transmitted by ticks, mites, ceratopogonid flies, fleas, tabanids, simuliids, and muscoid flies.

12

HORSE FLIES, DEER FLIES, AND SNIPE FLIES

ORDER DIPTERA; SUBORDER BRACHYCERA

(Bloodsucking Members)

The Suborder Brachycera, aside from the Tabanidae, does not contain many flies of medical importance. However, the genus *Symphoromyia* of the family Rhagionidae includes a number of species of vicious blood-suckers; and *Hermetia illucens* (Linnaeus), family Stratiomyidae, is sometimes involved in myiasis, on the one hand, yet may, as a larva, compete with the house fly to the dis-advantage of the latter. This chapter is con-cerned with the bloodsucking members of the suborder.

HORSE FLIES AND DEER FLIES

(Clegs, Breezeflies, Greenheads, and so forth)

FAMILY TABANIDAE

The large and cosmopolitan Family Tabani-dae includes the avidly bloodsucking flies known by a variety of names including horse flies, deer flies, clegs, breeze flies, greenheads, and mango flies. In Australia the term "March flies" is used, although in the Northern Hemi-sphere this name applies to an entirely different family of Diptera (Bibionidae). Tabanids are usually quite large and heavy bodied, measur-ing in length from 6 to 10 mm in the smaller species to about 25 mm in the larger ones. They are strong fliers and notorious pests of horses, cattle, deer, and many other warm-blooded animals; at times these flies, particu-larly the persistent members of the genus *Chrysops*, annoy man. The males feed on vege-table materials and do not bite; in fact they cannot do so because they have no mandibles. The eyes are very large and widely separated (dichoptic) in the females, and usually contiguous (holoptic) in the males. The antennae are short (though fairly long in some genera such as *Chrysops*) and are porrect (that is, projecting horizontally), consisting of three segments, the terimnal one, or flagellum, elongated and subdivided into flagellomeres, or subsegments, but not bearing an arista. The wing venation is characteristic in that the branches of vein R_{4+5} diverge broadly, thereby enclosing the apex of the wing between them. The mouth parts of the female are blade-like and function as cutting instruments, though the labella are fitted for sponging (Fig. 3-6).

Most species are aquatic or semiaquatic in breeding habits. In these, the eggs are normally deposited in layers on objects over water or situations favorable for the larvae, such as overhanging foliage, projecting rocks, sticks, and emergent aquatic vegetation (Figs. 12-1, 12-2). The narrow cylindrical eggs, 1.0 to 2.5 mm long, vary in numbers from 100 to 1,000

Fig. 12-1 A deer fly, *Chrysops* sp., in the act of oviposition. Note also an egg mass lower down on the leaf. × 1. (Photograph by Hine.)

and are deposited commonly in layers covered with a waterproof secretion that also binds the eggs together tightly.

The larva (Figs. 12-2, 12-3) has a slender, cylindrical, contractile body tapering at both ends and consisting of a small head and twelve additional segments. The head is retractile, with pointed mandibles capable of inflicting a sharp bite; at the posterior end is situated a tracheal siphon that telescopes into the anal segment. The pupa (Fig. 12-3) resembles those of naked Lepidoptera, is obtect, abruptly rounded anteriorly, tapering posteriorly, with leg and wing cases attached to the body; the abdominal segments are free and about equal in length, segments two to seven each bearing a more or less complete ring of spines near the posterior third. The adult fly emerges from the pupal case through a slit along the dorsum of the thorax, as do the rest of the Brachycera.

Breeding Habits and Life History. The eggs are deposited during the warmer months of the year. The incubation period is greatly influenced by weather conditions, but during midsummer the usual range is from five to seven days. The larvae of the aquatic species, on hatching, fall to the surface of the water, upon mud or moist earth, in clumps, and quickly drop to the bottom or burrow individually into the wet or damp earth, where they begin to feed on organic matter. Species of *Tabanus* and *Haematopota* are voracious predators on insect larvae, crustaceans, snails, earthworms, and other soft-bodied animals; cannibalism has been observed in several species. *Chrysops* larvae are probably vegetarians, according to Oldroyd (1964). The larvae of Tabanidae are commonly encountered buried in wet soil in such places as along the edge of marshy ponds and salt marshes, roadside ditches, and the overflow from rice fields; certain species may be found in moist leaf mold and debris, rotting logs, or in the water. Some inhabit tree holes and brackish water. Some species have terrestrial larvae. Schomberg and Howell (1955) have shown

Fig. 12-2 *Tabanus punctifer.* Egg mass on willow leaf, larva, pupa, and adult female.

that *Tabanus abactor* Philip and *T. equalis* Hine breed in soil, in the shade of trees, and under either dry grass or sparse short grass, where standing water never or seldom occurs, and Jones and Anthony (1964) have cited references to similar habitats for *Tabanus sulcifrons* Macquart and *T. quinquevittatus* Macquart; the latter mistakenly identified as *T. vicarius* Walker, was reported by Logathetis and Schwardt as an open-pasture breeder in New York State.

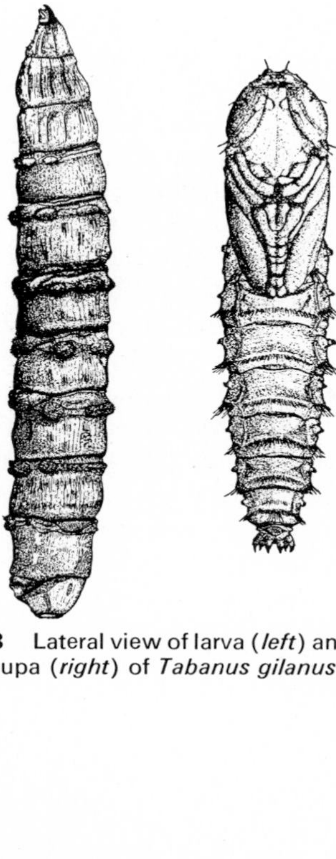

Most temperate climate species produce one generation a year. In these, the larva (Figs. 12-2, 12-3) grows rapidly during the summer and autumn, and very slowly, if at all during the winter; it attains full growth in the following early spring. Some species, however, such as *Tabanus vittiger schwardti* Philip, may have two generations a year, whereas others, such as *Tabanus calens* Linnaeus, require two or three years to complete their development. Individual larvae of other species may take two or three seasons for development if conditions are unfavorable the first season or if they do not get enough food (H. Oldroyd, personal communication to James).

It is difficult to determine the number of larval instars; this varies, according to some authors, from four to nine, the first molt evidently taking place shortly after hatching. An excellent account of the early stages of Tabanidae may be found in the study of Marchand (1920).

When the full-grown larva prepares to pupate, it usually moves into drier earth, usually an inch or two below the surface, and

Fig. 12-3 Lateral view of larva (*left*) and ventral view of pupa (*right*) of *Tabanus gilanus.*

in a day or two the pupal stage is reached. This stage requires from five days to three weeks, varying with the species. The flies emerge from the pupal case, and make their way to the surface, the wings soon unfold, and the insects take refuge among nearby foliage or rest on objects near at hand; in a short time they begin to feed, the females seeking blood and the males feeding on flowers and vegetable juices.

In some species, according to Oldroyd (personal communication to James), mating may take place during the hardening period following a mass emergence of both sexes together. The flies then disperse, and presumably the males soon die. Other species emerge individually, and mating takes place through the agency of male swarms, which are visited by the females. The swarms may be small; in fact a so-called swarm may consist of a single male.

Much important information based on rearing experience with many species may be obtained by consulting various publications such as those by Stone (1930), Schwardt (1936), Philip (1931), and Jones and Anthony (1964).

Bites. Female horse flies have broad, bladelike mouth parts (Fig. 3-6) that inflict a deep, painful wound, causing a considerable flow of blood, which they lap up by means of their sponging labella. Man may be seriously annoyed, particularly by *Chrysops, Silvius*, and some species of *Tabanus, Hybomitra, Diachlorus*, and other genera, but he is better able to protect himself by driving the flies away and by use of repellents than are wild and domestic animals. Nevertheless, tabanids may be annoying in certain recreational or work areas, such as where timber is being harvested, to the extent that economic loss may result.

Blood loss in livestock may constitute a serious problem. Philip (1931) estimated that, in Minnesota, an animal subjected to steady attack by fifty flies at any one time throughout a ten-hour period in one day would lose 300 ml, or nearly a third of a quart, of blood.

Infestations much heavier than fifty flies per animal frequently occur. Tashiro and Schwardt (1949) reported that, in New York State, it was not uncommon for 720 *Tabanus quinque-fasciatus* Wiedemann or 320 *T. sulcifrons* Macquart to feed on one animal for eight hours, with an estimated blood consumption of 0.074 and 0.359 ml per fly for these two species, respectively. These figures do not include loss of blood that exudes from tabanid punctures. Jones and Anthony (1964) observed, on one occasion, an estimated loss of 75 to 100 ml of blood oozing from a single puncture made by *T. atratus*, although this probably was the result of a physiological condition in the animal rather than the effect of the anti-coagulin injected by the fly. Heavily infested livestock commonly show hair on exposed areas matted with blood that has come from such punctures.

Feeding habits vary with the genera and even species. Oldroyd (1964) believes that *Haematopota*, which feeds especially on Bovidae, has evolved along with its mammalian hosts. He points out that there are no members of this genus in Australia or South America, where native Bovidae are lacking; that only five species occur in North America; but that 50 occur in the Palaeartic, 70 in the Oriental, and 180 in the Ethiopian region, areas where cattle and antelopes have likewise undergone their great development. *Tabanus* has a much wider host range, some species attacking reptiles as well as mammals. *Chrysops*, which commonly lives in broken woodland areas, commonly attacks members of the deer family but many species readily and severely attack man. No tabanid is absolutely host-specific, even though definite preferences may be shown. Most tabanids are daylight feeders, though some feed at dawn or dusk or even at night.

Leclercq (1952) has pointed out that, although members of the horse, cow, and camel family are most commonly attacked, with man chosen by the fly in the absence of the more preferred hosts, other mammals and also such reptiles as lizards and land and sea turtles are attacked. He points out, however, that there are no records of feeding on birds or amphibians.

The intermittent feeding habit of tabanids increases their likelihood to be involved in mechanical transmission of disease. A fly, interrupted in or ceasing its feeding activities on one individual, may readily pass on to another, so that sick and healthy individuals may be attacked in succession by the same fly. This behavior is particularly noticeable where animals are bunched together for mutual protection from their tormentors. A single feeding puncture is sufficient to contaminate the proboscis of a fly, and the subsequent biting of another animal within a short period of time may easily transfer the pathogen to the blood stream of the second host.

Excellent accounts of Tabanidae as vectors of disease-causing organisms are given by Leclercq (1952) and more recently by Anthony (1962). Leclercq's tabulation of records of pathogen transmission is especially valuable, though in need of being brought up to date.

Relation to Anthrax. Anthrax, also known as malignant pustule, carbuncle, wool sorter's disease, or charbon, is caused by *Bacillus anthracis*. Nearly all species of domestic mammals and man are susceptible; the herbivores and rodents are most likely to become infected.

After the inoculation of the organism into the animal, its incubation period is from three to six days. The bacilli are seen in the blood stream in advanced cases as chains of rod-shaped bodies. Entrance to the body is gained in various ways: through local pricks and lesions, including insect bites; through inhalation of the spores; through infected animals and animal products; through ingestion of food, as in grazing by livestock in contaminated pastures; through dried insect feces, and through drinking from contaminated streams and ponds.

Horse flies relate directly to the first mode of infection (inoculation), and it is not altogether improbable that an epizootic of

anthrax might thus be started and spread. Nuttal (1899) cites two early references to tabanid transmission of anthrax. The first of these was by Hintermayer, in 1846, in which several horse fly species were apparently involved in an epizootic of deer by first feeding on the fallen carcasses and then immediately turning to healthy animals. The second was by Bollinger, in 1874, who captured horse flies on a cow that had died from anthrax and then observed the bacilli in preparations made from the digestive tracts of the insects; two rabbits that were inoculated therewith died of anthrax.

Mitzmain (1914), in a series of experiments with *Tabanus striatus* Fabricus, showed that direct mechanical inoculation of guinea pigs could be readily effected by the bite of the fly. He permitted the flies to feed on an inoculated guinea pig shortly before its death and transferred the flies, within forty-five seconds to thirty minutes, to a healthy guinea pig. The death of these animals followed in three to three and one-half days.

Instances are recorded in which apparently the simple bite of an infected fly was all that was needed to produce malignant pustules in human beings. Several veterinarians have related instances to Herms in which this had occurred, notably one case in which a man was in the act of burying a cow that had died of anthrax when he was severely bitten on the back of the neck by a horse fly and in due time developed a malignant pustule at the site of the bite. Similar cases have been cited in the literature.

Tularemia. In 1919 a disease of man of hitherto unknown etiology occurring in Utah was reported by Francis as deer fly fever or Pahvant Valley plague. It was later identified by the same author with a disease reported among rodents in Tulare County, California, by McCoy and Chapin in 1912 and was given the name tularemia. It is a specific infectious disease traceable to *Francisella tularensis* (McCoy and Chapin). It was described by Francis as a disease of rural population occurring during the summer months, coinciding with the prevalence of the newly discovered vector, *Chrycops discalis* Williston, a deer fly. Francis states:

Following the fly bite on some exposed surface of the body (neck, face, hands or legs) the onset is sudden, with pains and fever; the patient is prostrated and is confined to bed; the lymph glands which drain the bitten area become tender, inflamed and swollen, and commonly suppurate, requiring incision. The fever is of a septic type, lasting from three to six weeks, and convalescence is slow.

The disease occurs not only in the United States, but also in Canada, Alaska, northern Europe, Russia, Japan, and many other parts of the world. The pathology of tularemia is described in great detail by Lillie and Francis (1936). In the acute form of the disease a primary ulcer (eschar) develops at the site of the inoculation. Pneumonic complication may result. In highly susceptible persons it may assume the form of a septicemia, which may result in death between the fourth and fourteenth days.

Francis and his coworkers found that rabbits constitute an important reservoir for the bacillus and that it is transmitted from rabbit to rabbit by *Chrysops discalis*. As Jellison (1950) has pointed out, the geographical distribution of this fly corresponds roughly with that of tularemia in the western United States. The fly is undoubtedly merely a mechanical vector, and is only one of a number of arthropods that can be involved as such. There is evidence to indicate that ticks may be much more important than flies. According to Steinhaus (1946), at least fifty-four different arthropods can harbor the pathogen. These include several species of ticks (see Chapter 18). Tularemia is now known to exist in nature in many species of vertebrates; among these are meadow mice, ground squirrels, beavers, coyotes, sheep, and quail and other game birds.

Loiasis. The mango fly, *Chrysops dimidiata* van der Wulp, was shown by Leiper to be a vector of *Loa loa* (Cobbald), an African eye worm that occurs in various regions in the tropical rain forests of western and central Africa. *Chrysops silacea* Austen was proved to be a carrier of the organism by Connal and Connal (1922), who elucidated the life cycle of the parasite not only in this fly but in *C. dimidiata* as well. Microfilariae of *Loa loa* are found in the peripheral blood vessels during the daytime, showing a diurnal periodicity. The larvae (Fig. 12-4) measure about 300 microns in length by 7.5 microns in thickness, resembling *Wuchereria bancrofti* (Cobbald) very closely. In this stage, they are ingested by the *Chrysops* flies, and undergo development similar to that of *Wuchereria bancrofti* in the mosquito. Metamorphosis is completed in from ten to twelve days, the larva increasing in length "tenfold." When the infected fly bites, the mature larvae issue from the proboscis, come to lie upon the skin of the host, and quickly disappear by burrowing.

The adult worms, females measuring from 50 to 70 mm in length and the males about half this length, inhabit the superficial subcutaneous connective tissue and are known to move about from place to place quite rapidly, giving rise to transient itching swellings known as Calabar swellings. The parasites have been observed in many parts of the body, such as the scrotum, penis, breast, eyelids, anterior chamber of the eye, tongue, finger, and back. The worms may be most readily excised when they travel across the bridge of the nose or the conjunctiva.

So far as known, only *Chrysops* species are involved in the transmission of *Loa loa*. *C. silicea* is undoubtedly the most important vector, according to Anthony (1962); this species readily bites man and readily enters houses, the latter possibly in part a result of the attraction of this fly to wood smoke. *C. dimidiata*, likewise a domestic species, is also important. At least five other species have been shown to be capable of supporting the development of the parasite. Some of these may be associated with epizootics in monkeys, which

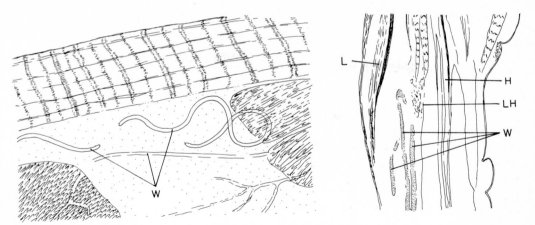

Fig. 12-4 Sections of *Loa loa* in the tissues and mouth parts of *Chrysops silacea*. On the left larvae may be seen among muscles of the head region. On the right infective larvae are in the process of escaping through the labiohypopharyngeal membrane. *H,* Hypopharynx; *L,* labium; *W,* worms. (Redrawn from photomicrographs by Lavoipierre, *Ann. Trop. Med. Parasit.,* **52**:103.)

are also known to be hosts of closely related species of *Loa.*

Animal Trypanosomiases. Surra is a highly fatal disease of horses in southeastern Asia and other parts of the Far East; it occurs also in parts of Africa and of Central and South America. It was first described from India by Evans in 1885. The causal agent is *Trypanosoma evansi* (Steel). Several domestic and wild animals are involved as hosts and reservoirs. The disease may occur in a highly fatal form in dogs; in horses it is usually fatal, and camels are seriously affected. The acute form may occur in cattle and buffaloes when the parasite is introduced into a new area, but these animals are usually not seriously affected and may serve for months as reservoirs.

The trypanosomes (Fig. 12-5) are found in the blood of infected animals, and especially in the lymph and swollen glands, from the beginning of the first symptoms. During the early stages of the disease virtually no clinical manifestations are visible except a variable appetite and an intermittent fever; there is progressive emaciation and edema of the abdomen and genitalia. Guinea pigs, white mice, and monkeys are highly susceptible laboratory animals.

Mitzmain (1913) succeeded in transferring the pathogen from animal to animal through the agency of a horse fly, *Tabanus striatus* Fabricius. The transfer of the parasite took place within fifteen minutes of the infectious meal, despite the fact that the trypanosomes could survive as long as thirty hours in the digestive tract of the fly. Transmission is mechanical. About twenty-five species of Tabanidae, in the genera *Tabanus, Atylotus,* and *Haematopota,* have been reported as vectors of *Trypanosoma evansi.*

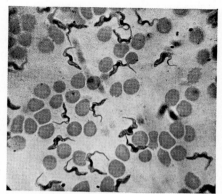

Fig. 12-5 *Trypanosoma evansi,* the causal organism of surra. (After Yutuc.)

Several other pathogenic trypanosomes can be transmitted by tabanids (Anthony, 1962). The transmission of *T. equinum* Voges, the cause of a disease similar to surra that occurs in South America, has been attributed to *Stomoxys* and tabanids. *T. hippicum* Darling, highly pathogenic to hoires in Panama, the Canal Zone, and probably Colombia, is transmitted chiefly by the bite of vampire bats, but tabanids are also involved. Transmission of these pathogens, as well as that of surra, is mechanical, but *T. theileri* Laveran undergoes cyclical development in the midgut of tabanids, the infective forms of the protozoon passing to the hindgut and then voided with the feces. This species is commonly regarded as non-pathogenic, but it has been shown to be associated with at least one case of bovine abortion.

Other Animal Diseases. Anaplasmosis, or infectious anemia, a frequently fatal disease of cattle, is caused by *Anaplasma marginale* Theiler, an organism that has been generally considered a protozoon but whose biological nature and consequently taxonomic position is now in question. Ticks transmit this organism biologically, but tabanids are frequently involved mechanically. Anthony (1962) lists eleven tabanids in the genera *Hybomitra, Tabanus, Chrysops,* and *Silvius* that have been shown to be experimental vectors. Anthony concludes that tabanids are probably highly important vectors in some parts of the world, for example the southeastern United States, but are of little importance in others.

Equine infectious anemia, or swamp fever, of horses, is a viral disease that may result on occasion from tabanid transmission. Some success has been had in the experimental transmission of this disease.

The Species of Tabanidae. The family Tabanidae is a fairly large one of almost worldwide distribution, being absent only in high altitudes and latitudes and in such insular areas as Hawaii. There are about 3,000 species distributed through thirty to eighty genera, depending upon the interpretation of

the authority. The Nearctic forms have been treated in monographs by Stone (1938) and Brennan (1935). Many important studies have been made in other parts of the world, and some excellent regional treatments exist; among the more comprehensive publications are the general studies of MacKerras (1954–55); those of Kröber (1925) and Leclercq (1960) for the Palearctic Region; those of MacKerras (1956–1961) for Australia; and those of Oldroyd (1952–1957) for the Ethiopian region. Surcouf (1921) has treated the family in the "Genera Insectorum," and J. Moucha has a list of the Tabanidae of the world in preparation.

The family is divided into three subfamilies. Of these the Pangoniinae comprise those genera in which the flagellum of the antenna consists of six or eight flagellomeres; the proboscis in many species is elongated and the labella and palpi are small. Some Pangoniinae suck blood, but the majority of them are flower feeders. In the other two subfamilies, in which those tabanids of greater medical and veterinary importance are found, the flagellum has only five flagellomeres and the proboscis is shorter, with large labella and palpi. Of these, the Chrysopinae, which include such genera as *Chrysops* and *Silvius*, have apical spurs on the hind tibiae, while the Tabaninae, which include *Tabanus, Hybomitra,* and *Haematopota*, lack these spurs. The Chrysopinae are included in the Pangoniinae by some authorities, but the tendency is to recognize these two subfamilies as distinct.

Tabanus atratus Fabricius (Fig. 12-6), the widespread black horse fly of eastern North America, is uniformly black, and the thorax and abdomen in well-preserved specimens are thinly covered with a whitish pollen, or dust. In certain lights, unless this pollen is rubbed off, the abdomen shows a distinctly bluish cast. Curran believes, probably correctly, that this is the "blue-tailed fly" of the well-known ballad.

Among the more serious pests of livestock in the United States are *Tabanus punctifer*

Fig. 12-6 The black horse fly, *Tabanus atratus*. *A*. Male. *B*. Female. × 1.5. (Photograph by Hine.)

A   B

Osten Sacken in the West, *T. stygius* Say east of the Rocky Mountains, and *T. sulcifrons* Macquart in the Midwest and the Great Plains states. These are large, black species that will readily attack cattle but not man. *Tabanus quinquefasciatus* Wiedemann, the notorious "greenhead," and *T. lineola* Fabricius, the striped horse fly, are very annoying pests in the eastern United States. *T. striatus* Fabricius is well known by virtue of the investigations on this fly as a vector of the pathogens of anthrax and surra. In the western and northern United States and in Canada, various species of *Hybomitra* are annoying to man and animals alike.

The genus *Chrysops* (Figs. 12-1, 12-7) contains about eighty North American species. Leclercq lists forty-five species, some with several subspecies each, in the Palearctic region, and Oldroyd lists thirty-eight Ethiopian species. Many members of this genus attack man readily and persistently. They are smaller than most *Tabanus* and have pictured wings that are usually definitely cross-banded. The term deer fly is commonly applied to this genus. *Chrysops discalis* Williston, which breeds in shallow alkaline waters in the western United States, has been particularly associated with the transmission of the tularemia pathogen, and several African species, including *C. silacea* Austen and *C. dimidiata* van der Wulp,

are associated with the transmission of *Loa loa*.

Haematopota americana (Osten Sacken) occurs from central Alaska to New Mexico. It is quite different in appearance from *Tabanus* and *Chrysops* in that its wings are quite characteristically densely mottled. As was previously pointed out, this genus, though poorly represented in the New World, is richly represented in some parts of the Old

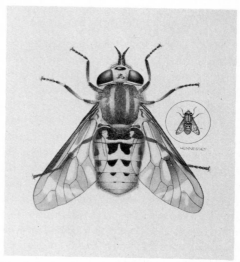

Fig. 12-7 *Chrysops discalis* Williston adult female. (Courtesy Canada Department of Agriculture.)

World but absent in others; for example, Oriental species are numerous but there are none in New Guinea or Australia. *Silvius pollinosus* Williston and *S. quadrivittatus* (Say), small gray species with distinctly but rather sparsely mottled wings, are viciously annoying to both man and animals in the area just east of the Rocky Mountains.

SNIPE FLIES

FAMILY RHAGIONIDAE

Snipe flies belong to the family Rhagionidae, also known as the Leptidae. This family comprises nonbloodsuckers as well as bloodsucking species. Leonard (1930), who has written the only comprehensive work on the North American species to date, characterizes the family as follows:

Flies of moderate to large size usually more or less elongated and nearly bare to moderately pilose, rarely rather densely hairy, never, however, with distinct bristles. Males usually holoptic; more rarely dichoptic. Empodium pulvilliform, there being three pads of about equal size between the tarsal claws ... Veins of the wing distinct, not crowded anteriorly; third longitudinal (vein)* furcate; basal cells large; five posterior cells usually present.

Several genera have been reported as containing bloodsucking species, but in some of these the statements to that effect are poorly documented or based on supposition. Some species of the Holarctic *Symphoromyia* (Fig. 12-8), however, are without doubt important annoyers of man and animals. In this genus the antennae, which are highly variable in the family as a whole, are characteristic, the flagellum being kidney-shaped (sometimes concave in dorsal profile below the arista and then not exactly kidney-shaped) with a subterminal arista. The Mexican *Suragina longipes* (Bellardi), which has been reported, apparently authentically, as a bloodsucker, has

* Leonard says "cell" (lapsus).

Fig. 12-8 A snipe fly, *Symphoromyia hirta.* (After Hearle.)

similar antennae but the wings are banded, whereas those of *Symphoromyia* are clear. The Australian genus *Spaniopsis*, which also sucks blood, has an elongated antennal flagellum that terminates in a style.

The females of several species of *Symphoromyia* are vicious biters, behaving somewhat as do the tabanid flies of the genus *Chrysops*. They alight on the exposed parts of the body quite silently and singly, and inflict a sudden painful bite usually before their presence is known. Both the severity of the bite and the accompanying pathology vary with the individual bitten. Man is the most commonly recorded host for the genus, but Hoy and Anderson (1966) record its frequent attacks on deer; other hosts include cattle, horses, and dogs. Some species of *Symphoromyia* may be mistaken at first for stable flies. Among the severe biters are *Symphoromyia atripes* Bigot, *S. hirta* Johnson, and *S. sackeni* Aldrich. The genus is best represented in mountainous and coastal terrains in the western North America, although it also occurs in eastern North America and in Europe. The Australian species of *Sapniopsis* (as *Spania*) are reviewed by Paramonov (1962).

The mouth parts are of the tabanid type, the strongly sclerotized piercing and cutting structures being enclosed in a retractile labial sheath; as in the tabanids, blood is lapped up by the labella. The mouth parts have been studied in detail by Ross (1940).

Very little is known about the breeding habits and life history of the species of *Symphoromyia*. According to the studies of Frohne (1957), Sommerman (1962), and Hoy (1966), larvae breed in wet, peaty soil and moss along temporary stream banks and similar places, a characteristic of the family as a whole, so far as is known.

The potential medical and veterinary importance of *Symphoromyia* is at the present time undetermined. Shemanchuk and Weintraub (1961) have shown that a fly probes repeatedly in taking a meal. This, plus the facts that in some species, such as *S. sackeni*, females are relatively abundant, may take large volumes of blood, and may feed several times in a lifetime, suggests that such species may serve as vectors of deer parasites or may even be involved in the epidemiology of zoonoses (Hoy, 1966). The annoyance value may be considerable and, when man is the host, may interfere with the efficient use of resort areas.

13

SYRPHID FLIES, MUSCOID FLIES, AND LOUSE FLIES

SUBORDER CYCLORRHAPHA

Special Structural Characteristics of Adults. In the higher Diptera, certain anatomic structures peculiar to this group are used as a basis for the construction of keys and descriptions. The most important of these will be considered here.

The most conspicuous feature of the head (Fig. 13-1) is the pair of large *compound eyes* that, though widely separated from each other in the female, are often contiguous or very narrowly separated in the male, thereby greatly constricting the areas that lie between them. The *ocelli* are located on an *ocellar* or *frontal triangle* that is usually clearly demarcated; in the Chloropidae, this triangle is very large and may occupy most of the vertex and a considerable area of the front. The median area extending from the ocelli to the base of the antennae is the *frontal stripe* or *frontale*; to each side, adjoining the eye, lie the *parafrontals*, which, below the base of the antennae, become the *parafacials*. The central part of the face, set off by a suture that extends above the base of the antennae, terminates below an area called the epistoma, which may be produced forward over the *oral margin*. The ridges between the center of the face and the parafacials are called the *facialia* or *facials*.

The *antenna* (Fig. 10-2) is aristate, with an undivided flagellum; the second segment is set at a distinct angle to the first, so that the antenna is pendant rather than produced horizontally forward (porrect), as in most insects. The second antennal segment, in the calyptrate muscoids, is partially divided by a seam or suture that runs most of the length of its outer dorsal side. The *arista*, a large bristlelike structure arising high on the third

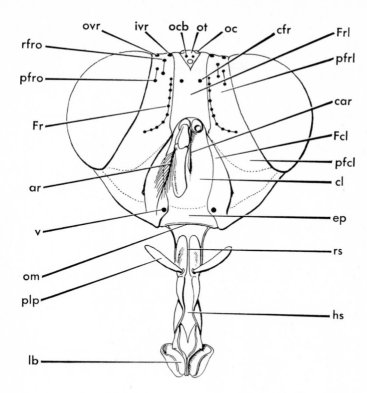

Fig. 13-1 Diagrammatic drawing of the head of a muscoid fly, from front view. Explanation of abbreviations: *ar*, arista; *car*, facial carina; *cfr*, cruciate frontal bristle (scar); *cl*, clypeus; *ep*, epistoma; *fcl*, faciale; *fr*, frontal row (bristle scars); *frl*, frontale (frontal stripe or vitta); *hs*, haustellum; *ivr*, inner vertical bristle (scar); *lb*, labella; *oc*, ocellus; *ocb*, ocellar bristle (scar); *ot*, ocellar triangle; *ovr*, outer vertical bristle (scar); *pfcl*, parafaciale; *pfrl*, parafrontale; *pfro*, proclinate fronto-orbital row (bristle scars); *plp*, palpus; *rfro*, reclinate fronto-orbital row (bristle scars); *rs*, rostrum; *v*, vibrissa. (Drawing by Arthur Cushman; U.S.D.A. photograph.)

segment, actually consists of several terminal flagellomeres of the antenna that have migrated onto a dorsal position and fused. The arista may be bare or hairy; the hairs may be situated above or below (plumose) or above only; if the latter, they may be simple (cf. Fig. 15-6) or, as in the tsetse flies (Fig. 15-2), plumose.

Chaetotaxy (the arrangement of macrochaetae or bristles) is important in the taxonomy of the muscoid flies. That of the head is shown in Figure 13-1, that of the thorax in Figures 13-2 and 13-3. The more important bristles mentioned in this text are the *vibrissae* (an unusually strong bristle on the lower part of each facial) and the following thoracic bristles: the *notopleurals, dorsocentrals, acrostichals, sternopleurals, hypopleurals,* and *scutellars*. These, as well as others not mentioned here, may be identified from Figures 13-2 and 13-3. The bristles of the abdomen are not so important, but the median marginals, i.e.,

erect bristles at the apices of the segments and near the median line (measured from left to right), will be mentioned in subsequent descriptions.

In addition to the chaetotaxy, mention should be made of the following thoracic structures. The two *thoracic spiracles* have been shown to be the *mesothoracic* and *metathoracic*, respectively (Fig. 13-2, *mss* and *mts*). The *propleuron* lies in front of the mesothoracic spiracle; whether its centrally depressed area is hairy or not may be of important taxonomic significance. In the calyptrate muscoids, a well-defined *mesonotal suture* is present, and the area between the wing base and the side of the *scutellum*, known as the *postalar callus*, is well differentiated. Two pairs of *squamae* are present, one (the alar) more closely associated with the wing, and the other (the *lower* or *thoracic*) closer to the wall of the thorax. The latter may be hairy above, and this may be of taxonomic significance. The

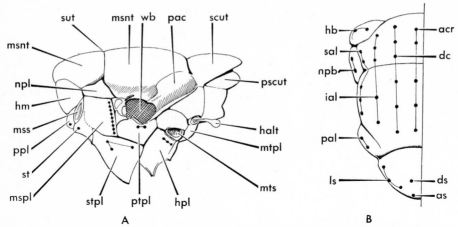

Fig. 13-2 Diagrammatic drawing of the thorax of a muscoid fly. *A.* Side view. *B.* Left half, dorsal view. Abbreviations of areas and bristle scars: *acr,* acrostichal row; *as,* apical scutellar; *dc,* dorsocentral row; *ds,* discal scutellar; *halt,* halter; *hb,* humeral row; *hm,* humerus; *hpl,* hypopleuron; *ial,* intra-alar row; *ls,* lateral scutellar row; *msnt,* mesonotum; *mspl,* mesopleuron; *mss,* mesothoracic spiracle; *mtpl,* metapleuron; *mts,* metathoracic spiracle; *npb,* notopleural row; *npl,* notopleuron; *pac,* postalar callus; *pal,* postalar row; *ppl,* propleuron; *pscut,* postscutellum; *ptpl,* pteropleuron; *sal,* supra-alar row; *scut,* scutellum; *st,* stigmatal; *stpl,* sternopleuron; *sut,* mesonotal suture; *wb,* wing base. Bristle scars not labeled are named in accordance with the sclerite on which they are located (propleural, sternopleural, mesopleural, hypopleural, pteropleural). (Drawing by Arthur Cushman; U.S.D.A. photograph.)

postscutellum (Fig. 13-2) in some of the calyptrate muscoids is strongly convex as in the figures; in others, it is inconspicuous or undeveloped.

The abdomen of a muscoid fly usually consists of four apparent segments, plus several others that are usually telescoped into the apparent fourth and that involve the male terminalia and the so-called "ovipositor." The term "apparent" is used here because in actuality the true first and second segments are fused into one.

In describing the covering of the integument the term *pubescence* refers to a very short, fine, downy hair that often escapes notice in casual examinations; the usual hairy covering of the adult consists of *pile*, which is soft and rather dense, and *setulae*, which are coarser. The bristles, or *macrochaetae*, are sometimes hard to distinguish from setulae, but in general they are quite distinct and tend to be arranged

in a definite order. The color of the body may be affected by *pollen*, a fine dustlike substance that may cover parts of the integument and give it a bloom, or that may be dense enough even to conceal the ground color. The term *pollen* in Latin means a "fine dust," and the aptness of its application also to the microspores of seed plants is obvious.

The following keys will aid in the identification of some of the higher Diptera of greater medical importance. To make identifications below the generic level, the student will need to consult specialized works that deal with the family and geographic area in question. Several useful manuals of recent date are James (1948), Van Emden (1954), Zumpt (1965), and Shtakelberg (1956); the last mentioned is an excellent work that will be useful even in dealing with the Nearctic fauna, but its use depends on the student having a reading knowledge of Russian. A very useful work that deals with

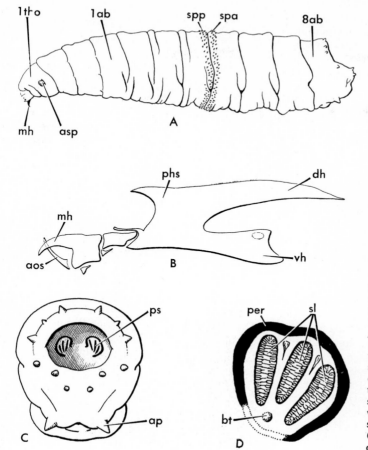

Fig. 13-3 Diagrammatic drawing of the mature larva of a muscoid fly. *A.* Lateral view. *B.* Cephalopharyngeal skeleton. *C.* Posterior view. *D.* A posterior spiracle. Explanation of abbreviations: *ab*, abdomen; *aos*, accessory oral sclerite; *asp*, anterior spiracle; *bt*, button; *dh*, dorsal horn of the pharyngeal sclerite; *mh*, mouth hooks; *per*, peritreme; *phs*, pharyngeal sclerite; *ps*, posterior spiracle; *sl*, slits of the posterior spiracle; *spa*, spines of the anterior margin of the segment; *spp*, spines of the posterior margin of the segment; *tho*, thorax; *vh*, ventral horn of the pharyngeal sclerite. (Drawing by Arthur Cushman; U.S.D.A. photograph.)

the third-stage larvae only is Ishijima (1967). Though based on the Japanese fauna, this is of wide use because of the broad distribution of the flies involved.

The following keys will aid in identification of the higher Diptera of greater medical importance. The family key does not include the Stratiomyidae, which belong in the Brachycera; *Hermetia illucens* (Linnaeus), in this family is a myiasis-causing fly of some importance. The key to the genera of Calliphoridae does not include some genera that may be involved in myiasis of wild vertebrates; for these, see Zumpt (1965). In this key, nestling bird parasites of the genus *Protocalliphora* (=*Apaulina*) will trace to couplet 5.

KEY TO THE FAMILIES OF HIGHER DIPTERA (CYCLORRHAPHA) THAT CONTAIN FORMS OF MEDICAL IMPORTANCE (ADULTS)

1. Body strongly flattened in a dorsoventral axis and with a tough leathery or horny integument; coxae widely separated at the base, the legs attached laterally and spreading away from the body (except in some Streblidae); ectoparasitic forms, frequently without wings. (Section Pupipara)....2
   Body usually not flattened and without an especially tough integument; coxae close

together, the legs attached ventrally and not particularly spreading; wings present, with rare exceptions. (Section Myodaria) 4

2. Head small, when at rest folded back into a groove on the dorsum of the thorax; prosternum produced................. ....Family Nycteribiidae
Head larger, not folding back into a groove on the dorsum of the thorax; prosternum not produced.............3

3. Palpi leaflike, broader than long, and not ensheathing the proboscis............. ....Family Streblidae
Palpi elongated, forming a sheath for the proboscis........Family Hippoboscidae

4. Wing with a spurious vein, that is, a vein-like fold in the membrane between the radius and the media and transversing the cross vein r-m; anal cell closed very close to the wing margin ....Family Syrphidae
Wing without a spurious vein; anal cell not prolonged toward the wing margin..5

5. Wing with only the veins toward the fore margin thickened, the others weak, oblique and not connected by cross veins........ ....Family Phoridae
Wing not as described, but with the normal muscoid type of venation.............6

6. Mouth parts nonfunctional, reduced to three knoblike structures (the two palpi and the rudimentary proboscis); bot and warble flies 7
Mouth parts well developed and functional 9

7. Postscutellum distinctly formed; squamae large; apical cell greatly narrowed or closed at its apex......Family Oestridae
Postscutellum undeveloped; squamae large or small, apical cell sometimes narrowed 8

8. Squamae small; apical cell gradually broadening to the wing margin.......... ....Family Gasterophilidae
Squamae large; apical cell greatly narrowed at its apex.....................
...................Family Cuterebridae

9. Second antennal segment with a longitudinal seam or suture extending along its outer upper edge; squamae usually large; postalar callus distinct 10
Second antennal segment without a longi-

tudinal suture; squamae usually small; postalar callus not differentiated.......12

10. Hypopleural bristles present; apical cell greatly narrowed toward its apex......11
Hypopleural bristles absent; apical cell sometimes narrowed toward its apex but often broadly open....................
....Families Muscidae and Anthomyiidae

11. Two strong notopleural bristles present; if there is a weak third, the abdomen is metallic blue, green, or coppery, and the depression of the propleuron is hairy; base of the radius before the humeral cross vein often hairy posteriorly.................
..................Family Calliphoridae
At least three or four notopleural bristles present, (*Wohlfahrtia* usually has only two) abdomen, in medically important forms, black (often reddish at the apex) with grayish or silvery pollen; depression of the propleuron bare; base of radius before the humeral cross vein bare posteriorly..........Family Sarcophagidae

12. Subcosta distinctly differentiated from vein R and ending independently in the costa............................13
Subcosta absent or only partially developed, not reaching the costa..........14

13. Metathoracic spiracle with one to several hairs (visible only under high magnification) on its border; palpi, vestigial; head, spherical; slender, wasp-waisted, somewhat resembling winged ants...........
......................Family Sepsidae
Metathoracic spiracle with only ordinary soft pubescence; palpi well developed; eyes round; bristles of the front confined to the upper part and consisting of at most two pairs...........Family Piophilidae

14. Frontal triangle very large, often occupying a large part of the front; vein Cu_1 with a slight, though quite distinct, crook or curvature near the middle of the discal cell; species of medical importance with a spur, usually curved, at the apex of the hind tibia. (*Hippelates*) ....
..................Family Chloropidae
Frontal triangle small; vein Cu_1 without a noticeable crook or curve at the middle of the discal cell; hind tibia without a curved spur at its apex.................
..................Family Drosophilidae

KEY TO THE GENERA OF MUSCIDAE OF MEDICAL IMPORTANCE (ADULTS)

1. Arista bare or virtually so; apical cell broadly open at its apex..............2
   Arista long-haired, at least above; apical cell narrowed at its apex (Figs. 2-2, 10-1*E*, *F*); anal veins not as in *Fannia*...3
2. Second anal vein short and the third anal vein curved forward in such a way that, if the second were prolonged, the two would intersect.....................*Fannia*
   Second anal vein long, the third very short and not bent forward...........*Ophyra*
3. Proboscis fitted for bloodsucking, long, slender, rigid, with small labella (Fig. 3-7)...............................4
   Proboscis shorter, fleshy, with well-developed labella, at most with rasping labellar teeth, which may be fitted for lapping but not for siphoning blood (Fig. 3-8); arista with hair above and below 7
4. Arista with hair above and below........
   ....*Lyperosiops*
   Arista with hair above only...........5
5. Proboscis thin, with a strongly developed bulb at the base of the lower portion (haustellum) (Fig. 15-2); hairs of arista in turn plumose; discal cell of wing shaped like a meat cleaver.................*Glossina*
   Proboscis somewhat thicker, enlarged but not bulbous at the base of the haustellum (Fig. 15-6); hairs of arista simple; discal cell not shaped like a meat cleaver......6
6. Palpi short and small, not nearly as long as the haustellum; flies of about the same size as the house fly (Fig. 15-6).......
   ....*Stomoxys*
   Palpi very prominent, about as long as the haustellum and ensheathing it in life; size considerably less than that of the house fly (Fig. 15-6)............*Haematobia*
7. Vein M_{1+2} broadly rounded at its bend; longest hairs of arista not half so long as the terminal aristal segment.....*Muscina*
   Vein M_{1+2} angularly rounded at its bend; longest hairs of arista almost as long as the terminal aristal segment.......*Musca*

KEY TO THE GENERA OF CALLIPHORIDAE OF MEDICAL AND VETERINARY IMPORTANCE (ADULTS)

1. Base of the radius (before the humeral cross vein) with a row of hairs posteriorly on the upper surface.................2
   Base of the radius bare posteriorly on the upper surface 6
2. Hind coxa with a row of hairs posteriorly; green to violet-green species, with three prominent black longitudinal stripes on the mesonotum......................3
   Hind coxa bare posteriorly; green to bluish-black species, sometimes with transverse bands or two narrow longitudinal stripes or both on the mesonotum, but never marked as above 4
3. Palpus short and filiform, not nearly reaching the margin of the epistoma.....
   ....*Cochliomyia*
   Palpus elongated and clavate, almost reaching the margin of the epistoma.....
   ....*Paralucilia*
4. Lower squama hairy above....*Chrysomya*
   Lower squama bare..................5
5. Mesonotum convex; mesothoracic spiracle with bright orange hair, preacrostichal bristles well developed......*Phormia*
   Mesonotum flattened on the disc; mesothoracic spiracle with dark hair; preacrostichal bristles absent or very poorly developed...............*Protophormia*
6. Depression of the propleuron bare; yellow, brown, or gray species........7
   Depression of the propleuron pilose; abdomen blue, green or violet, except in some Australian *Calliphora*...........10
7. Arista short, not or very slightly longer than third antennal segment, thickened on at least basal half, the aristal hairs very short ....*Booponus*
   Arista thin, much longer than third antennal segment, the aristal hairs long......8
8. Prosternum hairy; lower section of proboscis (haustellum) somewhat swollen; yellowish species with only ordinary hairs and bristles on the thorax.............9
   Prosternum bare; lower section of pro-

boscis not at all swollen; blackish species with abundant crinkly yellowish hairs (except when they are abraded) on the sides and dorsum of the thorax...*Pollenia*

9. Vein R_5 with a row of erect hairs extending nearly to cross vein r-m; eyes of both sexes broadly separated; second abdominal segment especially long............ .... *Auchmeromyia* Vein R_5 with a row of erect hairs extending less than halfway to cross vein r-m; eyes of the male nearly contiguous; second abdominal segment of ordinary length ....*Cordylobia*

10. Lower squama bare above............11 Lower squama hairy above..........12

11. Subcostal sclerite with only soft pubescence not interspersed with stiff black hairs.......................*Phaenicia* Subcostal sclerite with wiry, erect black hairs in addition to the fine pubescence... .... *Lucilia*

12. Abdomen either dull or shining, but the sheen somewhat dulled by overlying pollen; scutellum usually with four or more strong lateral bristles on each side.......................*Calliphora* Abdomen brilliantly shining, without overlying pollen to dull the sheen; scutellum with three strong lateral bristles on each side.....................*Cynomyopsis*

Identification of Cyclorrhaphous Larvae. The typical muscoid larva, called a maggot, is legless, more or less cylindrical but strongly tapering anteriorly and truncated posteriorly. It is distinctly segmented, with twelve segments including the so-called "cephalic" segment (Fig. 13-3) usually clearly visible; however, Zumpt (1965) has pointed out that the last segment is a composite of two, and sometimes thirteen segments may be counted. Some muscoid larvae differ from this general pattern; the cattle grub, sheep nose bot, for example, and Oestridae in general are robust and more oval, and the larva of *Fannia* is flattened with conspicuous processes extending from the body. Fully grown larvae differ greatly in length according to species, ranging from less than 5 mm to about 35 mm.

At the narrow, somewhat pointed anterior end the *mouth hooks* are prominent, unless the mouth parts are nonfunctional, as in the tsetse or the mature cattle grub. The mouth hooks form a part of the *cephalopharyngeal skeleton*, the form of which may be useful in the identification of larvae (Fig. 13-3B, 13-4). In some Calliphoridae, an *accessory oral sclerite*, lying below the basal part of the mouth hooks, may be of taxonomic importance. The *anterior spiracles*, located on the posterior part of the second segment (first thoracic) are used in taxonomic discrimination; so are the *spines* of the body, which may be fine or coarse, and located in rows, in particular areas, or generally distributed over the body.

At the blunt or posterior end are found the *posterior spiracles*, which afford useful diagnostic characters (Figs. 13-3C, 13-4). The spiracles, or *stigmatal plates*, are more or less separated from each other; each usually consists of a sclerotized (hardened) outer rim, or *peritreme*, within which are the *spiracular slits*, three in number in the mature larva, but only two in the second-stage larva and one or two in the first. These slits may be straight, bowed, or highly sinuous; sometimes, as in *Hypoderma*, the slits are replaced by multiple small round openings. A prominence known as the *button* is often present in the peritreme or the area that would ordinarily be enclosed by an incomplete peritreme; it may be absent or variously situated depending on the species, and therefore has taxonomic value.

In using the posterior spiracles for purposes of identification the following characters are to be noted: (1) diameter of the stigmatal plate, the space occupied by one stigmatal plate on a line drawn through the center of both; (2) the distance between the plates; (3) the general form and shape of the plates; (4) presence or absence of a button; (5) the form of the peritreme, whether complete or broken, regular or irregular, its thickness, and its relation to the button; (6) the form of the spiracular slits, if present, and their relation to one another and to the peritreme and the button; (7) the location of the plates in respect to the segment that bears them, for example,

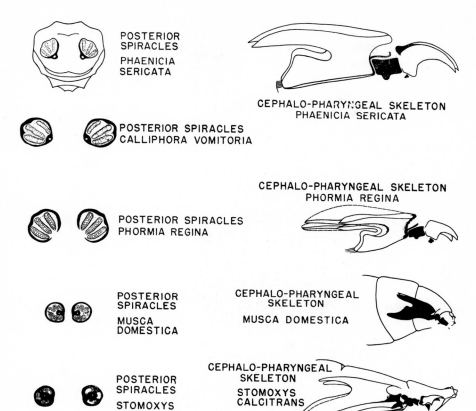

Fig. 13-4 Taxonomic details used in the classification of muscoid fly larvae.

whether they lie flush with the posterior wall of the segment or whether they are sunken into concavities.

The following keys, based largely on James (1948), but taken in part from other sources, will aid in the identification of the mature (third-stage) larvae of the higher Diptera.

KEY TO THE FAMILIES OF HIGHER DIPTERA (CYCLORRHAPHA) THAT CONTAIN FORMS OF MEDICAL IMPORTANCE (MATURE LARVAE)

1. Free larval stage of very brief duration or lacking (that is, developing larva retained within body of female)..........Family Muscidae (in part, Glossina, and so forth); Pupipara
   Free larval stage present.............2
2. Conical maggots, the body broad and truncated behind, tapering to a narrow anterior end, without prominent tubercles or processes on any segment but the last (Fig. 13-3); posterior spiracles flush with the posterior face of the anal segment or sunken into a concavity or depression...3
   Not such larvae; that is, the body either not conical (Fig. 16-4, Fig. 16-13) or with lateral or dorsal spinous processes (Fig. 14-4), or with the posterior spiracles at the end of two processes or of a respiratory tube 5
3. Posterior spiracles deeply sunken into a round concavity; inner slits of posterior spiracles directed away from the median line ventrally......Family Sarcophagidae

Posterior spiracles flush with the posterior face of the anal segment; or, if they are sunken into a shallow slitlike concavity, their inner slits are directed toward the median line ventrally 4

4. Slits of posterior spiracles either sinuous or short and radially arranged . . . .
. . . . Family Muscidae (in part)
Slits of posterior spiracles long and slender, more nearly parallel to one another. . . . Family Calliphoridae (in part)

5. Body robust, ovate or pear-shaped, without fleshy protuberances or stalked posterior spiracles 6
Body, if ovate, flattened and not robust, and with either fleshy protuberances or stalked posterior spiracles 12

6. Each posterior spiracle with three distinct slits 7
Each posterior spiracle with numerous small openings, but without well-defined slits 10

7. Larva either nude, wrinkled, with the posterior spiracles separated by several times the diameter of each (*Auchmeromyia*), or the slits sinuous (*Cordylobia*) . .
. . . . Family Calliphoridae (in part)
Larva spine-bearing, the slits in the posterior spiracle not sinuous 8

8. Pear-shaped species; spiracular slits straight and elongated, deeply sunken into a concavity (*Dermatobia*) . . . .
. . . . Family Cuterebridae (in part)
Ovate species; spiracular slits at most a shallow concavity 9

9. Spiracular plates united at their inner sides . . . . Family Gasterophilidae
Spiracular plates well separated (*Booponus*)
. . . . Family Calliphoridae (in part)

10. Mouth hooks rudimentary . . . .
. . . . Family Hypodermatidae
Mouth hooks well-developed 11

11. Body with spines weak and located on the ventral surface only or on the anterior margin of each segment dorsally; integument only moderately tough . . . .
. . . . Family Oestridae
Body with spines stronger or in the form of spinose plates and more evenly distributed; integument very tough . . . .
. . . . Family Cuterebridae (in part)

12. Body with tubercular, fleshy, or spinous processes dorsally and laterally on the segments 13
Body without such processes 15

13. More or less cylindrical larvae with short or moderately short, unbranched, lateral and dorsal tubercles on the segments . . .14
Flattened larvae with long, filiform processes branched at least basally and may appear feathery, on the dorsum and sides of the segments; posterior spiracles borne on stalks, each stalk with four lobes on which are found the three slits and the button (*Fannia*) . . . .
. . . . Family Muscidae (in part)

14. Small, dirty-white, slightly flattened larvae, measuring up to 4 mm, with short processes on the dorsal and lateral surfaces; posterior spiracles on brown, hardened tubercles, each with a narrow opening . . . .
. . . . Family Phoridae
Larger, more nearly cylindrical larvae, with longer, pointed fleshy processes laterally and dorsally; posterior spiracles in a cleft on posterior face of the last segment and consisting of flattened plates perforated by three slits (*Chrysomya*, in part) . . . . . . Family Calliphoridae (in part)

15. Posterior spiracles at the end of a long retractile respiratory tube that, when extended, is longer than the length of the body proper; rat-tailed maggots . . . .
. . . . Family Syrphidae
Posterior spiracles on short tubercles or a short respiratory process much shorter than the body length 16

16. Posterior spiracles situated at the end of the branches of a forked respiratory process . . . . Family Drosophilidae
Posterior spiracles situated at the apices of short cones 17

17. Last abdominal segment with a pair of fingerlike processes on the sides ventrally; mature larvae do not skip . . . .
. . . . Family Sepsidae
Last abdominal segment with a pair of processes on the sides ventrally that are tapered and point slightly upward; mature larvae move in a skipping fashion . . . .
. . . . Family Piophilidae

KEY TO THE GENERA OF MUSCIDAE OF MEDICAL IMPORTANCE (MATURE LARVAE)

1. With only brief free stage prior to pupation; mouth hooks lacking; posterior end with a very sharply demarcated collar posterior to which are two shiny, black lobes separated by a deep cleft or pit. . . . .
. . . . *Glossina*
With a distinct free stage during which at least most of the larval development takes place; larvae not as described above. . . .2
2. Larvae of the normal muscoid shape (cylindrical, tapering anteriorly), without lateral processes 3
Larvae flattened, with prominent lateral processes . . . . *Fannia*
3. Slits of posterior spiracle strongly sinuous
. 5
Slits of posterior spiracle arcuate (with a simple bow). 4
4. Slits slightly sinuous and lying almost parallel to one another. . . . . *Ophyra*
Slits arcuate and distinctly divergent. . . . .
. . . . *Muscina*
5. Slits of posterior spiracle each with three or more loops, usually W-shaped. . *Musca*
Slits of posterior spiracle each with two loops, S-shaped. 6
6. Posterior spiracles triangular, separated from each other by 1.5 to 2 times the diameter of a spiracle. 7
Posterior spiracles kidney-shaped, separated from each other by 1/4 to 1/3 the diameter of a spiracle. . . . . . . *Haematobia*
7. A ventral tubercle, covered with small spines, present behind the anus. . . . .
. . . . *Stomoxys*
No such tubercle present. . . . . *Lyperosiops*

KEY TO THE GENERA OF CALLIPHORIDAE OF MEDICAL IMPORTANCE (MATURE LARVAE)

1. Robust larvae, oval in outline, not noticeably tapering anteriorly. 2
Slender larvae, tapering anteriorly. 4

2. Blood-sucking maggots; posterior spiracles very widely separated, each with three straight, short, outwardly directed slits . . . . *Auchmeromyia*
Maggots burrowing into the dermis; posterior spiracles not widely separated. 3
3. Posterior spiracles with three almost parallel slits (Eastern Palaearctic and Oriental species). . . . . *Booponus*
Posterior spiracle with three sinuous or tortuous slits (Ethiopian species). . . . .
. . . . *Cordylobia*
4. Peritreme of posterior spiracle incomplete, not enclosing the button, which may be weakly defined .5
Peritreme of posterior spiracle complete, enclosing the button. 6
5. Posterior spiracle without a definite button. . . . . *Callitroga, Paralucilia*
Posterior spiracle with a button. . . . .
. . . . . . *Chrysomya, Phormia, Protophormia*
6. Peritreme of posterior spiracle weakly sclerotized. . . . . *Pollenia*
Peritreme of posterior spiracle strongly sclerotized 7
7. Accessory oral sclerite present. . . . .
. . . . *Calliphora, Cynomyopsis*
Accessory oral sclerite absent. . . . .
. . . . *Lucilia, Phaenicia*

HIPPELATES FLIES—EYE GNATS

FAMILY CHLOROPIDAE

Hippelates Flies. Hippelates flies are members of the Chloropidae, the family of the frit flies and related forms. Members of the genus are as a rule very small flies (1.5 to 2.5 mm in length); they are frequently called "eye gnats" or "eye flies" because they frequently come to the eyes of the victim, as well as to mucous and sebaceous secretions, pus, and blood. Some species are attracted to exposed genital organs of mammals (e.g., *Hippelates pallipes* clustered around a dog's penis), and others to sores on the lower limbs (e.g., *H. flavipes* on yaws sores). *Hippelates* gnats approach their mammalian host quietly, usually alighting some distance from their feeding site (Mulla, 1959). To reach the feeding site, they will then crawl over the skin or resort to intermittent flying and alighting, thus adding to the anoyance of the host. They are extraordinarily persistent and if brushed away will quickly return to continue engorging themselves. They are nonbiting; however, the labella are provided with spines that have been thought by some authors to act as scarifying instruments capable of producing minute multiple incisions, likely to assist in entrance of pathogenic organisms.

Unlike the gnats discussed in Chapter 9, all of which are Nematocera, the Chloropidae have short aristate antennae and are more like the house fly in form and structure though much smaller. The pomace or vinegar flies, *Drosophila*, resemble some *Hippelates*, but they have a distinctly feathered arista, whereas that of *Hippelates* is at most pubescent. A distinct feature that will distinguish the Chloropidae from related families is the very large frontal triangle, the sclerotized plate on which the ocelli are situated. *Hippelates* may be distinguished from most members of the same family by the presence of a distinct shining black apical or subapical spur on the hind tibia. The larvae of many Choropidae live in grass and other plants (stem maggots); however, those of the genus *Hippelates* develop in a wide variety of materials such as decaying vegetables, plant rootlets, and animal matter, incorporated into the soil during farming operations.

Relation to Conjunctivitis. Hippelates flies have long been looked upon with suspicion in certain parts of the southern United States as possible vectors of a form of conjunctivitis commonly known as "sore eye," "pinkeye," and so forth. Schwarz, in 1895, was the first to suggest this relationship. Since 1912 the correlation between outbreaks of pinkeye and adult *Hippelates* abundance in Southern California has been noted and documented by several workers, particularly Tinkham and Mulla. Roy (1928) shows that the seasonal prevalence of *Siphunculina funicola* de Meijere,

a close relative of *Hippelates*, coincides with epidemic conjunctivitis in Assam, India. The literature dealing with the Chloropidae as vectors of conjunctivitis has been reviewed with great care by Graham-Smith (1930). This review indicates a paucity of experimental evidence but a large amount of circumstantial evidence involving flies as spreaders of conjunctivitis in Egypt, the West Indies, India, Ceylon, Java, and the United States.

The *Hippelates* species most closely associated with human annoyance and probable pinkeye transmission are *H. collusor* (Townsend) (Fig. 13-5), in the Southwestern United States and Mexico, and *H. pusio* Loew, a common species in the Southern United States. In India, Ceylon, Java, and other parts of the Oriental region *Siphunculina funicola* de Meijere, which is known there as the "eye fly," fulfills this role.

Relation to Yaws. As pointed out in Chapter 1, flies have for many years been suspected as vectors of the pathogen of yaws (framboesia tropica), and some experimental evidence has been advanced from time to time; however, the evidence collected by Kumm (1935) in Jamaica with *Hippelates flavipes* Loew (as *pallipes* Loew) is most convincing. Kumm, as well as others, has shown that it is relatively easy to demonstrate motile *Treponema pertenue* Castellani in the "vomit drops" of eye gnats after they have fed on infectious lesions of yaws. He found, however, that the spirochetes were presumably digested in the midgut and hindgut of the gnats very soon after they were ingested, none being seen after an interval of two days. There was no evidence of cyclical development.

The gnats receive the infection most readily by feeding on available primary lesions that exude freshly infected serum with large numbers of spirochetes. Inoculation is affected mechanically; i.e., the unchanged spirochetes are deposited in "vomit drops" (Kumm and Turner, 1936) when infected gnats feed on exuded serum from wounds, excoriated areas, or susceptible surfaces. The manner in which

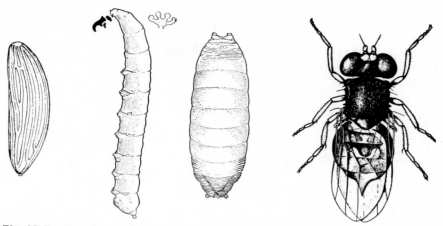

Fig. 13-5 *Hippelates collusor.* From *left to right:* egg ; larva, showing cephalopharyngeal skeleton and anterior spiracle ; pupa ; adult. (After Herms and Burgess, except adult fly which is redrawn after D. G. Hall.)

the gnats receive the infection and their general feeding habits are well described by Kumm, Turner and Peat (1935).

Bovine Mastitis. Sanders (1940) reports investigations at the Florida Agricultural Experiment Station that incriminate *Hippelates* (species not given) as well as the house fly, *Musca domestica*, as vectors of bovine mastitis. *Hippelates* flies were seen to hover around natural openings of calves, yearlings, pregnant heifers, and lactating cows. They fed on lacrimal fluid, fatty body secretions, milk droplets accidentally spilled, and on secretion at the tip of the teats of animals in herds where mastitis has prevailed. Exposure tests were made with flies feeding alternately on infected material and the teat orifice; also the teat orifice was exposed to flies taken directly from premises where mastitis prevailed. "Mastitis developed in each of the experimental animals by the exposure technique employed."

Life History of Hippelates collusor. The biology of *Hippelates collusor* has been extensively investigated in Southern California. The adult flies are present throughout the year in the desert and foothill regions and are particularly annoying from April through November. During the peak months the adults are noticeable early in the morning and late in the afternoon, and then in deep shade, such as densely planted shrubbery, in date gardens, and in the shade of the house. The fluted, distinctly curved eggs of about 0.5 mm length (Fig. 13-5) are deposited on or below the surface of the soil; the average incubation period under optimum conditions (90°F) is about two days. The larvae feed on a great variety of decaying organic matter including excrement, provided the material is rather loose and well aerated. According to Burgess (1951) the larvae will not develop naturally in closely compacted soil or putrid material, neither will they breed in excrement unless it is mixed with loose earth. The larval stage under optimum conditions requires about seven to eleven days. During the winter months the larval and pupal stages may last for many weeks.

Pupation takes place close to the surface of the material in which the larvae develop. The prepupal stage requires about one day, the pupal about six, and the preovipositional adult about seven, giving a total of about twenty-one days from egg to adult fly, or about twenty-eight days from egg to egg. Eggs are deposited in batches up to fifty, usually followed by a second but smaller batch after about seven days (Burgess, 1951). The development of all stages may be slowed down in the winter season, in areas where breeding may be continuous throughout the year. Experiments performed by Hall (1932) show that the larval stage averaged about 11.4 days on human excrement, 8.7 days on dog manure, and about seventeen days on decaying oranges. Burgess (1951) and Mulla (1958) point out that the majority of *Hippelates* gnats are bred in light, well-drained sandy soils that are freshly plowed (i.e., plowed not over three weeks before) and contain abundant humus or vegetable matter (cover crops, manure) and sufficient moisture. The disturbed soil habitat is characteristic also of the true *H. pusio* and the related *H. bishoppi* Sabrosky (Dow, Bigham, and Sabrosky, 1951).

Hippelates eye gnats are generally strong fliers. They fly with and against the general direction of the wind, although wind velocities of five miles or more per hour considerably reduce their flight activity. In the desert regions of California flight is more noticeable in the early morning and the late afternoon hours when the temperature is over 100° F. In the spring and fall months the gnats probably fly throughout the day and infest residential areas, golf courses, schoolyards, motels, and, the like.

Dow (1959) investigated the dispersal of *H. pusio* in Georgia with the use of phosphorus-32. The insect was found to fly as far as one mile from the release point. In a more extensive study on the flight range and dispersal pattern of *H. collusor* in the Coachella Valley of California, Mulla and March (1959) tagged a large number of this eye gnat with radioactive phosphorus. Thousands of labeled gnats were released in each of two experiments in two different areas of the Valley. The gnats were found to become widely distributed within four to six hours from the time of release. In both the experiments the insects traveled as far as four to 4.5 miles from the release point.

Classification. Sabrosky (1941) gives a valuable review of the *Hippelates* of the United States. In addition to the stout and distinct tibial spur, the following characteristics will assist in the identification of this genus: cephalic bristles short, weak, and not conspicuous; ocellars very short, erect, and convergent or cruciate; fronto-orbital hairs minute, slightly reclinate; no intrahumeral bristles present. The species most important from the medical standpoint belong to the *pusio* group; in this group the body color is black, and the thorax is polished and shiny, with at most a trace of pollen at the base of the wing. Sabrosky places *H. pusio* Loew, *H. flavipes* Loew, *H. pallipes* (Loew), *H. bishoppi* Sabrosky, *H. collusor* (Townsend), and two other species in this group. *Hippelates flavipes* and *H. pallipes* have been confused with each other in the literature, but *H. flavipes* is a tropical species and *H. pallipes* belongs to the temperate regions (Sabrosky, 1951). Some members of other groups of *Hippelates* may be seriously annoying, but some species (e.g., *hermsi* Sabrosky) do not attack man (Tinkham, 1953).

LOUSE FLIES AND BAT FLIES

SERIES PUPIPARA

Characteristics of Hippoboscidae. Four families of flies constitute the Pupipara, three of which attack warm-blooded animals: (1) Hippoboscidae (louse flies); (2) Nycteribiidae (spiderlike bat flies); and (3) Streblidae (bat flies). The bloodsucking parasitic flies belonging to the family Hippoboscidae are readily recognized as Diptera when winged. The larvae are retained within the body of the female, being nourished by special glands within the mother until time for pupation is reached; they are then extruded, and pupation quickly follows, whence the term, "pupipara." The adult flies are flattened, leathery in appearance, often wingless; the legs are short and strong, and broadly separated. The antennae are inserted in pits or depressions near the border of the mouth; they appear to consist of but one segment, which may terminate in a bristle or long hairs.

The members of this family are all parasitic in the adult stage upon birds or mammals. There are about 400 species widely distributed throughout the world. They range in size from 2.5 to 10 mm. The American species have been admirably monographed by Bequaert (1953–57).

The sheep ked, *Melophagus ovinus* (Linnaeus), is a wingless bloodsucking species, reddish brown in color, about 5 to 7 mm in length. It is a worldwide parasite of sheep and goats. The head is short and sunken into the thorax, the body saclike, leathery, and spiny (Fig. 13-6).

Life History. The eggs are retained and hatch within the body of the female ked, where the larvae develop in about seven days and are extruded fully grown ready to pupate. The extruded larva pupates during the course of a few hours, becoming chestnut brown in color; the secretion with which it is covered hardens and serves to glue the pupa firmly to the wool of the host. The pupae are commonly found on infested animals in the region of the shoulders, thighs and belly. Pupae may be found on sheep at all times of the year; the time for development in the summer is about three weeks, but may be twice as long in the winter. Females reach sexual maturity in from fourteen to thirty days and over, when they begin extruding young at the rate of one about every seven to eight days. The average life of the insect is about four months; each female deposits from ten to twelve pupae.

The entire life of the ked is spent on its host: when off the sheep, the insects die in from two to eight days, the majority in about four days.

Damage Done. The presence of a few louse flies on the body of a sheep does not materially affect it. In heavy infestations the presence of the insect is indicated by the fact that the animal rubs itself vigorously, bites the wool, and scratches. Badly infested animals show emaciation and general unthriftiness. The injury to lambs is especially marked.

Other Louse Flies of Mammals. *Lipoptena depressa* (Say) and *Neolipoptena ferrisi* (Bequaert) are common parasites of deer in North America. These species are smaller than *Melophafus ovinus*, but otherwise resemble it; they are wingless when established on the host, but have well-developed wings on emergence from the pupal stage. The parasites have been found in chains, three or four individuals attached to one another, the first fly drawing blood from the host, the second with its proboscis thrust into the abdomen (dorsally) of the first, the third drawing on the second, and so on to the last individual. *Lipoptena cervi* (Linnaeus), known as the "deer ked," is reported to be a common species on European deer, and according to Bequaert (1953–57) has become naturalized in the northeastern United States on the Virginia white-tailed deer and on wapiti. *Lipoptena mazamae* Rondani occurs on deer in South and Central America and in the southeastern United States.

Nine species of the genus *Hippobosca* are recognized as valid by Bequaert (1937). The wings are always well developed in the genus and are functional throughout adult life. With the exception of the ostrich louse fly, *H. struthionis* Janson, the species of the genus are ectoparasitic on mammals. *Hippobosca equina* Linnaeus, known in England as the "forest fly," is usually found on horses, mules, and

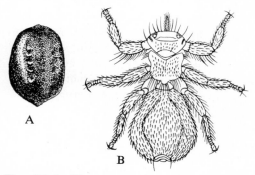

Fig. 13-6 The sheep "tick" or louse fly, *Melophagus ovinus. A.* Pupa. *B.* Adult. (Courtesy of U.S. Public Health Service.)

donkeys, sometimes on cattle and other animals; *H. longipennis* Fabricius is commonly found on domestic dogs in the far East and in many parts of the Mediterranean region; *H. variegata* von Mühlfeld occurs on domestic cattle and equines and is widespread in distribution; *H. camelina* Leach is a parasite of the camel and dromedary. No species of *Hippobosca* seem to be established in America.

Louse Flies of Birds. The pigeon fly, *Pseudolynchia canariensis*, is an important parasite of domestic pigeons throughout the tropics and warmer regions of the world. It is found throughout the southern United States and northward along the Atlantic Coast to New England. The dark-brown flies have long wings, 6.5 to 7.5 mm, and are able to fly swiftly from the host, but usually alight nearby. They move about quickly among the feathers of the host and bite and suck blood from parts that are not well feathered.

The mature larvae, at first yellow and later jet black in color, are deposited on the body of the bird while it is quiet, but they soon roll off and collect in the nests. Bishopp (1929) gives the duration of the pupal stage at from twenty-nine to thirty-one days when the mean daily temperature is about 73° F. Thus, the thorough and regular cleaning of the nests at intervals not to exceed twenty-five days is probably the most important single step in control.

In addition to its evil effects as a bloodsucking parasite, the pigeon fly is the vector of a pigeon blood protozoon, *Haemoproteus columbae* (Celli and San Felice), the parasite undergoing sporogeny in the body of the insect and consequently requiring it as a link in its life cycle. Also, a similar pathogen of the California valley quail, *Haemoproteus lophortyx* O'Roke, is transmitted by *Lynchia hirsuta*

Ferris and *Stilbometopa impressa* (Bigot), and other bird hippoboscids may be involved in transmission of other species of *Haemoproteus*.

Hippoboscids Attacking Man. This subject has been reviewed critically by Bequaert (1953–57). No known hippoboscid has man as its normal or habitual host, but at least thirteen species, including *Hippobosca equina* Linnaeus, *H. camelina* Rondani, *H. variegata* Megerle, *H. longipennis* Fabricius, *Melophagus ovinus* (Linnaeus), *Lipoptena cervi* (Linnaeus), and *Pseudolynchia canariensis* (Macquart), have been authentically reported as biting man. The sheep ked may become quite annoying to persons employed in shearing sheep or handling wool. The pigeon fly may readily attack perons who handle squabs and adult birds; the bite is said to be as painful as a bee sting and its effects may persist for five days or more (Soroker, 1958).

Streblid and Nycteribiid Bat Parasites. Bat flies are pupiparous bloodsucking parasites belonging to the family Streblidae; they are all parasitic on bats in tropical and subtropical climates. Little is known about the life history of these insects. The species of the family Streblidae have been reviewed by Kessel (1925). Spiderlike bat flies belong to the family Nycteribiidae. They are very small (2 to 3 mm long), wingless, spiderlike parasites of bats. Except for a very few species described from North and South America, they are primarily parasites of Old World bats. Ferris (1924) has reviewed the New World species. The fact that vampire, fruit-eating, and insectivorous bats are involved in the epidemiology of rabies is of interest in this connection, because until proven otherwise, there exists the possibility that bat parasites may help to maintain the virus in bat populations.

14

THE HOUSE FLY
AND ITS RELATIVES

ORDER DIPTERA,
SUPERFAMILY MUSCOIDEA

House-Invading and Other Man-Associated Flies. Many species of robust flies belonging to various families of Diptera are commonly found indoors. Some of these are actual or potential menaces to human health in that they habitually enter the house and come in contact with human food or drink, after breeding or feeding in excrement, dead animal material, or other contaminated media. Other species, which do not necessarily enter houses, may be

so clearly associated with man as to form a definite threat to his health. These same flies, and others that have no relationship to the transmission of pathogenic organisms, may be of further importance because of their annoyance and interference with human comfort. Flies of such character belong chiefly to the Muscidae (including the Anthomyiidae), Sarcophagidae (flesh flies), and Calliphoridae (blow flies).

The bionomics of the house fly and related forms of medical and sanitary importance have been treated in an admirable monograph by West (1951), and a condensed account of the relationship to disease, with an extensive list of citations, has been presented by Lindsay and Scudder (1956). A very useful account of flies of public health importance and their control is that of Scott and Littig (1962), and Greenberg's research on the house fly and relationships to disease and his well-written article in the *Scientific American* (Greenberg, 1965) are valuable contributions to the subject.

Those flies that have entered the man-dominated ecological community (or human biocoenosis), and consequently coexist with man over an extended period of time, have been referred to by European workers as synanthropic species. A monograph by Greenberg (1969), in collaboration with European workers, contains an extensive treatment of synanthropy, with a wealth of tabular material. A significant fact is that a large number of Northern Hemisphere synanthropes are very widespread, being often holarctic or circumpolar.

Various degrees of synanthropy exist, from a total association with man to one that is quite loose and purely facultative. Total association involves a complete dependence upon the man-controlled environment, including households, food-processing plants, slaughterhouses, and so forth, for their complete development (the true or eusynanthropes). Requirements for this development include larval food as well as other biotic needs of the environment. Most synanthropic flies (the hemisynanthropes) do not depend totally on man's environment, though they readily take advantage of it and under its influence show marked increases in population density; they can exist however, independently of it. A still looser association involves those species whose contact with man is through his domestic animals, either in stables or barns or in the pastures (symbovines).

The chief medical significance of synanthropy lies in the potential epidemiologic and hygienic implications of the individual requirements of those flies. A classical synanthrope, like the house fly over most of its range, is highly significant medically; its pathogen-transmitting potential, because of its breeding and feeding habits, is great. The degree of synanthropy for many man-associated flies may vary considerably within the species; a closely synanthropic species in temperate areas may be totally disassociated with man, or almost so, in the tropics and subtropics, or even within temperate regions may have strains with a lower degree of synanthropy. The human habitat does, however, provide a breeding and living ground for many species, to their very definite advantage and often with a threat to the human key-occupant of the habitat.

The Family Muscidae. The family Muscidae, to which the house fly and several other groups of synanthropic species belong, is characterized as including usually dull-colored flies of medium to small size, with well-developed squamae. The hypopleural bristles are absent, whereas in the closely related Calliphoridae and Sarcophagidae (also the Tachinidae) they are present; the mouth parts are well developed. The limits of the family are a controversial matter, varying according to the usage of different authors; those accepted here are in conformance with the usage in the Stone, *et al.* (1965), catalog of the Nearctic Diptera.

The house fly, *Musca domestica* Linnaeus, is the most familiar and, medically, the most important member of this family. It is a gray species, 6 to 9 mm in length, with four dark stripes running lengthwise on the thoracic dorsum. The eyes are separated in both sexes but are much closer in the male than in the female. The central part of the hypopleuron, unlike most other species of *Musca*, bears at least a few fine hairs; however, these might be difficult to see or may be rubbed off.

The prevalence of house flies in houses has been commented upon by Howard (1900). Of a total of 23,087 flies collected by him in dining rooms in different parts of the United States, about 99 per cent of the whole number were *Musca domestica*. However, there are extensive areas in the United States today where other muscoids, for example *Fannia* or certain blow flies, predominate. The changes that have accompanied progress have evidently altered the composition of the domestic fly fauna since Howard's time. As West (1951) points out, "in many parts of the United States today *Musca domestica* is less a housefly than a 'picnic fly', 'park fly', 'dairy fly' or 'stable fly', but wherever found it is almost certain to be the availability of human food or drink which brings it there." *Musca domestica* is almost cosmopolitan, but in some parts of the world its place is taken by other species, particularly *Musca sorbens* Wiedemann.

Life History of the House Fly. The house fly passes through a complex metamorphosis, i.e., egg, larva (maggot), pupa, and adult or fully winged insect (Fig. 14-1). Under warm summer temperatures, under what may perhaps be considered representative conditions, the egg stage requires eight to twelve hours, the larval stage about five days, the pupal four to five days; a total of about ten days from egg to adult insect. This allows for the development of from ten to twelve generations in one summer. Under more nearly ideal conditions, the length of the life cycle may be shortened and the number of annual generations consequently increased. In California the minimum time from egg to adult is estimated at seven days (Arthur C. Smith,

personal communication), with two or three generations a month in warm weather. The more usual length of the life cycle, under temperate conditions, is about three weeks.

The larval stage is the growing period of the fly, and the size of the adult will depend entirely upon the growth that the larva attains. An underfed larva will result in an undersized adult. The mature maggots usually crawl away from their breeding place, many of them burrowing into loose ground beneath the manure pile, or under boards or stones, or into dry manure collected under platforms and the like. Herms recorded 2,561 pupae from one and three quarter pounds of manure taken from beneath a platform. The larvae spend three or four days in the prepupal or migratory stage before actually pupating.

As in the case of other muscoids, the adult fly, when transformation is completed, pushes

Fig. 14-1 Developmental stages of the house fly, *Musca domestica.* (*Upper left*) eggs; (*upper right*) larvae; (*lower left*) pupae; (*lower right*) adult. (Photograph of adult by Edward S. Ross, others by Arthur C. Smith; courtesy of California Bureau of Vector Control.)

the end of the puparium open by means of the ptilinum; then, by alternate expansion and contraction of this organ, the fly opens a passageway through the loose soil and debris to the surface. Compaction of the soil impedes its progress (Black and Barnes, 1958).

The house fly is highly prolific, and several authors have commented on the fantastic potential for multiplication, if all eggs produced by the fly were to develop adult flies that, in turn, could reproduce to their full capacity. With one adult fly depositing from 120 to 150 eggs per lot, with at least six lots at intervals of three to four days, Hodge (1911) gives us the following statement: "A pair of flies beginning operations in April may be progenitors, if all were to live, of 191,010,000,-000,000,000,000 flies in August. Allowing one-eighth of a cubic inch to a fly, this number would cover the earth forty-seven feet deep." The practical value of such fantasy is, of course, to demonstrate how rapidly a badly depleted population can recover.

Influence of Temperature on Life History. Temperature influences materially both the survival of the immature stages and the time required for the development from the egg to the adult. The temperature of an average manure pile to which material is added daily varies from 18° to 66° C. Young growing larvae are most numerous where temperatures vary from 45° to 55° C. Below 45° C, half-grown and full-grown larvae occur; above 55° C, the temperature seems to become too great. Therefore, there is a definite zone in the manure pile which produces at least most of the flies.

According to Herms, the average time required to develop from egg to adult, at various temperatures, were: 16° C, 44.8 days; 18° C, 26.7 days; 20°, 20.5 days; 25°, 16.1 days; and 30°, 10.4 days. The shortest time required for the development of *Musca domestica* may, depending on local conditions, be less than the minimum time observed above. The determination of this minimum may be an important consideration in fly control.

Breeding Places. Excrement is one material upon which *Musca domestica* habitually deposits its eggs, the larvae feeding on this material and the contained microorganisms. To gain an estimate of the number of larvae developing in an average pile of horse manure, Herms took four samples of three to four pounds each, after four days exposure to flies the four samples gave a total of 10,282 larvae in fifteen pounds. All larvae were nearly or quite fully grown. This gives an average of 685 larvae per pound. The weight of the entire pile from which the sample was taken was not less than 1,000 pounds, of which certainly two thirds was infested. A little arithmetic gives us the astonishing estimate, in round numbers, of 450,000 larvae (Herms, 1911).

Horse manure is a favorite larval food, and at one time it was regarded as the chief factor in the production of house flies in many rural village areas in the United States. Cow manure is frequently an important factor in the development of flies. Flies will also breed in hog manure, but the swarm of flies around pig pens usually originates in the waste feed, slops, and so forth. Chicken manure is the most important factor in the breeding of flies in poultry districts. Human excrement, if exposed to flies in open privies becomes not only a prolific breeding medium but an important source of pathogens; this consideration emphasizes the need for making privies flyproof or for using other means to prevent flies from breeding in them.

In this day of automobiles and tractors, however, other sources of breeding may be vastly more important then excrement. Smith (1956), studying conditions in dairy barns in California, concludes that "the fly-breeding potential of these enormous amounts of organic waste material [chicken and cow manure, garbage, etc.], is far greater than it could possibly have been back in horse-and-buggy days." Great swarms of flies are often found around feed troughs; the animals (hogs and cattle) may be literally covered with them. An examination of the waste feed behind or beneath the troughs or in and about the mixing vats will almost invariably reveal numerous maggots. Storage recepticles for slop sometimes present a wriggling mass of maggots. Waste brewer's grain or spent hops, bran mash, and ensilage that is partly consumed by the animals may commonly be a source of enormous numbers of flies (nearly all *Musca domestica*) about dairies where otherwise conditions may be good and where no apparent reason for the swarm of flies exists. Commercial wastes and freeze plant wastes, when used as feed for beef and dairy cattle, may likewise constitute a major problem.

Garbage heaps, particularly when fermentation and decomposition begin, are commonly sources of many flies of several kinds (Fig. 14-2). Heaps of decaying onions, Lima beans, and other vegetables may become infested with maggots. The fly-breeding potential of a garbage can (Fig. 14-3), under certain circumstances, is amazing; single garbage cans

under experimental conditions produced more than 20,000 larvae each week, according to Arthur C. Smith (personal communication).

In the country, in the absence of septic tanks and sewers, the dishwater from the kitchen is frequently piped from the sink to a ditch in the backyard. On occasions these ditches become clogged and vile smelling, and an examination will reveal numerous maggots developing in the muck—a source of flies that is commonly overlooked. Also, maggots may be found in countless numbers in the soft sludge mat covering the liquid in defective septic tanks, chiefly those of older construction.

Other breeding places have been recorded by Hewitt (1910) and West (1951). There are even records of house fly larvae parasitizing other insects. In brief, the house fly is remarkably versatile in its breeding habits.

Range of Flight. Ordinarily under city conditions it may be safely said that where flies are abundant they have bred in the

Fig. 14-2 Fresh trash and garbage on an open dump may be a prolific breeding ground for flies. (Photograph by Arthur C. Smith; courtesy of California Bureau of Vector Control.)

Fig. 14-3 An uncovered, ill-kept garbage can may breed flies even when "empty." An examination of the bottom of this can revealed larvae of the house fly, the lesser house fly, the greenbottle fly, and the drone fly. (Photograph by Edgar A. Smith; courtesy of California Bureau of Vector Control.)

immediate vicinity. The house fly can, however, use its wings effectively and may also be carried by the wind, although it usually seeks protection very quickly when there is a strong breeze. The use of radioactive isotopes as markers has indicated that flies can fly as far as twenty miles from their source and that under certain conditions they may migrate from one to four miles in considerable numbers; the dispersal capacity, however, is usually limited to a distance of 0.5 to two miles (Schoof and Siverly, 1954). Where houses are situated close together, flies have the opportunity to travel considerable distances by easy flights, and they are often carried on garbage vehicles and animals.

Longevity of Flies. Several factors, such as the availability of food and water, but particularly temperature, influence the longevity of adult flies. Herms determined that in California the average life span of the adult fly was about thirty days, with a maximum of sixty days. In Texas, flies lived two to four weeks under midsummer conditions, whereas at Ithaca, New York, survival reached seventy days (Knapp and Knutson, 1958). In hibernation, flies may live over winter, that is, from October to April, in the eastern and central United States; in warmer portions of California they emerge from pupal cases throughout the winter, and their adult life span is then considerably longer than in summer.

Other Synanthropic Muscids. There are many species (seventy-four, including subspecies, according to West, 1951) belonging to the genus *Musca*, but only a few of these are comparable in their habits to *M. domestica.*

Of these, *M. vicina* Ma quart, *M. calleva* Walker (=*cuthbertsoni* Patton), and *M. nebulo* Wiedemann are now generally considered merely subspecies of *M. domestica*. A quite distinct species, *M. sorbens* Wiedemann, is widespread in Africa, the Orient, the Pacific Islands, and Australia, where it is important as a bazaar and house fly. It breeds in both human and animal excrement. Adults are frequently attracted to wounds and ulcers and will persistently settle on the human body, especially around the eyes, nose, and mouth. It has much the same potential as *M. domestica* for transmitting human and animal pathogens. Some that have been associated with it, experimentally or through examination of vomit spots or gut contents, are the causative organisms of leprosy, yaws, tuberculosis, and several enteric infections.

In Australia this species or a very similar one, *Musca vetustissima* (Walker), is very important because of its nuisance value to man and animals and possible relationship to pathogen transmission. This species, known in Australia as the bush fly, has been considered the same as *M. sorbens*, but the Australian workers prefer to consider it a separate species or at least subspecies until its taxonomic status can be more definitely determined. A valuable review of its biology is that of Norris (1966). This fly has been a pest of man in Australia since before the advent of Europeans, but it is attracting more and more attention in recent years, probably because of the increasing standards of health and comfort. It breeds in the excrement of man, cattle, horses, sheep, dogs, and swine, and has been reported breeding in the paunch contents of dead ruminants. Norris, however, believes that human excrement is of importance, at the present time, only under local conditions, where the feces are left exposed without burial; under aboriginal conditions, the situation may have been quite different. The fly may migrate, according to experimental evidence, as far as 3.5 miles from the point of release.

Another species, *Musca crassirostris* Stein (sometimes placed in a separate genus, *Philaematomyia*) is a habitual if not obligate bloodsucker. Though its proboscis is similar to that of other *Musca* species, it is more bulbular, with strong labellar teeth, by means of which it can scratch the skin or scabs and cause blood to flow. Thus, this fly marks a transition between the house fly type and the bloodsucking *Stomoyxs* type. Some other *Musca* species, such as *M. sorbens*, are facultative bloodsuckers, and Garcia and Radovsky (1962) have shown that this habit extends to other muscids such as the *Fannia benjamini* Malloch and the Phaoniine *Hydrotaea armipes* (Fallén). These bloodsuckers should be considered as potential vectors of blood parasites.

The face fly, Musca autumnalis De Geer, has different habits. It is a little larger than the house fly; the abdomen of the female is black on the sides, in contrast to the yellowish coloration of that area in the house fly, whereas that of the male is orange or cinnamon-buff laterally. The propleura are bare; there is a tuft of stiff black hairs at the base of and between the squamae (difficult to see unless the wings are expanded) that are absent in the house fly. The eyes of the male almost touch each other, the frontal stripe, unlike that of the house fly, being almost interrupted. Sabrosky (1959) has given, graphically, the means for separating the two species.

The face fly, though common in Europe and parts of Asia and Africa, has apparently been of little or no importance there, but, after being introduced into North America, probably in 1950 (it was first recorded in 1952), it has spread rapidly and assumed considerable importance. It now extends from coast to coast in southern Canada and in all but the most southern parts of the United States.

A concise discussion of this insect, with an annotated bibliography of the American literature, is given by Smith, Linsdale, and Burdick (1966) and Smith and Linsdale (1967). The eggs, which differ from those of the house fly in the possession of a respiratory stalk, are laid just beneath the surface of fresh cow droppings. In about a day they hatch. The larva is yellowish rather than creamy white but otherwise looks much like that of the house fly. Its development requires two and one-half to four days. The puparium is dirty white in distinct contrast to the reddish-brown color of the house fly. The life cycle is completed in about fourteen days.

Unmated adults hibernate, often entering houses and massing together in large groups, where their presence can, like that of the cluster fly, cause considerable annoyance. Face flies may be associated in hibernating groups. During the summer months the adult females feed on secretions around the heads of cattle and other animals. In areas where the flies are common, 75 to 100 flies per animal are not unusual. Males are found on fence posts, tree leaves, and such places, rarely on animals. Flies of both sexes spend the night on vegetation, away from the animals.

In addition to the annoyance to man and animals, the potential for mechanical transmission of pathogens should be considered. The fly has been incriminated in Europe as a vector of an eye worm, *Thelazia rhodesii* Demarest, and it is a possible vector of other human and animal pathogens. A significant bit of information has been given by Steve and Lilly (1965) and Cheng (1967). These authors have shown, first, that the habits and structure of the face fly provide a suitable means for the transmission of the bacterium *Moraxella bovis* (Hauderoy), which is considered the most probable pathogen of infectious bovine keratitis (pink eye of cattle), and, second, that in Pennsylvania there is a significant correlation between numbers of face flies on the heads of cattle and the incidence of pink eye. It is noteworthy that this information gives as conclusive evidence for pathogen transmission as we have in most cases of house fly pathogen vectorship.

Fannia canicularis (Linnaeus), the lesser house fly (or little house fly), is frequently seen hovering in midair or flying hither and thither in the middle of a room. Whereas the house fly is encountered most abundantly in the kitchen or dining room, particularly on food, the lesser house fly will be seen as frequently in one room as another and very seldom on the spread table. These little flies are commonly observed to dance weirdly in the center of a room midway between the floor and the ceiling. Various observers have estimated that flies of this species constitute from 1 to 50 per cent of the total population of flies in an average house.

The lesser house fly is more slender than the species of *Musca*; it is largely black, but the sides of the abdomen are marked with yellow, more noticeably so in the male. The thorax has three brown longitudinal stripes, which remain evident even in somewhat rubbed specimens. The genus *Fannia* is easily distinguished from *Musca* by the broadly open cell R_5 and by the characteristic bend of vein 3rd A, which would intersect the 2nd A if the latter were produced.

The eggs of this species are deposited chiefly on decaying vegetable matter and excrement, particularly of chickens, humans, horses, and cows. The larvae emerge in about twenty-four hours and may be recognized as flattened, spiny organisms about 6 mm long when full grown (Fig. 14-4A). The pupal period lasts about seven days under favorable conditions. The complete life cycle requires from fifteen to thirty days.

Fannia scalaris (Fabricius), the latrine fly, is very similar to the foregoing. In size the two flies are about the same; if anything the latrine fly is somewhat larger. The thorax and abdomen are bluish black; the antennae, palpi, and legs are thick. The abdomen has a dark median stripe that, with segmentally arranged transverse bands, produces a series of dorsal triangular markings. In contrast to the preceding, the middle tibia of the male is provided with a distinct tubercle.

The eggs of this fly are deposited chiefly on excrement of humans, horses, cows, and so forth, also on decaying vegetable matter. The

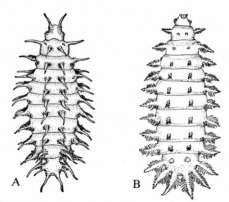

Fig. 14-4 *A.* Larva of *Fannia canicularis. B.* Larva of *Fannia scalaris.* × 6. (After Hewitt.)

egg stage lasts about twenty-four hours, the larval stage about six days and over, and the pupal stage about nine days.

Though the larva of the latrine fly resembles that of the lesser house fly in general, it is readily distinguished because its lateral protuberances are distinctly feathered (Fig. 14-4*B*).

Both *Fannia canicularis* and *Fannia scalaris* are Old World as well as New World in their distribution. Other similar species, with similar breeding habits, likewise found in both hemispheres, are *F. manicata* (Meigen) and *F. incisurata* (Zetterstedt). *Fannia benjamini* Malloch, an American species, not only enters houses, but also may cause annoyance by darting about the eyes, ears, and mouths of persons who may enter its habitat (Arthur C. Smith, personal communication). There is some possibility that this fly might be involved in pathogen transmission.

The Genus Muscina. Muscina stabulans (Fallén), the false or nonbiting stable fly, is larger and more robust than the house fly, varying in length from 7 to nearly 10 mm. Its general appearance is dark gray. The head is whitish gray, the antennal arista bears setae on both the upper and lower sides. The thorax is gray with four longitudinal black lines; the scutellum is broadly yellowish at its apex; the abdomen is almost black in color, covered

with gray in places, which gives it a blotched appearance. The legs are slender and are largely reddish-gold or cinnamon in color. The wings are folded like those of *Musca domestica*; vein M_{1+2} is not elbowed and converges but gently toward the vein before it (R_{4+5}). The eggs of this species are laid upon decaying organic matter and excrement, including human feces and rotting cow dung in which the larvae develop. The complete life cycle is said to require from five to six weeks. *Muscina assimilis* (Fallén), a similar species with wholly black legs, has much the same habits.

Family Calliphoridae (Blow Flies). The blow flies are the common bluebottle, greenbottle, and related forms, including many species of medical and veterinary importance. The more familiar ones are at least in part metallic blue, green, or copper, but there are many nonmetallic species, particularly in the Old World. The family is characterized by James (1948) as follows:

The arista is plumose, the hairs being usually long and extending almost to its apex; there is no postscutellum except in some genera of little medical importance; hypopleural and pteropleural bristles are present; there are three sternopleurals, two in front and one behind; there are two notopleurals, rarely an adventitious third; vein M_2 bends strongly forward, greatly narrowing but usually not closing the apical cell; and the first abdominal sternite overlaps the lateral margins of the tergites.

The larvae usually feed on dead animals or meat scraps or wastes contained in garbage; less frequently they are scavengers on excrement and plant materials; some are facultative or obligatory parasites. An extensive study of the life histories and nutritional requirements of several common species has been made by Kamal (1958, 1959).

Calliphora. Among the several species of bluebottle flies (metallic blue in color), two are quite common, namely *Calliphora vomitoria* (Linnaeus) (Fig. 14-5), which has black genae

Fig. 14-5 A common blow fly, *Calliphora vomitoria.*

clothed with golden-red hairs, and *C. vicina* Robineau-Desvoidy (=*erythrocephala* Meigen), which has fulvous genae clothed with black hairs. The eggs of these species hatch in from six to forty-eight hours; the growing larvae feed on the flesh for from three to nine days, and after attaining full growth leave the food and bury themselves in loose earth and debris. This period (prepupal) lasts from two to seven days, after which the puparium is formed. Although it is now known that a fourth larval stage, of brief duration, occurs within the puparium, for the sake of simplicity the pupal stage, as considered here, is reckoned as beginning with the formation of the puparium. The pupal period varies considerably according to temperature, lasting from ten to seventeen days, commonly eleven days. Thus, the life history of the blow fly requires from sixteen to thirty-five days, usually twenty-two days. The life span of the adult is about thirty-five days on an average.

Several nonmetallic species of *Calliphora* are important scavengers in Australia, where they may also be involved in sheep strike (see Chapter 16). The most important of these are *C. augur* (Fabricius) and *C. stygia* (Fabricius).

Phaenicia and Lucilia. *P. sericata* (Meigen) is of a yellowish-green or cupreous green metallic color with the abdomen varying from metallic blue and green to copper. It may occur indoors but is typically an outdoors scavenger. The palpi are yellow, as are the scales at the base of the wing (epaulet and basicostal scale); there are usually three postacrostichal bristles; and the second abdominal segment lacks strong, erect marginal bristles. At $80° \pm 2°$ F, ($27–28°$ C) with beef lung or fish as food, the entire cycle of *P. sericata*, from the deposition of the egg to the emergence of the fly, requires about twelve days, broken down as follows: egg stage, about eight hours; larval stage (feeding period), about two and one-half days; prepupal stage (migrating larva), about three days; pupal period, about six days. It is the most abundant species in the genus in the temperate parts of the Holarctic Region and is an important synanthropic fly, some strains being strongly eusynanthropic. *Phaenicia sericata* lends itself well to rearing in large numbers for experimental purposes. Procedures are described by Dorman, Hale, and Hoskins (1938) and more recently by Smith (1967).

Lucilia illustris (Meigen) is a widely distributed holarctic species. In the midwestern portion of the United States it ordinarily deposits its eggs on carcasses in competition with *Phaenicia sericata*. It is, however, largely an open woodland and meadow species. In North American literature prior to 1948, it was confused with the Palaearctic *Lucilia caesar* (Linnaeus). The two species resemble each other very closely; they can be separated, in both sexes, by differences in the terminal abdominal segments and in the genitalia. The thorax in both is metallic blue-green with bronze and purple reflections and the legs are black. *Lucilia papuensis* Macquart is a common and widespread scavenger in southeastern Asia, New Guinea, and other Pacific islands.

The black blow fly, Phormia regina (Meigen), is a widely distributed holarctic species; it is a broadly feeding scavenger and is often involved in sheep strike. It is a cold-weather fly, occurring more abundantly during the early spring months and becoming less abundant as hot weather approaches. The thorax is black with a metallic bluish-green luster; there are darker black longitudinal stripes on the dorsum extending somewhat beyond the suture; the prothoracic spiracles are clothed with bright yellow hairs; the legs are shining black; the abdomen is olivaceous or bluish-green to black, and shiny; the length of the fly is 6 to 11 mm.

The cluster fly, Pollenia rudis (Fabricius), may be distinguished from other common synanthropic blow flies of North America and Europe, by its pollinose, nonmetallic abdomen. It measures about 8 mm in length; it is thus, as a rule, a much larger insect than the house fly, which it superficially resembles. It is also more heavily built and slower in its movements. The thorax, particularly on the sides, is clothed with silky, curly yellow hairs that are clearly visible to the naked eye unless they are rubbed off.

The larvae of this fly parasitize earthworms, so far as is known. Several species of worms occurring in Europe and North America are known as hosts, including *Allolobophora chlorotica* Sav., the species from which Keilin first reared the fly in 1908. The name "cluster fly" is applied to this species because of its habit of entering houses and clustering together in large numbers for purposes of hibernation. Its presence can cause a severe nuisance problem, but it is of no importance otherwise. Mixed clusters of this and other species, such as *Musca autumnalis*, may occur.

Family Sarcophagidae. The family Sarcophagidae is considered by some authorities to be a part of the Calliphoridae. It contains a variety of biotic types, including the familiar medium-sized grayfish flies found around carrion and excrement. The abdominal pattern in the more familiar species consists of a tessellated gray and black, that is, a checkerboard pattern in which the spots change from black to gray and back with the light incidence. An exception in a medically important group is the myiasis-producing *Wohlfahrtia*, in which the abdominal pattern, though variegated, does not depend on light incidence. The arista

of the antenna is bare or, if hairy, the plumosity does not reach the apex; there are usually three or more notopleural bristles. The larvae may breed in carrion, excrement, or decaying vegetable matter; some parasitize grasshoppers, Lepidoptera, snails, and other invertebrates, and a few parasitize vertebrates, including man.

Sarcophaga haemorrhoidalis Fallén may be taken as representative of this group. This is one of the many species of flesh flies; it occurs throughout much of North America and Eurasia. It measures 10 to 14 mm in length; its general color is gray and the terminalia of the male are red. It reminds one of an oversized house fly but it is lighter gray, the eyes are brighter red-brown in color, and it is larviparous, like most other members of the family. The larvae have a wide range of feeding habits but they are primarily scavengers. They feed on dead insects, carrion, mammalian excrement, and so forth.

The life cycle in the presence of ample food and warm temperature requires from fourteen to eighteen days. The growth of the larva is very rapid after extrusion when food such as carrion is available. The larval stage may be completed in about three days. The pupal stage requires from eight to ten days.

Sarcophagids are not as apt to enter houses as calliphorids are, but many of them are definitely synanthropic, including a number of carrion and excrement feeders.

FLIES AND HUMAN WELFARE

Flies as Pests. Lindsay and Scudder (1956) have pointed out the importance of flies as nuisances or pests "in an age when those who enjoy a high standard of living are spending progressively more and more for creature comforts." There is no reason why we should tolerate a fly nuisance such as that shown in Figure 14-6 any more than we should endure hordes of biting mosquitoes. This is particularly true in an age in which we are

Fig. 14-6 Such a fly nuisance as this is intolerable. (Photograph by Edgar A. Smith; courtesy of California Bureau of Vector Control.)

recognizing more and more the importance of mental, as well as physical, health.

Control of fly nuisance must, like mosquito control, be a public responsibility. An outstanding as well as pioneering piece of work in this direction has been done by California's Bureau of Vector Control and by the Health Department of Santa Clara County; these agencies have thoroughly recognized the importance of the nuisance aspect and of public responsibility in its abatement.

One can only speculate as to what effect buzzing flies in the home may have on mental health. It is an established fact that some per-

sons have a pathologic fear of insects (entomophobia), whether the cause of this fear be real or imagined. The effect on more normal persons is unknown, but certainly a noisily buzzing blow fly or a swarm of house flies within the house does not lead to mental well being.

Flies as Germ Carriers. The house fly, *Musca domestica*, is by accident of habit and structure an important and dangerous pathogen-transmitting insect. Its importance in this respect can be fully appreciated if one considers the following facts. (1) The house fly is a eusynanthrope over most of its range, at least; it freely enters houses and areas where persons congregate, as well as restaurants, stores, and other places where human food is available; it just as freely frequents human and animal excrement. (2) It freely feeds on human food and excrement alike. Because the fly can take in only liquid food, it may emit vomit spots for the purpose of liquefying solid materials. In the feeding process, droplets of excrement may be deposited. (3) Structurally, the fly is well adapted for picking up pathogens. Its proboscis is provided with a profusion of fine hairs that readily collect germs and filth. The foot of the fly, when examined under the microscope, presents an astonishing complexity of structure; each of the six feet is fitted with hairy structures and pads that secrete a sticky material, thus adding to its collecting ability. Habit and structure therefore combine to result in a remarkably effective mechanism for mechanical transmission of any pathogen small enough to be so carried, particularly of microorganisms and helminth ova.

Studies going back as far as those of Esten and Mason (1908) have shown that the number of bacteria on the body of a single fly may exceed a million. Esten and Mason found as many as 6,600,000 bacteria on a single fly, with an average of one and a quarter million per fly for 414 flies. Yao, Yuan, and Huie (1929), in a study involving 384,193 flies, estimated an average of 3,683,000 bacteria per fly in a slum district and an average of 1,941,000 for the cleanest district studied, in Peiping, China.

The fly usually acquires microorganisms by walking over materials containing them, both its feet and wings being contaminated. The intestinal contents of flies, while they are feeding, also becomes charged with infectious agents, and these are ejected in the fly specks and vomit droplets. In some cases flies might become infected in the larval stage by developing in infectious matter, and newly emerged and unfed flies can then be dangerous. The great majority of organisms present in the digestive

tracts of fly larvae fail to carry over to the adult, and larvae reared in an abundance of them may produce completely bacteria-free flies (Greenberg, 1959, 1965). However, some *Salmonella*, including one species that is responsible for food poisoning in man and another that is the agent of the deadly pullorum disease of poultry, can pass thus from the larva to the adult fly. The opportunity for flies to become infected, therefore, is so great in all communities, even the most sanitary, that no fly should be trusted to alight on food prepared for human consumption.

The evidence for incriminating flies as mechanical vectors of human pathogens is, however, essentially circumstantial. Flies are known to become contaminated with more than 100 species of pathogenic organisms, including the causative organisms of amebic and bacillary dysentery, typhoid fever, cholera, salmonellosis, anthrax, leprosy, yaws, trachoma, poliomyelitis, and infectious hepatitis; they can also carry certain helminth eggs, such as those of pinworm, whipworm, hookworm, Ascaris, and tapeworm (Hale, *et al.*, 1960). In consideration of this fact, as well as the fly's potential, by habit and structure, of transmitting microorganisms, plus the epidemiologic picture in epidemics of such diseases as trachoma and shigellosis, the evidence seems so conclusive as to be virtually undeniable. We do, however, lack a clear-cut picture such as that which exists in relation to the transmission of such diseases as malaria, plague, and Rocky Mountain spotted fever.

Gastrointestinal Diseases. The house fly is primarily a food contaminator and vector of pathogens found in filth because of its feeding and breeding habits, as already explained. Pathogenic organisms are collected on the feet and mouth parts and ingested while feeding, then deposited mechanically while the fly is crawling on human food, by regurgitation or with the fly's excrement.

It is in respect to gastrointestinal diseases that the role of the house fly in pathogen transmission has been most firmly established.

The results of studies on bacillary dysentery, or shigellosis (causative organisms *Shigella dysenteriae* and *S. paradysenteriae*), are particularly enlightening. The work of Watt and Lindsay (1948) in semiarid, subtropical Texas near the mouth of the Rio Grande, where shigellosis is so highly prevalent and epidemic in some areas that a reduction of 50 per cent in rate would be readily detectable in a sample of feasible size, has given particularly significant results. Lindsay and Scudder (1956), citing that work, say:

Through cooperation with the Texas State Health Department, fly control was achieved with DDT spraying in five out of nine similar towns. It resulted in substantial reduction in (a) *Shigella* infections, as determined by rectal swab cultures in representative groups of children under 10 years of age, (b) reported attacks of diarrheal disease, and (c) reported deaths of children under two years of age. Fly control operations were routinely established early in 1946, a few weeks in advance of the establishment of direct epidemiological measurements. Thus differentials between reported illnesses and actual infections were evident when first measured, although reported deaths of infants under two years of age prior to fly control were essentially at the same rate in the two groups of towns. In September, 1947, after nearly 20 months of fly control in five of the nine study towns, the treatment order was reversed, and the four previously untreated towns were subjected to fly measures with DDT. This change in schedule coincided with the normal seasonal increase in flies in the area and within a few days the Scudder fly grill indices for the previously treated towns had risen sharply. This was followed a few weeks later by a comparable condition in the rates of cultured infections of *Shigella* and of reported diarrheal disease. Concurrently with these rising trends, fly indices for the currently treated towns abruptly declined. This reversal in trends, coinciding with the change in fly controlled areas, decisively eliminated the possibility of chance and demonstrated the role of flies in vectoring a human disease in this study area and under the conditions involved.

Transmission of *Eberthella typhosa*, the causative organism of typhoid fever, and of *Salmonella paratyphi* and *S. schötmuelleri*, the causative organisms of two strains of paratyphoid, is by fecal contamination of food and drink. Faichnie (1929) found that both *E. typhosa* and *S. paratyphi* multiplied in the intestines of flies fed on fecal material. Greenberg, *et al.* (1963), in a study made at a slaughterhouse in central Mexico, recovered twelve types of *Salmonella* from ten species of flies taken over offal and manure. The Salmonella types and percentages of positive recoveries were much higher in flies than in livestock or rats. The paratyphoid pathogens, however, were not represented. The epidemiological picture for typhoid fever and paratyphoid, together with repeated isolations of the bacteria from flies, points strongly to the incrimination of flies; however, evidence such as we have in shigellosis is absent.

The pathogen of Salmonella enteritis has been considered in part to be fly-borne. However, in the studies of Watt and Lindsay, as well as in subsequent studies in Georgia, the transmission of salmonellosis bacteria was not established. Either the vectoring potential of the fly is low, or the host qualifications of man are unnatural (Lindsay and Scudder, 1956). It is probable that the low dosage transmission of the fly removes it from serious consideration and that human cases of the disease, even in areas where domestic animal infection rate is high, are due to consumption of food contaminated by other agencies.

Cholera. Cholera, the causative organism of which is the bacillus *Vibrio comma*, was among the first diseases in which the house fly was incriminated as a carrier. Tizzoni and Cattani in Bologna, Italy, in 1886 isolated cholera vibrios from flies caught in cholera wards. Simmonds in 1892 captured flies in the postmortem morgue in Hamburg and isolated cholera vibrios from these in large numbers. In the study of the epidemiology of cholera Gill and Lal (1931) found evidence to support the startling suggestion that possibly one phase of the life cycle of the cholera vibrio may be passed in the body of the house fly. The results of this work show that the vibrios disappeared on or about the fifth day, at which time the fly was capable of infecting food by its feces.

Yaws. Yaws (Frambesia) is caused by the spirochete *Treponema pertenue* Castellani. This disease is widely distributed in the tropics. The spirochetes are found in superficial ulcers on the hands, feet, face, and other parts of the body. As early as 1907 Castellani demonstrated the presence of the yaws organism on the mouth parts and legs of flies that had been feeding on ulcers in yaws patients; moreover, he was able to transfer the pathogen to scarified areas on the eyelids of monkeys by means of such flies. The work of Satchell and Harrison (1953) in Samoa indicates quite convincingly that wound-feeding flies, particularly *Musca domestica* and *M. sorbens*, are involved in the transmission of the yaws organism in that area.

Ophthalmia. Evidence concerning the role of the house fly in the transmission of organisms that cause eye infections is conflicting. It has been pointed out that, in Egypt, eye infections are most prevalent in areas where the house fly is most numerous, whereas in the desert, where flies are absent, eyes as a rule are not affected (Howard, 1900). The role of the house fly in the transmission of conjunctivitis is apparently not as great as was once supposed. In the United States, *Hippelates* gnats are much more important than house flies in the transmission of that complex of bacteria that cause infections known as "pink eye" and "sore eye." The more important trachoma of the Near East, a viral disease, that frequently results in blinding, is, according to Siniscal (1955), a family disease resulting from poor sanitary practices under crowded conditions. Lindsay and Scudder (1956) believe that "if his (Siniscal's) conclusions are sound, flies would seem very unimportant as carriers during ordinary levels of the disease."

Poliomyelitis. Though flies, biting and nonbiting, as well as mosquitoes, have long been under suspicion as vectors of the virus of poliomyelitis, suspicion now rests only on flies breeding and feeding in excrement, carrion, and garbage. The virus has been isolated repeatedly from human stools and sewage, and its presence has been demonstrated in flies collected in the field during both urban and rural epidemics by various investigators. The fly species involved most frequently in field isolations are *Musca domestica* and toe blow flies *Phaenicia sericata* and *Phormia regina.* Positive experimental evidence of potential transmission has been secured by intraperitoneal inoculation of etherized fly extract into *Cynomolgus* monkeys and by the introduction of unetherized material both intranasally and by mouth. Persistence of the virus on and in the fly seems to vary with the strain of the virus, but ranges from about forty-eight hours to twelve days or more, ample time for the fly to contact the food or person of a susceptible individual.

The conclusion that the house fly and certain flesh flies and blow flies can harbor the poliomyelitis virus, and, under proper circumstances, can transmit it either by external contamination or contact, or by internal passage following ingestion, seems quite secure. However, any role that flies may play is undoubtedly incidental. The exact mechanism of the transmission of poliomyelitis, despite all the work that has been done on the subject, is not known; it is probably through the oropharyngeal route and by close association with the human carrier, either by transfer from the pharynx of the carrier to the oropharynx of the susceptible individual, or by a fecal route. Any involvement of flies probably just adds to the severity of an epidemic. It has been assumed that such involvement takes the form of food contamination or other initiation of the oropharyngeal route, although Nuorteva (1959) has presented some cogent arguments to indicate that, with flies, infection may come through the cutaneous route, specifically through infection of wounds and cuticular lesions by the carrion-feeding blow flies, particularly *Phormia regina* and *Phaenicia sericata*. This would require the transfer of the virus from a carrion rather than a fecal source. Certain facts regarding the epidemiology of poliomyelitis tend to support Nuorteva's contention (cf. Nuorteva, 1959).

Tuberculosis. Though flies have the mechanism and habits for the transmission of the tubercle bacillus, no conclusive work has established the relationship of flies to such transmission. Flies have been observed to feed on the sputum of tuberculosis patients and to pass infective bacilli in their feces. Lamborn, working with *Musca sorbens* in Nyasaland, found that the tubercle bacilli might remain viable in the body of the fly for a week. West (1951) reported:

As an experimental procedure Lamborn injected a guinea pig intraperitoneally with the gut contents of three flies that had fed eight days previously on positive sputum. The animal died four months later of a generalized tuberculosis, as did a second animal injected five days after the flies had fed.

Intestinal Protozoa. Roubaud (1918) found that the cysts of *Entamoeba coli* (Grassi), *Entamoeba histolytica* (Schaudinn), and *Giardia lamblia* Stiles passed through the intestine of the fly uninjured, and that free amebae (both *coli* and *histolytica*) when fed to flies were found dead in the fly's intestine in less than an hour. The supposed role of the house fly in the transmission of *Entamoeba histolytica* cysts has been supported by the research of other workers. Pipkin (1949) believes that the external carriage of both trophozoite and cyst of *E. histolytica* is of no significance except where sanitary conditions are generally ignored, but that transmission by way of the alimentary tract is important on a community basis, especially in backward areas. Root (1921) found mobile *Chilomastix mesnili* (Wenyon) in a fly's feces seven minutes after it had fed on an infectious stool.

Eggs of Parasitic Worms. Extensive and careful work on the dispersal of eggs of

parasitic worms by the house fly has been done by Nicoll (1911). The following is a summary of his investigations. Flies feed readily on excrement in which eggs from parasitic worms occur. Eggs may be conveyed by flies from excrement to food in two ways, namely, on the external surface of the body and in the intestines. The latter is possible only when the diameter of the eggs is less than 0.05 mm. Eggs with a diameter up to 0.09 mm may be conveyed on the external surface; however, these adhering eggs are usually shed by the fly within a short time, whereas those harbored in the intestine may remain for several days. It was found that material containing eggs of parasites, and in particular gravid segments of tapeworms, remains a source of infection through flies for as long as two weeks.

The eggs of the following parasitic worms were shown experimentally to be carried externally by *Musca domestica*: *Taenia solium* Linnaeus, *Taenia pisiformis* (Bloch), *Taenia hydatigena* Pallas, *Hymenolepis nana* (von Siebold), *Dipylidium caninum* (Linnaeus), *Diphyllobothrium latum* (Linnaeus), *Enterobius vermicularis* (Linnaeus), *Trichocephalus trichiurus* (Linnaeus), both internally and externally; *Necator americanus* (Stiles), *Ancylostoma canium* (Ercolani), *Ascaris equorum* Goeze, *Toxascaris leonina* (von Linstrow), *Hymenolepis diminuta* (Rodolphi). No trematode parasites were experimented with, and the observations of Stiles that the larval fly can ingest ascarid eggs and pass them on to the adult were not confirmed. In addition to the above, West lists the eggs of *Ascaris lumbricoides* Linnaeus, *Ancylostoma duodenale* (Dubini), and the hydatid *Echinococcus granulosus* (Batsch).

Diseases of Domestic Animals. House flies are thought to be one means by which *Trypanosoma hippicum* Darling, the causative organism of murrina of horses, mules, and burros can be transmitted. The causative organism of bovine mastitis, *Streptococcus agalactiae* Lehmann and Newmann, was thought by Sanders (1940) to have *Musca* *domestica* as well as Hippelates gnats for natural vectors, although Ewing (1942) did not consider the house fly to be an important natural agent.

Larvae of the nematode *Habronema* may cause persistent ulcerations, or summer sores, on the lower portions of bodies of horses, also *habronemic conjunctivitis*, which manifests itself as sores on the eyes. Adults of *Habronema muscae* Carter occur in the stomach of the horse, where they lay their eggs, which pass out with the feces. The newly hatched larvae find their way into the bodies of the fly larvae, which are evidently true intermediate hosts, and in which further development of the nematode occurs. The worm larvae escape from the adult fly and attack the host, or the fly may be accidentally ingested.

Another nematode, which produces hump sores in cattle, *Stephanofilaria assamensis* Pande, family Stephaniidae, is transmitted mechanically by muscoid flies, according to Rahman (1957). The flies, when visiting the sores to feed, pick up the nematodes and transmit them to other cattle, where new sores are produced. However, Hawking and Worms (1961) believe that this theory requires confirmation before it can be accepted.

Domestic fowls are commonly infested by tapeworms, several of which may have the house fly or the stable fly as intermediate hosts. This relationship was first demonstrated by Guberlet (1916). The most important of the fowl tapeworms is *Choanotaenia infundibulum* (Bloch). Parasitized flies may be ingested in food, such as buttermilk, which is attractive to both chickens and flies.

The role of the face fly in the transmission of pathogens of domestic animals has been discussed earlier in this chapter.

15

BLOODSUCKING MUSCOID FLIES

ORDER DIPTERA, FAMILY MUSCIDAE

TSETSE

The genus *Glossina*, family Muscidae, comprises the tsetse of Africa. According to Buxton (1955) the word "tsetse" comes from the Sechuana language of Bechuanaland and means "fly destructive to cattle." As Glasgow (1963) points out, the term "tsetse fly" is therefore a tautology, though well established in the literature and in common usage. "Tsetse" may

be used either as a singular or a plural noun. Bequaert (1930) states that the word was introduced into the English language by R. Gordon Cumming in 1850 in his "Five Years of a Hunter's Life in the Far Interior of South Africa," and David Livingstone in 1857 "focused the attention of the scientific world upon the ravages of the fly."

Evidently tsetse enjoyed a wide distribution in earlier geological times; four species of fossil *Glossina* have been described from the Oligocene shales of Colorado. Today, so far as is known, tsetse are restricted to continental Africa south of the Tropic of Cancer and possibly southern Arabia, where they occur in so-called "fly belts." They remain an obstacle to the development of tropical Africa over an area of over four million square miles.

Several large monographs on tsetse have been published. The ones by Buxton (1955) and Glasgow (1963) will be especially useful to the student. An important review of significant advances in our knowledge of tsetse bionomics is given by Glasgow (1967), and Willett (1962, 1963) has reviewed the relationships of these flies to the epidemiology of trypanosomiases.

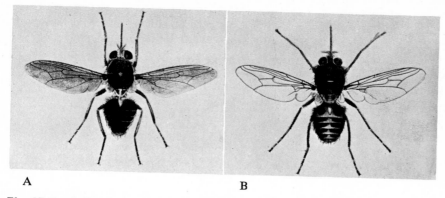

Fig. 15-1 *A. Glossina palpalis. B. Glossina morsitans.* (After Newstead.)

General Characteristics. The tsetse (Fig. 15-1) are flies of medium size, ranging from that of a house fly to that of a blow fly. They are brownish in color; the body is wasplike; and the wings, when at rest, are crossed scissorslike and extend well beyond the tip of the abdomen. The wing venation is characteristic in that the fourth longitudinal vein (M_{1+2}) bends suddenly upward before it meets the anterior transverse vein, which is very oblique. The discal cell is shaped remarkably like a meat cleaver and is referred to as the "cleaver cell" (Fig. 10-1*F*).

The palpi are nearly as long as the proboscis, which points bayonetlike in front of the head. The antennal arista (Fig. 15-2) bears a series of long bilaterally branched and regularly arranged hairs on the upper surface. This type of antenna is distinctly characteristic of *Glossina.* The mouth parts are of the third dipterous, or stable fly, subtype described in Chapter 3. A characteristic "onion-shaped" bulb is situated at the base of the haustellum (Fig. 15-3).

Food Habits. Both sexes feed avidly and exclusively on blood. This food source has to

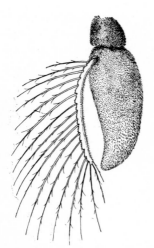

Fig. 15-2 Antenna of *Glossina,* showing arista with branched hairs. (Much enlarged.)

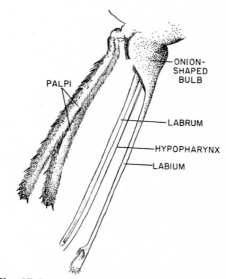

ONION-SHAPED BULB

PALPI

LABRUM

HYPOPHARYNX

LABIUM

Fig. 15-3 Mouth parts of *Glossina.* × 17.

suffice for all stages of the fly, because the larva takes no nourishment other than that furnished by the mother. The flies are attracted to moving objects. They usually feed in broad daylight. As a group, tsetse feed on a wide variety of mammals, reptiles, and, rarely, birds. Some species seem to be restricted in their food habits, whereas others are largely opportunistic, though with certain food preferences. Though man is freely attacked by some tsetse, he is not considered, in general, a favored host.

Weitz (1963) has shown that there are five main patterns of tsetse feeding: (1) those that feed mainly on suids (pigs) such as the warthog, e.g., *Glossina swynnertoni, G. austeni, G. fuscipleuris,* and *G. tabaniformis*; (2) those that feed on suids and bovids (cattle and antelope), e.g., *G. morsitans* and its subspecies; (3) those that feed mainly on bovids, e.g., *G. pallidipes, G. longipalpis,* and *G. fusca*; (4) those that feed mainly on mammals other than bovids and suids, e.g., *G. longipennis* and *G. brevipalpis*; and (5) those that feed on most available hosts, human and otherwise, e.g., *G. palpalis* and its subspecies, *G. fuscipes* and *G. tachinoides.* Jordan, Lee-Jones, and Weitz (1962) found, by serologic tests, that *G. tachinoides* feeds on a variety of hosts including primates (mostly man), porcupine, oxen and other Bovidae, and various other mammals, reptiles, and birds. They considered that this species, like *G. palpalis,* is an opportunistic feeder that can feed on various game animals and reptiles but can also survive in close association with man, in the absence of its wild hosts.

Life History. The female tsetse gives birth to full-grown larvae, which are extruded singly at intervals of about ten to fifteen days during the lifetime of the mother. During the intrauterine state, which involves the first two larval stages, the larvae feed on fluids from special glands commonly referred to as "milk glands." The newly extruded, or third-stage larva, is creamy white to pale yellow and has a pair of intensely black, shining lobes at the posterior end. Thoracic spiracles are lacking.

The female fly requires three blood meals to complete the developmental period of each larva, the last being about three days prior to larviposition. Evidence concerning the number of larvae produced during the lifetime of one female is inconclusive, but the average number is probably eight to ten.

The flies are said to avoid excrementous matter, and the larvae are ordinarily deposited in the root tangles of the mangrove and shade of other vegetation where the soil is not too dry and loose. The presence or absence of organic material seems to be immaterial (Nash, 1939). The larvae are unable to crawl, as do other muscid larvae, because of the reduced cephalopharyngeal armature and the lack of spinose pads. Lewis (1934) points out that the larva moves and burrows by peristaltic movements and longitudinal contractions of the whole body. Coarse, pebbly sand favors the larva in burrowing, although a depth of only a few centimeters is reached. The behavior of the larva at this time, Lewis points out, is of great importance in determining its chances for survival. "If it is slow to penetrate the soil, it is exposed for a longer period of time to the possible attack of predators and parasites." Hardening of the integument to form the puparium takes place within an hour of larviposition. The puparium rapidly darkens to a blackish brown color with the posterior lobes and general form as shown in Figure 15-4. A fourth larval stage occurs within the puparium prior to true pupation. The pupal stage lasts three to four weeks or longer, depending on soil temperature and moisture. A great deal of work has been done on the ecology of the puparium (Nash, 1939). The fly emerges from the puparium by breaking loose the end of the pupal case through pressure from the ptilinum.

Glossina Species. Twenty-one species of Glossina, several of which are divided into subspecies, are recognized today. These are placed in three species groups: (1) the **fusca** group, which consists of *fusca* (Walker), *brevipalpis* Newstead, *fuscipleuris* Austen,

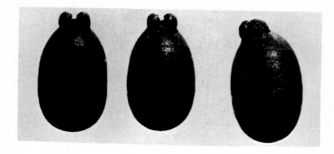

Fig. 15-4   Pupae of *Glossina.* ×4.8.

haningtoni Newstead and Evans, *longipennis* Corti, *medicorum* Austen, *nigrofusca* Newstead, *schwetzi* Newstead and Evans, *severini* Newstead, *tabaniformis* Westwood, *vanhoofi* Henrard, and *nashi* Potts; (2) the **palpalis** group, consisting of *palpalis* (Robineau-Desvoidy), *pallicera* Bigot, *caliginea* Austen, and *tachinoides* Westwood; and (3) the **morsitans** group, consisting of *longipalpis* (Wiedemann), *morsitans* Westwood, *pallidipes* Austen, *austeni* Newstead, and *swynnertoni* Austen. Recent keys to the species of *Glossina* may be found in the works of Buxton (1955) and Smart (1965).

Glossina palpalis (Fig. 15-1) is the most important vector of *Trypanosoma gambiense.* Its distribution covers an enormous area in Africa, but it occurs chiefly in the Congo and West Africa. It is usually found on the shores of rivers and lakes, but may occur far back from them. As Swynnerton points out, it requires a combination of several types of country, one of which must be a relatively massive woodland or thicket of more or less evergreen type. It feeds mainly on large reptiles, such as crocodiles and monitor lizards, but it can live on the blood of mammals as well. Although man is not regarded as one of the favored hosts, the fly will nevertheless feed freely on persons available in its riparian habitat.

Glossina morsitans (Fig. 15-1) is a most efficient vector of the trypanosomes of both Rhodesian sleeping sickness in man and nagana in animals. It has a wide distribution in Africa; it is of importance in the Sudan, Congo, Zambia, Rhodesia, and many other areas. This species requires savanna "of sufficient shade value, and with sufficient logs, rocks, or tree rot holes to form a good rest-haunt and breeding ground, and relatively open glades or plains in which to hunt for its prey." It is essentially a game fly but, since it attacks human beings readily, it is important from the human standpoint.

Glossina swynnertoni, like *G. morsitans*, is an important vector of trypanosomes of both Rhodesian sleeping sickness and nagana. It is largely confined to the northern parts of Tanzania, according to Swynnerton, who describes it as "the fly of the driest and most open areas and apparently unable to inhabit the more mesophytic savannas. It breeds normally in the thicket, though rock suits it as well. ... It utilizes open spaces as feeding grounds.... It is primarily and essentially a 'game' fly." It attacks human beings readily, however, and like *G. morsitans* is an important tsetse.

Glossina tachinoides is an important species in West Africa. It is essentially a reptile feeder, though it freely attacks mammals, including man. It is one of the more important vectors of *Trypanosoma gambiense* and is involved in the transmission of *T. brucei, congolense,* and *vivax. G. pallidipes*, widely distributed through Kenya, Tanzania, Rhodesia, and other parts of East Africa, is one of the more important vectors of the Rhodesian parasite.

Trypanosomiasis.   The term trypanosomiasis applies to all infections with flagellate parasites of the genus *Trypanosoma.* Many species of trypanosomes are regarded as nonpathogenic. Nearly all require an intermediate host. Trypanosomes invade the blood, lymph, cerebrospinal fluid, and various organs of the body, such as the liver and the spleen, of many species of vertebrates, from fish to man. Forms of trypanosomiases have been dealt with in other chapters, namely Chagas' disease (Chapter 8) and surra (Chapter 12). In this chapter we are concerned chiefly with two kinds of sleeping sickness in man and nagana, a related disease complex in cattle. Tsetse are the vectors of the causative organisms of these diseases.

Although human sleeping sickness has been known as a disease since the fourteenth century (Willett, 1963), its cause and vector were not known until 1901, when Dutton discovered the parasites in human blood smears, and 1903, when Bruce and Nabarro proved *Glossina morsitans* to be a vector. Dutton named these parasites *Trypanosoma gambiense*; a second species of human parasite, *T. rhodesiense* Stephens and Fantham, was described in 1910.

Sleeping sickness is now widely distributed in Africa, extending along the west coast from Senegal to Angola and eastward to Mozambique and the valley of the upper Nile. Apparently, human trypanosomiasis was limited to relatively small areas until the late nineteenth century when, as a result of the penetration of Europeans and the lessening in conflict between native tribes, migration in Africa became more prevalent (Willett, 1963). Even when the disease was more limited geographically, it made a definite impact upon the natives. Willett says that slave traders in the seventeenth and eighteenth centuries were well aware of the dangers of "Negro lethargy" and would not accept slaves that showed the characteristic swellings in the neck now known as Winterbottom's sign. More recently, devastating epidemics have occurred. It has been estimated that between 1896 and 1906 from 400,000 to 500,000 natives perished from this pestilence. Dutton and Todd found that in some villages from 30 to 50 per cent of the population was infected. An epidemic, in Uganda near Lake Victoria over a five-year period, took 200,000 human lives, according to Bell (1906, cited by Buxton, 1955); the population of the area involved was 300,000 before the epidemic, the mortality consequently being 67 per cent.

Duggan (1962) cites a case where an entire tribe, the Rukuba of northern Nigeria, was virtually brought to extinction by an epidemic of sleeping sickness following the close of a local war. As the war ended, these people left their overcrowded hilltop fortresses and mingled with returning farmers who harbored the trypanosomes, with tragic results.

Currently, human trypanosomiasis is fairly well under control in many areas, but constant vigilance is necessary. The situation concerning animal trypanosomiasis, however, is quite a different matter.

The bite of an infected tsetse appears to produce more local reaction than that of an uninfected fly. The usual duration of the incubation period is ten to twenty days, but clinical symptoms may be delayed as long as two to five years. In some individuals trypanosomiasis is asymptomatic and such persons may serve as carriers; the extent to which this condition prevails is unknown. During the first phase of the disease, which may continue for many months, the trypanosomes are in the blood, the trypanosomiasis stage; this phase is characterized by an irregular fever, glandular enlargement, debility, and languor. In the second phase, the sleeping sickness stage, the trypanosomes are consistently found in the cerebrospinal fluid; a constant accompaniment is the enlargement of the posterior cervical lymph nodes, *Winterbottom's sign*; there are tremors of the tongue and a speech impairment; there are nervousness, pronounced languor, and drowsiness, which give way to lethargy, and finally the victim falls into a comatose state, wasting rapidly, largely as a result of starvation, until death ensues. Gambian sleeping sickness, caused by *Trypanosoma gambiense*, tends to be mild and to endure for months, with the result that man is of greater importance as the reservoir; Rhodesian sleeping sickness, caused by *T. rhodesiense*, on the other hand, progresses much more rapidly, and the patient, usually too sick to leave his village, assumes less importance as a reservoir (Buxton, 1955).

Transmission. The natives of French Guinea long attributed the transmission of sleeping sickness to flies. After the discovery that the nagana pathogen was transmitted by tsetse, Bruce and his coworkers demonstrated that *Glossina palpalis* could transmit *Trypanosoma gambiense* mechanically for a period of less than forty-eight hours; the virulence of the organism became more and more attenuated after the fly had bitten the infected individual, and soon the power of infection was lost. Thus, the tsetse may be a mechanical vector for a short period of time, during which the trypanosomes are introduced into the wound produced by the bite, before the proboscis is completely cleaned. Interrupted feeding would thus be a factor. Mechanical transmission from man to man in nature is believed to be very uncommon; firm evidence as to the extent of its occurrence is lacking.

Kleine (1909) was evidently the first to demonstrate the development of *Trypanosoma brucei* in *Glossina palpalis*. Robertson (1913) reported that *T. gambiense* is first established in the posterior part of the midgut of the insect, where multiplication occurs. From the tenth or twelfth day onward, slender, long forms are found to be increasing in numbers. These finally move forward to the proventriculus and are the dominant type. The proventriculus becomes infected as a rule between the twelfth and twentieth days. The salivary glands become infected by the slender proventricular type, which reaches the glands by way of the hypopharynx; arriving in the glands, they become attached to the wall, multiply, and produce the metacyclic form, which becomes infective in two to five days. The preinfective cycle in the fly requires a period of at least eighteen days.

The fly is never infective until the salivary glands are invaded, the only exception to this being in case of mechanical transmission. Infectivity in the fly lasts at least ninety-six days. Only a relatively small percentage of the flies become infective, however. The life span of a female *G. palpalis* in captivity has been observed to be about four and one-half months.

Despite the extensive study that has been made of the epidemiology of human African sleeping sickness, some important problems remain unsolved. One is the question of reservoirs. Man is generally considered the sole reservoir of Gambian sleeping sickness. If this is so, the disease can be eliminated from a given area by breaking the cycle of transmission. However, Willett (1963) has pointed out that the low incidence of disease that persists in many areas in spite of prophylactic measures suggests the existence of an additional reservoir or reservoirs. There is evidence, cited by Willett, that pigs may serve as asymptomatic carriers. The evidence that game animals may serve as reservoirs of Rhodesian sleeping sickness is stronger. The reedbuck and eland have been shown to remain infective to the flies for as much as ten and a half and four and a half months, respectively, and some epidemiologic facts seem inexplicable on any basis other than the assumption of a wild-animal reservoir.

Another problem concerns the relative roles of given vectors in the transmission of the trypanosome. Willett (1962), in discussing the relative roles of *Glossina palpalis* and *G. tachinoides* in the transmission of the Gambian parasite, advances the interesting theory that the riverine tsetse are more dangerous when circumstances are such that they find difficulty in surviving at all. Under favorable conditions the fly is more generally distributed over the area that it occupies, but, when conditions are marginal for existence, which in this case means a critically low humidity, it will concentrate near temporary pools, which it may be unable to leave. Man often visits such pools for water, washing, and other activities, thus bringing the victim and fly together. This theory explains such anomalies as the apparent greater ability of the fly to transmit the parasite in areas near the limits of the tsetse's geographical range. *G. palpalis* requires moister conditions for its existence, so may show the restricted distributional pattern where the associated *G. tachinoides* may enjoy a general distribution. Consequently, where *G. palpalis* and *G. tachinoides* coexist, the former may be the effective vector; where only *G. tachinoides* can survive, it assumes that role.

The taxonomic position of *Trypanosoma rhodesiense* has not yet been definitely determined. The generally accepted view is that *T. rhodesiense*, *T. gambiense*, and *T. brucei* are morphologically indistinguishable but biologically distinct species. Willett (1962), however, points out that if this were so, passage of the trypanosome through game animals by tsetse transmission would cause the parasite to lose its infectivity for man. This has been proven experimentally not to be so. After reviewing a considerable amount of evidence, Willett contends that *T. rhodesiense* is a virulent strain of *T. gambiense* that has been able to continue its spread by transmission through game animals and that has thus been able to survive under circumstances that would suppress all less virulent strains.

The principal vectors of *Trypanosoma gambiense* are *Glossina palpalis* and *G. tachinoides*; those of *T. rhodesiense* are *G. morsitans*, *G. swynnertoni*, and *G. pallidipes*.

Nagana. *Trypanosoma brucei* Plimmer and Bradford is the causal organism of classical nagana, a disease that has denied man the use of any domestic animals except poultry over an enormous area estimated to be as great as one fourth of the African continent. The result is not only a loss of the much-needed protein supply, so essential to the future development of an already protein-starved continent; there is also the influence on the mores of African peoples of certain tribes to whom the possession of cattle is an important status symbol.

The disease is fatal to horses, mules, camels, and dogs. Cattle, sheep, and goats usually survive, except when parasitized by certain strains and except when the trypanosome is transmitted by game tsetse rather than by *G. palpalis*; pigs may be chronically infected, without symptoms. Many other mammals are susceptible to the infection and may serve as reservoirs; wild ungulates, however, show no evidence of harm.

Other forms of nagana are caused by *Trypanosoma vivax* Ziemann and *T. congolense* Broden, likewise *Glossina*-transmitted. The effect on the host and the developmental histories of these trypanosomes differ in certain respects from those of *T. brucei*. In *T. vivax*, for example, there is no proventricular stage; the parasite, which would be destroyed if it were to reach the midgut, becomes attached instead to the food canal of the proboscis of the fly. Vivax nagana is known as *souma* in French. The effects of both vivax and congolense nagana on domestic animals may be serious or even fatal. Taxonomically, *T. vivax* and *T. congolense* belong to groups separate from each other and from the *brucei-gambiense-rhodesiense* group.

Glossina morsitans, *G. longipalpis*, and *G. pallidipes*, and, to a lesser extent, other species, relate to nagana in nearly the same way that *Glossina* species relate to African human sleeping sickness, that is, the flies are infective for a day or two after feeding, then become noninfective for a period of about three weeks, when they again become infective and remain so for life. The incubation period after inoculation into the body of the host is said to be about ten days.

THE STABLE FLY

The stable fly, *Stomoxys calcitrans* (Linnaeus), is the most familiar and widely distributed member of its genus and the only one to occur in the New World. The Ethiopian species of *Stomoxys* have been treated by Zumpt (1950) and those of the Palearctic region by

Zimin (1951). The discussion in this section is confined to *Stomoxys calcitrans*.

General Characteristics. Owing to similarity in color and size, the stable fly is often mistaken for the house fly, *Musca domestica*. However, the former is more robust and has a broader abdomen. In color the stable fly is brownish gray with a greenish-yellow sheen; the outer of the four longitudinal thoracic stripes are broken, and the abdomen is more or less checkered. The wings when at rest are widely spread apart at the tips and are distinctly irridescent; the apical cell is open. The proboscis protrudes bayonetlike in front of the head. (For its structure, see Chapter 3.) The antennal arista, unlike that of the house fly, bears hairs on the upper side only.

Habits. Although *Stomoxys calcitrans* is commonly called the "stable fly," it occurs much less abundantly around stables, at least in many areas, than does the house fly. It is sometimes called the "biting house fly" because it may occur indoors, especially in the autumn and during rainy weather, and at such times it bites human beings viciously. It is often very annoying along the sandy, vegetation-strewn shores of lakes and along the seashore where seaweed is windrowed by the tides. The name "dog fly" is sometimes applied to this species. The stable fly is typically an out-of-doors, day-biting fly and is usually to be found in abundance during summer and autumn where large numbers of domestic animals occur, horses and cattle affording an abundant food supply. Sunny fences, walls, and light-colored surfaces in general, when in the proximity of animals, are abundantly frequented by stable flies.

The stable fly is a vicious biter that draws blood quickly and fills to full capacity in three to four minutes if undisturbed, but ordinarily, even when undisturbed, it changes position frequently or flies from one animal to another, where the meal is continued. Characteristic interrupted feeding makes it an excellent vector of pathogens. The fly feeds readily on many species of mammals, such as rats, guinea pigs, rabbits, monkeys, cattle, horses, and man. Both sexes suck blood. The flight of the stable fly is direct and swift and of long range, the fly sometimes traveling many miles.

Breeding Habits and Life History. Although the stable fly can be successfully reared in the manure of horses, cattle, and sheep, it may be safely said that it does not breed commonly in excrement under field conditions unless this is mixed with decaying vegetable matter, straw, or hay. Very good breeding places are afforded by the leftover soggy hay, alfalfa, or grain in the bottoms of or underneath out-of-doors feed racks in connection with dairy feed lots. This material becomes soggy and ferments, and here virtually pure cultures of stable fly larvae may be found. The materials must be moist, for dryness prevents larval development. Old straw piles that remain in the field through the year may produce an abundance of stable flies in the moist fermenting straw near the ground, particularly if cattle have access to it and moisten it with urine. Other fermenting and decaying vegetable matter, such as windrowed seaweed, piles of moist fermenting weeds and lawn cuttings, piles of waste vegetables, and fermenting peanut litter, may provide breeding places.

The larvae of the stable fly (Fig. 15-5) and of the house fly can readily be differentiated by the form, size, and position of the posterior spiracles; otherwise, they resemble each other closely. The pair of posterior spiracles of the stable fly are roughly triangular, widely separated from each other, and situated near the periphery; in the house fly larva they are elliptical, large, close together, and more central in position (Fig. 13-5). The pattern of the spiracular slits, also, is different.

The eggs of the stable fly are about 1 mm long, curved on one side, and straight and grooved on the opposite side. In depositing her eggs, the female fly often crawls far into the loose material, placing them usually in little pockets in small numbers, often in pairs. Egg depositions range in number from 23 to

A   B

Fig. 15-5 *Stomoxys calcitrans. A. Larvae and pupae. B. Adult.* (Photographs by Arthur C. Smith; courtesy of California Bureau of Vector Control.)

100, usually between twenty-five and fifty; there are ordinarily four or five layings, but there may be as many as twenty. Egg production exceeding 600 by a single female has been reported.

The incubation period varies from two to five days, commonly three days, at a temperature of 26° C. Higher temperatures result in a shorter incubation period. The newly hatched larvae bury themselves in their food at once, thus protecting themselves against dryness. At temperatures of 21° to 26° C the larvae reach their full growth in from fourteen to twenty-six days. A developmental period as short as twelve days may be attained at a slightly higher temperature.

Before pupation the larvae usually crawl into the drier parts of the breeding medium, where the chestnut-colored puparia may be found in enormous numbers. The puparia are 6 to 7 mm long and may be recognized by the posterior spiracles as in the larvae. The pupal period, including the last larval stage that begins with the formation of the puparium, varies, depending on temperature. At 21° to 26° C, this period varies from five to twenty-six days, with the greatest frequency nine to thirteen days.

If not handicapped, the imago (Fig. 15-5) emerges with astonishing rapidity, unfolds its wings, and is ready to fly in less than an hour. The fact that the proboscis is temporarily attached beneath the thorax gives the newly emerged insect a very peculiar appearance, and it may then be mistaken easily for a house fly. The total time for development of the fly, from egg laying to emergence of adults, was determined by Herms to be thirty-three to thirty-six days at 21° C. As short a developmental period as twelve days has been reported (Mitzmain, 1913).

Longevity. With approximately 4,000 flies under continuous daily observation in glass quart jars, fifty to a set, Herms has found that the average length of life of a stable fly under favorable laboratory conditions of feeding is about twenty days, with a maximum of sixty-nine days. A maximum of seventy-two days for the female and ninety-four for the male, in the Philippine Islands, was determined by Mitzmain (1913).

The Stable Fly as a Cattle Pest. Bishopp (1939) regards this fly as one of the most important sources of annoyance to livestock. Injury is brought about in various ways, for example, worry caused by the mass attack of flies, loss of blood, and loss of flesh.

Freeborn, Regan, and Folger (1925) have shown that the reduction in milk production caused by the stable fly amounted to 9.26 per cent, which for a five-month period means a loss of fifty gallons of milk per lactating animal. The total loss occasioned by the three dairy cattle pests—house flies, stable flies, and horn flies—amounts to 15 per cent, according to these studies.

The Stable Fly and Disease. The stable fly is no exception to the rule that any blood-sucking fly must be suspect in the transmission of causative organisms of disease in man and animals. Yet, there is little evidence against it. Its supposed relationship to the transmission of the poliomyelitis virus is now only of historical interest, as shown by Sawyer and Herms (1913) and substantiated by subsequent workers. It is, however, known to have some importance in the mechanical transmission of the virus of infectious anemia of horses, the anthrax bacillus, and several pathogenic trypanosomes. One of the latter is *Trypanosoma evansi* (Steel), the causative organism of surra, a disease nearly always fatal to horses and mules and often with serious effects on camels and dogs; it may under certain circumstances be a serious disease to cattle, though in these animals it is usually mild or asymptomatic, but with the result that cattle may serve as carriers. Though the role of the stable fly as a vector of surra is purely a mechanical one, its transmission by this and other bloodsucking flies, particularly *Tabanus*, is quite important. Mechanical transmission of *Trypanosoma brucei, T. rhodesiense,* and *T. gambiense* also occurs, but is of very little importance. The fly is infective for only a brief period of time. Nevertheless, the restless, intermittent type of feeding characteristic of the stable fly is very conducive to this type of transmission.

On rare occasions, the stable fly becomes involved in accidental traumatic myiasis or enteric pseudomyiasis in man.

THE HORN FLY

The horn fly, *Haematobia irritans* (Linnaeus), is a well-established pest of cattle through-out many of the tropical and temperate areas of the Northern Hemisphere. It was originally described from southern France. It was first reported in the United States, in the fall of 1887, from Camden, New Jersey; its spread was very rapid, and by 1892 it was found over the entire continent, east of the Rocky Mountains, from Canada to Texas. California cattlemen report that it made its appearance in that state in 1893 or 1894. It now occurs on the American mainland as far south as Venezuela. It appeared in Honolulu, Hawaii, in 1897.

The nomenclature of this species is confusing to the nonspecialist. The combination *Siphona irritans* has been used extensively in recent American literature as a result of a confusion as to just what fly the generic name *Siphona* should apply. The names *Lyperosia irritans* and *Haematobia stimulans* have been applied to it. The true *H. stimulans* is a different, though closely related, European fly that is not known to occur in America, although another similar but uncommon species, *H. alcis* Snow, torments moose and perhaps other members of the deer family in Canada and the northern United States.

Characteristics. The horn fly is about half the size of the house fly, that is, about 4 mm long. It has the same general color as the stable fly and in most respects resembles it, though it is a much more slender species. The mouth parts (Fig. 15-6) are like those of the stable fly except that the labium of the horn fly is relatively heavier and the palpi, almost as long as the proboscis, are flattened and loosely ensheath that structure. The wing venation is similar to that of the stable fly.

The season of horn fly abundance varies with climate and latitude. In southern Alberta, for example, there is one peak of abundance in midsummer, whereas in Texas there are two peaks, in early and late summer. The adult fly remains on the host night and day, the females leaving only briefly to deposit their eggs. The feeding position depends on the length of the hairs of the host. On bare areas

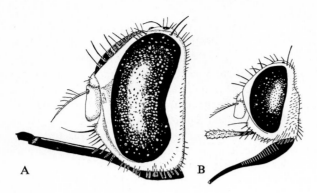

A   B

Fig. 15-6 *A*. The stable fly, *Stomoxys calcitrans,* head from side view. *B*. The horn fly, *Haematobia irritans,* same; both drawn to the same scale. (Drawings by Bruce Eldridge.)

the fly holds its body almost parallel to the surface, whereas when it is among long hairs it must put its head down to reach the skin. In feeding, the fly characteristically orients itself with its head downward, toward the ground, in contrast to the stable fly, which usually orients itself with the head directed upward. At least in western North America, the habit of clustering around the horns of cattle, which gives the horn fly its common name, seems to relate to weather conditions. It often is evident when a storm front is approaching and may be influenced by a change in temperature, moisture, pressure, or a combination of these. (Much of the information in this paragraph was furnished by Dr. Kurt Depner, personal communication.)

Life History. A comprehensive study of the life history and habits of this fly was published by McLintock and Depner (1954). The fly deposits its eggs chiefly, if not exclusively, on freshly passed cow manure. These are deposited sometimes singly but more often in groups of four to six, usually under the sides of the cake of dung or in the grass or soil beneath it. A maximum of twenty to twenty-four eggs may be laid at one time, but a female is capable of producing 375 to 400 eggs in her lifetime. The eggs measure 1.3 to 1.5 mm in length, larger than those of the stable fly. At temperatures of 24° to 26° C they hatch in twenty-four hours. A relative humidity of close to 100 per cent is required for maximum hatching.

The larvae burrow through the droppings, reaching full growth in from four to eight days, more or less. They then crawl into drier areas and form the puparia. The so-called "pupal" period, or development within the puparium, which, as in related forms, includes one larval stadium, requires six to eight days. In cooler climates overwintering is in the pupal stage in a state of diapause made possible by the shortening photoperiod and related to lower environmental temperatures. Even in southern regions a percentage of pupae enter this state.

Temperature has a profound effect on the length of time required for the development of this fly. Depner (1961), for example, found the developmental period from hatching to puparium formation to require 10.5, 5.6, and 3.7 days at respective temperatures of 18°, 24°, and 30° C.

Damage and Relation to Disease. The damage occasioned by the horn fly is chiefly through irritation and annoyance, which in dairy animals results in disturbed feeding and improper digestion, causing loss of flesh and reduced milk production. Cattle heavily attacked by these flies may suffer a loss of 0.5 pound of flesh per day, and milk production may be reduced from 10 to 20 per cent.

It is not uncommon, in areas where the horn fly abounds, for from 1,000 to 4,000 flies to be on one animal at any one time. Depner (personal communication) has observed numbers as high as 10,000 flies per animal in southern Alberta, and he states that claims as high as 20,000 per animal have been made. Under such conditions the actual loss of blood must certainly be significant. From ten to twenty minutes are required for the fly fully to engorge itself; during this time it withdraws and reinserts its proboscis in the same puncture as in a pumping motion. Much digested blood is discharged from the anus of the fly while it is in the act of feeding.

As in the case of other bloodsucking pests of man and domestic animals, the horn fly becomes suspect as a possible transmitter of pathogens. However, there is no direct incriminating evidence, and Stirrat, *et al.* (1955), have shown that, though horn flies do harbor a number of bacteria, these are normal associates of cattle.

Man is only rarely attacked; the importance of the horn fly is chiefly veterinary rather than medical. A surprising case of human myiasis is on record (Knapp, Padilla, and Philips, 1955).

OTHER SPECIES OF BLOODSUCKING MUSCOID FLIES

Haematobia exigua de Meijere, commonly known as the "buffalo fly," is particularly important to the cattle and dairy industries of Australia (Kriggsman and Windred, 1933).

Among the animals it attacks are buffalo, cattle, horse, dog, and man. The fly oviposits in fresh dung, particularly of cattle and buffalo.

The genus *Stomoxys* is represented by a number of Old World species, in addition to *S. calcitrans.* Of these, the Ethiopian *S. nigra* Macquart, *S. omega* Newstead, and *S. inornata* Grünberg resemble *S. calcitrans* in their feeding habits. *S. nigra* is reported to be a vicious biter.

Musca crassirostris Stein, sometimes referred to a separate genus *Philaematomyia*, is of particular interest because of the form of the proboscis, which is intermediate between the biting and nonbiting muscoid type. This is a widely distributed African and Oriental species resembling *Musca domestica* in size and general appearance. The proximal portion of the proboscis is a strongly swollen, polished, sclerotized bulb; the distal portion is fleshy and, when not in use, is folded back under the distal end of the bulb; when in use, its terminal section, consisting of a tubular extension, surrounded at its extremity with a circlet of stout, sclerotized teeth, is protruded from between the labella. By means of this proboscis the fly scratches the skin until blood exudes. Blood forms the main, if not the only, food of both sexes. The larva breeds in cow and horse manure. Cases of human pseudomyiasis reportedly caused by this fly are on record.

16

MYIASIS

Myiasis is a term meaning an infestation of the organs and tissues of man or animal by fly maggots that, at least for a period of time, feed upon the living, necrotic, or dead tissues or upon the ingested food of the host. Though the host may, in the broad sense, be any animal, myiasis usually implies the infestation of a vertebrate. Such invasions may be benign in effect or even asymptomatic, or, on the other hand, may result in more or less violent disturbances, even death.

Various terms have been used to indicate the localization of the myiasis, such as gastric, intestinal, or enteric (digestive system); urinary or urogenital (urogenital tract); auricular (ears); ophthalmic (eyes); dermal, subdermal, or cutaneous (skin); or naso-pharyngeal (nose and pharynx). When wounds are involved, the term "traumatic" may be used; when the lesion is boil-like, it may be called furuncular. When larvae burrow in the skin in such a way that the progress may be followed as the larva advances, the term "creeping myiasis" (creeping eruption) is applied. Finally, larvae may be bloodsuckers; although this is an aberrant type of myiasis, it is recognized as such by Zumpt (1965), who calls it "sanguinivorous myiasis."

As is the case with other types of parasitism, myiasis may be obligatory, when the parasite is dependent upon the animal or human host, at least for a certain period of its life, to complete its development; and facultative, when the maggot, though normally free-living, can under certain circumstances adapt itself to a parasitic existence.

Some studies of significance on the subject of myiasis are those of James (1948), Zumpt (1965), and Morikawa (1958). A useful review of myiasis in recent times in North America was given by Scott (1964), and a similar review for Australia is that of Lee (1968).

ENTERIC MYIASIS AND
PSEUDOMYIASIS

Fifty species of fly larvae have been reported, either positively or questionably, from cases of enteric "myiasis" in man. These species are mainly members of the families Muscidae, Calliphoridae, and Sarcophagidae, which commonly deposit their eggs or larvae on cold meat, cheese, and other foods of man and are thus ingested. Also, flies may deposit their eggs on or near the anus, particularly in the use of old-fashioned, nonsanitary privies, and the larvae on hatching may make their way into the intestine.

The reality of enteric involvement as a pathologic condition in man has been questioned by many workers. The subject has been discussed in considerable detail by Riley (1939), James (1948), and West (1951), who come to the conclusion that, in spite of experimental evidence to the contrary (which these authors do not consider to be conclusive), "there seems no doubt that genuine enteric myiasis does occur from time to time, when chemical and physical conditions within the patient's alimentary tract are such as to favor survival of the parasites" (West). The evidence for the reality of enteric myiasis rests on the number of clinical cases by competent entomologists and physicians. Nevertheless, great care should be used in diagnosing enteric myiasis.

Zumpt (1965) does not consider the kind of enteric infestation that occurs in man as a true type of myiasis, and he proposes the term "pseudomyiasis" for it. Such dipterous larvae as occur in the human intestinal tract, he points out, are accidentally ingested and are not able to continue their development there. What is involved is merely the ability of the fly maggots to resist an extremely unfavorable environment, rather than adaptation to a facultative type of parasitism. A true enteric myiasis, however, occurs in the case of those Gasterophilidae that invade the digestive tract of mammals.

Human pseudomyiasis, however, may show clinical symptoms that are sometimes severe. These depend on the number as well as the species of fly larvae and on their location within the digestive tract. No doubt many instances occur in which living fly larvae are passed in the stool without having caused any enteric disturbances. In severe infestations, there will be nausea, vertigo, and more or less violent pain in the abdomen; diarrhea with discharge of blood may occur as the result of injury of the intestinal mucosa by the larvae. Living and dead larvae are expelled with either the vomit or stool, or both.

An obstinate case was reported by Herms and Gilbert (1933). The patient was a female, aged thirty-eight years. In addition to the symptoms mentioned above, there were recurring attacks of nervousness. The patient was considerably depressed at times, and treatment was difficult because of lack of cooperation except after she had experienced an acute attack. The condition lasted for more than three months. Adult flies of the genera *Calliphora*, *Phaenicia*, and *Lucilia* were reared from maggots obtained from vomit and bowel discharge. The recurrence of violent symptoms with evacuation of larvae in vomit and stools can be interpreted as the result of repeated infestations. The patient's physical condition and apparent susceptibility to parasitism were undoubtedly contributing causes. The author's suggestion that pedogenesis (reproduction by fly larvae) is involved cannot be substantiated.

Etiological Agents in Pseudomyiasis. The larvae of the cheese skipper, *Piophila casei* (Linnaeus), of the family Piophilidae, frequently are reported in enteric pseudomyiasis, as they are able to pass through the digestive tract without injury. Simmons (1927) cites a number of instances indicating the frequency of their reported occurrence in the digestive tract of man. The adult flies measure 2.5 to 4 mm in length; superficially they appear shining black, with reddish brown eyes and wings held flat over the dorsum when at rest. The eggs are deposited on cured meats, old cheese, dried bones, smoked fish, and similar materials. The eggs hatch in from thirty to forty-eight hours at 65° F; the larval stage requires about eight days, the pupal about twelve. The length of these stages is influenced greatly by temperatures. The larvae have the peculiar habit of curving the ends of the body together and then suddenly springing to a distance of as much as 15 cm (6 inches); this habit is responsible for the popular name of the fly.

Several cases of enteric pseudomyiasis caused by the larvae of a soldier fly, *Hermetia illucens* (Linnaeus), Family Stratiomyidae, are on record. This fly may deposit its eggs on overripe or decaying fruits, vegetables, and animal matter, where they or the larvae may be ingested accidentally. Another fly frequently involved in this way is the drone fly, *Eristalis tenax* (Linnaeus), whose rat-tailed larvae has reportedly been passed with stools on a number of occasions. The frequency with which these larvae occur in liquid excrement, however, suggests the use of extreme caution in accepting reports that they have been evacuated with discharges from the bowels.

There are, however, several recorded cases that seem to be incontrovertible. One of these was reported by Hall and Muir (1913), who also brought together all information relative to *Eristalis* and myiasis. The case involved a five-year-old boy who, after suffering from digestive disturbances for about five weeks, discharged rat-tailed larvae upon receiving treatment. After passage of the larvae, the child is said to have improved in health and become normal; the nervous symptoms and vomiting disappeared. Three chances for infestation were pointed out; namely, first, eating overripe or probably decayed peaches in which the rat-tailed larvae might have occurred; second, drinking ditch water polluted with kitchen and other refuse; last, playing in a neighbor's yard in which stable manure was present.

Eristalis tenax, the drone fly (Fig. 16-1), is an insect larger than a honey bee and resembling the drone bee very closely; indeed, it is commonly referred to as its mimic. It is probably the "bee" that was supposed to arise by spontaneous generation from carcasses of buried steers in ancient times. The fly deposits its eggs on liquid manure or

Fig. 16-1 *A.* The drone fly, *Eristalis tenax.* × 3.5. *B.* The "rat-tailed" larva of *Eristalis tenax.* × 2.

excrement by-products in cans, slop jars, privies, septic tank effluent, and so forth.

Among other species that are involved in enteric pseudomyiasis are several muscids, including the house fly, *Musca domestica* Linnaeus, the lesser house fly, *Fannia canicularis* (Linnaeus), the latrine fly, *Fannia scalaris* (Fabricius), and the false stable fly, *Muscina stabulans* (Fallén).

Rectal Myiasis. Certain fly larvae may invade the intestine after having gained entrance through the anus. Some cases of "intestinal" myiasis caused by the drone fly, *Eristalis tenax*, and by certain species of *Sarcophaga* may be explained in this way. These larvae are excrement feeders and may complete their life cycle in the rectum or terminal part of the intestine. Parasitism of this type may occur in man, where human beings live under filthy conditions, or in animals that are partially paralyzed or otherwise helpless.

Enteric Myiasis. True enteric myiasis does not occur in man, although it does affect horses, donkeys, mules, zebras, elephants, and rhinoceroses. Zumpt (1965) lists six species, all in the genus *Gasterophilus*, as attacking domestic Equidae. These are *G. intestinalis* (De Geer), *G. haemorrhoidalis* (Linnaeus), *G. nasalis* (Linnaeus), *G. inermis* (Brauer), *G. pecuorum* (Fabricius), and *G. nigricornis* (Loew). All are widely distributed in the Old World, and the first three have been introduced into and are now widespread in America; *G. inermis* also was introduced into North America but apparently never established there.

The flies of this genus are about the size of, or slightly smaller than, a honey bee; superficially they are honey-bee-like in appearance. The ovipositor is strong and protuberant. They are strong fliers. Larvae are restricted to the digestive tracts of Equidae, but within that family they are not highly host-specific. A taxonomic review of the group has been presented by Zumpt and Paterson (1953), and keys to adults, eggs, and larvae are included in Zumpt (1965).

Fig. 16-2 Eggs of the horse bot fly, attached to a hair of the host. × 20.

Gasterophilus intestinalis (De Geer) (Fig. 16-5*A*) [*Gasterophilus equi* (Clark)] is the common horse bot fly or nit fly. Each female deposits about 1,000 light yellow eggs (Fig. 16-2), which are firmly attached to the hairs of the forelegs, belly, flanks, shoulders, and other parts of the body of the horse, but chiefly on the inside of the knees where they are accessible to the tongue, teeth, and lips. The sudden increase in temperature arising from the warmth of the tongue (not friction and moisture, as was previously considered the case) provides the necessary stimulus for the hatching of the eggs. The incubation period is five days, but hatching may be greatly delayed by cool weather so that viable eggs may be found unhatched on the horse until late autumn, long after the flies have disappeared. The larvae on hatching (Fig. 16-3) are provided with an armature that enables them to excavate galleries in the subepithelial layer of the mucous membrane of the tongue. From the mouth the larvae apparently pass rapidly to their preferred site in the alimentary canal, the left sac or esophageal portion of the stomach, where second- and third-stage larvae remain fixed with little or no change in position until the following spring and early summer, when they detach themselves and pass out of the intestine with the droppings.

Fig. 16-3 Newly emerged larva of the horse bot fly. × 60.

Fig. 16-4 Mature larva of the horse bot fly, *Gasterophilus intestinalis.* × 4.

They are then from 1.6 to 2 cm in length (Fig. 16-4). Pupation takes place shortly thereafter in loose earth or in dry droppings. The pupal stage varies considerably, depending upon moisture and temperature, but the usual time is from three to five weeks. The winged bot fly emerges, copulation soon takes place, and egg laying begins in early summer. The life cycle requires about a year.

Gasterophilus haemorrhoidalis (Linnaeus) (Fig. 16-5*B*) is commonly known as the "nose fly" because the female forcibly "strikes" the animal in the region of the nose, where it attaches its black eggs to the fine hairs of the lips. Because of the orange-red terminal segments, this fly is known as the "redtailed bot." The fully grown larvae have the habit of moving from the stomach during the early spring and attaching close to the anus before finally dropping to the ground.

Gasterophilus nasalis (Linnaeus) [*G. veterinus* (Clark)] (Fig. 16-5*C*) is the chin fly or throat bot fly. This fly is very annoying to horses because its eggs are attached to hairs under the jaws, and when the fly darts at the throat it causes the animals to throw their heads up as though struck under the chin. Egg deposition takes place during late spring and early summer. The larvae hatch without the need for

heat, moisture, or friction, in from four to five days. The newly hatched larvae travel along the jaw and enter the mouth between the lips. They travel to their preferred site in the alimentary tract, the pyloric portion of the stomach and the anterior portion of the duodenum, where they are found in groups.

Gasterophilus pecuorum (Fabricius), the dark-winged horse fly, is the most common and, apparently, the most pathogenic species of this genus, in the Old World, though it does not occur in America. The eggs are deposited on grasses and other plants and hatch only when they are taken into the mouth of the host with the food. The larvae mature in the stomach of the host.

Gasterophilus nigricornis (Loew), the broad-bellied bot fly, is a strikingly stout species. Eggs are deposited on the cheek or nose of the host, and the act of oviposition is said to greatly disturb the animal. The eggs of *Gasterophilus inermis* (Brauer), the unarmed bot fly, are deposited on the hair of the cheeks of the host; when hatched, the larvae penetrate the epidermis and work their way under it until the mouth is reached.

Other genera of Gasterophilidae are involved in a similar type of myiasis in two groups of wild mammals: *Gyrostigma* in

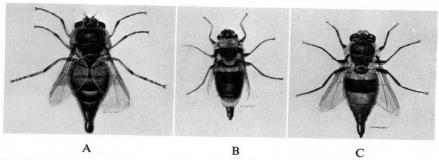

Fig. 16-5 Horse bot flies. *A. Gasterophilus intestinalis. B. G. haemorrhoidalis. C. G. nasalis.* (After Hearle.)

rhinoceroses and *Cobboldia, Platycobboldia,* and *Rodhainomyia* in elephants.

Pathogenesis. Though a moderate infestation of bots will give no outward indications, a heavy infestation will be indicated by digestive disorders (which may, of course, be traceable to other causes as well). The discovery of bots in the manure is sufficient evidence. A light infestation is probably of no consequence; there are, indeed, some individuals who erroneously maintain that to be well a horse must have at least a few bots. On the other hand, infestations of horses by *G. pecuorum* may result in such serious injury as to require that the animal be destroyed (Zumpt, 1965).

The injuries bots produce are (1) abstraction of nutriment, both from the stomach and its contents; (2) obstruction to the food passing from the stomach to the intestine, particularly when the larvae are in or near the pylorus; (3) irritation, injury, and secondary infections to the mucous membrane of the stomach (Fig. 16-6) caused by the penetration of the oral hooklets; (4) irritation of the intestine, rectum, and anus in passage.

Gasterophilus parasitism of man will be discussed in a later section.

FACULTATIVE MYIASIS

Urinary Myiasis. As in enteric pseudomyiasis, the symptoms of urinary myiasis depend on the number and kind of larvae

and their localization. There may be obstruction and pain; pus, mucus, and blood in the urine; and a frequent desire to urinate. Larvae are expelled with the urine. *Fannia canicularis* (Linnaeus), the lesser house fly, is the species most frequently found in urinary myiasis, although *F. scalaris* (Fabricius), *Musca domestica* Linnaeus, and other species have been encountered. Hoeppli and Watt (1933) believe that albumen and sugar in the urine may provide food, as may mucus and leukocytes;

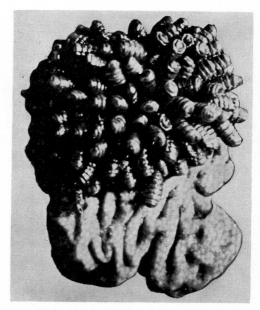

Fig. 16-6 Horse bots, *Gasterophilus intestinalis,* attached to mucous lining of the stomach of a horse. × 0.75. (Photograph by Wherry.)

the shortage of oxygen presents the chief difficulty for larvae, athough they need oxygen in only small amounts.

Infestation is probably usually accomplished at night in warm weather when persons may sleep without covering. Oviposition may be stimulated by discharges from diseased organs; the eggs are laid around the orifice, and the larvae, upon hatching, enter it. Use of unsanitary toilets may be another source of infestation.

Facultative Traumatic and Cutaneous Myiasis. Many species of larvae that normally breed in meat or carrion may become involved in traumatic and cutaneous myiasis. These include the phorid *Megaselia scalaris* (Loew), the house fly, *Musca domestica*, several species of *Calliphora* including *C. vicina* Robineau-Desvoidy, *Phaenicia sericata* (Meigen) and *P. cuprina* (Wiedemann), *Lucilia illustris* (Meigen) and *L. ceasar* (Linnaeus), *Phormia regina* (Meigen), *Cochliomyia macellaria* (Fabricius), several *Chrysomya* species, and such species of *Sarcophaga* as *S. haemorrhoidalis* (Fallén).

Stewart (1929) describes in detail a case of myiasis of this type resulting from parasitism by the black blow fly, *Phormia regina* (Meigen). The adult female fly was obviously attracted by the foul odors of suppurating scalp wounds. Treatment of the patient's wounds brought forth numerous larvae, both from the extensive scalp areas and from the ears. The emergence and activities of the larvae, following this treatment, caused the patient such great pain that she became delirious.

As a human wound parasite, *Phaenicia sericata* is usually benign, feeding on necrotic tissues; indeed, certain strains of bacteriologically sterilized maggots of this fly were previously used in treatment of osteomyelitis, where they removed the necrotic tissue and produced secretions that had a healing effect on the diseased living tissue. However, healthy tissue may be invaded, more so apparently in some parts of the world than in others. The role of this species as a sheep maggot should

be kept in mind. It seems that certain strains of the fly are more malignant than others. Wounds in cattle and other domestic animals may be invaded.

The secondary screw-worm of the Americas, *Cochliomyia macellaria* (Fabricius), may be a secondary wound invader of some consequence, particularly in domestic animals. In the earlier literature, however, much of the damage attributed to this fly really was caused by its close relative, the primary screw-worm fly, *C. hominivorax* (Coquerel).

A similar situation occurs in the Old World, where *Chrysomya bezziana* Villeneuve, the Old World screw-worm, was responsible for much of the traumatic myiasis previously attributed to *C. megacephala* (Fabricius). The latter species, however, may be involved in traumatic myiasis in man and animals, either alone or in association with another species such as *C. bezziana*. On some occasions *C. megacephala* assumes considerable importance. Other *Chrysomya* species may be either primary or secondary parasites, but their role is usually a minor one. However, there is evidence that *C. rufifacies* (Macquart), whose "spiny" larvae are usually predatory, may become an important pest. In Hawaii, where *C. bezziana* does not occur, *C. rufifacies* produces a strange type of myiasis in newborn calves on the island of Maui; the larvae eat the epidermis, causing death by dehydration and possibly by the production of a toxic element. As many as 30 per cent of the calves on one ranch have been attacked (D. Elmo Hardy, personal communication).

Wool Maggots (Fleeceworms). Flies of the wool maggot group were undoubtedly at one time solely scavengers feeding in the maggot stage on carrion and animal wastes, but with the introduction of herds of domesticated animals they have acquired the habit of attacking living animals. Froggatt (1922) has suggested that, prior to the introduction of cattle and sheep into Australia, blow flies existed on the continent as simple scavengers, ovipositing on animal matter that happened to be festering in the sun. The transition from wool of dead sheep to infesting damp or soiled wool of living animals was not a great one. The increase in carcasses of slaughtered rabbits, of poisoned dingoes, hawks, and carrion crows, added great quantities of decaying flesh in which the scavenger flies could breed.

The next, and perhaps the most important, factor in the development of the sheep-maggot pest is the work of sheep-breeders themselves. Forty years ago there were many thousands of Merino sheep of the bare-belly, bare-legged type, which did not produce a third of the weight of wool of the modern, improved Merino. The ambition of every sheep-breeder has been to make every inch of the sheep's skin grow wool, and in the case of some classes of Merinos to produce a wrinkled skin, giving even more woolbearing surface. A sheep clothed with such a mass of thick, close, fine wool, fitting closely over the rump and round the tail, is sure to get more or less stained and damp around the crutch, and to attract flies. This artificial increase in weight, quantity, and fineness of wool is accompanied, too, by an increased secretion of yolk, which rising from the skin and spreading all through the wool fiber, forms an additional attraction for the flies, and supplies food for maggots (Froggatt, 1922).

Zumpt (1965, p. 50) gives a concise account of sheep myiasis. Though exact reasons for primary strike are not thoroughly understood, the main predisposing cause is bacterial activity in the wool, the result of excess water and profuse sweating. Hard driving of the animals, for example, may tend to set up the proper conditions for strike. Larvae may remain on the surface or they may bore inward in susceptible areas or enter previously existing wounds, even small ones. Parasitized sheep may refuse to feed, and death may occur, probably the result of a toxemia or even a septicemia.

The wool maggot problem is most severe in Australia, where it is considered one of major importance. The most important species there,

as well as in South Africa, is *Phaenicia cuprina* (Wiedemann). *P. sericata* (Meigen) replaces this species in importance in some areas, such as in Scotland. In the United States, the relative roles of the two *Phaenicia* species are reversed from what they are in Australia, *P. sericata* being, along with *Phormia regina* (Meigen) and *Cochliomyia macellaria* (Fabricius), the most important species, whereas *P. cuprina*, which occurs throughout the southern states, is of little or no importance in this respect.

Calliphora stygia (Fabricius) is an important species in New Zealand, less so in Tasmania and Australia, whereas another native species, *C. augur* (Fabricius), is important in Australia. Some other calliphorids, such as *Chrysomya rufifacies* (Macquart) in Australia and *C. chloropyga* (Wiedemann) in South Africa, are secondarily involved in sheep strike; at least one muscid, *Ophyra rostrata*, is sometimes involved in a secondary capacity.

OBLIGATORY MYIASIS

The Primary Screw-Worm. The several changes in the scientific name of the primary screw-worm since the time of the discovery of its distinctness from the secondary screw-worm in 1930 has been confusing to the non-taxonomist. The name is now accepted as *Cochliomyia hominivorax* (Coquerell). Unlike the secondary screw-worm fly, *C. macellaria* (Fabricius), which is more particularly a scavenger fly, *C. hominivorax* is an obligatory parasite and is responsible for the great majority of cases of screw-worm infestations in man and animals in the United States and the entire Neotropical Region. It is also known as the cause of nasopharyngeal myiasis in man.

Cochliomyia hominivorax (Fig. 16-7) is definitely the most important producer of human myiasis and of traumatic animal myiasis in the New World. It is strongly attracted to the wounds and sores of animals; even a tick bite may be sufficiently attractive

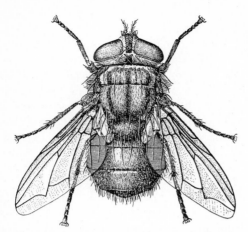

Fig. 16-7 *Cochliomyia hominivorax*, adult female. (Drawing by Arthur Cushman; U.S.D.A. photograph.)

to produce an infestation. Laake (1936) estimated that at the time of his writing the loss occasioned by this fly in the southwestern United States was $5,000,000 annually. He found the following predisposing causes of attack: among sheep and lambs, wounds caused by needle grass take first rank; among goats and kids, shear cuts; among cattle, injuries by the horns of other cattle; among calves, exposed tissues at birth; and among horses and mules, wire cuts.

Laake points out that the most common causes of screw-worm attack are due to farm practices that can be corrected. He stresses particularly care in shearing, dehorning, and removal and disposal of old barbed wire from fences; also the timing of dehorning, castrating, and branding so as to expose the wounds as little as possible to flies during the season of abundance.

As a human parasite, the primary screw-worm has assumed an importance that cannot be overlooked. In 1935, when a serious outbreak in Texas resulted in more than 1,200,000 cases in livestock, there were fifty-five reported human cases and probably twice as many unreported ones (James, 1948).

An epidemic of human myiasis caused by *C. hominivorax*, eighty-one cases in five provinces in Chile during the months of December to April, 1945–46, is reported by Gajardo-Tobar and Honorato (1947), who also describe the biology of the fly concerned.

An early description of a human case was given by Richardson in the Peoria, Illinois, *Medical Monthly* for February, 1883. A traveler in Kansas, in August, while asleep, apparently received a deposit of eggs in the nose. A nasal discharge probably was the attractant to the fly. The first symptoms were those of a severe cold. As the larvae cut away through the tissues of the head, the patient became slightly delirious and complained about the intense misery and annoyance in his nose and head. When the larvae finally cut through the soft palate, his speech was impaired. Despite attempts to remove the larvae (there were more than 250 in all), the patient, after an apparent trend toward recovery, had a relapse as the eustachian tubes were invaded, and died. The tissue damage was extensive, and the head and face showed the characteristic swelling of severe screw-worm head myiasis.

Life History of the Screw-Worm Fly. The adult *Cochliomyia hominivorax* has a deep greenish-blue metallic color with yellow, orange, or reddish face, and three dark stripes on the dorsal surface of the thorax. It is difficult, unless one is experienced, to separate this species from *C. macellaria* (Fig. 16-8). Females of *C. macellaria* may usually be distinguished from *C. hominivorax* by the fact that the basicostal scale (a small sclerite at the base of the wing) of the former is of a yellowish color, whereas in the latter it is black. Also, both sexes of *C. macellaria* have yellow hairs on the lower half of the parafrontals (just above the antennae and between the frontal bristles and the eyes), whereas in *C. hominivorax* these hairs are black. The two species can be accurately separated from each other by characters of the male terminalia.

Individual females of *C. hominivorax*, according to Laake, Cushing and Parish, may lay more than 2,800 eggs, which are deposited in characteristic batches of 10 to 393 eggs each;

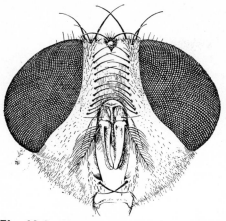 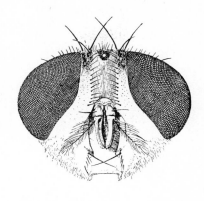

Fig. 16-8 Head, front view, of females of *Cochliomyia hominivorax* (*left*) and *C. macellaria* (*right*). Note small proclinate fronto-orbital bristles of *C. macellaria,* absent in *C. hominivorax.* The hairs of the lower parafrontalia are black in *C. hominivorax,* pale in *C. macellaria.* (Drawings by Arthur Cushman; U.S.D.A. photographs.)

the laying of as many as 300 eggs may be completed in from four to six minutes. The incubation period of the eggs on wounds of animals ranges from 11 to 21.5 hours, under natural conditions. The larval feeding period ranges from 3.5 to 4.5 days or more; the prepupal period from a few hours to about three days; the pupal stage, which is in the ground, lasts about seven days. The prepupal and pupal stages are greatly influenced by temperature and moisture. The life history from egg to egg, under natural conditions, requires about twenty-four days.

Migration of adult flies or transportation by moving vehicles and transportation of infested animals may carry flies a considerable distance beyond their winter range. It is in this way, for example, that temporary summer breeding sites have, in the past, been established in the United States far to the north of the permanent breeding areas.

The screw-worm is a true parasite and lives only in the living flesh of warm-blooded animals; it is not found in snakes, lizards, or other cold-blooded animals, nor in carcasses, dead fish, decaying meats, or decaying vegetable matter. Parasitism is apparently due to oviposition habits of the female, as mass rearing experience proves that larvae readily grow in meat and animal products. The maggots found in dead animals are not true screw-worms. This fact was not realized until 1930, when Cushing and Patton first recognized the distinctness between the primary screw-worm fly, which they called *Cochliomyia americana,* new species, and the secondary screw-worm, *C. macellaria* (Fig. 16-9).

Today, the primary screw-worm exists as an important economic problem and a threat to man throughout the warmer temperate, subtropical, and tropical parts of the New World, from Mexico to northern Argentina and Chile. Though still present in the United States at the time of this writing, it has been eradicated, through the use of male sterilization techniques from the Southeast and has been pushed back to a level of relatively low incidence in the Southwest. The problem of eradication in the latter area is important, however, since we are dealing with a population that is broadly in contact with the continuous, large, and potential breeding area to the south.

The Old-World Screw-Worm Fly. In Africa, India, and the nearby island areas of the Pacific and Indian Oceans, including such areas as Indonesia, New Guinea, and the

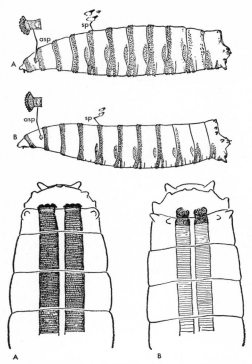

Fig. 16-9 Mature larva of *(A) Cochliomyia hominivorax, (B) C.* macellaria. (*Above*) Larva, side view. (*Below*) Dorsal view of posterior segments, showing pigmented tracheal trunks of *C. hominivorax* and unpigmented tracheal trunks of *C. macellaria*. (After Laake, Cushing, and Parish.)

hatching; at this time they are imbedded in the wound to such a depth that only their posterior ends are visible. The larval stage lasts five to six days, the pupal seven to nine days under tropical conditions but longer in cooler areas.

Norris and Murray (1964) have presented an excellent study of the biology of this fly in New Guinea, and Zumpt (1965) has given a very good summary of human and animal myiasis caused by this fly. Human parasitism is much more common in India and other parts of the Oriental region than in Africa. Numerous cases have been reported by Patton and others. Zumpt suggests that the fewer cases in Africa may be the result of different conditions and ways of life; animal cases are apparently as common there as in the rest of the range of the fly. All parts of the body where pre-existing wounds or ulcers occur— but particularly areas where the skin is soft or mucous tissue is present—may be affected. The genital openings and the orifices of the head may be attacked, as by its American counterpart.

The most commonly attacked domestic animals, as in the case of the American screwworm, are cattle. Zumpt cites Cuthbertson as stating that in Rhodesia this species is, next

Philippine Islands, another calliphorid fly, *Chrysomya bezziana* Villeneuve (Fig. 16-10), occupies a position similar to that of *Cochliomyia hominivorax* in America. It is also an obligatory parasite, differing in this respect from other members of the genus, including the widespread *C. megacephala* (Fabricius), which it closely resembles. It is interesting to note that the relationship between these two *Chrysomya* species in the Old World parallels that which exists between the two American *Cochliomyia* species. The Old World screwworm fly is attracted to the same kinds of wounds as is *Cochliomyia hominivorax*. About 150 to 500 or more eggs are deposited in a batch, around the edges of the wounds. Larvae attain the third instar about two days after

Fig. 16-10 The Old World screw-worm fly, *Chrysomya bezziana*. (Drawing by Arthur Cushman; U.S.D.A. photograph.)

to tsetse flies, the most important pest of cattle and other domestic animals; it is also a major pest of cattle and other domestic animals in New Guinea (Norris and Murray, 1964). Parasitism may lead to the death of the animal within a short time if the wounds are not treated. Other hosts of the fly include sheep, goats, buffalo, horses, pigs, and dogs.

Wohlfahrtia Traumatic Myiasis. A third screw-worm fly, belonging to the family Sarcophagidae, is *Wohlfahrtia magnifica* (Schiner). The ecological relationship of this obligatory parasite to the common closely related scavenger *W. meigeni* (Schiner), which occurs in the same area, parallels the primary-secondary screw-worm relationships of the *Chrysomya* and *Cochliomyia* species in other parts of the world.

This fly is widespread over the warmer parts of the Palaearctic Region. The female does not lay eggs; as in most other Sarcophagidae, she gives birth to active first-stage maggots. Skin lesions in prospective hosts, even as small a one as a tick bite, may be the site of larviposition, but the mucous membranes of the head openings, the eyes, ears, and female genital orifices may be used. Five to seven days are required for larval development, during which time tissue destruction may be considerable. Fatal cases in man are on record. Domestic animals that are attacked include dogs, horses and donkeys, cattle, goats, pigs, sheep, water buffalo, camels, and poultry, especially geese.

The most comprehensive work on this type of *Wohlfahrtia* myiasis is that of Portschinsky (1916), which, after half a century, remains the classical reference. A concise treatment of the subject, along with references to the more recent literature, is included in Zumpt (1965).

Gasterophilus as a Human Parasite. The larvae of the horse bot flies burrow freely and may cause a form of creeping cutaneous myiasis in human beings. Since man is a very unusual host, the larvae do not live beyond the first stage. The newly hatched larva enters the unbroken skin and begins to burrow in much the same fashion as it does in the tongue or mucous membranes of the mouth of its normal host. This burrow is very tortuous and plainly visible. It may cause severe itching but never any serious consequences. The larva, which measures 1 to 2 mm in length, is easily detected a short distance beyond the apparent end of the burrow. *Gasterophilus intestinalis* and several other species of the genus may be involved in this way.

Cattle grubs are the larvae of flies of the genus *Hypoderma*, the heel flies or ox warble flies. These are now generally considered as belonging to the family Oestridae, although a separate family, Hypodermatidae, has been recognized for them. Although the normal hosts are cattle and Old World deer, they occasionally parasitize horses and humans. Persons dealing with cattle are familiar with the tumerous swellings on the backs of cattle during late winter and early spring, and most stockmen have squeezed out the large grubs that inhabit these tumors. Two well-known species infest cattle: *Hypoderma lineatum* (de Villers), the common cattle grub or lesser cattle warble fly, widely distributed in the United States, Europe, and Asia; and *Hypoderma bovis* (De Geer), the northern cattle grub or larger cattle warble fly, which broadly overlaps the preceding species in distribution but extends farther northward. At least four Old World species attack native deer.

Hypoderma bovis is the larger of the two species, the adult measuring about 15 mm in length; *H. lineatum* (Fig. 16-11) measures about 13 mm. The former has the thorax covered with dense yellow hairs in front and black ones behind, with the terminal hairs on the abdomen yellow, whereas the latter has a fairly uniform hairy covering of mixed brownish-black and white with four prominent smooth and polished lines on the thorax, the hairs of the terminal segment of the abdomen being reddish orange. The full-grown larvae are easily distinguished by examination of the spiny armature, *H. bovis* having the last two segments entirely devoid of spines, *H. lineatum*

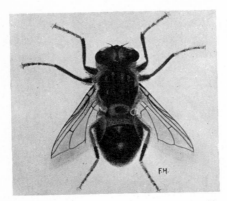

Fig. 16-11 The common cattle grub, *Hypoderma lineatum.* (After Hearle.)

having only the last one smooth; the posterior spiracular plates, also, are different, that of *H. bovis* being deeply excavated, funnel shaped, toward the button, whereas that of *H. lineatum* is more shallowly and broadly excavated (Fig. 16-12). The full-grown larva of the former measures from 27 to 28 mm in length and that of the latter about 25 mm (Fig. 16-13).

Life History and Habits. The eggs of both species are laid on the hairs of cattle, *H. lineatum* attaching five to fifteen to a single hair; *H. bovis* attaches but one egg to a hair. As many as 800 eggs may be laid by a female of either species (Warburton, 1922). Although no pain is inflicted at the time of oviposition, cattle become terror-stricken when the fly is discovered and gallop madly for water or shade in which to stand to escape the enemy. This

is termed "gadding" and often spreads to the whole herd.

In both species the eggs hatch within a week, and the tiny armored larvae crawl down the hairs of the host and bore either directly into the skin or into the hair follicles. In doing so, they cause considerable irritation. The first-stage larva then migrates through the body of the host, finally lodging beneath the skin of the back. Details of this migration vary with the species, and some aspects of the migration have not been thoroughly determined. *H. bovis*, after about four months, reaches the spinal cord, where it burrows between the periosteum and dura mater for a period of time before leaving the spinal canal and cutting through muscle and connective tissue to the back. *H. lineatum* rests for awhile in the walls of the esophagus, probably without having entered the spinal canal. Soon after reaching the skin, the larva cuts a small opening to the surface.

From one to five days after reaching the back, this molt, the skin of the larva is closely set with spines. The body of the host now begins to isolate the invading parasite by forming a pocket around it. The growth of the grub from this time on is rather rapid, and a second molt occurs about twenty-five days after the first. In the last stage of the larval development, the color gradually darkens, first becoming yellow, then brown, and finally almost black, During the entire development in the warble.

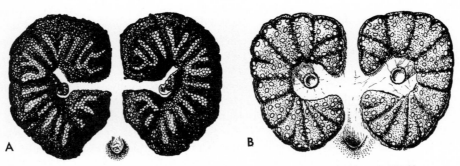

Fig. 16-12 Posterior spiracles of mature larva of *(A) Hypoderma bovis* and *(B) H. lineatum.* (Drawing by Arthur Cushman; U.S.D.A. photograph.)

Fig. 16-13   Larva of the common cattle grub, *Hypoderma lineatum.* × 1.3.

a breathing hole is kept open to the surface, and the grub lies with its two spiracles, which are located on the posterior end, applied rather closely to the opening. As growth proceeds, this hole is gradually enlarged. At the end of the developmental period in the warble, which requires five to eight weeks for *H. lineatum* and up to eleven weeks for *H. bovis*, the grub works its way out and falls to the ground. There it crawls away, enters loose earth or debris, becoming rapidly dark brown to black in pupation, and in from four to five weeks emerges as a warble fly. The complete life cycle requires about a year.

Seasonally, the occurrence of the two species does not coincide; *H. lineatum* adults appear in the spring about a month earlier than *H. bovis*.

Literature on the cattle grub is voluminous; a good comprehensive work is that of Gebauer (1958).

Injury Done.   The injury done by the larvae is, first, irritation caused by their migrations in the body of the animal and later by their emergence from beneath the skin; second, the escape of the larva from the warble leaves an open, running wound that persists for a long time and is subject to bacterial infection and attractive to screw-worm flies and other tormenting insects. The direct pathogenesis, however, is of minor importance in comparison with the economic loss produced by this insect.

Economic Losses.   The economic losses include: (1) Reduction in the milk production of the cattle, which is estimated at from 10 to 20 per cent of the normal yield. (2) Loss of flesh resulting from the wild efforts of the animals to escape from the flies. As is pointed out by Holstein, "A cow quietly grazing will suddenly spring forward, throw up her tail, and make for the nearest water at a headlong gait. Seemingly deprived at the moment of every instinct except the desire to escape, she will rush over a high bluff on the way, often being killed by the fall. This, with miring in water holes and the fact that cattle are prevented from feeding, causes the loss." The excitement and overexertion accompanying gadding may cause a pregnant cow to abort, thus resulting not only in the loss of the calf but also of milk for one lactation period. (3) Depreciation of the value of the carcass because flesh becomes greenish yellow, jellylike in appearance, and unfit for consumption at the points where the grubs are located. (4) Injury to the hide, which becomes "grubby," full of holes, where the grubs have emerged (Fig. 16-14).

Hypoderma as a Human Parasite.   Numerous records of attacks on man by *H. lineatum*, *H. bovis*, and *H. diana* Brauer, a European parasite of deer, have been published. Most case histories reveal some association with cattle during the summer or fall preceding the attack. The incidence on children is proportionately higher than on adults. A typical case, described by Herms (1925), involves a ranch superintendent, Mr. C., who was apparently parasitized while sleeping in the open in late July with his body partly exposed. Herms says:

Several days later, exact time not remembered, soreness was experienced and a slight swelling in the region of the right groin appeared. In about a week the swelling had increased to the width of a hand with no discoloration. The swelling then crept downward toward the left side affecting the scrotum, thence downward along the left leg to the knee and calf, thence back up the left leg following

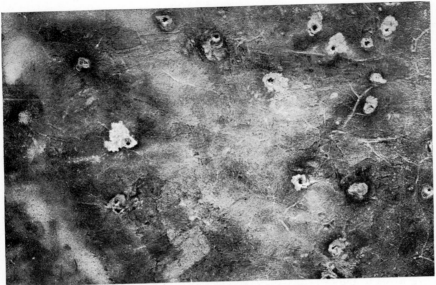

Fig. 16-14 A piece of sole leather 21 × 31.5 cm, showing work of the cattle grub. × 0.3.

about the same course to the left groin, thence across to the right groin and back again to the left and upward along the left side of the body, slightly anterior to the shoulder, thence downward to the upper right arm to near the elbow, when the arm could not be raised without great pain, thence the swelling traveled upward again to the neighborhood of the shoulder blade where a "hive-like" local swelling was formed without any itching sensation. Mr. C. stated that at this point he was "bothered" all night, and while rubbing his arm and manipulating his shoulder muscles a larva of some insect "popped" out.

The first larva was expressed in late October; a second cut through a typical warble on February 3. The species was identified as *Hypoderma bovis*, though the known distribution of the species would make it more likely to be *H. lineatum*.

As in cattle, ingress is probably through the skin. The wanderings of the larvae may cause severe discomfort, itching, pains and cramps, and may be associated with stomach disorders. When the larva is reaching the end of its wandering stage, it moves upward, as in cattle, but, because of man's upright position,

it usually forms its warble in the upper part of the chest, the neck, or the head. Because of the abnormal host the larva may make several attempts to reach the surface, thus resulting in a dermal creeping myiasis. The pain and discomfort accompanying parasitism may be severe. An apparently increased nocturnal activity of the larva may interfere with sleep. Local paralysis may be due to invasion of the spinal canal; in one case, a boy parasitized by seven larvae suffered almost complete paralysis of the lower extremities for about a year. There are cases on record of an eye being invaded and destroyed; in another case, a small boy died after a larva had produced a fetid ulcer around the back teeth of the lower jaw. Surgical removal of the larva may often be accomplished.

The caribou or reindeer warble fly, *Oedemagena tarandi* (Linnaeus), is widely distributed over the range of its host in northern Eurasia and northern North America. The fly is yellowish-orange in color and has a beelike appearance. The life history and pathology resemble those of the warble flies of cattle. It is unknown as a human parasite.

Oestrid Head Maggots. The sheep bot fly, *Oestris ovis* Linnaeus, is a widely distributed species whose larvae are known as sheep head maggots or grubs-in-the-head. The fly (Fig. 16-15) is about 12 to 14 mm in length, smaller than a honey bee, which it somewhat resembles; it is yellow to brownish gray in color and hairy. The abdomen is variegated with brown and straw-yellow; the legs are brown. The lower part of the head is puffed out and white; the antennae are small and located in a cavity; and the mouth parts, as in other bot and warble flies, are rudimentary, the proboscis and the two palpi appearing like three minute tubercles arranged in a triangle.

The sheep bot fly normally deposits active young during early summer to autumn in the nostrils of sheep and goats and related wild hosts. One female fly may deposit as many as 500 larvae. The larvae at once begin to move up the nasal passages, working their way into the nasal and frontal sinuses often as far as the base of the horns in rams, and attach themselves to the mucous membranes. Here numbers of these whitish grubs may be found wedged closely together in various conditions of development. The grubs reach full growth with a length of 25 to 30 mm by the following spring, a larval period of from eight to ten

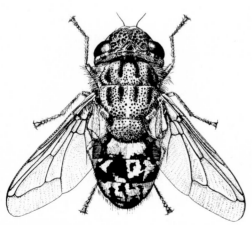

Fig. 16-15 The sheep bot fly, *Oestrus ovis* (Drawing by Arthur Cushman; U.S.D.A. photograph.)

months. At the end of this time they work their way out of the nostrils (they are usually sneezed out), fall to the ground, and pupate in a few hours. The pupal period lasts from three to six weeks and over, sometimes much more in areas where low temperatures prevail. Adults may live as long as twenty-eight days. Complete development of the parasite stage in spring lambs may be shortened to twenty-five to thirty-five days.

In the presence of the fly, the sheep or goats are very much excited, shake the head, rush with their noses into the dust, snort, and otherwise indicate that they are trying to escape something that persists in entering their nostrils. In parasitized animals, there is a purulent discharge from the nostrils, vigorous shaking of the head, and perhaps the occasional discharge of a maggot, loss of appetite, grating of the teeth; and when the animals walk, the forefeet are lifted in a pawing movement. The great majority of cases do not terminate fatally, but death may come in a week or less after the appearance of aggravated symptoms.

Head Maggots of Horses. An important species of head maggot attacking horses in parts of Europe, Asia, and Africa is *Rhinoestrus purpureus* (Brauer). Its habits are similar to those of *Oestrus ovis*, differing mainly in the details of its life history. The incidence of fatality in parasitized horses in parts of Russia may be high, according to reports reaching as high as 82 per cent (cf. Zumpt, 1965).

Parasitism of Man by Oestrus and Rhinoestrus. Ophthalmomyiasis of man is commonly traceable to the larvae of *Oestrus ovis* and *Rhinoestrus purpureus*. Because man is not a normal host the larva is unable to progress beyond its first stage, and the infestation is consequently short lived. In the typical case history, the patient, who usually has had a close association with sheep or goats, will report being struck in the eye by an insect or small foreign object, with pain and inflammation developing a few hours later. The condition is similar to acute catarrhal conjunctivitis and may be diagnosed as such. It is apparently always benign, though irritating; reports involving destruction of extensive ocular tissue or the entire eye are probably the result of misidentification. This type of myiasis is most common among nomadic shepherds whose food consists to a large extent of goat's milk and cheese.

Larvae of *Oestrus* and *Rhinoestrus* may affect the nose and throat, as in sheep, but, as in ophthalmomyiasis, they never progress beyond the first stage in the human host. Considerable irritation and headaches may result before the larvae are removed.

Head Maggots of Deer. Deer, elk, caribou, and other related wild animals are commonly infested with head maggots (Fig. 16-16); among these are the European species *Cephenemyia stimulator* (Clark) in the roe deer, *C. auribarbis* (Meigen) in the red deer, *C. ulrichii* in the European elk, and *C. trompe* (Modeer) in reindeer. *C. trompe* is also American; other New World species are *C. phobifer* (Clark) from the white-tailed deer, *C. pratti* Hunter from mule deer, and *C. jellisoni* Townsend from the Pacific black-tailed deer. These species are unknown from humans.

Cutaneous Wohlfahrtia Myiasis. The larvae of *Wohlfahrtia vigil* (Walker), family Sarcophagidae, frequently cause cutaneous myiasis of a furuncular (boil-like) type in the northern United States and southern Canada. A typical case is described by Walker (1922) as follows, the patient being a five-month-old boy:

Most of the lesions were clustered together on the left side of the neck under the angle of the jaw, one being on the left cheek. They had been first noticed by the mother 24 hours earlier, and when seen by the writer they were already secondarily infected with pus organisms, the child being in poor general condition and suffering from an intestinal disorder. They were similar to the lesions observed in the previous cases, each being a boil-like sore with an external opening, and from these openings six larvae had already been expressed. Only three additional larvae were obtained, these measuring 5 to 7 mm in length.

In western North America, parasitism of this type has been attributed to *W. opaca* (Coquillett) (Fig. 16-17), but this is no more than a subspecies of the eastern form. Biologically, the two forms are very similar, if not identical. *W. vigil opaca* has been reported in furuncular myiasis of human infants in many parts of the western United States and Canada; it is also a pest of mink and fox fur ranches, where it can kill the newly born or very young animals. The larvae penetrate the unbroken skin and usually infest dermal tissue, although in mink kits and fox pups they may exceptionally enter the body cavity.

Human patients are almost without exception infants, and economic damage to fur ranches is always from parasitism of the very young animals. However, there is strong evidence that adult rodents and rabbits may be involved in maintaining populations of the fly other than in the whelping season of the carnivore hosts (Eschle and De Foliart, 1965).

Fig. 16-16 Head maggots of deer attached to tissues in the nasal sinuses.

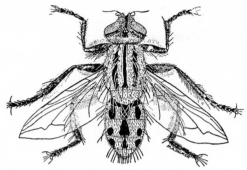

Fig. 16-17 *Wohlfahrtia opaca*. (Drawing by Miriam A. Palmer.)

In Europe, *W. meigenii* (Schiner) is a very similar species, considered by some as identical to the *opaca* form of *vigil*. However, it is strictly a scavenger and, so far as known, is not involved in human or animal myiasis. Other Old World species of *Wohlfahrtia*, the obligatory parasite *W. magnifica* (Schiner) and the facultative *W. nuba* (Wiedemann), are involved in myiasis of wounds or head cavities, not the dermal type.

Rodent and Rabbit Bots. The larvae of the genus *Cuterebra* are commonly parasitic on rodents and wild and domestic rabbits and hares in the New World. These animals may be severely infested with dermal tumors in which the large, spiny grubs lie. The adult flies are bumble-beelike, although as a rule they are much less hairy; they may be predominantly shining blue or black. The taxonomy of the group is in an unsatisfactory state.

Occasionally animals other than rodents and lagomorphs are parasitized by *Cuterebra* larvae. These include dogs, cats, New World monkeys, and man. Human cases are very rare, the larvae forming boil-like lesions in the dermal and subdermal tissues. The larvae are easily removed.

The human bot fly, *Dermatobia hominis* (Linnaeus Jr.) (Fig. 16-18), is common in parts of Mexico and Central and South America. The larva is known by several names, the most common of which are torcel, tórsalo, and berne. The fly measures 12 to 16 mm in length

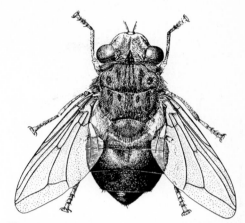

Fig. 16-18 The human bot fly, *Dermatobia hominis.* (Drawing by Arthur Cushman; U.S.D.A. photograph.)

and superficially resembles a bluebottle fly. It parasitizes a large range of mammals and even birds. It has been reported from cattle, swine, cats, dogs, horses, mules, sheep, goats, monkeys, man, and several wild mammals; toucans and ant birds are also known as hosts. It is a serious pest of cattle in parts of Brazil and Central America, where young animals that are heavily infested may be killed and where the loss of meat and milk and damage to hides may run to many millions of dollars annually. In man the larva has been reported from various parts of the body, mainly the head, arms, back, abdomen, scrotum, buttocks, thighs, and axilla.

The life history of this fly is extremely interesting. The adult is a forest-inhabiting insect. The female does not deposit eggs directly on the human skin; rather, she captures another fly or, rarely, a tick, and glues the eggs, by use of an adhesive, quick-drying cement, along one side of the carrier's body. The carrier (Fig. 16-19) is an active, day-flying zoophilous species of moderate size. Guimarães and Papavero (1966) list, as known carriers, forty-eight species of flies and one tick (*Amblyomma cayennense*); the flies include twenty-four species of mosquitoes as well as black flies, the deer fly *Chrysops, Fannia*

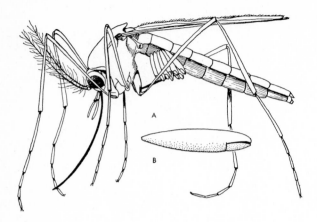

Fig. 16-19 *A. Psorophora* mosquito carrying a load of Dermatobia eggs. *B.* Egg enlarged. (Drawing by Arthur Cushman; U.S.D.A. photograph.)

species, *Musca domestica, Stomoxys calcitrans,* and others.

Eggs are attached to the carrier by the posterior end, so that when the carrier makes contact with a prospective host, the anterior end of the egg is pointed downward. This end of the egg develops an operculum, through which the larva emerges. The larva may, however, remain alive and inactive within the egg for as much as twenty-eight days. The larva, upon emergence, penetrates the skin to the subcutaneous tissues.

The larval period in the body of the host requires about six weeks; then, like *Hypoderma,* the larva leaves the warblelike swelling it has produced, drops to the earth, and enters the ground to pupate. Unlike *Hypoderma,* the larva of *Dermatobia* (Fig. 16-20) remains for the full period of its development in the lesion it makes upon entering the skin; there is no wandering period prior to the warble formation. The entire life cycle requires three to four months.

Dunn (1930) has described the life history of the human bot fly on the basis of an infestation he permitted himself to suffer in the Canal Zone. In his case the fly *Limnophora,* not a bloodsucker, was the carrier. Two larvae were observed to enter the skin of his arm, requiring forty-two minutes for the first and one hour and thirty-five minutes for the second. Dunn experienced "absolutely no sensation caused by the entrance of the (first) larva

after the first 30 minutes. Then, as the posterior end was being drawn inside, a sharp pricking, which lasted for about two minutes, was experienced." He states that there was at first a sharp itching at night, and by the end of two weeks the lesions had the appearance of small boils, and by the end of three weeks they were excruciatingly painful. At the end of 46 days and 15 hours, and 50 days and 15.5 hours, respectively, the larvae emerged from the skin, causing "absolutely no pain or sensation." The pupal periods were from twenty-two to twenty-four days.

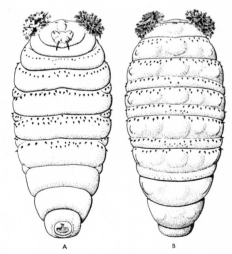

Fig. 16-20 *Dermatobia hominis,* mature larva. *A.* Ventral view. *B.* Dorsal view. (Drawing by Arthur Cushman; U.S.D.A. photograph.)

An important review of the biology, systematics, pathogenesis, economic importance, and control of *Dermatobia hominis* is given by Guimarães and Papavero (1966). A very valuable part of this paper is its bibliography of 375 titles, in chronological order, a considerable number of which are partially abstracted or more or less extensively quoted.

The Tumbu Fly. The tumbu fly, an African calliphorid fly, *Cordylobia anthropophaga* (Blanchard), causes a boil-like (furuncular) type of myiasis. It is heavy-bodied, predominantly yellowish-brown, with two poorly defined longitudinal stripes on the thorax and with transverse black bands on the abdomen. It measures 6 to 12 mm in length. Though restricted to Africa south of the Sahara Desert, it is widespread there.

The female deposits her eggs, in batches of 100 to 300, usually in dry sand that has been contaminated by urine or feces. Sometimes soiled diapers of babies, if dry, may stimulate oviposition. Eggs are never deposited on the naked skin or attached to hairs. After hatching, a larva may remain alive up to nine to fifteen days without feeding. Once it finds a host, it burrows into the subcutaneous tissues, where the characteristic boil-like lesion is found. The three larval instars are quite different from one another in appearance; the first is more maggotlike; the second is a club-shaped larva with strong, recurved tegumentary hooks; the third is 13 to 15 mm in length, rather cylindrical, and densely set with spines.

Penetration of the human skin may be accomplished with no more discomfort to the host than a mild itching. As the boil-like lesion is enlarged, a serous fluid is exuded and the surrounding tissues become hardened. Later, febrile reactions and malaise may occur. The patient's sleep may be interfered with. Secondary microbial infection is a possibility.

A wide range of vertebrate hosts has been recorded. Dogs are the domestic animals most commonly affected; wild hosts include native cats, apes, monkeys, rats, mice, and other rodents. Rats form the main reservoir. Other species of *Cordylobia* parasitize other native African mammals.

Bloodsucking Maggots. A calliphorid fly commonly referred to in the literature on myiasis is *Auchmeromyia luteola* (Fabricius), the larva of which is a bloodsucker known as the Congo floor maggot (Fig. 16-21). This fly is restricted to Africa south of the Sahara Desert, including the Cape Verde Islands but excluding Madagascar. It is commonly found in and about human habitations. The eggs are deposited in various situations, such as on sleeping mats on the ground in huts, in dusty crevices, and in dry sand, situations where the larvae, when hatched, may readily find food. The time required for hatching depends upon relative humidity and temperature, but may vary from thirty-six hours to seven days. The larvae are remarkably resistant to extreme dryness and lack of food. They are nocturnal in their feeding habits, sucking the blood of sleeping persons, producing a wound by means of the powerful mouth hooks and the associated maxillary plates. They feed for fifteen to twenty minutes, detach, and hide in the crevices of mats, and so forth during the day; the attacks are repeated almost nightly if hosts are available. They attack persons sleeping on the ground or in low beds; they cannot reach beds of ordinary height. The duration of the larval period has not been determined, but it may be as short as two weeks or, in the absence of food, perhaps as long as three months. The

Fig. 16-21 Congo floor maggot, *Auchmeromyia luteola.* (After Blacklock, in Martini's *Zoönosen der Haut in wärmeren Ländern.*)

larvae then pupate in protected situations. The pupal period lasts from nine to sixteen days, depending on temperature.

The bite of the larva is normally felt as a slight prick. But like bed bugs, the effects of their attacks may vary considerably according to the susceptibility of the host. Heavy infestations of huts may cause the natives considerable discomfort. No relationship to the transmission of any disease-producing organism is known.

Bloodsucking Maggots of Birds. Though the Congo floor maggot is the only dipterous larva that is known to suck the blood of man, there are several genera that consist largely or wholly of parasites of this type of nestling birds. One of these is the calliphorid genus *Protocalliphora*, which is widespread in the Northern Hemisphere. Hall (1948) lists more than fifty species of birds, mostly passerines but including several species of hawks and other nonpasserines, that are parasitized by various species of *Protocalliphora* in America, and Zumpt (1965) lists thirty-four avian hosts of this genus in the Old World.

The effect of parasitism on the host is a matter on which there is some disagreement. According to Plath (1919), 5 to 10 per cent of the parasitized nestlings die from loss of blood, and some of those that become full-fledged are so weakened by the loss of blood that they fall an easy prey to rapacious animals. The presence of the maggots may at times lead to desertion of the nest by the mother bird. One species of the genus, *P. lindneri* (Peus), does not suck blood, but rather forms abscesses in the skin of the nestlings.

Several genera in other families may also have bloodsucking larvae that attack nestling birds. These include *Neottiophilum*, family Neottiphilidae, and *Passeromyia*, family Muscidae, in the Old World, and *Philornis*, family Muscidae, in the New.

Toxic Effects of Ingested Fly Larvae. Botulism, known as "limber-neck" in chickens, is traceable at least in part to the ingestion of large numbers of fly larvae such as *Lucilia caesar*, *Phaenicia sericata*, and no doubt other species of flies, or of meat containing the botulism organism. This organism multiplies in the unburied bodies of dead animals, where it may be picked up by fly larvae breeding in that medium and in turn passed on to the chickens that eat the maggots. This is one reason why dead animals should be speedily and safely disposed of, preferably by incineration.

Surgical Maggots. Though now of only historical interest, the use of sterile maggots, maggot therapy, in the disinfection of osteomyelitis and other wound infections was introduced into professional medical practice shortly after the end of World War I. Baer (1931) had noticed that when men wounded in battle had been lying out on the ground for some time before being carried into dressing stations, their wounds were infested with maggots. He noticed particularly that these men whose wounds were crawling with maggots did not develop infections, as did the men whose wounds had received treatment. It was discovered that the maggots were eating the dead tissue in which the bacterial infection throve; the maggots actually served as a "viable antiseptic." Baer's work attracted a great deal of attention, and much experimentation followed, resulting in numerous publications by many investigators.

The fly larvae used in earlier osteomyelitis treatment apparently belonged indiscriminately to the species *Phaenicia sericata, Lucilia caesar,* and *Phormia regina.*

It is interesting to note, in passing, that the use of maggot therapy was known in at least one instance to an aboriginal tribe. Lee (1968) cites the work of Dunbar with the Ngemba Tribe of New South Wales, Australia, in which the author states that these primitive peoples used maggots for cleansing wounds, the practice apparently dating from ancient times.

17

FLEAS

Fleas are insects, the order Siphonaptera (Suctoria or Aphaniptera of some authors), which are exclusively bloodsucking in the adult stage. They number about 1,900 species and subspecies. The degree of permanence of attachment to the host as adults permits segregation into three distinct groups (Suter, 1964): (1) The majority of fleas, as represented by *Xenopsylla cheopis* (Rothschild), may easily leave their host and may transfer to other hosts of the same or a different species. (2) Another group, which includes the sticktight flea, *Echidnophaga gallinacea* (Westwood), is

one in which the females become stationary ectoparasites anchored by their mouth parts to the host's skin. (3) The third group, represented by the chigoe, *Tunga penetrans* Linnaeus, is characterized by females that develop into proper stationary intracutaneous parasites, though they maintain an opening with the outside. From the standpoint of pathogen transmission, free-living fleas are the main vectors, and attached species play no important role. Rate of development and optimal ecological conditions are similar for all three types of fleas. A fourth group may be recognized as being collected in abundance in the host's nest and seldom on the host (Jellison, personal communication to Harwood).

Typical Flea Life History. The eggs of a flea (Figs. 17-1, 17-2) are comparatively large (5 mm long), glistening white, and rounded at both ends. Relatively few, from three to eighteen, are deposited at one laying; however, during the entire lifetime of a female the number may be considerable. Bacot (1914) records 448 eggs over a period of 196 days deposited by a single female *Pulex irritans*. Fleas often oviposit among the hairs of the host, but the eggs are dry and will not attach. Oviposition usually occurs in the nest of the host where flea excrement and other detritus serve as larval food. Captured fleas readily oviposit in glass vials or other receptacles. In the case of a heavily infested dog or cat large numbers of eggs may be found on the sleeping mat.

Temperatures of 65–80° F (approximately 18–27° C) combined with a humidity of 70 per cent and over appear to favor egg laying. High mean temperatures of 95–100° F (approximately 35–38° C, close to the normal body temperature of most mammals) inhibit growth of the developmental stages, which may account for the fact that the eggs do not hatch well on the host. Low temperatures also inhibit the developmental stages. The incubation period normally varies from two to twelve days. Sensitivity of adult and developing fleas to low humidity and to temperature extremes may be a principal reason why fleas occur in large numbers on animals that live in burrows or nests; or perhaps their development under conditions of high humidity and relatively stable temperatures, characteristic of animal lairs, may have resulted in the loss of ability to withstand environmental extremes. For

whatever reason, it has been noted that cottontail rabbits (*Sylvilagus*) which inhabit burrows, harbor many more fleas than do hares and jackrabbits (*Lepus*), which live and rear their young in the open (Holland, 1949).

The flea embryo is provided with a sharp eggburster spine on the head by means of which the eggshell is cut by a tumbling motion of its inhabitant (Kessel, 1939). Larvae (Figs. 17-1, 17-2) are very active, slender, thirteen-segmented, and yellow-white with segmentally arranged bristles. The larval mouth parts are of the biting type.

Flea larvae feed on a variety of materials found in the den and associated areas of the host. It was early noted that droplets of blood and egested blood products are deposited freely by adult fleas in such surroundings, which led to the impression that larvae need blood derivatives in their diet, but such a specific requirement is not evident in a nutritional study of the Oriental rat flea, *Xenopsylla cheopis* (Rothschild), by Pausch and Fraenkel (1966). In their investigation rich protein sources provided maximum growth rates and weight. Such sources could be provided by blood proteins, but also by other complete proteins. They note that the rather large size

Fig. 17-1 Life cycle of a flea: (*upper left*) egg; (*center*) larva; (*lower left*) pupa; (*upper right*) female; (*lower right*) male.

of the flea egg, one twelfth the weight of a fully grown larva in the species studied, suggests that essential nutritional factors are received from the female parent, reducing the need for many specific nutrients required in the diet of most mature insects.

Under favorable conditions the flea larval period may be but nine to fifteen days, if unfavorable it may extend over 200 days. At the end of the active feeding period when full growth has been achieved, the larva enters a quiescent stage, spins a cocoon, and pupates. The cocoon is whitish in appearance and so loosely spun that one may see the pupa within it (Fig. 17-2). Debris from the surroundings may adhere to the surface of cocoons.

The pupal period is influenced by temperature and varies greatly, from as short a time as seven days to nearly a year. The life cycle (egg to adult) accordingly may vary from eighteen days to twenty months or more. Under laboratory conditions at a temperature of 24° C, Kerr (1946) reports the life cycle of *Ctenocephalides felis* to be twenty to twenty-four days (larval stage eleven to twelve days). His cultures were from fleas fed on a cat. Since adult fleas await the near approach of a host, rather than setting out in search of their blood meal, newly developed adults may remain quiescent until vibrations or other stimuli associated with the presence of a host cause them to be activated.

Figures obtained by different workers have varied greatly even within a species, but most fleas seem to require thirty to seventy-five days for a complete life cycle. Of course inadequate nutrition and suboptimal temperatures will greatly prolong the growth period.

Longevity of Adult Fleas. In common with other types of lair parasites, adult fleas may survive prolonged periods of starvation while awaiting the return of a host. Bacot (1914) states that with nearly saturated air at 45–50° F (approximately 7–10° C) unfed *Pulex irritans* Linnaeus survived for 125 days, *Nosopsyllus fasciatus* (Bosc) for 95 days, *Xenopsylla cheopis* (Rothschild) for 38 days, *Ctenocephalides canis* for 58 days, and *Ceratophyllus gallinae* (Schrank) for 127 days. If fed on their natural host, adults of *P. irritans* may live upward of 513 days, *N. fasciatus* for 106 days, and *X. cheopis*, fed on man, 100 days. *Ctenocephalides canis* (Curtis) and *Ceratophyllus gallinae* have lived for periods of 234 and 345 days, respectively, when fed on man. Bacot further indicates that the maximum observed length of life cycle for the various species mentioned is 966 days for *P. irritans*, 738 days for *C. canis*, 680 days for *N. fasciatus*, 481 days for *C. gallinae*, and 376 days for *X. cheopis*. Adult longevity in nature permits foci of flea-transmitted diseases to persist in the absence of susceptible vertebrates.

Hosts and Occurrence of Species. About 100 species of fleas are parasites of birds, the remainder are associated with mammals (Holland, 1964). It is apparent that ordinarily a certain species of flea predominates on a given host, e.g., *Ctenocephalides canis* on the dog, *Nosopsyllus fasciatus* on the rat in Europe and the United States, *Xenopsylla cheopis* on the rat in Asia, *Leptopsylla segnis* on the domestic mouse, *Pulex irritans* on the human, and so forth, but host specificity is not characteristic of many other flea species. This lack of absolute host specificity increases the potential acquisition and transmission of pathogens.

Of the fleas recovered from rats during the San Francisco plague epidemic of 1907 (Link, 1955), a great preponderance were *Nosopsyllus fasciatus*. Percentages based on 10,972 specimens were as follows:

	Per Cent
Nosopsyllus fasciatus (Bosc)	68.1
Xenopsylla cheopis (Rothschild)	21.3
Pulex irritans Linnaeus	5.6
Leptopsylla segnis (Schönherr)	4.5
Ctenocephalides canis (Curtis)	0.5

Certain fleas, particularly those of medical or veterinary importance, readily pass from

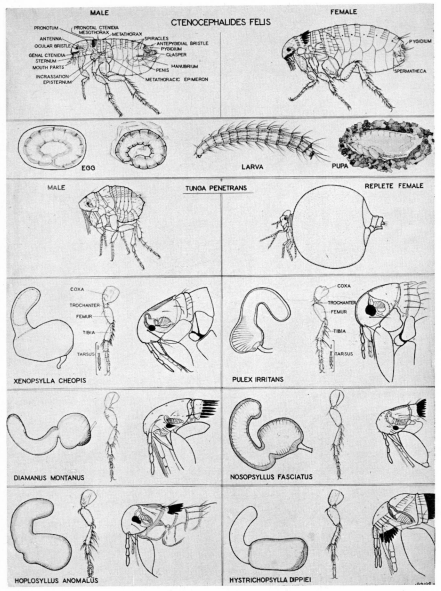

Fig. 17-2 Showing the structural details used in the classification of the Siphonaptera; also, the life history.

one host to another. *Pulex irritans* attacks not only man, but also pigs, dogs, cats, goats, domestic rats, and such wild animals as skunks, coyotes, and badgers; it has even been recorded from the echidna (*Tachyglossus aculeatus*), mallard duck (*Anas platyrhynchos*), and short-eared owl (*Asio flammeus*) (Hopkins and Rothschild, 1953, 1956, 1962). It may breed in the litter inside pig shelters. *Ctenocephalides canis* and *C. felis* freely attack both dogs and cats; they readily bite man. Rodent fleas may divide their attentions among various rodent species.

An extended study on host relationships of

fleas has been made by Hubbard and incorporated in his book, *Fleas of Western North America* (1947). From several sources, Hubbard lists the following fleas as attacking man in the United States: *Tunga penetrans* Linnaeus, *Echidnophaga gallinacea* (Westwood), *Pulex irritans* Linnaeus, *Ctenocephalides canis* (Curtis), *C. felis* (Bouché), *Diamanus montanus* (Baker), *Xenopsylla cheopis* (Rothschild), *Hoplopsyllus affinis* (Baker), *Cediopsylla simplex* (Baker), *Nosopsyllus fasciatus* (Bosc), *Orchopeas howardii* (Baker), *Ceratophyllus niger* C. Fox, *C. gallinae* (Schrank), and *Dasypsyllus gallinulae perpinnatus* (Baker). Holland (1949) lists the following additional species: *Ceratophyllus garei* (Rothschild), *Hystrichopsylla* sp., *Monopsyllus ciliatus protinus* (Jordan), *M. eumolpi eumolpi* (Rothschild), *M. vison* (Baker), *M. wagneri wagneri* (Baker), and *Oropsylla arctomys* (Baker). *Hoplopsyllus anomalus* (Baker), a common parasite of ground squirrels in California and a proven vector of plague, is also known to bite man (Pollitzer, 1954).

Morphology of Fleas. Many of the external features of fleas are unique among the Insecta. As Snodgrass (1946) so aptly states: "No part of the external anatomy of an adult flea could possibly be mistaken for that of any other insect. The head, the mouth parts, the thorax, the legs, the abdomen, the external genitalia, all present features that are not elsewhere duplicated among the hexapods." Yet internally the flea is a fairly generalized insect (Fig. 2-6*E*).

Adult fleas are laterally compressed, wingless, and minute bloodsucking ectoparasites of warm-blooded vertebrates. The wingless condition appears to be a secondary adaptation to obligate parasitism in adults, as Sharif (1935) has demonstrated the presence of wing buds in pupae of three common species of fleas. The posterior pair of legs is strikingly adapted for jumping, though some fleas attaching to birds and squirrels in the nest have secondarily become crawlers (Holland, 1964). Commoner species vary from 1.5–4 mm in length, with males as a rule being smaller

than females; both sexes feed on blood exclusively.

The head is a highly specialized cranial capsule set closely against the pronotum; this near fusion limits the head's movement. On the sides of the head are depressions (grooves) in which are held the tiny knobbed and segmented antennae; in front of the antennae are located the inconspicuous eyes, if these are present. The position of a conspicuous ocular bristle in front of or below the eye may be useful in classifying fleas; also useful in classification is the presence in some species of a conspicuous comb of heavy spines located just above the mouth parts—the *oral* or *genal ctenidium* (Fig. 17-2). The head is sometimes divided into an anterior and a posterior part by the interantennal suture and associated ridge, known collectively as the *falx*. Mouth parts of the adult flea are of the piercing-sucking type (Chapter 3). The thorax of the flea is compact, consisting of the pro-, meso-, and metathorax. The *pronotum* lies immediately behind the head, and at its posterior margin in many species is a comb of spinelike processes known as the *pronotal ctenidium*, useful in group classification. The *mesonotum* is a simple arched plate. The *metathorax* is highly developed to sustain the jumping mechanism. The chaetotaxy of the thoracic sclerites is of some systematic importance. The arrangements and numbers of bristles on the tarsi are likewise of importance on the generic level; other leg characters are not much used in identification.

The abdomen consists of ten segments (actually eleven according to Kessel, 1939), which like the thoracic segments are made up of plates (sclerites), except that the pleurites are concealed. There are numerous backward-pointing spines. On the apical edge of the seventh tergite are the *antepygidial bristles*; the ninth tergite consists of a peculiar pincushion-like structure known as the *pygidium*, probably a sensory organ.

The male terminalia are particularly important in classification. Among the parts to be observed are the *claspers*, movable and nonmovable portions, and the *manubrium* (Fig. 17-2). In cleared specimens the springlike *penis* may be seen lying in the region of the fifth and sixth segments. In copulation it projects out from between the upper and lower claspers (see Rothschild, 1965). The females possess a sacculated spermatheca (Figs. 17-2, 17-3), situated in the region of the eighth or ninth segment and easily visible in cleared specimens. Some species have two spermathecae. The shape of this organ is unique for many species and is, therefore, an important taxonomic character.

Digestive Tract (Fig. 2-6*E*). As soon as blood flows from the feeding wound it is drawn up into the *pharynx* by the action of both cibarial and pharyngeal pumps. The blood is carried to the long narrow *esophagus*, which begins in the region of the brain and passes through the circumesophageal ring. The esophagus opens into the stomach through the bulbous *proventriculus*, which is provided internally with radially arranged (seven rows) proventricular spines (Fig. 17-4). When the encircling bands of muscle contract, these spines meet as a valve that prevents regurgitation from the stomach. The *stomach* (midgut) is a capacious distensible organ nearly as long as the abdomen, emptying into the short *intestine*, which in turn empties into the wide *rectum* with its six rectal glands. Where the stomach joins the intestine, four filamentous *Malpighian tubes* arise.

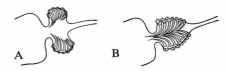

Fig. 17-4 Spinelike epithelial cells in the proventriculus of *Xenopsylla cheopis*. *A.* At rest. *B.* Showing opening into stomach closed.

Systematics. According to Holland's estimates (1964), by 1968 some 1,900 species and subspecies of fleas had been described. Jordan (in Smart, 1965) has estimated about 3,000 species and subspecies comprise the total existing fauna. The most complete catalog is that of Hopkins and Rothschild (1953, 1956, 1962, and still in preparation). For America north of Mexico (including Greenland), Jellison, *et al.* (1953), list 72 genera containing 243 species and 55 subspecies. Holland (1964) discusses the difficulties encountered in classifying Siphonaptera. These are largely because many groups of mammalian hosts and their associated fleas have become extinct and there are gaps in apparent phylogenetic relationships; in addition flea taxonomy is based mainly on external structures for which there has been much convergent development. The family classification used here is that of Jellison and Holland. Only a key separating the most frequently encountered North American genera is provided, because family level characteristics are very difficult for the initiate to follow. The genera selected include:

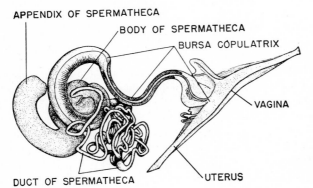

APPENDIX OF SPERMATHECA

BODY OF SPERMATHECA

BURSA COPULATRIX

VAGINA

DUCT OF SPERMATHECA

UTERUS

Fig. 17-3 Copulatory organs of the female of *Nosopsyllus fasciatus*. (After Fox.)

(1) those known to attack man; (2) those commonly on the Norway rat; and (3) rodent fleas generally recognized as involved in transmission of plague.

More inclusive works on North American fleas include Fox (1940), Ewing and Fox (1943), Hubbard (1947), and Holland (1949). Traub (1950) covers the fleas of Central America and Mexico. Jordan's chapter in Smart (1965) is useful in recognizing Old World fleas, and Hopkins and Rothschild as well as Smit (1954) provide additional valuable taxonomic information. Indexes to the literature of Siphonaptera of North America, through 1960, have been prepared by Jellison and Good (1942), Jellison, et al. (1953), and Jellison and Glesne (1967).

KEY TO THE MEDICALLY MORE IMPORTANT GENERA OF FLEAS OF TEMPERATE NORTH AMERICA (After Holland, 1949, and other sources)

1. Pronotal ctenidium absent; genal ctenidium absent or represented by a single inconspicuous tooth..................2
   Pronotal ctenidium present; genal ctenidium present or absent...............6
2. The three thoracic tergites together shorter than the first abdominal tergite.........3
   The three thoracic tergites together as long or longer than the first abdominal tergite 4
3. Hind coxa with a patch of spinelike bristles on its inner apical surface..*Echidnophaga* Hind coxa with only scattered bristles on its inner surface.................*Tunga*
4. Two rows of bristles on a typical abdominal segment............*Rhopalopsyllus* One row of bristles on a typical segment 5
5. Mesopleuron divided by a pleural ridge or rod that runs upward from the base of the middle coxa................*Xenopsylla* Mesopleuron without such a pleural ridge or rod........................*Pulex*

6. Genal ctenidium present..............7
   Genal ctenidium absent..............12
7. Anterior abdominal terga each with one row of setae; eyes well developed......8
   Anterior abdominal terga each with two or more rows of setae; eyes absent or vestigial..........................9
8. Genal ctenidium more or less horizontal, with sharp, slightly curved spines........
   .... *Ctenocephalides*
   Genal ctenidium oblique, with blunt spines
   ....*Cediopsylla*
9. Genal ctenidium of two spines only, overlapping each other....*Epitedia, Neopsylla*
   Genal ctenidium of three or more spines
  10
10. Genal ctenidium of three spines; apical segment of labial palpus with a hooklike seta...................*Ctenophthalmus*
    Genal ctenidium of more than three spines; labial palpus not as above.....11
11. Genal ctenidium of four spines, arranged vertically.................*Leptopsylla*
    Genal ctenidium of four or more, long, slender spines, arranged in an oblique row...................*Hystrichopsylla*
12. First abdominal tergite with a ctenidium which is as prominent as that of the gena
    ....*Stenoponia*
    First abdominal tergite without a ctenidium.............................13
13. Anterior abdominal terga each with but one row of setae...........*Hoplopsyllus*
    Anterior abdominal terga each with two or more rows of setae...............14
14. One or no lateral setae on fore femur....
    ....*Orchopeas*
    A number of lateral setae on each fore femur............................15
15. Anterior inner surface of mid and hind coxae with long thin setae from base to apex, aside from those fringing the anterior margin of coxa..................16
    Basal part of mid and hind coxae with no setae except those along the anterior margin........................17
16. Basal abdominal sternum with a patch of lateral setae...............*Opisocrostis*
    Basal abdominal sternum without a patch of lateral setae......................
    ....*Thrassis, Oropsylla, Diamanus*

17. Total of 24 or more spines in pronotal ctenidium. Usually on birds. . . . .
. . . . *Ceratophyllus*
Less than 24 spines in pronotal ctenidium. On mammals. .18
18. Eye somewhat reduced, its longest diameter shorter or barely as long as distance from eye to heavily incrassated portion of genal lobe. . . . . *Malaraeus*
Longest diameter of eye greater than this distance. . . . . . . *Monopsyllus, Nosopsyllus*

COMMONER SPECIES OF FLEAS

Family Tungidae. *Tunga penetrans* Linnaeus, the chigoe, is also known as the "jigger," "chigger," "chique," or "sand flea" (Fig. 17-5). The head of this flea is definitely angular and is usually larger proportionately than the head of other fleas; there are no ctenidia on the head or pronotum; mouth parts are conspicuous, the palpi four-segmented.

Family Pulicidae. *Pulex irritans* Linnaeus (Fig. 17-6) is commonly known as the human flea. It is cosmopolitan in distribution and occurs on a surprisingly wide range of hosts, including domesticated animals, particularly swine. This species has neither oral nor pronotal ctenidia. The metacoxae have a row or patch of short spinelets on the inner side; the mesosternite has an internal rodlike incrassation extending dorsoanteriorly. The maxillary laciniae extend about halfway down on the fore coxae, which distinguishes this species from *Pulex simulans* Baker (laciniae extending at least three fourths the length of the fore coxae), also known as a human flea but restricted to the New World (northwestern United States to the northern half of South America).

Pulex simulans has long been confused with *P. irritans*, and undoubtedly some of the published information relative to the latter belongs properly to the former (Smit, 1958). *Pulex irritans* transmits plague under laboratory conditions and may be the chief vector of two unusual types of plague, e.g., *viruola pestosa* (a vesicular form) and *angina pestosa* (a tonsillar form) found in Ecuador.

Echidnophaga gallinacea (Westwood), the sticktight flea of poultry (Fig. 17-12), resembles *Tunga penetrans* in the great reduction of the thoracic segments; it differs in having the angles of the head acutely produced, while in *T. penetrans* the head is obtuse instead of rounded and the eyes and antennae are in the posterior half of the head. It is 1–1.5 mm in length.

Ctenocephalides canis (Curtis) and *Ctenocephalides felis* (Bouché) are the dog flea and cat flea, respectively. Both species attack cats and dogs as well as man. Both have the genal ctenidium consisting of seven or eight sharp black teeth, a character that distinguishes them from all other fleas (Hubbard, 1947). *Ctenophalides felis* (Fig. 17-7) may be separated (from *C. canis*) by observing that in the female the head is fully twice as long as high and pointed (less than twice as long as high and rounded); first and second genal spines of approximately equal length (first spine shorter than second); pronotal ctenidium with about sixteen teeth (about eighteen); two or three bristles on metathoracic episternum (three or four bristles); bristles on metathoracic epimeron, first row, four to eight (seven to eleven), second row, five to seven, (seven to

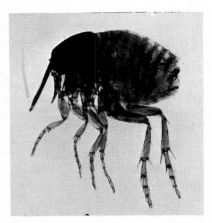

Fig. 17-5 The chigoe flea, *Tunga penetrans*.

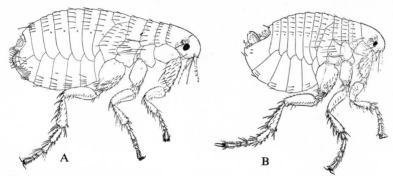

Fig. 17-6 *Pulex irritans*, the human flea. *A.* Female. *B.* Male. × 17.

nine); seven to ten bristles on inner side of hind femur (ten to thirteen).

Xenopsylla cheopis (Rothschild) (Fig. 17-8) is the Oriental rat flea. This species is largely cosmopolitan, occurring just about wherever *Rattus rattus* is found, though it is scarce or absent from northern areas. It habitually inhabits buildings and bites man freely. It resembles *Pulex irritans* in that both oral and pronotal ctenidia are absent. The ocular bristle is in front of and just above the middle of the eye; there are two bristles on the gena; oral bristles placed low down just above the base of the maxillae; each abdominal tergite has but one row of bristles; the hind femur has a row of about eight bristles. The maxillary laciniae reach nearly to the end of the anterior coxae.

Mellanby (1933) has performed experi-

ments proving that *X. cheopis* can complete its life history between 18–35° C in moist air. Between 18–29° C, air with a relative humidity of 40 per cent is unfavorable, but with 60 per cent relative humidity pupation takes place successfully. Pupation at 18° C required eight days; at 22° C, it required six days; and at 29–35° C, it required four days. The developmental zero for pupation is about 15° C.

Xenopsylla brasiliensis (Baker), an African species, is the predominant rat flea in Uganda, Kenya, and Nigeria. It has spread to South America and certain areas in India. Because it is "the flea of the hut," it is regarded as a more important vector of plague than *X. cheopis* in Kenya and Uganda; *cheopis* infests rats in stone or brick buildings.

Xenopsylla astia Rothschild has a restricted distribution:

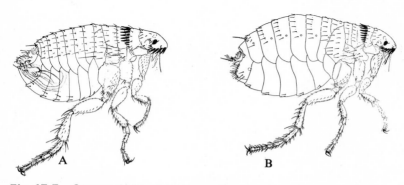

Fig. 17-7 *Ctenocephalides felis*, the cat flea. *A.* Male. *B.* Female. × 17.

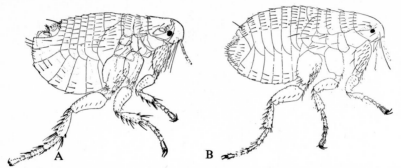

Fig. 17-8 *Xenopsylla cheopis,* the Oriental rat flea. *A.* Male. *B.* Female. × 17.

... being found mostly along the low-lying coast of Ceylon, the east coast of India, and along the opposite coast of Bengal ... while *X. astia* may be the responsible vector (of plague) in certain circumscribed and isolated outbreaks, the available evidence ... points to its inferior position in the epidemiological picture ... Moreover, *astia* outbreaks, if and when they do occur, are not known to carry over from one season to another.

Xenopsylla vexabilis Jordan is a common flea of the Hawaiian rat, *Rattus hawaiiensis.* According to Eskey, reported by Jordan (1932), this species has a very peculiar distribution:

It has not been found in Honolulu or vicinity, while it is quite common on rats caught about nine miles away on the opposite side of the island. It is essentially a flea of field rats and rarely found on rats caught in buildings.

Family Ceratophyllidae. *Nosopsyllus fasciatus* (Bosc) is the Northern rat flea (Fig. 17-9).

It is widespread over Europe and America, less common in other parts of the world. It has been recorded on rats, house mice, pocket gophers, skunk, man, and many other host animals. It has but one ctenidium, the pronotal, which has a total of eighteen to twenty spines. Females have two bristles in front of the eye, males have three bristles plus an additional group of four in front of these. There are three or four hairs on the inner surface of the hind femur. *N. fasciatus* (Bosc) is regarded as unimportant in the causation of natural outbreaks of plague.

The genus *Nosopsyllus* may be distinguished from the genus *Diamanus* by the fact that in *Diamanus* there are long, thin bristles on the inside of the mid and hind coxae from the base of the apex; in *Nosopsyllus* such bristles occur at most in the apical half.

Diamanus montanus (Baker) (Fig. 17-10) is a common squirrel flea abundant in California. This species may be recognized by a

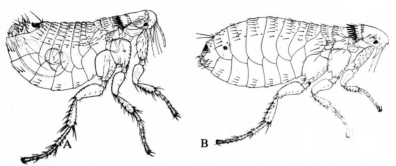

Fig. 17-9 *Nosopsyllus fasciatus,* the northern rat flea. *A.* Male. *B.* Female. × 17.

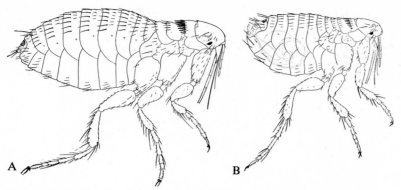

Fig. 17-10 *Diamanus montanus*, the squirrel flea. *A*. Female. *B*. Male. × 17.

spine at the tip of the second joint of the hind tarsus, longer than the third joint and reaching over onto the fourth joint; each abdominal tergite has two rows of bristles; the male claspers are long and sickle-shaped.

Ceratophyllus niger C. Fox, the western chicken flea, was originally described from specimens taken from man and from *Rattus norvegicus*. This flea is considerably larger than the sticktight flea of poultry (*Echnidnophaga gallinacea*), and unlike that latter species does not attach except for brief periods of feeding. Additional hosts include cats and dogs. It breeds primarily in fowl droppings. *Ceratophyllus gallinae* Schrank is commonly known as the European chicken flea (Stewart, 1927), although it has a wide range of hosts. The large number of spines on the pronotal ctenidium furnishes a striking

characteristic for distinguishing these bird fleas from the others discussed here.

Leptopsylla segnis (Schönherr) is the cosmopolitan mouse flea (Fig. 17-11), also common on rats. It bites man reluctantly, and is regarded as a weak vector of plague; its role in human outbreaks is considered negligible.

THE MEDICAL AND VETERINARY IMPORTANCE OF FLEAS

Plague. Plague, caused by the bacterium *Pasteurella pestis* (the genus will likely be changed to *Yersinia*) has been known from ancient times. It has had a very great influence on the course of history, being a decisive factor affecting military campaigns, and weakening besieged cities or their attackers. More

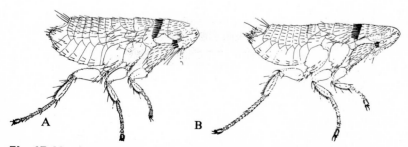

Fig. 17-11 *Leptopsylla segnis*, a mouse flea. *A*. Female. *B*. Male. × 17.

significantly this disease has been characterized by epidemics that have decimated human
populations of entire countries or even continents (pandemics). The early historic highlights of this disease are covered in Chapter 1.
In the discussion that follows here, events will
be covered from the time of the last major
pandemic, which apparently started in the
interior of north China toward the end of the
nineteenth century.

The Disease in Man. In addition to the
work of Wu, *et al.* (1936), two valuable
general references are the well-documented
monograph of Pollitzer (1954) and Hirst's
interestingly written book, *The Conquest of
Plague* (1953).

Wu, *et al.*, give the period of incubation as
two to ten days; the onset usually occurs within three to four days. Fox in *Insects and
Disease of Man* (1925) describes the disease as
follows:

It develops suddenly with a rapid rise of
temperature, reaching 103° or 104° F in two
or three days, after which it is more or less
irregular. There is headache, the eyes are injected and the facies are characteristic of extreme illness. Prostration is profound and
comes on early. Delirium also appears early.
The characteristic lesion of the disease, the
bubo, usually is sufficiently pronounced by
the second day to be readily detected. The most
common site for the bubo is the femoral or
inguino-femoral region, then the axillary
region, cervical, iliac and popliteal. Over the
enlarged glands oedema appears and pressure
elicits great tenderness. The individual lymph
nodes cannot be palpated. This swelling forms
the primary bubo. Secondary bubos may
appear in other parts of the body. In these, the
glands are not matted together as in the
primary bubo. Four forms of skin eruption
may be described—a petechial eruption,
ecchymoses, a subcuticular mottling, and the
so-called plague pustule ... a bulbous-like
formation containing thin, turbid material
teeming with plague bacilli. It is believed to
indicate the original point of inoculation, the
flea bite. Extending from this to the nearest
lymphatic glands faint red lines indicating
lymphangitis may be observed. A secondary
pneumonia due to the deposit of plague

bacilli in the pulmonary tissues may occur.
In about a week if the patient survives, the
bubo breaks down leaving an ulcer which
heals slowly.

Plague is essentially a disease of rodents,
usually transmitted by rodent fleas, but it may
under certain conditions cause serious epidemics among human beings. The term *bubonic
plague* is applied when inflammation of lymph
glands results from the infection, and buboes
are formed; these first foci may remain so
localized and cause little discomfort. The
pathogenesis of plague infection follows a
standard course: from the lymphatics and
lymph nodes, to the blood stream, to the liver
and spleen. When, because of the rapidity of
the multiplication of the bacteria or for other
reasons, the liver and spleen cannot cope with
the invaders, the infection massively invades
the blood stream and becomes *septicemic*
plague. As Meyer (1955) points out, septicemic
plague is really plague in which the buboes are
inconspicuous; it is better to distinguish only
two forms of human plague: the *primary
bubonic*, or zootic form, and the *primary
pneumonic* (pulmonary), or demic form. The
latter is not transmitted by fleas; it is transmitted from human to human by infective
droplets coming from the respiratory system
of a plague patient.

Several preventive and therapeutic practices
greatly reduce the dangers of human plague.
Immunization can be accomplished with
killed organisms or avirulent cultures, and
antiplague serum. The sulfonamides, streptomycin, chlortetracycline, and chloramphenicol are useful in treating the disease once
contracted.

Fleas as Vectors. Ogata (1897) concluded
on epidemiologic grounds that fleas were the
agents of transmission, noting that fleas leave
a rat as it becomes cold after death, and so
may transmit the pathogen directly to man.
He pointed out that the flea ingests plague
bacilli while feeding, having produced plague
in mice by injecting a suspension of crushed

fleas taken from plague rats. Simond (1898) first succeeded in transmitting plague from a sick rat to a healthy rat through the bite of infected fleas. His work, initially discredited, was successfully repeated in 1903 (Verjbitski, 1908).

Liston (1905), working in Bombay in 1904, concluded: (1) one flea, *Xenopsylla cheopis*, infested rats in India far more commonly than did any other; (2) fleas acquired plague bacilli by feeding on a plague rat and these bacilli multiplied in them; (3) infested fleas were at large during the incidence of plague fatalities; and (4) after an epizootic of rat plague, man acquired rat fleas, and might become infected as had guinea pigs used in his experiments.

The following briefly summarizes experiments that proved the association of fleas with plague, conducted by the Indian Plague Commission organized in 1905. Plague was transferred from rats to guinea pigs, and between the latter, only through the agency of infected fleas. When guinea pigs free of fleas were introduced into rooms in which persons had died from plague, or from which plague-infected rats had been taken, they attracted fleas and many of the guinea pigs died under subsequent ordinary confinement. When pairs of susceptible animals were confined in plague-associated rooms without access to soil, with one of each pair in a flea-proof cage, only some of those animals accessible to fleas developed plague. Of fleas trapped in plague-associated rooms no cat fleas, less than 0.5 per cent of human fleas, and nearly 30 per cent of rat fleas harbored plague organisms.

Further observations relating dead rats to human acquisition of plague were reported from San Francisco in 1906 by Blue (1910), and from Manila (*Pub. Hlth. Repts.*, Nov. 7, 1913, p. 2356).

Role of the Flea in Plague Transmission. The Indian Plague Commission showed that the average capacity of *Xenopsylla cheopis* for blood was 0.5 cubic millimeter, and that it might receive as many as 5,000 plague organisms from an infectious rat. The Commission found that the bacillus multiplies in the stomach of the flea and the percentage of fleas with bacilli varies seasonally. In the epidemic season the percentage was greatest for the first four days, and on one occasion the stomach was filled with the organisms on the twentieth day; in the nonepidemic season, no plague bacilli were found in the stomach after the seventh day. In the epidemic season fleas might remain infective up to fifteen days; in the nonepidemic season, but seven days; and in the latter case the percentage of infection in animals was much less than in the epidemic season. Both male and female fleas could transmit the bacilli. As to the manner of dissemination, the Commission found bacilli in the stomach and rectum only, never in salivary glands or body cavity, and rarely in the esophagus if the flea was killed immediately after feeding. After digestion, the blood in the stomach passes into the rectum and is ejected as a dark-red or tarry droplet, containing virulent plague bacilli, which if rubbed into recent flea bites causes infection of the animal. The actual inoculation was therefore believed accomplished indirectly by the flea-bitten person's scratching or rubbing the site of the bite after the infected flea had discharged fecal material upon the skin. There is a great deal of difference in the consistency and other characteristics of the fecal deposits of the various species of fleas, e.g., the human flea, *Pulex irritans*, defecates freely while feeding but is not a ready vector of bubonic plague; the Oriental rat flea, *Xenopsylla cheopis*, seldom defecates while feeding and is a potent vector.

Bacot and Martin (1914) demonstrated the most frequent and normal mechanism of infection, based on observations made by Swellengrebel (1914) that *X. cheopis* seldom defecates when feeding. They showed infection resulted when the flea's only contact with the experimental animal was by means of the proboscis, i.e., the infection is introduced with the bite directly. This mode of infection by regurgitation is due to a temporary obstruction at the entrance to the stomach, described by Bacot and Martin, who state that on:

... examining the contents of the stomach of a flea a day or two after it has fed upon infected blood, clusters of minute brown specks darker in colour and firmer in consistency than the rest of the contents are visible.... The plague-culture grows in the proventriculus as well as in the stomach. Owing to its gelatinous consistency, it not infrequently leads to incompetence and even complete blocking of the proventricular valve.... Although with the proventriculus obstructed in this manner fresh blood cannot find its way into the stomach, this does not prevent the insect sucking.... Given the opportunity, the insects suck blood again and again and if the pharyngeal pump ceases for a moment, some of the blood will by the elastic recoil of the oesophageal wall be driven back into the wound and carry with it plague bacilli.

Bacot and Martin found that infected fleas lived as long as fifty days at 10–15° C and twenty-three days at 27° C, and died infected. Working with the rat fleas, *Xenopsylla cheopis* and *Nosopsyllus fasciatus*, fed on septicemic blood, they concluded that these species were capable of transmitting plague during sucking and that certain fleas with a temporary obstruction at the entrance to the stomach were responsible for most if not all of the infections obtained. In the course of time the plague culture forming the proventricular plug undergoes autolysis and the normal passage of blood is re-established.

Figure 17-4*A* shows the position of the spinelike epithelial cells in the proventriculus when at rest, the opening into the stomach being free for the passage of blood. Figure 17-4*B* shows the opening into the stomach closed against the outward passage of blood on contraction of the muscular bands. Bacot (1915) points out that the adherence and growth of the bacilli among the spines constitute the initial stage of the blockage.

In describing the mechanism of plague transmission by fleas, Eskey and Haas (1940) show numerous photomicrographs of blood-distended stomachs of fleas after feeding. The elapsed interval between an infective blood meal and an infective bite (transmission) for *Xenopsylla cheopis* averaged about twenty-one days (range five to thirty-one days); for *Diamanus montanus* the average was fifty-three days. The average length of life of fleas after being plague-infected was seventeen days (maximum forty-four days) for *X. cheopis*, and forty-seven days (maximum eighty-five) for *D. montanus*.

Another factor concerned with proventricular blockage involves the strain of *P. pestis*. Kartman and Quan (1964) fed *X. cheopis* on six strains of the pathogen. Three of the strains multiplied and eventually caused blockage, whereas the others failed to develop. A direct relation was found between the number of bacilli in an infective meal and the rate of proventricular blockage. Thus for different species of fleas there may be threshold degrees of bacteremia in infected rodents that determine the ability of each flea species to serve as vectors.

Eskey (1938) has shown that virulent plague organisms are more constantly present in the feces of some species of fleas than in others. He reports that plague followed every inoculation of feces deposited by infected *Diamanus montanus*; less than one third of fecal inoculations of *Nosopsyllus fasciatus* caused infections. He also reports that feces of *Xenopsylla cheopis* gave positive reactions, but these fleas did not survive long enough to determine whether or not the results would be constant for any length of time. Eskey points out that there seems to be danger of infection from virulent plague organisms present in the feces of all plague-infected fleas.

Still another possible mode of transmission has been suggested, namely the host may crush infected fleas with its teeth, and then infection through the mucosa of the buccal cavity will cause lymph node involvement in the region of the neck. This mode of transmission usually applies only to rodents, though tonsillar plague among the Indians of Ecuador seems to be transmitted in this manner (Pollitzer, 1954).

Efficiency of Vectors in Experimental Studies of Plague. Kartman and associates (1957) have ascertained those factors that make for efficiency in flea vectors of the plague pathogen in studies similar to those of Wheeler and Douglas, 1941. Their findings bring additional insight into the classical observations of the Indian Plague Commission, and of Bacot and Martin. The terms used in their investigations could often be applied to other arthropods and to their ability to transmit any vertebrate pathogen. *Vector efficiency* is the percentage of fleas becoming infected after feeding on an infected host. In practical usage this is derived simply by taking the percentage of plague transmissions accomplished within the group of fleas tested. The *vector* or *blocking potential* is the percentage of fleas with a blocked proventriculus. The *transmission potential* is the number of infected rodents to the number of transmitting fleas fed daily until the death of individual rodents.

From an ecological point of view all important factors contributing to vector success under the conditions studied must be considered. Field data should include the natural infection rates of fleas, their prevalence and length of life, their transfer potential between wild and commensal rodents, their ability to retain plague bacilli and to become infective (capable of transmission) under given conditions of temperature and humidity, and their predilection for known rodent reservoirs of plague. Also of importance are quantitative data on flea habits and movements, and habits and prevalence of the principal rodents concerned. As an example the fleas *Hystrichopsylla linsdalei* Holland and *Malaraeus telchinum* (Rothschild) were both associated with a plague epizootic in the San Francisco Bay region. *H. linsdalei* had an experimental blocking index, field infection index, field prevalence index, and vector potential respectively of 0.02, 0.11, 0.08 and 0.02; these same factors for *M. telchinum* were 0.0, 0.04, 0.43, and 0.0 (Kartman, 1957). Vector potential on an individual basis showed *M. telchinum* to be inefficient, yet this flea apparently transmitted plague by sheer numbers, and its known prevalence and infection rate in the field suggested it to be important in the epizootic.

In comparing the vector efficiency of *H. linsdalei* with *Xenopsylla cheopis*, Kartman, *et al.* (1958), found the former to block more rapidly, but the rate of blocking in the latter was much greater. When all factors comprising the vector indices were combined, *X. cheopis* had a considerably higher rating. Mice dying from plague bacilli transmitted by *X. cheopis* died sooner than those infected by bites of *H. linsdalei*, suggesting the former introduces more bacilli in the act of feeding.

Urban and Campestral Plague. The epidemiology of plague, as it has thus far been treated, primarily involves commensal rodents, particularly *Rattus rattus*, the Oriental rat flea, *Xenopsylla cheopis*, and man. These are the conditions of typical urban plague, and wherever poor sanitation places large numbers of rats in close association with man there is the distinct possibility that an epidemic can occur.

Because rodents other than rats were known to harbor large numbers of fleas, and rodents are variably susceptible to the plague pathogen, the question naturally arose as to whether plague is maintained in other than urban situations. The existence of a plague epizootic in wild rodents in California was suspected as early as 1903, and plague was demonstrated in ground squirrels, *Citellus beecheyi beecheyi* (Richardson), under natural conditions in 1908 by McCoy. According to that author (1910), about a dozen persons had contracted the disease under circumstances that pointed conclusively to ground squirrels as the source. The two species of fleas commonly infesting the ground squirrel in California are *Diamanus montanus* (Baker) and *Hoplopsyllus anomalus* Baker, of which the former is far more numerous. McCoy proved the first-named species capable of transmitting the plague bacillus from an infected to a healthy ground squirrel.

The designation *sylvatic (selvatic) plague* was proposed by Ricardo Jorge (1928) for the plague of field rodents. The designation *campestral plague* (wild-rodent plague), relating to fields or open country, is more apt, since the term "sylvatic" implies woodland, which is not typical plague territory. Fleas play an important role in transmission from rodent to rodent and consequently in the endemicity of the disease. It is now known that under certain ecologic conditions in vacated rodent burrows fleas can harbor virulent *P. pestis* for many months, thus providing an important part of the reservoir for the infection under campestral conditions. Another distinction, termed *telluric plague* is sometimes made, referring to plague that survives in the soil in rodent burrows.

On a worldwide basis some 220 species of rodents have been shown to harbor plague (Dubos and Hirsch, 1965). Wherever plague is characterized by occasional human cases due to man coming in contact with wild rodents, or wherever the initial stages of urban outbreaks cannot be accounted for by spread from commensal rodents, there is a strong likelihood that plague is present in wild rodents. A number of studies have shown that the maintenance of plague in focal rural areas is associated with resistant species of wild rodents that survive epizootics, yet maintain bacteremia for a prolonged time. Lengthy bacteremia in wild rodents, and the ability of some rodent fleas to survive for long periods, even under starvation conditions, are both mechanisms for maintaining a plague reservoir.

A summary of observations on wild rodent plague in the San Francisco Bay area by Kartman and associates (1958, 1960) related the danger of plague spreading to man with expansion of suburban building, and with increased visitation of wild areas by man. Most serious was the threat of transfer of plague by fleas from wild rodents to commensal rats. Of the wild rodents concerned, various inconspicuous small species appeared to have closer associations with rats than did ground squirrels and other colonial species.

The Pattern of Plague in Various Parts of the World. The last pandemic of plague originated at the close of the nineteenth century in north China. It soon reached Hong Kong via routes of commerce and was transferred to other continents by way of rats on steamships. The devastating epidemics that followed in India for some twenty years served as the impetus for the studies of the Indian Plague Commission. Northern China has been regarded as the cradle of plague, with permanent foci in wild rodents and transfer to man and commensal rodents resulting in passage along ancient land trade routes to European urban centers, resulting in the severe epidemics of the past. With the last pandemic, and the transfer along steamship routes, epidemics occurred in seaports of India (Bombay), the United States (San Francisco), South Africa, the Far East, and the Near East. Permanent foci are established in these areas, with maintenance in wild rodents during times when commensal rats and humans appear unaffected. The general opinion prevails that plague was introduced to these areas at seaports, that native rodents became infected and epizootics resulted, and that infection of urban areas may take place from contact of man or *Rattus* with wild rodents.

Plague is endemic in parts of India, Kurdistan, Burma, Java, China, Madagascar, South, Central, and East Africa, and the Americas. Sporadic outbreaks occur in North Africa, Iraq, Thailand, and Vietnam. For 1962 the World Health Organization listed a total of 1,256 cases, the majority occurring in India, Ecuador, and southwest Africa. In recent decades plague has been declining on a worldwide basis (Dubos and Hirsch, 1965), but the fact remains that permanent foci smolder with varying intensity among native rodents and their fleas, and only the appropriate circumstances are required to permit the recurrence of human epidemics. Disruptions in general sanitation, and medical and public health services, as well as malnutrition and other debilitating conditions, can all readily lead to epidemics. Unstable conditions currently existing in Southeast Asia have increased the number of human cases, with cases in Vietnam jumping from 353 in 1966 to a provisional total of 4,725 in 1967 (WHO *Epidem. Vital Statist. Rep.* 20:380).

The circumstances surrounding campestral plague, as stated, involve resistant and susceptible rodents and their fleas. Each region can be analyzed for its own peculiarities with respect to these factors and from the standpoint of unique ecological conditions.

In the United States the major studies have been conducted by Kartman and associates, particularly in the San Francisco Bay area of California. Flea-host relationships of that region have been described by Miles, *et al.* (1957), and by Murray (1957). After tagging the mouse flea *Malaraeus telchinum* (Rothschild) with radioactive cesium[144] it could be shown that this vector transferred from the field vole *Microtus californicus* to *Rattus norvegicus* and their nests under certain conditions (Hartwell, *et al.*, 1958). Further studies indicated that the direction of transfer of fleas occurred principally from wild rodents to rats (Stark and Miles, 1962).

Under campestral conditions typical of the western United States, man rarely acquires the plague pathogen even though he may be in rather frequent contact with wild rodents. Nonetheless, there is occasional evidence of the disease in such conditions. Lechleitner and others (1962) found that plague exterminated an isolated colony of prairie dogs (*Cynomys*) in Colorado. In this epizootic the fleas *Opisocrostis labis* (Jordan and Rothschild) and *O. tuberculatus cynomuris* Jellison were found infected with the pathogen, the latter species being more numerous and with a higher infection rate. These authors conclude that the fleas acted as reservoirs and, while infected, remained alive in prairie dog burrows for at least one year after the epizootic ceased.

There is no evidence that rabbits constitute basic reservoirs of the disease in the United States, yet in New Mexico cases of plague occurred in men who shot and skinned rabbits, and the pathogen was isolated from the cottontail rabbit (*Sylvilagus*) and two species of fleas (Kartman, 1960). Apparently rabbits can be affected when rodent epizootics are occurring.

In South Africa, according to Davis (1964) and De Meillon, *et al.* (1961), plague-infected rats left ships following the great pandemic spreading from Hong Kong. Between 1899 and 1905 outbreaks occurred in the major port cities, as well as at inland centers such as Johannesburg. These outbreaks were confined to house rat areas, the last epidemic of this phase taking place in Durban in 1912.

During the urban phase of the disease in South Africa wild rodents appear to have become infected, probably at fodder and remount depots established on main lines of communication from the ports inland during the Anglo-Boer war. Gerbils (*Tatera* and *Desmodillus*) with the fleas *Xenopsylla philoxera* Hopkins and *X. piriei* Ingram, respectively, are the most likely primary reservoir, with many other indigenous rodents and hares implicated. Most likely *Xenopsylla philoxera* on *Tatera brantsi* maintains the infection, and the multimammate mouse *Rattus* (*Mastomys*) *natalensis*, with a mixed flea fauna derived from wild and domestic hosts, carries the infection to the human environment. In the human environment *Xenopsylla brasiliensis* (Baker) transmits the pathogen among commensal rodents and man. The probable means of bridging the gap between epizootics is by reinfection of gerbils or other rodents entering deserted warrens still containing some infective fleas.

In South Africa, for reasons not understood, *Rattus rattus* and its fleas, including a high proportion of *Xenopsylla cheopis*, could not provide the right conditions for persistence of plague in the domestic environment. The campestral foci spread to include areas with a mean rainfall of five to twenty-five inches, but not into winter rainfall areas of the western Cape or coastal zone having year-round rain. The distribution of implicated gerbils and flea vectors coincides, with minor exceptions, with the enzootic plague areas.

In India both urban and campestral plague is found. An analysis of major urban centers shows *Rattus rattus* to be most important, and *Rattus norvegicus* to be of minor significance. In Calcutta *Xenopsylla astia* is the predominant rat flea, whereas in Bombay *X. cheopis* predominates (Seal, 1960). However, in Calcutta, wards with plague have rats more heavily infested with *X. cheopis* (Seal and Bhattacharji, 1961). In the province of Uttar Pradesh (north central India) it was thought that only *R. rattus* and its fleas were implicated in the genesis of rural plague in man, but a reservoir was found in a relatively resistant and abundant field rodent, the gerbil, *Tatera indica*. The domestic rat acts as a liaison agent between wild rodents and man, with the flea *Ceratophyllus punjabensis* Jordan and Rothschild being abundant on wild and commensal rodents, along with *Xenopsylla astia* Rothschild on the latter (Baltazard and Bahmanyar, 1960).

In Java the propagation and persistence of plague are under conditions much as described for rural India. *Rattus exulans* is the predominant wild rodent with high resistance to *P.* (= *Yersinia*) *pestis*, *R. rattus* acting as the liaison rodent between wild rodents and man. *Xenopsylla cheopis* predominates on *R. rattus*, and the flea *Stivalius cognatus* Jordan and Rothschild predominates on rodents in mountain regions but is also found in domestic areas (Baltazard and Bahmanyar, 1960).

There are some interesting characteristics of human plague in the Kurdistan ethnogeographical region (parts of Persia, Iraq, Turkey, Syria), a plague focus considered united with the southwestern portion of the Soviet Union. Commensal rodents are a rarity in much of this region and even appear to be lacking in some village environments. Yet rare human cases are contracted in the field,

apparently from fleas normally biting plague-resistant or susceptible species of gerbils (*Meriones*). Epidemics spreading the disease from man to man are then by way of the human flea, *Pulex irritans* Linnaeus (Baltazard and others, 1960).

Pollitzer (1966) has reviewed the subject of plague and plague control in the Soviet Union. Plague regions in that country have been divided into four general foci: (1) the Caspian focus, a region surrounding the northern part of the Caspian Sea; (2) the Central-Asian focus comprised of plains and mountain areas; (3) the Transcaucasian focus, lying predominantly west of the mid to southern portion of the Caspian Sea; and (4) the Transbaikalian focus, encompassing Mongolia and surrounding areas. These are all campestral foci, as plague never became established in commensal rat populations. The last of six short-lived outbreaks in urban rats occurred in 1921, and all of these urban-centered outbreaks were invariably due to recent importations of infection.

Campestral plague is well established, in fact it was probably from the Transbaikalian focus that the great pandemic of plague originated at the end of the last century. In that outbreak plague started in men engaged in trapping tarabagans (marmots, *Marmota sibirica*) for their highly valued fur. From man the pathogen was transferred to the parasites of commensal rats along trade routes, and resulted in an epidemic in Hong Kong in 1894 that was transported by shipping to many parts of the globe. An epidemic of pneumonic plague in Manchuria, resulting in 60,000 deaths in 1910–11, was also a consequence of trapping tarabagans. Apparently the low body temperature of the tarabagan during hibernation enables this animal to survive infection and thus to maintain plague bacilli from one season to the next. The flea, *Oropsylla silantiewi* (Wagner), and possibly other bloodsucking ectoparasites as well, transmits the infection from animal to animal.

Wherever they occur in sufficient numbers,

the following rodents and fleas seem primarily involved in campestral plague in the Soviet Union, with occasional outbreaks of the disease resulting in man. Marmots (*Marmota sibirica, M. baibacina, M. caudata*) and the fleas *Oropsylla silantiewi* (Wagner), *Rhadinopsylla ventricosa*, and *Citellophilus lebedewi*; ground squirrels or susliks (*Citellus pygmaeus, C. dauricus, C. fulvus*) and the fleas *Citellophilus tesquorum* (Wagner), *Neopsylla setosa* Wagner, *Ctenophthalmus breviatus*, and *C. pollex*; the large gerbil *Rhombomys opimus* and various *Xenopsylla* fleas; the gerbils *Meriones meridianus, M. tamariscinus, M. libycus* and the fleas *Xenopsylla conformis* (Wagner), *Nosopsyllus laeviceps* and some others. Other rodents, particularly mice and hares as well as their fleas, are at times involved.

Attempts at plague control in the Soviet Union have included rodent control by using poisoned baits against wild rodents, and by using similar baits and baits with bacterial pathogens to control commensal rodents.

Murine Typhus (Endemic Typhus, Shop Typhus, Flea Typhus, Rat Typhus). Sporadic cases of typhus in Europe, Australia, and Mexico were suspected as being different from epidemic louse-borne typhus. The agent was found to be different from that of the latter disease, and suspected rodent-flea relationships were confirmed, the disease being called murine typhus to identify it as a natural infection of rats (Mooser, 1932). Upon investigation murine typhus was found in most parts of the world. The causative agent is *Rickettsia mooseri* Monteiro.

The incubation period in man is six to fourteen days. The disease greatly resembles epidemic typhus but is relatively mild with negligible mortality except in persons over fifty; rash is shorter in duration, skin lesions less numerous, involvement of nervous system and kidneys less severe, and serious complications infrequent. In the United States, from 1931–46 approximately 42,000 cases were reported. Since that time there has been a

dramatic reduction in incidence, with only forty-six cases reported in 1961.

The normal biocenose of murine typhus involves rats and the rat flea *Xenopsylla cheopis*. The fleas *Nosopsyllus fasciatus* (Bosc) and *Leptopsylla segnis* (Schönherr) have also been incriminated. Transmission from rat to rat also occurs by way of the rat louse *Polyplax spinulosa* (Burmeister), and the tropical rat mite *Ornithonyssus bacoti* (Hirst) may be similarly involved. In the United States rats on scattered farms are believed to be the most important reservoirs in endemic murine typhus areas, as since 1943 most human cases have occurred in rural regions. In that country the monthly incidence of *Rickettsia mooseri* antibodies in the commensal rats *Rattus norvegicus* and *R. rattus* was strongly correlated with the monthly abundance of the flea *Xenopsylla cheopis*, and showed little relationship to the abundance of *Polyplax spinulosa* and *Ornithonyssus bacoti* (Smith, 1957). Transmission from flea to man is accomplished when infective feces are scratched into the skin; contact of infective flea feces with conjunctiva or mucous membranes is another possible route of infection.

Control of this disease consists of (1) flea reduction by dusting rat runs and harborages with insecticide; (2) rodent control. Once contracted the disease is readily cured with modern antibiotics.

Myxomatosis. Myxomatosis is a virus disease of rabbits that is mechanically transmitted by a variety of bloodsucking arthropods (Fig. 11-19) especially by mosquitoes (see Chapter 11). However, in England there is abundant evidence that fleas play the major role as vectors. The rabbit flea of England, *Spilopsyllus cuniculi* (Dale), is primarily involved, readily transferring between rabbits (*Oryctolagus*) but seldom feeding on hares (*Lepus*) (Mead-Briggs, 1964). This species of flea has become specifically adapted to hormonal changes in rabbit does, undergoing ovarian maturation only on pregnant does, or experimentally in response to topically applied hydrocortisone or related hormones (Rothschild and Ford, 1964). In central England, where myxomatosis caused a scarcity of rabbits, *S. cuniculi* was found in a much higher than normal ratio on hares, suggesting that the scarcity of rabbits and increase in hares caused a change in the host relationships of the flea (Rothschild and Ford, 1965).

There is no evidence that the myxoma virus multiplies in the flea, or harms the flea directly, but fleas feeding on sick rabbits undergo maturation of the ovaries and have internal organs often characteristic of a spent or aged flea. Rothschild (1965) feels this condition may be due to a sudden rise in the temperature of affected rabbits, which causes increased defecation and feeding of fleas; the increased passage of blood through the flea automatically increases the amount of corticosteroid hormones ingested. Virus survival on the fleas in southern England, under starvation conditions in artificial burrows, was demonstrated to occur for as long as 105 days (Chapple and Lewis, 1965).

Fleas as Intermediate Hosts of Cestodes. Although Melnikoff in 1867 showed that the biting louse of the dog, *Trichodectes canis* De Geer, serves as an intermediate host of the double-pored dog tapeworm, *Dipylidium caninum* (Linnaeus), it has since been shown by other workers that fleas play a more important role in the transmission of this helminth, particularly the cat and the dog flea, *Ctenocephalides felis* and *C. canis*. This tapeworm normally affects dogs, cats, and certain wild carnivores, but also occurs in man, particularly in young children. The embryonated eggs of the tapeworm are discharged in the fecal material of the host and are ingested by the larval flea, and develop into cysticercoids in the body cavity of the insect. Thus the mature flea, which would not be able to ingest the tapeworm eggs itself, is infected, and when ingested by a cat or dog or human, the cysticercoids are liberated and develop into tapeworms in the animal's digestive tract.

A common tapeworm of rats and mice, *Hymenolepis diminuta* (Rudolphi), has numerous intermediate arthropod hosts, among them *Nosopsyllus fasciatus* and *Xenopsylla cheopis*. A related rodent tapeworm, *H. nana* Siebold, has among its intermediate hosts the fleas *X. cheopis, Ctenocephalides canis*, and *Pulex irritans*. Both cestodes frequently infest children.

Damage by Permanently Attached Fleas. Among the permanently attached fleas are included the chigoe flea of man, and the stick-tight flea of poultry.

The chigoe or sand flea, *Tunga penetrans*, is a tiny "burrowing" species of the tropical and subtropical regions of North and South America, also of the West Indies and Africa (Fig. 17-5). According to Hoeppli (1963), the first reference to the chigoe was from tropical America in 1526, and it was reported from Africa in 1732. Very probably *T. penetrans* was introduced in the seventeenth century from tropical America into Africa. It was reintroduced in 1872 by a British ship from Rio de Janeiro to Angola, followed by a rapid spread along the west coast, and dissemination by expeditions across the tropical part of the whole African continent. Indian laborers returning to their homeland from Africa carried the parasite to Bombay and later to Karachi.

The chigoe is reddish brown and measures about 1 mm in length, though the impregnated female may become as large as a small pea. The adult fleas are intermittent feeders but adhere closely to the host. The female when impregnated "burrows" into the skin of the host, frequently between the toes or under the toe nails and into the soles of the feet, causing nodular swellings that ulcerate. Actually, as Jellison (1959) has pointed out, there is no obvious way for the insect to burrow; "somehow the skin envelops the flea except for a small sinus with an external opening through which eggs and dejecta are passed." The larvae that emerge in a few days from the eggs are typical flea larvae. Some hatch within the sinus; these usually drop to the ground to develop under conditions similar to those having hatched on the ground. Faust and Maxwell (1930) do report a case in which the eggs had hatched in or on the body around the sites of the burrows of the gravid females, and the larvae had thrived and grown there. The larval period under favorable conditions probably requires not more than ten to fourteen days, and the cocoon or pupal period about the same time.

The chigoes commonly attack bare feet, infesting the skin between the toes and soles, but no part of the body is exempt from attack. The attached female flea causes extreme irritation; the area surrounding it becomes charged with pus, producing a distinct elevation. The ulcerations due to the presence of numerous chigoes become confluent. Wellman (personal communication to Herms) attributes the commonly observed autoamputation of toes of natives in Angola to the work of the chigoes and attendant secondary infection. Tetanus and gangrene frequently result, and the latter may require amputation of affected structures.

Where the chigoe flea occurs, walking in bare feet should be avoided. Parts of the body attacked by the fleas should receive immediate attention. The insect can be removed quite easily by means of a sterile needle or very fine-pointed knife blade. The wounds caused by this treatment must be carefully dressed to heal.

The flea, *Echidnophaga gallinacea*, also known as the "sticktight," is a serious poultry pest in many parts of subtropical America. It commonly attacks poultry of all kinds, also cats, dogs, rabbits, horses, and man.

Before copulation, both sexes are active, hopping about much as do other species of fleas. Shortly after feeding, the females attach themselves firmly to the skin of the host and copulation takes place. The females deposit eggs in the ulcers that have been produced by the infestation. Eggs are also deposited in the dust or dry droppings of poultry or in old nests, etc. The usual incubation period according to Parman (1923) is six to eight days at a temperature average of 76° F (approximately 25° C). If the eggs are deposited in the ulcer, the larvae crawl out and drop to the ground, where they grow rapidly if conditions are favorable and feed on nitrogenous matter, dry droppings, and so forth. The full-grown larva, which is not unlike other flea larvae, is about 4 mm in length, reaching this stage in about two weeks. The larva then spins a cocoon, pupates, and in about two weeks emerges as a fully developed flea. The life history requires thirty to sixty days.

Sticktight fleas are most likely to attack the skin around the eyes, the wattles and comb, and the anus or other bare spots (Fig. 17-21). The ulceration and wartlike elevations around the eyes often become so aggravated that blindness occurs, the host is unable to find its food, and death results. Because this flea also lives on dogs, cats, rats, quail, blackbirds, and sparrows, suitable precautions should be taken to exclude these animals from chicken pens.

Fig. 17-12 Sticktight fleas, *Echidnophaga gallinacea*, clustered on the head of a young chicken. (After Suter.)

18

TICKS AND TICK-BORNE DISEASES

CLASS ARACHNIDA, ORDER ACARINA, SUPERFAMILY IXODOIDEA

Most species of vertebrate animals higher than fishes are subject to attack by ticks, but particularly vulnerable are mammals, whose warmth and odor are highly attractive to these parasites. The food of both sexes of adults and all active immature stages is blood, other tissue fluids, and cellular debris. Hunters have long observed heavy infestations on the bodies of wild animals. Stockmen suffer enormous losses due to ticks on cattle, horses, and other stock; poultry is often severely parasitized. Hunter and Hooker (1907) reported that as many as 200 pounds of blood may be withdrawn from a large host animal by ticks in a single season.

Woodward and Turner (1915), using the common cattle tick, *Boophilus annulatus* (Say), found that infested cows under experimental conditions gave only 65.8 per cent as much milk as tick-free cows. Furthermore, tick-free cows gained 6.1 per cent in body weight during the time of the experiment, while the infested animals gained but 3.6 per cent. Beef cattle, rather than dairy animals, are probably mainly affected, the losses for Australia being recently calculated as $25 million annually. Death due to exsanguination by ticks is believed possible. Jellison and Kohls (1938) found that an adult female *Dermacentor andersoni* Stiles withdrew from 1.7 to 2 gm of blood and fluids in the act of engorgement, and they concluded that "tick-host anemia is not only an experimental disease but occurs with some frequency in nature, and may be the immediate cause of death in animals." During the months of

October to March, 1935–36, one riding academy in Alameda County, California, lost eighty-three horses, whose deaths were reported to be due to loss of blood (exsanguination) through huge infestations of *Dermacentor albipictus* (Packard). Autopsies, blood examinations, and inoculation of blood into other horses produced no symptoms characteristic of pathogens. All exsanguination losses are probably accompanied by some toxicosis.

Although ticks were referred to as "disgusting parasitic animals" by Aristotle in the fourth century B.C., the orderly classification of these parasites dates from the publications of Linnaeus in 1746 (*Fauna Suecica*), where they were placed among the Acari in the genus *Acarus* specifically, according to Nuttall (Monograph of the Ixodoidae, Cambridge University Press, May, 1911). The scientific nomenclature of ticks began in 1804 when Latreille set up eleven genera; in 1844 Koch separated the ticks from the Acari, which included both ticks and mites. In 1896 Neumann placed the ticks in the order Acarina and divided them into two subfamilies, namely, (1) Argasinae and (2) Ixodinae. Finally, in 1901, Salmon and Stiles raised the two subfamilies of Neumann to family rank and placed them in the superfamily Ixodoidae established by Banks in 1894. An alternative recent higher classification is provided by Baker and Wharton (1952). Among more recent publications on the general biology of ticks, that of Arthur (1962) includes their relation to disease, and Theiler (1964) discusses ecogeographical aspects of their distribution.

There are many disorders and diseases of man and animals traceable to ticks; among these are (1) *dermatosis*, inflammation, itching, swelling, and ulcerations at the site of the bite, also skin ulceration and lesions resulting from improper or partial removal of tick mouth parts. Breaking of the skin also predisposes the host to myiasis and secondary bacterial infections; (2) *envenomization*, inoculation of toxic salivary fluids at the site of the bite often resulting in severe systemic disturbances; (3)

exsanguination, a serious matter when an animal is badly infested with ticks, resulting in a secondary anemia and possibly death; (4) *tick paralysis*, an acute ascending, flaccid type of paralysis, often fatal, caused directly by the bite of certain species of ticks, affecting humans and sheep, cattle, horses, pigs, and dogs; (5) *otoacariasis*, invasion of the auditory canal by ticks; (6) *infections* transmitted by ticks including *piroplasmoses* (*babesioses*), e.g., Texas cattle fever; *rickettsioses*, e.g., Rocky Mountain spotted fever; *viroses*, e.g., Colorado tick fever; and *spirochetoses*, e.g., tick-borne relapsing fevers; ticks may also assist in the spread of *tularemia*.

High Vector Potential of Ticks. Some of the factors that account for the potency of ticks in the spread of diseases of man and animals are the following: they are first of all (1) *persistent bloodsuckers*—they *attach firmly* while feeding and cannot be dislodged easily; their (2) *slow feeding* permits wide dispersion while attached to a host; the later stages (nymphs and adults) are (3) *highly sclerotized*, hence very resistant to environmental stresses; they are (4) *relatively free from natural enemies*; most species have a (5) *wide host range*, thus insuring a relatively certain source of blood. Cooley (1932) reported twenty-eight species of hosts for the adult *Dermacentor andersoni* Stiles, and thirty-two for the immature stages; over 100 species of hosts could be listed for *Ixodes persulcatus* Schulze. Other factors adding to the vector potential of ticks are: (6) *longevity*—the life span of some argasid species may be fourteen years or more; (7) *transovarian transmission* of pathogens in many species, passing infectivity on to the next generation; (8) the *reproductive potential* of ticks is great, as some species may deposit as many as 18,000 eggs, and parthenogenesis sometimes occurs.

Ticks are generally parasites of wild animals in nature; they parasitize man and his domesticated mammals fortuitously, though the latter may be heavily attacked due to conditions provided by man. Certain tick-borne infections in wild animals have persisted for so long that a host-parasite relationship has developed resulting in a benign (nonpathogenic) infection; when man intervenes as a fortuitous host he may receive a severe infection. Diseases limited to animals, i.e., not transmissible to man, also possess similar tick-host relationships. Thus, the causal agent of bovine anaplasmosis is harbored by wild deer without causing apparent symptoms, but when it is transmitted to domestic cattle by ticks a severe disease results.

Characteristics of Ticks. Ticks are easily distinguished from insects, as the body is not definitely divided; a strong fusion of the thorax and abdomen produces a saclike leathery appearance. A distinct head is lacking, but the mouth parts, together with the *basis capituli* in many species, form a structure known as the *capitulum*. Like most other Arachnida the mature ticks and nymphs have four pairs of legs; the larvae three pairs.

All adult and nymphal ticks have a pair of spiracles, situated lateroventrally on the abdomen, one on each side near the third and fourth coxae. In ixodids, the dorsum of the adult male is largely or wholly covered by a plate called the *scutum*. In immature ticks and females, the scutum covers only the anterior part of the dorsum, behind the capitulum. The scutum is *ornate* if it has a pattern of gray or white imposed upon a dark background, *inornate* without such a pattern. A pair of simple eyes may be located on the lateral margins or submargins of the scutum in hard ticks, or along the submargins in certain soft ticks. Many species of ticks are eyeless. In certain hard ticks more or less rectangular areas, separated from adjacent ones by grooves, along the posterior submarginal area of the dorsum are known as *festoons*. Festoons may be present in both sexes, though not evident in engorged females. Ventrally (Fig. 18-1), an *anal* groove may set off a plate or area on which the anus is located; the anal groove may be evident only in front of the anus, or it may occur only beside and behind the anus. Other

plates of the ventral surface may be of some taxonomic significance, such as *adanal plates* (to each side of the anal plate) and *accessory plates* (anterior to the adanal plates).

Ticks vary considerably in size according to species, but even fully engorged females rarely exceed 20 mm in length. Females can be greatly distended and, when fully engorged, are beanlike in form.

The mechanism for penetration and anchoring of the mouthparts is discussed in Chapter 3. One remarkable feature, considering the extensive laceration of tissues during the act of feeding, is that in most cases the bite is not felt. Once it has attached, great care should be exercised in removing a tick, for the mouth parts are easily left embedded in the flesh, serving as an irritant and source of secondary infection. Concluding a study of many materials singly and in combination, Knight and Bryan (1963) found 0.6 per cent pyrethrins in methyl benzoate and camphorated phenol greatly reduced the mean force required for detachment of embedded lone star ticks. They suggest application at least twenty minutes before detachment, and the use of a slow and steadily increasing pulling force.

The length of time a tick remains attached in the act of uninterrupted feeding depends on the family, the species, whether mating has taken place, and the stage of development. As a rule ixodid ticks stay attached to a host for a prolonged time; many argasids are parasites associated with the lairs, roosts, or dens of their hosts, attaching only briefly to the host and remaining the remainder of the time in or near its habitation. As examples, nymphs and adults of the ixodid cattle tick *Boophilus annulatus* (Say), feed six to eight days to become fully engorged; the common argasid poultry tick, *Argas persicus* (Oken), feeds nightly and intermittently. However, nymphs of the spinose ear tick, *Otobius megnini* (Dugès), an argasid, are known to feed for months. Both male and female ticks suck blood; with great distention in female Ixodidae only, but in both sexes in Argasidae.

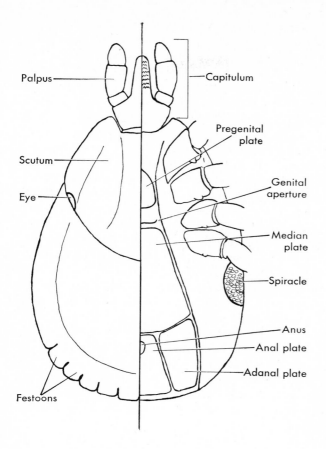

Palpus

Capitulum

Pregenital plate

Scutum

Genital aperture

Eye

Median plate

Spiracle

Anus

Anal plate

Adanal plate

Festoons

Fig. 18-1 Diagrammatic illustration of the anatomy of an ixodid tick. (*Left*) Dorsal view; (*right*) ventral view. (Redrawn and adapted as a composite of two illustrations from Gregson, 1956.)

Life History. Under natural conditions a few species of ticks show a rather marked host specificity, e.g., *Boophilus annulatus* on cattle, and *Dermacentor parumapertus* Neumann on jack rabbits. However, other species have a fairly wide range of hosts. The life histories of ticks vary among the many species; hence, it is quite impossible to generalize, except that it may be said all species pass through four stages (*egg, larva, nymph*, and *adult*) in from six weeks to three years. Depending on the timing of infestation, the Rocky Mountain wood tick, *Dermacentor andersoni* Stiles, normally requires one or two years to complete its life history. Fully engorged female ticks usually deposit their eggs on the ground, the number varying from 100 in some species to 18,000 in others. The larvae are hexapod

(six-legged) and remain in this condition until after the first molt. The nymph emerging from the first molt has four pairs of legs and remains in this stage until transformation to the sexually mature form, or adult. Ixodid ticks have only one nymphal stage, but there may be as many as five nymphal molts in argasids. In studying three species of argasids it was found that a blood meal one third of normal size resulted in molting and the presence of additional instars, resulting in adults with abnormal chaetotaxy (Balashov, 1963). Copulation takes place after the last molt when the females engorge and then deposit eggs. In the majority of species the ticks drop off the host animal to molt, but in several species, notably *Dermacentor albipictus* (Packard) and those of the genus *Boophilus*, the molting takes place on the host. In *Boophilus* there may be two or possibly three generations per year under favorable climatic conditions.

Tick eggs may withstand rather harsh environmental conditions, though they generally do not bear desiccation well. The eggs are coated with a waxy secretion from a structure called Gene's organ (Lees and Beament, 1948). According to Theiler (1964) there are records of tick eggs hatching after as long as eighty days of submersion, and even adults have been submerged three weeks without ill effects. Larval ticks emerging from eggs on the ground commonly climb up grasses and other low vegetation to come within easy reach of grazing or passing animals. The height of larval ascent varies markedly with species.

Upon reaching the body of the host the tick follows a sequence of feeding and molting until maturity is reached. When this is completed on one animal, as in the case of *Boophilus annulatus* (Say), the species is said to be a *one-host tick*. When two host animals are involved, as with the African red tick, *Rhipicephalus evertsi* Neumann, the species is said to be a *two-host tick*. The larva of this two-host species hatches on the ground like other ticks, then proceeds to attach itself to the inner surface of the ear of the host animal where it becomes fully engorged and molts. The nymph engorges and drops off to molt, after which the adult tick emerges and must now find a second host upon which it engorges and then drops to the ground, where the female lays her eggs. When a tick requires three different hosts to complete its cycle, it is called a *three-host tick*, as for example, *Dermacentor andersoni* Stiles, the Rocky Mountain wood tick. In this species the larva engorges on smaller mammals, such as ground squirrels, after which the larva drops to the ground to molt. The nymph also feeds on one of the smaller mammals, after which it drops to the ground, molts, and becomes adult. It once more finds a host (usually one of the larger animals or sometimes man) upon which it

feeds, then drops to the ground where the female lays eggs. In ticks such as the argasid *Ornithodoros hermsi* Wheeler, Herms, and Meyer, of California and other western states, several individual host animals are utilized; such species are known as *many-host ticks*. There are usually five molts in this species, each completed off the host; hence, at least five host animals are needed to complete the cycle. Moreover, the adult may feed intermittently, consequently attacking additional hosts. Quite naturally the variety of hosts utilized by a tick species may be of great importance in determining its potential sources of pathogens, and its opportunities for transmission.

Longevity. The longevity and hardiness of ticks are truly remarkable, a matter not to be overlooked in applying control measures or in considering the persistence of tick-transmitted diseases. Particularly noteworthy have been observations on argasids, with longevity under starvation conditions for as long as sixteen years in some species (Chapter 4). Gregson (1949) has recorded an adult life span of seven years for the ixodid tick *Ixodes texanus* Banks, and a total life cycle of more than twenty-one years.

Classification. The ticks are considered by some authors to form a separate suborder of Acarina, the Ixodides; and by others to form, along with a number of mite families, the suborder Mesostigmata. They constitute the superfamily Ixodoidea, which includes well over 500 species, and which is divided into two major families. A third family, Nuttalliellidae, is morphologically intermediate and contains a single rare African species, *Nuttalliella namaqua* Bedford. The two major families may be readily separated by Table 18-1 and Figure 18-2. They are the (1) *Ixodidae* also known as the hard-bodied ticks; scutate ticks with a terminal capitulum; sexual dimorphism obvious; scutum of males covering the dorsum, males incapable of great distention; scutum of females a small shield immediately behind the capitulum; females capable of enormous

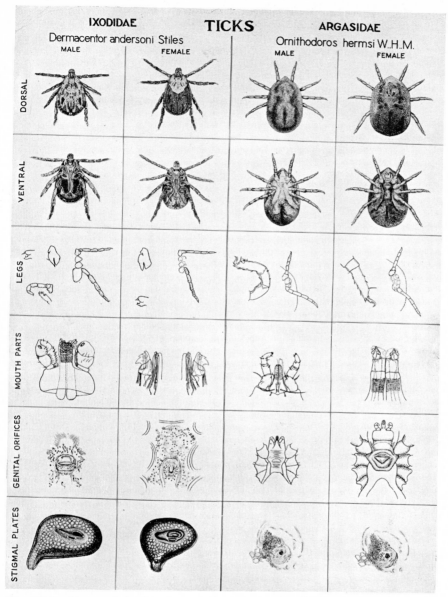

Fig. 18-2 Structural details of the two common families of ticks, Ixodidae and Argasidae.

distention. (2) *Argasidae*, also known as the soft-bodied ticks, include ticks without a scutum (nonscutate); sexual dimorphism not obvious; capitulum ventral and palpi leglike; eyes when present are lateral and on the supra-coxal folds; spiracles very small. The student will find papers by Bequaert (1946), Cooley (1938, 1946), Cooley and Kohls (1944a, b, 1945), Gregson (1956), and Hoogstraal (1956) very useful for the classification of ticks.

TABLE 18-1 Separation of the Two Families of the Ixodidae (Adapted from Nuttall)

	ARGASIDAE	IXODIDAE
Sexual dimorphism	Slight	Marked
Capitulum	Ventral	Anterior
Base	No porose areas	Porose areas in females
Palpi	Leglike, with subequal segments	Relatively rigid, of very varied form
Body		
Scutum	Absent	Present
Festoons	Absent	Generally present
Eyes (when present)	Lateral on supracoxal folds	Dorsal on the sides of the scutum
Legs		
Coxae	Unarmed	Generally armed with spurs
Tarsi	Without ventral spurs	Generally armed with one or two ventral spurs
Pulvilli	Absent or rudimentary	Always present

FAMILY IXODIDAE
(HARD-BODIED TICKS)

The Family Ixodidae. Nuttal and Warburton (1908) include nine genera in the family Ixodidae, namely, *Ixodes, Haemaphysalis, Dermacentor, Rhipicentor, Rhipicephalus, Margaropus, Boophilus, Hyalomma,* and *Amblyomma*. Two other genera of some importance that are not recognized are *Aponomma* and *Anocentor* (=*Otocentor*). Other genera proposed in recent years are either of no medical or veterinary importance or have not been generally accepted. The following key (see also Fig. 18-3) will separate the above genera.

KEY TO THE GENERA OF IXODID TICKS OF MEDICAL IMPORTANCE

1. Eyes absent.........................2
   Eyes present 4
2. Anal groove surrounding the anus in front; festoons absent; inornate...*Ixodes*
   Anal groove not surrounding the anus in front; festoons present; ornate or inornate
  3
3. Ornate or inornate tropical or subtropical ticks, occurring mostly on reptiles; second palpal segment much longer than wide...
   ....*Aponomma*
   Inornate ticks; second palpal segment about as long as wide.....*Haemaphysalis*

4. Mouth parts much longer than the basis capituli; second palpal segment much longer than wide....................5
   Mouth parts about as long as the basis capituli; second palpal segment as long as wide 6
5. Eyes submarginal; adanal plates present in the males; scutum inornate..........
   ....*Hyalomma*
   Eyes marginal; adanal plates absent in the male (though small, ventral sclerotized plates may occur close to the festoons); scutum usually ornate......*Amblyomma*
6. Festoons absent....................7
   Festoons present....................8
7. Male with a preanal plate that is continued backward as two prongs, one on each side of the anus; no adanal or accessory plates; segments of fourth leg greatly swollen....
   ....*Margaropus*
   Male without preanal plate but with adanal and accessory plates; segments of fourth leg not greatly swollen...*Boophilus*
8. Usually ornate; ventral plates absent in both sexes ....*Dermacentor*
   Usually inornate; ventral plates present or absent 9
9. Ventral plates present in the male.......
   ....*Rhipicephalus*
   Ventral plates absent in both sexes.....10
10. Basis capituli hexagonal dorsally; spurs on coxa IV of male very long..*Rhipicentor*
    Basis capituli rectangular dorsally; spur on coxa IV ....*Anocentor*

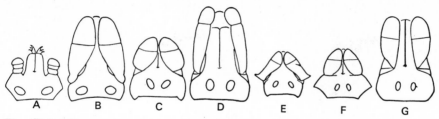

Fig. 18-3 Characteristic capituli of several genera of ixodid ticks. *A. Boophilus. B. Ixodes. C. Dermacentor. D. Amblyomma. E. Haemaphysalis. F. Rhipicephalus. G. Hyalomma.* (After Cooley.)

Genus Ixodes. The genus *Ixodes* is worldwide in its distribution. About forty North American species are recognized. It is clearly separated from all other genera of the family Ixodidae by the anal groove surrounding the anus in front (Prostriata). Eyes and festoons are absent; coxae either unarmed, trenchant, spurred, or bifid; tarsi without spurs; sexual dimorphism pronounced, especially with regard to the capitulum; venter of male covered by nonsalient plates; one pregenital, one median, one anal, two adanal, and sometimes two epimeral plates.

In Europe *Ixodes ricinus* (Linnaeus) and *I. persulcatus* Schulze are noted for their role in the transmission of viruses affecting man, and protozoa causing bovine piroplasmosis. The literature on these two species is widely scattered and conflicting, and a review by Arthur (1966) is the primary source for this account. Both species are many-host ticks utilizing an extraordinary range of hosts that includes birds, small rodents, insectivores, and intermediate-sized and large mammals. *Ixodes ricinus*, the European castor bean tick, is more western in distribution, extending eastward in places to about 55° longitude; westward along the westward margins of the British Isles and Norway to about 65° N latitude; southward to about 35° N latitude in Iran through the mountains to Turkey, Bulgaria, Italy, and the Pyrenees. *Ixodes persulcatus* Schulze is more Eurasian in distribution below 65° N to as far south as the island of Kyushu, Japan; westward into north Germany. Of these two species *I. persulcatus* is more

tolerant of temperature extremes and is more cold hardy. Where the two species overlap there are microclimatic conditions separating their distribution; *I. ricinus* occurs mainly in cut-over, secondary, small-leaved forests of alder, aspen, and birch intermingled with shrubby undergrowth and pastures, *I. persulcatus* is associated with small-leaved forests near primary coniferous forests, such as spruce-basswood combinations. This condition is commonly referred to as *taiga*, and *I. persulcatus* is known as the taiga tick.

An American species close to these European *Ixodes* is *Ixodes scapularis* Say (Fig 18-4) the black-legged tick, widespread in the southeastern United States and along the East Coast. It congregates along paths, trails, and roadways and may inflict a painful bite on man. *Ixodes pacificus* Cooley and Kohls (Fig. 18-5) is a common tick on deer in California but flourishes on cattle as well. It bites human beings freely and often causes severe disturbances.

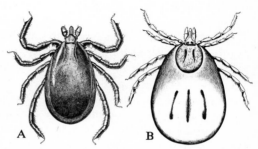

Fig. 18-4 *Ixodes scapularis.* A. Male. B. Engorged female (not to same scale). (U.S.D.A. illustration.)

Fig. 18-5 A common deer and cattle tick of the Pacific coast, *Ixodes pacificus;* (*left*) female; (*right*) male. × 3.5.

Severe disturbance may be characteristic of the bite of many *Ixodes* species. In Israel a case involving a four-year-old girl included fever, vomiting, and severe local pain caused by the attachment of a female of *I. redikorzevi* Olen to the neck; symptoms disappeared rapidly after the tick fell off naturally (Boger, *et al.*, 1964).

Genus Dermacentor. Ticks of the genus *Dermacentor* are ornate ticks with eyes; eleven festoons; palpi short, broad, or moderate; basis capituli rectangular dorsally. In some species coxae from I to IV of the male increase progressively in size, in all species coxa IV is much the largest; the male shows no ventral plates or shield. Coxa I is bifid in both sexes. The spiracles are suboval or comma-shaped. The genus includes about twenty species.

Dermacentor variabilis (Say), the American dog tick, is the principal if not only, vector of Rocky Mountain spotted fever in the central and eastern portion of the United States (Fig. 18-6). It is also an important vector of tularemia. It may cause canine paralysis and is a common pest of dogs, which are preferred hosts of adult ticks of this species; it also freely attacks horses and other animals, including man. Immature stages feed almost exclusively on small rodents with a decided preference for meadow mice [*Microtus pennsylvanicus pennsylvanicus* (Ord) in the Atlantic states] (Sonenshine and Atwood, 1967). A widely distributed North American species,

commonly referred to as the "American dog tick," it commonly congregates along paths and roadways where man is apt to be attacked (Smith, Cole, and Gouck, 1946). This tick has shown an increasing distribution in Nova Scotia, Canada, being present in considerable numbers in the western region (Hall and McKiel, 1961).

The fully engorged females drop from the host and in four to ten days lay 4,000 to 6,500 eggs on the ground. Incubation period during summer is about thirty-five days; however, temperature influences this stage greatly. Larvae remain on the ground or low-growing vegetation while awaiting a host, usually a field mouse. Larval engorgement period is from three to twelve days (average about four days), after which larvae drop to the ground and molt in about a week, although this period is often greatly prolonged. Nymphs engorge on a host (usually a mouse, *Microtus* or *Peromyscus*) three to eleven days (average about six days) and again drop to the ground and molt in from three weeks to several months. Unfed adults may live more than two years; however, the adults usually soon attack dogs and other large host animals. Females engorge in six to thirteen days. Mating occurs on the host as the attached female feeds. Like unengorged adults, immature stages have remarkable longevity in the absence of suitable hosts, which may prolong the life history two or more years, although under favorable conditions the life cycle from egg to adult may require no more than three months.

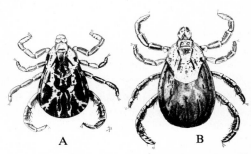

A   B

Fig. 18-6 *Dermacentor variabilis. A.* Male. *B.* Female. (U.S.D.A. illustration.)

In studying a Rocky Mountain spotted fever area of high incidence in the state of Virginia, United States, Sonenshine, *et al.* (1966), attributed bimodal seasonal larval activity curves of this tick to a spring larval population consisting of survivors from the previous season, and late summer larvae emerging from eggs of that spring and summer. Activity of larvae and adults in spring was found when a minimum daily average solar radiation was reached or exceeded (Atwood and Sonenshine, 1967).

Dermacentor andersoni Stiles, the Rocky Mountain wood tick, is widely distributed and very common throughout western North America from British Columbia near 53° N and eastward to 105° in Saskatchewan (Wilkinson, 1967) and North Dakota southward to New Mexico, Arizona, and California. "It is most abundant in regions or localities where the predominating vegetation is low, brushy, and more or less open, i.e., in areas where there is good protection for small mammalian hosts of the larvae and nymphs with sufficient forage to attract the large hosts (either wild or domestic) of the adult ticks. It is relatively scarce in heavily timbered areas or country of a strictly grassland prairie type" (Parker, *et al.*, 1937).

This three-host species is illustrated in Figure 18-7. Adults feed mostly on large animals, such as horses, cattle, sheep, deer, bear, and coyote; larvae and nymphs feed on small mammals such as rabbits, ground squirrels, pine squirrels, woodchucks, and chipmunks; all three stages may feed on intermediate-sized animals such as jack rabbits and porcupines.

There is some evidence that isolation, such as is provided by the Rocky Mountains, has separated out strains of this tick. Differences in size and color have been noted between populations from Alberta and British Columbia, Canada. Wilkinson and Lawson (1965) note further behavioral differences in that *D. andersoni* of Alberta attach on cattle to the brisket, undersurface, and tail, and questing adults concentrate in shrubby areas near water courses; in British Columbia cattle are almost exclusively infested on the head, withers, and back, and adults are concentrated on hillsides, often around rock outcrops. Also the incidence of tick paralysis in unsprayed cows is higher in British Columbia than Alberta.

The life cycle of the Rocky Mountain wood tick is fully described by Cooley (1932), and has been further detailed by Wilkinson (1967, and 1968 in press). Copulation occurs on the host, and the fully fed and greatly distended female drops to the ground. After a preoviposition period of about a week, egg-laying continues for about three weeks. If undisturbed, a large mass averaging some 6,400 eggs piles up ahead of the female. The eggs incubate about thirty-five days, when the larvae emerge, find suitable hosts, feed for three to five days, drop off and molt in six to twenty-one days, then emerge as nymphs with four pairs of legs.

Nymphs that find a host will feed, molt, and

A   B

Fig. 18-7 The Rocky Mountain spotted fever tick. *Dermacentor andersoni.* A. Male. *B.* Unengorged female. × 3.5.

overwinter as adults, a one-year life cycle being quite common where rodents are plentiful. If they do not feed, nymphs hibernate, then seek hosts the next spring to which they attach for feeding over a period of four to nine days. Thus a bimodal nymphal feeding period can be observed in one season, with spring-feeding nymphs on the two-year cycle and late summer nymphs on the one-year cycle. Fully engorged nymphs drop to the ground, molt in twelve to sixteen days or more, and transform into adults. The "normal cycle" can therefore be either one or two years. Wilkinson (personal communication to Harwood) suspects a three-year cycle may exist at high altitudes and at the northern limits of this tick's range. Larvae feed throughout the summer, and adults commonly disappear by about July 1, but nymphs continue in diminishing numbers until late summer. Since man is usually bitten only by adult ticks, danger from this source exists from early spring to about July 1, or well into August at high elevations.

Like other species of ticks, *Dermacentor andersoni* is remarkably resistant to starvation. Hunter and Bishopp (1911) report that all unfed larval ticks hatching from a mass of eggs usually die within one month after the first eggs hatch if food is not available. However, they later recorded more than 317 days between the beginning of hatching of the eggs and the death of the last larva. Unfed nymphs have been found to survive about a year and adults collected on vegetation during the spring have survived for 413 days without food. Students concerned with anatomy of this important tick should consult Douglas (1943). The medical and veterinary importance of *D. andersoni* is discussed in connection with specific diseases.

Dermacentor albipictus (Packard), the winter tick (sometimes called elk or horse tick), is widely distributed in North America (Fig. 18-8). It is found in Canada from the east to the west coast, and north to nearly 60° (Wilkinson, 1967). This one-host tick does not

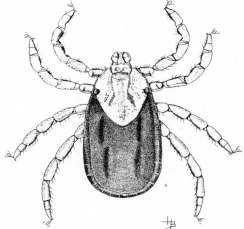

Fig. 18-8 *Dermacentor albipictus,* male. (U.S.D.A. illustration.)

attack during the summer months. The eggs are laid in spring and hatch in three to six weeks. Larvae bunch tightly together, remaining in torpor until the first cold weather in autumn, when they become very active and seek hosts. Molting occurs on the original host animal. Females reach maturity with the final molt and engorge, usually in about six weeks after larvae (seed ticks) attach. Although females drop off the host after final engorgement as do other ticks, egg-laying is delayed until spring, often after several months. In British Columbia, Canada, seed ticks are active from October to April, and fed females occur in late March (Gregson, personal communication to Harwood).

Heavy infestations on horses, moose, elk, or deer may cause their death by draining their vitality (Hearle, 1938). Cattle are seldom attacked (Gregson, 1956). Thomas and Cahn (1932) described a disease of moose, *Alces alces* (Linnaeus), caused by this tick in and adjacent to northeastern Minnesota. Man may be attacked through transfer of the tick by direct contact, as when skinning and dressing elk or deer. At least one case of Rocky Mountain spotted fever seems to have been transmitted by winter ticks under such circumstances, although the question as to how the tick acquired the infection is unsettled (Philip and Kohls, 1952).

Dermacentor occidentalis Marx (Fig. 18-9) is distributed in Oregon and California. Adults of this species have been taken from cow, horse, mule, ass, deer, rabbit, sheep, dog, man; and the immature stages from many species of smaller animals, such as ground squirrel, rabbit, skunk, and field mouse. *D. andersoni* and *D. occidentalis*, although distinct, have been hybridized experimentally.

Genus Anocentor (=*Otocentor*). Inornate ticks, eyes present but obsolescent, with seven festoons, basis capituli rectangular dorsally. No ventral plates present. Coxa I bifid in both sexes. Palpi short, the first and second segments fused. Spiracles oval, without dorsal prolongations. The only known species, *Anocentor nitens* (Neumann), chiefly attacks horses. It is known from Florida, Georgia, and extreme southern Texas to Brazil (Fig. 18-10).

Genus Haemaphysalis. Members of *Haemaphysalis* number about ninety species, of which two are North American; usually small with both sexes similar; inornate and eyeless, with festoons; the second segment of the usually short conical palpus projects laterally beyond the basis capituli forming an acute angle. Spiracles of males are ovoid or comma shaped. Most species parasitize mammals, but some are restricted to birds.

Haemaphysalis leporispalustris (Packard) is widely distributed in the New World from Alaska and Canada to Argentina (Fig. 18-11). Although commonly known as the rabbit tick,

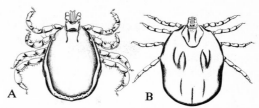

Fig. 18-10 *Anocentor nitens. A.* Male. *B.* Female (not same scale). (U.S.D.A. illustration.)

it has been taken on a number of species of birds and rarely on domestic animals such as horses, cats, and dogs. It rarely bites man but is important in the spread of Rocky Mountain spotted fever and tularemia among wild animals.

Haemaphysalis chordeilis (Packard) occurs commonly on upland game birds in North America, and rarely attacks cattle; of economic importance as a parasite of turkeys and vector of pathogens of wildlife. *Haemaphysalis leachii* (Audouin), the yellow dog tick of Africa, is common in parts of Asia and Africa; usually on wild and domestic carnivores, frequently on small rodents and rarely on cattle; a vector of malignant jaundice in dogs. *Haemaphysalis bispinosa* Neumann causes severe irritation of cattle and other farm animals. In New Zealand a basic population of this tick is maintained on the red deer, *Cervus elaphus*. It has been reported as reproducing by obligatory parthenogenesis in Queensland, Australia (Bremner, 1959), and in Japan it is present as a parthenogenetic and a bisexual strain.

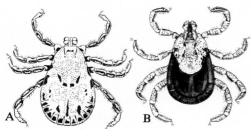

Fig. 18-9 *Dermacentor occidentalis. A.* Male. *B.* Female. (U.S.D.A. illustration.)

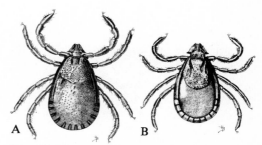

Fig. 18-11 *Haemaphysalis leporispalustris. A.* Male. *B.* Female. (U.S.D.A. illustration.)

Genus Rhipicentor. *Rhipicentor* is a small and relatively unimportant genus; inornate, with eyes and festoons; palpi short with basis capituli hexagonal dorsally and with very prominent lateral angles. Coxa I bifid in both sexes; coxa IV much the largest; no ventral plates or shields; spiracles subtriangular in females or comma-shaped in males. Exemplified by *Rhipicentor bicornis* Nuttall and Warburton.

Genus Rhipicephalus. About fifty species and subspecies make up the genus *Rhipicephalus,* all Old World except for the cosmopolitan brown dog tick and possibly one other introduced species. Usually inornate and with eyes and festoons; palpi short, and basis capituli usually hexagonal dorsally. Coxa I bifid. The male possesses a pair of adanal shields and usually a pair of accessory shields; some males when replete show a caudal protrusion. Spiracles bluntly or elongatedly commashaped.

Rhipicephalus sanguineus (Latreille), the brown dog tick; principal host is undoubtedly the dog, although known to attack numerous other animals, rarely attacks man (Fig. 18-12). Probably this is the most widely distributed of all ticks, inhabiting practically all countries between 50° N and 35° S, including most of the United States and parts of southeastern Canada. It is widely known as a vector of malignant jaundice of dogs and considered important in spreading the rickettsia of boutonneuse fever. It is a vector of Rocky Mountain spotted fever in parts of Mexico. Adults are found most often in the ears and between the toes of dogs, larvae and nymphs in the long hair at the back of the neck. Eggs are deposited in cracks and crevices of the kennel or other quarters frequented by dogs. The ticks have a strong tendency to crawl upward, hence are often hidden in cracks in the roofs of kennels or in the ceilings of porches. The eggs hatch in twenty to thirty days or more, depending on temperature. The life cycle corresponds to that of ixodine three-host ticks. Morel and Vassiliades (1962) conclude that ticks from Africa, including the Mediterranean area, generally identified as this species actually comprise five species separable by morphology, bionomics, and distribution.

Rhipicephalus appendiculatus Neumann is a vector of East Coast fever of cattle in east Africa. Annual rainfall of twenty to twenty-five inches is required for its survival, limiting it to western Kenya and in the highlands below 7,500 feet (Wiley, 1958). *Rhipicephalus evertsi* Neumann, an African red tick, was found on zoo animals in Florida and New York in 1960; it was eradicated from the United States the following year.

Genus Margaropus. Members of the genus *Margaropus* have an obsolete anal groove and no ornamentations or festoons; palpi short, capitulum highly sclerotized and similar in shape to that of *Boophilus.* Coxae conical and unarmed except for a small spine posteriorly on coxa I. Male with median plate prolonged into two long spines projecting beyond the anus on both sides, protruding caudally when replete. Separable from *Boophilus,* which it closely resembles, by greatly enlarged posterior legs and by prolonged median plate.

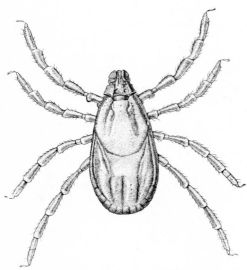

Fig. 18-12 *Rhipicephalus sanguineus,* female. (U.S.D.A. illustration.)

Margaropus winthemi Karsch, the winter horse tick, is restricted in South America to a few highland areas. Cattle and sheep are uncommonly attacked. When engorged the females may easily be mistaken for *Boophilus decoloratus* (Koch) but are distinguished by the dark bands at the joints of the legs. This one-host tick is usually seen only during the winter. It has similar winter habits in the Union of South Africa, attacking horses and cattle; there areas have been set up for its control (Theiler and Salisbury, 1958).

Genus Hyalomma. Usually large ticks; ornamentation, if present, confined to pale bands on legs; eyes convex; festoons more or less coalesced. Palpi are long, segment 2 less than twice as long as segment 3. Males have anal shields and usually also subanal shields. Coxae bifid and spiracles usually comma-shaped.

The genus, consisting of approximately twenty species, is distributed from the Indian subcontinent, through much of U.S.S.R., the Middle East, Arabia, and North Africa, into southern Europe and southern Africa. Adults parasitize all domestic and some wild animals; *H. aegypitum* (Linnaeus) infests tortoises. Larvae and nymphs of some species also attack domestic animals; others parasitize small wild mammals, birds, and/or reptiles. Life cycles are of the one-, two-, or three-host type; often variable within a single species.

Among the hardiest of ticks, many species exist under extreme conditions of cold, heat, and aridity; therefore they are variable in appearance and often difficult to identify. Arthur (1966) refers to problems of synonomy and nomenclature in vectors of this genus, and the distribution of three species that are vectors of equine piroplasmas. The number and variety of mechanical injuries caused and human and animal pathogens harbored and transmitted are exceptionally great. In Soviet Central Asia adults of *Hyalomma asiaticum* Schulze and Schlottke may penetrate the skin of Karakul lambs, forming an abscess invaded by fungi of the genus *Nocardia*, associated with so-called polyarthritis (Kusel'tan, 1964). In a study of the movement of ticks on birds migrating between Europe and Asia into Africa, *Hyalomma marginatum rufipes* Koch proved to be the commonest species (Hoogstraal, *et al.*, 1964).

Genus Amblyomma. Generally ornate ticks, with eyes and festoons; about ninety species; palpi long, segment 2 especially so; basis capituli of variable form. Male is without adanal shields, but small ventral plaques occasionally near festoons. Spiracles subtriangular or comma-shaped. *Amblyomma americanum* (Linnaeus) is the "lone star" tick (Fig. 18-13) of the southern United States, with its range extending considerably northward, and southerly into Mexico; wide variety of hosts, including wild and domestic animals, birds, and man (Cooley and Kohls, 1944). Unlike the common species of *Dermacentor*, this three-host tick attacks man in the larval and nymphal, as well as the adult stages; very pestiferous and a vector of Rocky Mountain spotted fever and tularemia.

Amblyomma cajennense (Fabricius) occurs in Texas, Mexico, Central America, the West Indies, and South America (Fig. 18-14). Larvae, nymphs, and adults commonly attack man, domestic, and many other animals. Abundant in a few counties in Texas (Cooley and Kohls, 1944). Considered a vector of Rocky Mountain spotted fever in Mexico, Panama, Colombia, and Brazil.

Genus Boophilus. No festoons or ornamentations, but eyes present; palpi and hypostome

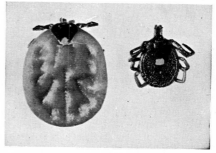

Fig. 18-13 The lone star tick, *Amblyomma americanum*. × 3.5.

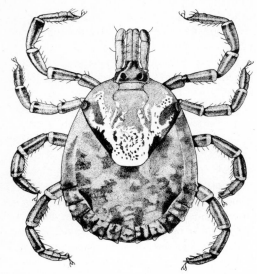

Fig. 18-14 *Amblyomma cajennense,* female. (U.S.D.A. illustration.)

short, compressed, and dorsally and laterally ridged; basis capituli hexagonal dorsally and slightly sclerotized. Coxa I bifid; anal groove obsolete in the female and faintly indicated in the male. Unfed adults small; scutum of females quite small, and spiracles circular or oval in both sexes. Only a few species known, some of uncertain taxonomic validity.

The cattle tick, *Boophilus annulatus* (Say) (Fig. 18-15), of the western hemisphere is normally restricted to the southern United States and Mexico. A similar if not identical species, *B. calcaratus* (Birula), occurs in the Mediterranean basin and the Near East.

Fig. 18-15 The cattle tick, *Boophilus annulatus.* *A.* Engorged female. *B.* Male. × 3.5.

Populations apparently referable to *B. annulatus* also occur in central Africa and certain other parts of the world. Although typically on cattle, this tick occurs at times on deer, horses, donkeys, sheep, goats, and other animals. This species and the tropical cattle tick, *B. microplus* (Canestrini), of similar habits and economic importance, have been eradicated from the United States except for a small, narrow quarantine zone along the Texas-Mexico border. Both species have been comparatively recently introduced to Tahiti where they attack cattle.

Engorged females of *B. annulatus* range in length from 10 to 12 mm, males 3 to 4 mm; body of female about equally rounded posteriorly and anteriorly, with a slight median incurving. Anterior pair of legs positioned well away from the capitulum (in *Dermacentor* close to the capitulum); palpi short and capitulum inconspicuous. The relatively small (about 1 mm long) scutum is solid chestnut brown in color.

Economic Importance. In 1906 it was estimated that the economic effect to the southern United States from all losses directly and indirectly occasioned by the cattle tick amounted to $130,500,000. From 1906–18, through cooperative tick-eradication work, a total of 456,529 square miles of territory was released from quarantine against Texas cattle fever. Subsequent eradication from the United States was accomplished.

Life History of Boophilus annulatus, a One-Host Tick. The life cycle of *Boophilus annulatus* is divided into two phases: (1) the *parasitic phase* during which the tick is attached to the host and that terminates when the mature tick drops to the ground after fertilization; (2) the *nonparasitic phase* when the tick is on the ground. After the mature female tick drops to the ground oviposition usually begins in about seventy-two hours and continues for eight to nine days, but may be greatly prolonged at adverse temperatures. According to Graybill (1911), 1,811–4,089 eggs are usual. The incubation period ranges from nineteen days in the summer to 180 days in early autumn, averaging about forty-three days for April, twenty to twenty-six days from May through August, and forty days for September. The eggs first deposited ordinarily hatch first. The larvae are immediately active, ascending to the top of blades of grass or other objects, where they remain clustered until they can attach to a suitable passing host. Longevity of the newly hatched larvae again varies with temperature, being about 39 days in July and 167 days in October. The entire life cycle may be completed in about forty days under most favorable conditions, usually nearer sixty days under natural conditions. The length of time cattle must be kept on tick-free fields to become free of ticks is about sixty-five days.

Boophilus microplus (Canestrini) is very prevalent in the Caribbean islands and the West Indies, Central America, parts of Mexico and South America, Africa, and the Oriental region (Fig. 18-16). In Australia it is particularly troublesome on cattle. Strict control schemes, including the restriction of stock movements, spraying of cattle and horses, and spelling of pastures may be practiced; and it is hoped to eradicate this tick from Papua and New Guinea (Anderson, 1963). Longest survival period in the field in northern Queensland, from engorged female to the death of all larvae without food was nineteen weeks (Hall and Wilkinson, 1960). Even in drought periods larvae can take up water from a moist

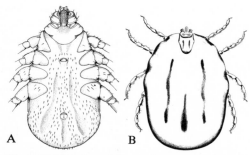

Fig. 18-16 *Boophilus microplus. A.* Male, ventral aspect. *B.* Engorged female, dorsal aspect (not to same scale). (U.S.D.A. illustration.)

atmosphere prior to dawn, and dew can also be drunk directly (Wilkinson and Wilson, 1959). Further survival of low populations is made possible by a fairly high incidence of parthenogenetic reproduction (Stone, 1963).

FAMILY ARGASIDAE (SOFT-BODIED TICKS)

The family Argasidae includes the so-called soft-bodied or nonscutate ticks in which sexual dimorphism is slight. The integument of all stages except larvae is leathery, wrinkled, granulated, mammillated, or with tubercles. The capitulum is either subterminal or distant from the anterior margin and in adults and nymphs lies in a more or less marked depression, the *camerostome*. The anterior part of the integument extending above the capitulum and forming part of the camerostome wall is called the *hood*. The articulations of the palpi of all stages are free; porose areas at the base of the capitulum are absent in both sexes. There are about eighty-five species. Cooley and Kohls (1944) provide an excellent account of this family. They recognize four genera, namely, *Argas, Ornithodoros, Otobius,* and *Antricola,* and give the following key for the separation of the genera.

1. With a definite sutural line separating dorsal and ventral surfaces........*Argas*
   Lacking a definite sutural line separating dorsal and ventral surfaces............2
2. Nymphs with integument beset with spines, hypostome well developed; adults with integument granular, hypostome vestigial......................*Otobius*
   Integument of adults and nymphs essentially alike, mammillated or tuberculated, and lacking spines; hypostome of various forms in nymphs and adults but not vestigial 3
3. Hypostome broad at the base and scooplike (associated with bats)......*Antricola*
   Hypostome of various forms but not scooplike (associated with various classes of animals and including bats).........
   ....*Ornithodoros*

Genus Ornithodoros. In the genus *Ornithodoros* the capitulum is either subterminal or distant from the anterior margin; the hypostome is well developed (Fig. 18-17). In the integument, discs and mammillae are interspersed in a variety of patterns; hood, camerostome, cheeks, and eyes are present or absent; dorsal humps and subapical dorsal protuberances on legs are progressively more prominent in successive nymphal stages. The body is more or less flattened but strongly convex dorsally when distended. The integument pattern is continuous over the sides from dorsal to ventral surfaces (Cooley and Kohls, 1944). The genus includes about sixty species, some twenty of which occur in North America, Central America, and Cuba.

The Ornithodoros moubata Complex. What was originally regarded as a single widespread species of eastern, central, and southern Africa, with several varieties, has been separated on the basis of crossing and morphological studies into four distinct species and a subspecies (Walton, 1962). Because this "species" is the only known vector of relapsing fever spirochetes in those areas, the feeding habits and ecology of each member of the separated species are matters of great importance. Until more current information is available, a discussion of detailed life history does not seem appropriate. Using the previously published information on *O. moubata sensu lato* (Fig. 18-18), it can be stated that adults feed chiefly at night, engorging rapidly. Eggs are

Fig. 18-18 African relapsing fever tick, *Ornithodoros moubata.* × 3.

deposited in batches of 35–340, with a total maximum per female of 1,217, according to Jobling (1925). The larvae are completely quiescent, molting in a few hours within the split eggshell to the first nymphal stage (Davis, 1947). About five feeding periods and molts follow to reach the adult stage. The list of hosts is believed to be very long.

Using Walton's classification (1962), the *moubata* complex is divided into: (1) *Ornithodoros moubata* (Murray), a domestic and sometimes wild species from Angola, Southwest Africa, Bechuanaland, Mozambique, Tanzania; a wild species from Kenya and Rhodesia. This is apparently a species of arid conditions that may be widely distributed in the wild state. (2) *Ornithodoros compactus* Walton, from tortoises in Cape Province, and in an area bounded in the north by the Zambesi river. (3) *Ornithodoros apertus* Walton, a large and rare species from the burrows of porcupines (*Hystrix*) in the Kenya highlands and probably also from Ghana and Bechuanaland. (4) *Ornithodoros porcinus* Walton, with two subspecies. Common and widely distributed in large burrows and animal lairs, and hollow baobab trees (*Adansonia*). The warthog (*Phacochoerus*) is its main host. *O. porcinus* is known from east, central, and southern Africa; also from Madagascar (Uilenberg, 1963). *O. porcinus domesticus* is common in native dwellings at all altitudes in East Africa and northern Mozambique, and overlaps *O. moubata* in southern Tanzania and areas of southwest Africa. *O. p. domesticus* occurs in three races (Walton, 1964) typified by their

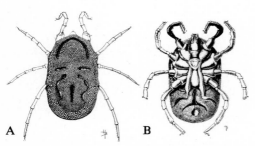

Fig. 18-17 *Ornithodoros turicata,* female. *A.* Dorsal. *B.* Ventral. (U.S.D.A. illustration.)

occurrence (1) in damp cool conditions at high altitude, feeding chiefly on man; (2) in hot climates with long dry periods, feeding on man and domestic fowls; (3) in hot moist climates, feeding almost exclusively on fowls. Typical *O. porcinus* in human dwellings survive starvation at least five years.

Ornithodoros erraticus Lucas occurs in Spain, Portugal, and northern Africa. It is an important vector of the relapsing fever pathogen in northern Africa. This tick is particularly sedentary and adapted to burrows. Because hybridization attempts among eight strains yielded no normally fertile offspring, Chabaud and Durette (1963) suggest further speciation is present.

Ornithodoros talaje (Guérin-Méneville) is a South and Central American (south to Argentina) and Mexican species, occurring also in Florida, Texas, Arizona, Nevada, Kansas, and California. It feeds on wild rodents, also swine, cattle, horses, man, and other animals, and in so doing inflicts a very painful bite. It is a vector of the relapsing fever spirochete *Borrelia* in Guatemala, Panama, and Colombia.

Ornithodoros rudis Karsch (=*venzuelensis* Brumpt) is a Central and South American species. It is considered the most important vector of relapsing fever spirochetes in Panama, Colombia, Venezuela, and Ecuador. Like *O. moubata sensu lato* this species appears to be essentially a parasite of man, although it is known to feed on other animals.

Ornithodoros tholozani (Laboulbène and Mégnin) is a vector of *Borrelia* in central Asia (Hindle, 1935). Several other species in Asia, Africa, and Europe are proven or suspected vectors.

Ornithodoros hermsi Wheeler, Herms, and Meyer, is a rodent parasite and proven vector of relapsing fever. It is widespread in the Rocky Mountain and Pacific Coast states. The life history of this species (Figs. 18-19, 18-20) as described by Herms and Wheeler (1936) is as follows: The very tiny amber-colored eggs are deposited at intervals in batches of 12–140 from May to October and range well over a total number of 200 per female. Under natural conditions, the eggs are deposited in the hiding places of the ticks; in summer cabins the eggs are laid in such corners and crevices as afford protection to the adult ticks.

The incubation period at a temperature of 75° F and 90 per cent humidity ranges from 15 to 21 days. The percentage of larvae hatching seems to grow less in the later egg-laying, decreasing from as high as 95 per cent for the first batches to less than 50 per cent in the last. After several days the larvae are ready to feed, remaining attached to the host for only about twelve to fifteen minutes; in later stages attachment may be for from a half hour to an hour in many cases. The larvae when fully engorged increase as much as three times in size and acquire a bright red color because of the imbibed blood. In this condition these tiny ticks have been referred to as a "strawberry seed insect" by persons living in relapsing fever areas.

Molting takes place about fifteen days after feeding. With this molt the fourth pair of legs appears, and this stage is termed the first nymphal instar. Ticks in the first nymphal stage may feed within a few days after molting, and again a period of eleven to fifteen days elapses before the third molt and the appearance of the second nymphal instar. Then follows the third feeding and again an elapsed period, in this case about ten to thirty-two days, before the fourth molt and the appearance of the third nymphal instar; or even the adult may appear with this molt. Usually a fifth feeding and a fifth molt are necessary before sexual maturity is reached. Egg laying may begin about thirty days after the last molt, fecundation and blood feeding taking place a few days after maturity is reached. The cycle from egg to egg under laboratory conditions requires about four months.

The life cycle may be greatly prolonged in the absence of food because of the ability of these ticks to withstand starvation; thus, larvae may

Fig. 18-19 *Ornithodoros hermsi.* (*Top left*) Mature female; (*top right*) mature male; (*bottom*) female depositing eggs.

live as long as ninety-five days without food; unfed first-stage nymphs may live as long as 154 days; unfed second-stage nymphs may live as long as seventy-nine days; third-stage nymphs, as long as 109 days, and adults well over seven months. Adult ticks have been kept alive in pillboxes with occasional feedings for a period of four years.

The mature female tick (Fig. 18-9) measures 5–6 mm in length by 3–4 mm in width. The male resembles the female closely in general appearance but is slightly smaller. This species is described as ovoid, conically pointed anteriorly, broadly rounded posteriorly. The anterior dorsal portion of the hood is visible from above. Unengorged individuals are of a light sandy color with the black of the intestinal diverticula visible through the integument of the dorsal surface; freshly engorged ticks are of a dull, deep garnet shade with

grayish sheen over the body. Legs and hood are pale yellow. In newly molted forms, the body and legs are lighter but gradually assume the light sandy appearance and darken correspondingly.

Genus Otobius. In adults the integument is granulated; nymphs have spines; sexes similar; capitulum distant from anterior margin in adults and near margin in nymphs. Hood and eyes absent; hypostome vestigial in adults but well developed in nymphs. Cooley and Kohls recognize two species, *O. megnini* (Dugès) and *O. lagophilus* Cooley and Kohls (1944), the latter a parasite on the face of rabbits in the western United States and Canada.

The spinose ear tick, *Otobius megnini* (Dugès), is a widely distributed species, being found in warmer parts of the United States, British **Columbia, South** America, South

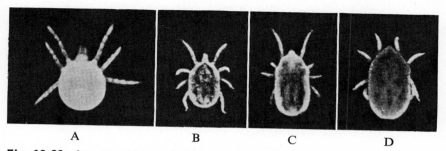

Fig. 18-20 Immature stages of *Ornithodoros hermsi. A.* Larva. *B.* First nymphal stage. *C.* Second nymphal stage. *D.* Third nymphal stage.

Africa, India, and no doubt in other parts of the world (Fig. 18-21). It was introduced to South Africa from the Americas, and has been recorded also from the Congo and Nyasaland, being apparently absent from areas with more than 40 inches annual rainfall (Theiler and Salisbury, 1958). It receives its common name from the fact that the nymph is covered with spines (Fig. 18-22) and that the larvae and nymphs invade the ears of cattle, horses, mules, sheep, cats, dogs, and other domesticated animals, as well as deer, coyotes, rabbits, and other wild animals. In British Columbia this tick has also been found in the ears of mountain sheep, and deaths of cattle are attributed to it (Rich, 1957). There are several records of the occurrence of nymphs in the ears of man. Rather large dark eggs are deposited by this species on the ground; under laboratory conditions at a temperature of about 21° C, the incubation period is eighteen to twenty-three days. In the field newly emerged larvae crawl up weeds and other vegetation, contact suitable host animals, and gradually work their

way to the shoulders, neck, and head, and thence to the deeper inner folds of the outer ear of the host, where they engorge and assume a peculiar saclike form.

After molting in the ear, nymphs attach and remain for long periods of time; this, the second nymphal stage, is the stage in which this species is most easily distinguished from other ticks. Individual ticks remain in the ear for as long as 121 days. On detaching, they drop to the ground and molt again (there are three molts), after which maturity is reached. Copulation takes place within a day or two after final molt, and oviposition occurs in fourteen to forty-two days, with a maximum

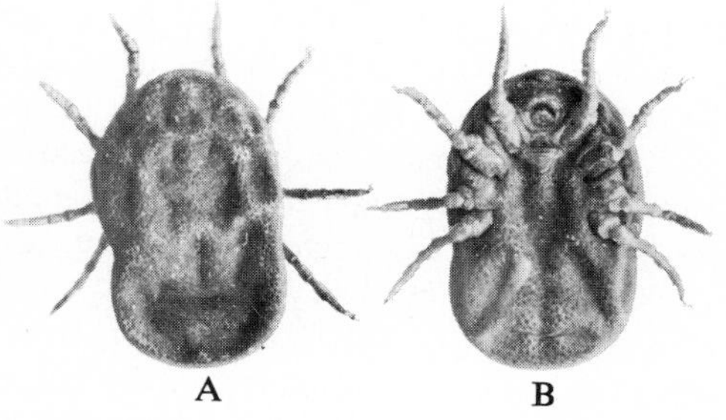

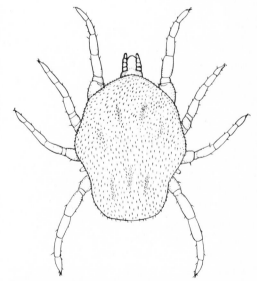

Fig. 18-21 *Otobius megnini,* female. *A.* Dorsal. *B.* Ventral. (U.S.D.A. illustration.)

Fig. 18-22 *Otobius megnini* nymph. (U.S.D.A. illustration.)

oviposition period of 155 days in the individuals observed, during which time 562 eggs are laid. The longevity of unfed larvae at room temperature was nineteen to sixty-three days, averaging forty-four days (Herms, 1917).

Genus Argas. Members of the genus *Argas* are distinctly flattened, with margins quite even when the tick is fully engorged; integument leathery, minutely wrinkled in folds, often intermingled with small, rounded "buttons," each with a pit on top and often bearing a hair in the pit; eyes absent; sexes similar.

Argas persicus (Oken), a cosmopolitan *fowl tick*, is one of the most important poultry parasites (Fig. 18-23). It is important to note, however, that, at least for the United States, what is termed *A. persicus* is in reality a complex of species (G. M. Kohls, personal communication to Harwood). At present, true *persicus* has been seen in the United States in Maryland, Pennsylvania, Georgia, and California. Species commonly identified as *A. persicus* in the United States are *A. sanchezi* Dugés and *A. radiatus* Railliet. *A. miniatus* Koch is a further member of the complex that has not been seen in the United States to date.

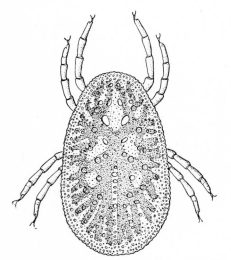

Fig. 18-23 The fowl tick, *Argas persicus*, dorsal view.

In addition to "fowl tick," this pest is commonly called "adobe-tick," "tampan," or "blue bug." It varies from light reddish brown to a dark brown, depending on the stage of engorgement. The obovate, flattened adults average about 8.5 mm long by 5.5 mm wide in the female, and 6.5 mm long by 4.5 mm wide in the male. When unengorged their thickness is about 0.75 mm, and when fully engorged may be nearly 3 mm. The margin of the body is composed of irregular quadrangular plates or cells that often have one or more circular pits. The genital orifice of the male is half-moon-shaped, and that of the female is slitlike and situated farther forward, i.e., immediately behind the capitulum as in other argasids. The capitulum has four long hairs, two hypostomal, and one near the articulation of each palpus, all directed forward. The palpi are about twice as long as the hypostome, second article longest, others equal in length. The hypostome, apically rounded, has six or seven fine denticles on each half distally, followed by stout teeth 2/2, the numbers increasing to 3/3, 4/4, 5/5 basally, the teeth decreasing in size, neither attaining the external border nor extending beyond half the length of the hypostome (Nuttall).

Nymphs and adults of *Argas persicus sensu lato* are strikingly active at night, migrating long distances to their host, and hiding inactively during the day. At night one may see hordes of these ticks climbing up to the roosts and upon fowls, filling leisurely with blood and before daybreak departing for hiding places. Females deposit their large reddish-brown eggs in crevices occupied during the day. The eggs are laid in masses of from 25–100 and more, and there are usually several layings, each preceded by a meal of blood, with a total of 700 eggs per female. Hatching takes place in from ten to twenty-eight days. The hexapod larvae are very active, attacking apparently as readily by day as by night.

Once attached, larvae feed about five days, occasionally longer, remaining firmly attached during this time. When fully engorged their appearance is that of little reddish globules. At the end of this feeding period, larvae detach, having flattened in the meantime, and crawl away from the host, hiding in some convenient crevice. Larvae molt in about a week, acquire a fourth pair of legs, and look like miniature adults. Nocturnal feeding now takes place, and in ten to twelve days another molt occurs, and the second nymphal stage is reached. Again the tick attaches, engorges in about an hour, and after something over a week, a third molt takes place (there may even be a fourth molt), resulting in the adult stage. The adults can engorge in twenty to forty-five minutes. Under favorable conditions the adult stage is reached in about thirty days. Absence of hosts to feed upon may greatly prolong the developmental time.

The species will bite man. Instances are recorded in which transient laborers occupying long-vacated but renovated poultryhouses have been badly bitten by the poultry tick. It could conceivably under certain circumstances become involved in the transmission of spirochetes to humans.

Argas reflexus (Fabricius), commonly known as the "pigeon tick," differs from *A. persicus* in that the body often narrows rather suddenly toward the anterior end and the thin margin is flexed upward; the margin of the body is composed of irregular striations. The capitulum has "two long post-hypostomal hairs ventrally, directed forward. Palps with articles sub equal, the third the shortest, denticulated hairs dorsally. ... Hypostome apically notched, some small denticles at the tip followed by 2/2 stout teeth merging into 3/3 to 6/6 progressively smaller teeth" (Nuttall). This species and *Ornithodoros coniceps* (Can.) infest pigeons in Spain, occasionally entering houses and biting man (Gil Collado, 1961). *Argas reflexus* is a European bird argasid and references to its occurrence in the United States prior to 1960, mainly in association with cliff swallows, are actually *Argas cooleyi* Kohls and Hoogstraal (G. M. Kohls, personal communication to Harwood).

An argasid found in chickenhouses, dovecotes, and human habitations of northern Chile was thought to be *A. persicus* or *A. reflexus*, but was found to belong to the reflexus group and named *Argas neghmei* Kohls and Hoogstraal. The species *A. brevipes* Banks has been recorded from wild birds of Arizona and California (Kohls, *et al.*, 1961).

Other species of *Argas* worth noting are: *A. brumpti* Neumann, the largest known species of the genus, measuring 15–20 mm in length by 10 mm in width; feeds on a variety of hosts in Africa and will attack man. *A. vespertilionis* (Latreille), a bat-infesting tick of wide distribution in the Old World; occasionally attacks man.

Genus Antricola. The dorsal walls flattened and marginated; below the dorsum the body is convex and deep; integument semitranslucent, surface smooth, shining, and with tubercles; the mouth parts adapted for quick feeding and not for clinging to host.

Antricola coprophilus (McIntosh) feeds on bats in Arizona and Mexico; *A. mexicanus* Hoffmann is known from a bat cave in Mexico; *A. marginatus* (Banks) is found in bat caves in Cuba and other parts of the West Indies.

TICKS AND DISEASE

Ticks are vectors of a number of important pathogens of man and domestic animals. Their role may involve more than simple transmission from one vertebrate to another, for in many cases the pathogens acquired by a female may be transferred through the reproductive system to her progeny; a situation referred to as *transovarial* or *hereditary transmission*. Likewise, differing from most insects having complex metamorphosis, an immature stage of a tick, such as a larva or nymph, may acquire a pathogen and transmit it while feeding after the next molt; a situation referred to as *transstadial transmission*. The dependence of all feeding stages on a blood meal for growth or reproduction affords many opportunities for pathogen acquisition and transmission, and the fact that different kinds of hosts may be attacked in different growth stages also increases the size of the potential reservoir.

ARBOVIRUSES

The viruses associated with ticks belong in Casal's B group of arboviruses, or are ungrouped. Several of these, particularly those of eastern Europe, have been misidentified so that literature from earlier studies has been confusing in its coverage. With very minor exceptions, all of these viruses are transmitted by Ixodid ticks. Much reliance has been placed on Horsfall and Tamm (1965), and especially on the review of Hoogstraal (1966), in preparing the present account.

B GROUP ARBOVIRUSES

Russian Spring-Summer Encephalitis Virus (RSSE). Russian spring-summer encephalitis has finally been distinguished from a complex that includes a number of closely related entities that have clinical and antigenic similarities, and that may also have considerable geographic overlap. Though clear distinction is still not always made, and some of these viruses are included in a tick-borne encephalitis complex (Horsfall and Tamm, 1965), the separation is made here on the basis of the review by Hoogstraal (1966). The disease is associated with taiga forest of the Soviet Union and with the tick *Ixodes persulcatus* Schulze; it also has been recorded from Prussia and East Germany. Incidence of this disease has increased with man's increasing development of Siberian and Far Eastern forest zones.

The disease caused by RSSE virus is characterized by a sudden onset of violent headache, rapidly rising fever, nausea, and vomiting. The incubation period is eight to 'fourteen days. At the height of illness delirium and coma may be present, as well as convulsions and paralysis. Bulbar center involvement and ascending paralysis occur, and residual paralysis is common. The mortality rate may be 25 to 30 per cent.

The severe paralytic form of RSSE virus is apparently transmitted to man solely by *Ixodes persulcatus*. A possible variant virus from northern China and the Khabarovsk region of the Soviet Union near the Sea of Japan is associated with the same tick, and with *Haemaphysalis concinna* Koch and *H. japonica douglasi* Nuttall and Warburton; it is clinically more severe than Central European tick-borne encephalitis (TE), but like that disease may be acquired from infected milk. Over 50 per cent of the permanent human residents of forest zones may have RSSE antibodies and no history of clinical symptoms, consequently clinical manifestations are more frequent in newcomers. The focal nature of virus distribution has even made it possible to relate highest incidence of clinical cases in some areas to coniferous foothill taiga forest indicated in aerial photographs.

Ixodes persulcatus Schulze is associated with a wide variety of small forest mammals and birds in immature stages, and with larger wild and domestic mammals as the adult. *Haemaphysalis concinna* Koch is found extensively in Europe, northern Asia, and western Siberia and may be the principal RSSE virus vector in regions where it outnumbers *Ixodes persulcatus*; it feeds in cut-over forest areas on small mammals and birds in immature stages, and often on cattle as the adult. *Haemaphysalis japonica douglasi* Nuttall and Warburton is an important vector of RSSE in the southern portion of the far eastern U.S.S.R.; it feeds on small and large vertebrates, and all stages attack humans. *Haemaphysalis neumanni* Doenitz has an ecology, distribution, and hosts somewhat similar to *H. j. douglasi*, but may have parthenogenetic generations; transstadial passage of RSSE virus has been demonstrated. *Dermacentor silvarum* Olenev is naturally infected in the easternmost U.S.S.R., but seems of less epidemiological importance than the other ticks mentioned.

Lack of tick relationship in the occurrence of some RSSE cases has raised the question of the role of other arthropods and other means of reservoir maintenance.

Central European Tick-Borne Encephalitis (TE). The Central European encephalitis virus causes a disease that is difficult to separate clinically from Russian spring-summer encephalititis. TE infection in humans is often a consequence of drinking infected milk. The virus reaches a high level in mammary glands, and at low temperature remains active for days in raw milk and uncooked milk products. By this mechanism, though TE virus is in low incidence in ticks and wild vertebrates in nature, milk-producing animals serve as a common infection route for man.

The tick *Ixodes ricinus* (Linnaeus) has been implicated as the main vector of TE virus, *Dermacentor marginatus* (Sulzer) being the only secondary species recorded as naturally infected. *Ixodes ricinus* feeds on a wide variety of vertebrates, and Central European tick-borne encephalitis virus has been isolated from rodents (*Apodemus, Clethrionomys*) and the European mole *Talpa europaea*. Antibodies have been found in a wide variety of wild mammals, including shrews, hares, bats, and several species of birds. Two hosts of *I. ricinus*, the dormouse *Glis* and hedgehog *Erinaceus*, can experimentally maintain the virus through torpor or hibernation. This virus may be very focal in nature; in Austria it is associated with high rodent populations in dense, moist, young mixed forest at least 10,000 square meters in area. Birds serve as a host for *I. ricinus*, which could readily explain how isolated but otherwise suitable ecological pockets can acquire the virus.

Omsk Hemorrhagic Fever Virus. Omsk hemorrhagic fever virus is the causative agent, antigenically close to RSSE and KFD viruses, of an acute febrile disease of man. It was first isolated in 1947 from human cases in the Omsk area of southwestern Siberia; further distribution in Central Asia is not clear, but a disease termed "Bukovinian hemorrhagic fever" from Bukovina, northern Romania, and a similar syndrome in the Ukraine may actually be identical.

The disease has an incubation period of three to seven days with an acute onset of headache and fever, often biphasic. There is frequent atypical bronchopneumonia, hemorrhagic rash, and extensive internal hemorrhage; the mortality rate is low (0.5–3 per cent).

The ticks *Dermacentor pictus* (Hermann), *D. marginatus* (Sulzer), and *Ixodes persulcatus* Schulze, along with small rodents, appear to constitute the reservoir. Introduced muskrats (*Ondatra*) along streams in the Omsk focus died in large numbers between 1960–62, and gamasid mites were implicated in passing the virus between these mammals and voles (*Arvicola*); a number of cases of Omsk hemorrhagic fever occurred among persons handling muskrat carcasses and pelts. The Bukovinian agent is associated with *Ixodes ricinus* infestation of people entering forests.

Kyasanur Forest Disease Virus (KFD). Kyasanur forest disease is a well-documented, seemingly new disease caused by an arbovirus. A number of excellent reviews of this disease are available (Work, 1962). Discovered in 1957, it was the first demonstration in Asia of disease caused by a virus of the Russian spring-summer B group complex. As an active clinical entity Kyasanur forest disease is thus far known only from a 600-square-mile area of Mysore State, India. Serological studies indicate presence of the virus in widespread foci elsewhere in that country. Curiously these other foci include arid regions sharply differing from the forest environment where human disease occurs.

Clinical manifestations of the disease are sudden onset of fever, headache, and severe muscle pains; prostration is common. In a significant number of cases a diphasic course is seen, with mild meningoencephalitis in the second phase. Bronchiolar involvement with a persistent cough and gastrointestinal disturbance are usual. Convalescence is prolonged.

but lasting damage is not seen; about a 5 per cent case fatality occurs.

Human KFD has been coincident with concurrent epizootics of local monkey populations. In fact, the first observations on the disease were in response to reports of monkey mortality, arousing the suspicion that sylvan yellow fever was present. Langur monkeys (*Presbytis entellus*) and bonnet macaques (*Macaca radiata*) were often fatally affected, and examination of these and humans in the disease area revealed the presence of ticks, especially of the genus *Haemaphysalis*.

Taxonomy of the tick species involved, particularly the immature stages, needed clarification before an accurate picture of the vectors was possible. Virus isolations obtained from a number of pools of ticks implicated *Haemaphysalis spinigera* Neumann in particular, but also *H. turturis* Nuttall and Warburton and five additional species in this genus; additional isolations included *Ixodes ceylonicus* Kohls, *Rhipicephalus* sp., and *Dermacentor* sp.

A variety of small rodents, squirrels, and shrews that serve as hosts of immature ticks in the Kyasanur Forest area have yielded KFD virus. Monkeys of the region are infested by *Haemaphysalis* ticks, particularly *H. spinigera*, and peak infestation, predominantly by larvae, occurs in the postmonsoon dry month of November. During dry months humans of the region turn from agricultural pursuits to wood gathering in forests, thereby entering infectious foci at a time of high virus activity.

Haemaphysalis spinigera Neumann is very inclusive in its host range. Small mammals are frequent hosts of the immature stages, but birds also are attacked; and from these KFD antibodies, but no virus, have been demonstrated. The adults prefer large mammals, either wild, or domestic forms such as cattle. Cattle grazing within forests can therefore also spread the principal vector tick and bring it into close association with villages; restricting roaming of cattle in forests, and tick control on village cattle, may be useful for KFD prevention.

Powassan Virus. Powassan virus is the only known American representative of the tick-borne B group complex. It was first isolated from a fatal encephalitis case in northern Ontario, Canada, in 1958. Though widely distributed foci are recognized in nature, no further clinical cases have been verified. Natural isolations have involved *Dermacentor andersoni* Stiles in Colorado and South Dakota, and *Ixodes spinipalpis* Hadwen and Nuttall from *Peromyscus* mice in Connecticut and South Dakota. Serological evidence from New York State implies exposure of racoons and foxes, and man only minimally. In northern Ontario (Canada), isolates of virus along with seasonal serological sampling, implicate the groundhog *Marmota monax* and the tick *Ixodes cookei* Packard; also the red squirrel *Tamaiasciurus hudsonicus* and the tick *Ixodes marxi* Banks. The evidence from other serological studies also reinforces the conclusion that wild rodents and hares, and their tick parasites, constitute the reservoir; man is highly unlikely to enter the picture because the ticks normally involved seldom bite him.

Other B Group Viruses Near the Russian Spring-Summer Complex. *Negishi encephalitis* virus is known from two fatal cases of human encephalitis in Japan, but the vectors are unknown; *Langat encephalitis* virus, from ticks and rats in Malaysia, is experimentally capable of causing human encephalitis and experimentally transmissible by several ticks.

UNGROUPED VIRUSES

Colorado Tick Fever Virus (CTF). In 1855 Ewing described what was apparently Colorado tick fever, calling it "mountain fever." In the Bitter Root Valley of Montana, United States, doctors alerted to Rocky Mountain spotted fever noted in 1902 that febrile cases occurred without skin rash. The etiological agent was subsequently shown to be a virus, transmitted by ticks, causing what is now recognized as the only tick-transmitted disease common in North America (Fig. 18-24). It occurs in all the Rocky Mountain states, the

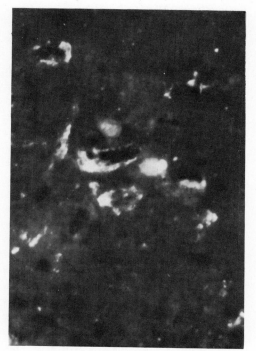

Fig. 18-24 Reaction between Colorado tick fever virus and fluoroscein isothiocyanate-labeled antibody globulin in mouse brain, approximately 2,250 ×. (Photograph by W. Burgdorfer, Rocky Mountain Laboratory, N.I.H.)

Black Hills of South Dakota and in western Canada.

There is usually a sudden onset of fever, headache, retro-orbital pain, and severe muscle pains; on inquiry there is a history of exposure to ticks. Incubation period, following the tick bite, is three to six days. Frequently the disease is diphasic, with symptoms and the remission period lasting two to three days. Rash is not usual but can occur. Almost exclusively in children, there may be serious complications in the form of encephalitis and severe bleeding. No lasting complications are reported.

Human cases of this disease are closely associated with the tick *Dermacentor andersoni* Stiles; and *Dermacentor occidentalis* Marx has been found infected in Oregon and California. The cycle in nature has also been associated with the rabbit and hare ticks *Dermacentor*

parumapertus Neumann, *Otobius lagophilus* Cooley and Kohls, and *Haemaphysalis leporispalustris* (Packard). Rodents having a prolonged viremia are important; in western Montana the golden-mantled ground squirrel, *Citellus lateralis tescorum*, is considered the main vertebrate host (Burgdorfer and Eklund, 1959); additional hosts include other *Citellus*, chipmunk (*Eutamias*), pine squirrel (*Tamiasciurus*), deer mouse (*Peromyscus*), and porcupine (*Erethizon*). Transstadial passage of virus occurs in *Dermacentor andersoni* Stiles, transovarial passage could not be demonstrated (Eklund, *et al.*, 1959); unfed nymphs overwinter the virus. Yunker and Cory (1967) have succeeded in growing the virus in tissue cultures of *D. andersoni* cells, with no differences observed in the cell growth of virus-infected and uninfected cultures.

Kemerovo Virus. In the Kemerovo region of western Siberia, the Kemerovo virus was isolated from unengorged *Ixodes persulcatus* Schulze females and from two patients with suspected tick-borne encephalitis. Clinical symptoms cannot be distinguished from Central European tick-borne B group encephalitis (TE), but laboratory studies show this agent to be ungrouped. The disease is febrile, benign, and nonparalytic.

Tribeč Virus. Subsequent to the finding of Kemerovo virus, an agent very close to it, termed Tribeč virus, was found in Czechoslovakia. This virus has been found in adults and nymphs of *Ixodes ricinus* (Linnaeus) and two species of rodents (*Pitymys, Clethrionomys*); it is not considered a significant danger for man.

Louping Ill. Louping ill, primarily a disease of sheep, has received extensive review by Varma (1964). The virus causes an encephalomyelitis of high mortality in sheep and can affect cattle and humans. Serious involvement in sheep is indicated by a jumping vertigo, or loup, known from Scotland for over a century and a half. The disease occurs in hills and moors of Scotland and northern England and is widespread in Ireland.

Cases in humans generally occur through

close contact with sheep by laboratory workers, butchers, veterinarians, and sheep farmers; infection of humans by tick bite is also apparently possible. In humans the disease resembles Central European tick-borne encephalitis, involving influenzalike symptoms; complications include temporary paralysis, and death is known from one case.

The virus seems to circulate chiefly among sheep and the tick *Ixodes ricinus* (Linnaeus), though because this tick feeds on a wide variety of animals many vertebrates have been examined. Isolations of louping ill virus have been made from red grouse (*Lagopus*), wood mouse (*Apodemus*), and shrew (*Sorex*); antibody surveys suggest the involvement of other mammals. Transstadial transmission of louping ill virus has been demonstrated in *I. ricinus*, transovarial transmission is suspected but not adequately proved.

Crimean Hemorrhagic Fever Virus. Crimean hemorrhagic fever was first noted in 1944–1945 among presumably nonimmune Russian troops helping farmers in the war-devastated Crimea. Later cases were noted from the Rostov and Astrakhan regions. Hemorrhagic symptoms occur along with seriously acute febrile conditions. Human cases originated from the wide Crimean steppe, not from cities, forests, or mountains, and were associated with the bite of the tick *Hyalomma marginatum* Koch. This tick occurs in a widespread complex, members of which infest birds readily and may be transported to nearby localities and even from Africa to Asia and Europe.

Uzbekistan Hemorrhagic Fever Virus. Known from Central Asia in the twelfth century, Uzbekistan hemorrhagic fever is antigenically close to Crimean hemorrhagic fever and felt by some to be identical. It is considered clinically more severe and causes higher mortality. Cattle and horses harbor the virus, and rural persons bitten by *Hyalomma anatolicum* Koch, a tick from these mammals, contract the disease. *Hyalomma detritum*

Schulze and *Rhipicephalus turanicus* Pomerantzev are suspected as secondary hosts of the virus. The disease may be spread among humans by contact.

Other Possible Tick Involvement with Viruses. There are other situations where ticks have been demonstrated to be potential vectors or reservoirs of arboviruses. The more important of these possibilities are listed here:

Japanese Encephalitis. This virus of antigenic group B is vectored by mosquitoes (see discussion under these insects). Soviet investigators have suggested certain ticks, especially *Ixodes persulcatus, I. ricinus, Haemaphysalis concinna* Koch, and *Dermacentor silvarum* Olenev could serve as natural virus hosts. Experimental work has demonstrated long survival (eleven to twenty-five months) and even transovarial passage in various ticks.

West Nile Virus. Experimental work has suggested the potential of ticks in maintaining this B group mosquito-transmitted virus. Schmidt and Said (1964) isolated West Nile virus in midwinter from *Argas reflexus hermanni* Audouin in pigeon cotes in Egypt.

Quaranfil Fever. The antigenically ungrouped virus that causes Quaranfil fever was isolated from a febrile child near Cairo, Egypt, and later from *Argas arboreus* Kaiser, Hoogstraal, and Kohls from heron and egret rookeries.

Equine Encephalomyelitis. American forms of virus have been experimentally demonstrated as capable of transmission by ticks, but natural infection of these vectors is lacking. A "near Eastern" variety of equine encephalomyelitis has been reported from horses, donkeys, and sheep in Egypt and Syria; and from *Hyalomma a. anatolicum* Koch infesting these animals.

Lymphocytic Choriomeningitis. The causative virus of lymphocytic choriomeningitis has been isolated in Ethiopia from the blood of human patients and from *Amblyomma variegatum* (Fabricius) and *Rhipicephalus sanguineus* (Latreille).

RICKETTSIAE

Ticks are known to be vectors of a number of important rickettsiae affecting man and animals. As background for the discussion here, Weyer (1964), Horsfall and Tamm (1965), and Hoogstraal (1967) are important review sources. In most cases studied, the rickettsiae transmitted by ticks do not occur for a prolonged period in the vertebrate host, thereby making ticks the essential reservoir.

Rocky Mountain Spotted Fever (RMSF, Mexican Spotted Fever, Tobia Fever, São Paulo Fever). Rocky Mountain spotted fever has been known in the Bitter Root Valley of Montana since 1872 (Stiles, 1905). It is also known as "tick fever," "black fever," "blue disease," and "black measles." The most characteristic and constant symptom is the rash that appears about the second to the fifth day on the wrists, ankles, and less commonly on the back, later spreading to all parts of the body. The most common complaints at the outset are frontal and occipital headaches, intense aching in the lumbar region, and marked malaise. The incubation period is two to five days in more severe infections and three to fourteen days in milder ones. The fever rises rapidly in the more virulent infections to 104–106° F. In fatal infections, death usually occurs between day nine and fifteen. Treatment employs broad-spectrum antibiotics such as chloramphenicol, chlortetracycline, and oxytetracycline. Commercial vaccines are available. Strains of spotted fever of different virulence occur in the same locality, such variations in virulence causing many points of dispute among early investigators. The agent of Rocky Mountain spotted fever is *Rickettsia rickettsi* (Wolbach).

Rocky Mountain spotted fever is endemic in the United States, in some parts of Canada, in Mexico, and in some parts of South America. The greatest number of cases occur in populations engaged in outdoor occupations, principally agriculture. Both sexes and all ages are subject to the disease. In the western United States, most cases occur in men; in the eastern part more women and children contract the disease. Parker suggests this is probably because the eastern vector is *Dermacentor variabilis*, which infests the dog, a household animal. The principal western vector, the Rocky Mountain wood tick, *Dermacentor andersoni*, is far less frequent on dogs.

In 1902, after a preliminary investigation, Wilson and Chowning advanced for the first time the theory that a tick ("wood tick") acts as the natural vector of Rocky Mountain spotted fever. According to Ricketts (in the 48th Biennial Report of the Montana State Board of Health, p. 106) as recorded by Hunter and Bishopp (1911):

… the first experiments which resulted in the proof of the transmission of spotted fever by a tick were conducted by Drs. McCalla and Brereton of Boise, Idaho, in 1905. In these experiments a tick which was found attached to a spotted fever patient was removed and allowed to bite a healthy person. In eight days this person developed a typical case of spotted fever. The experiment was continued by allowing the same tick to bite a second person. In this case again a typical case of spotted fever resulted.

The famous experiments of Ricketts have been brought together in a memorial volume (Ricketts, 1911) from which the following summary is made. First it was shown that the disease could be transmitted to guinea pigs by direct inoculation and this animal was used for further experimentation. Ricketts fed a female tick on the ear of an intraperitoneally infected guinea pig. Later feeding by this tick infected two healthy guinea pigs. Guinea pigs in association with the infected animals showed no symptoms, indicating mere association would not transfer the disease. Ricketts called the tick he used *Dermacentor occidentalis*, but undoubtedly the species was *D. andersoni*. In addition to other illuminating experiments, Ricketts found the disease can also be transmitted by the male tick and that "one attack of the disease establishes a rather high degree of immunity to subsequent inoculations." Furthermore, field-collected ticks transmitted the disease to a guinea pig in the laboratory, indicating infective ticks occur in nature in small numbers. It was also ascertained that any active stage of the tick could transmit the pathogen; larvae of an infective female are in some cases infective; transmission is probably through the salivary secretion.

The Infection in Nature. Parker thought, from field observations made in eastern Montana in 1916 and 1917, that some agent other than *Dermacentor andersoni* was likely involved in the natural maintenance of the pathogen. In 1923 he established the fact that the rabbit tick, *Haemaphysalis leporispalustris*, can transmit the infection from rabbit to rabbit, and also that infected rabbit ticks occur in nature; also the infection is transmitted by infected female ticks of this species to the egg as in the case of *Dermacentor andersoni*. The rabbit tick rarely bites man, but it is important in maintaining the pathogen and is furthermore the only known vector that occurs in all parts of the United States. Infection carried by this tick is reported by Parker to be extremely mild. Rabbits of all species studied are hosts of both wood ticks and rabbit ticks.

Small rodents and rabbits are possible reservoirs of the disease, though it has not been proved that they maintain rickettsemia for a prolonged period. Gould and Miesse (1954) first isolated the agent from a meadow mouse (*Microtus pennsylvanicus*) in Virginia, and later investigations in that same state by other workers isolated strains from cottontail rabbits (*Sylvilagus*), white-footed mouse (*Peromyscus*), pine vole (*Pitymys*), cotton rat (*Sigmodon*), and opossum (*Didelphis*). Burgdorfer, *et al.* (1962), isolated the rickettsia in western Montana from the blood of snowshoe hare, and spleen tissue of chipmunks (*Eutamias*) and golden-mantled ground squirrel (*Citellus*).

The American dog tick, *Dermacentor variabilis*, was proved a carrier of the eastern type of Rocky Mountain spotted fever by Dyer, *et al.* (1931), who used larvae bred from eggs. They also proved that transmission is transovarian. Parker (1937) reports successful stage-to-stage and generation-to-generation transmission with *Dermacentor occidentalis* Marx and *Rhipicephalus sanguineus* (Latreille). In the latter species, continuity of the rickettsia was shown from larval ticks of one generation through six successive stages to adults of the next. In *Amblyomma americanum* (Linnaeus), Maver had already reported larva-to-adult continuity, and transmission from female to larva was accomplished by Parker. With *Amblyomma cajennense* (Fabricius), the Cayenne tick, transmission from larvae to adult has been shown, and for *Dermacentor parumapertus* Neumann, a rabbit tick, transmission from nymphs to adults was shown by Maver, and continuity from larvae to nymphs as well as survival of the pathogens in adults was shown by Parker. Parker states that these data are considered sufficient to indicate that each of these six additional species is a possible natural carrier of spotted fever organisms and that four of these, *D. occidentalis*, *R. sanguineus*, *A. americanum*, and *A. cajennense* are possible present or future agents of transmission to man. Actually, *Amblyomma americanum* is now known to be a vector of spotted fever in Oklahoma and Texas (Parker, *et al.*, 1943); and *Amblyomma cajennense* is a vector in Brazil and Colombia.

Transmission of *Rickettsia rickettsii* by other ticks is a distinct possibility. Philip and Kohls (1952) have shown that *D. albipictus* may, under certain circumstances, transmit the disease to man. *Anocentor nitens*, species of *Amblyomma* other than *cajennense* and *americanum*, and even species of the argasid genera *Ornithodoros* and *Otobius*, may at times be involved. Philip, *et al.* (1955), have demonstrated the presence of the rickettsia in *Dermacentor parumapertus* feeding on native rabbits, so that species must also be considered as having some importance in maintaining the natural reservoir.

Mechanism of Infection. The infection is acquired from the reservoir animal by a feeding tick in any stage of its life history and is passed on from stage to stage; e.g., infected blood is ingested by the larva, the infection is passed on to the nymphs (which may be infective), and thence to the adult, which in turn may be infective; then at least some infected female ticks pass the pathogen on through their eggs to the larvae of the next generation.

When normal adult ticks were first fed on an infected host, just long enough to insure ingestion of the pathogen, and were then transferred directly to a normal host (the tick-feeding thus being interrupted but essentially continuous), Parker's (1928) tests showed a period of from nine to twelve days between the ingestion and the transmission of the pathogens. Except under experimental conditions, infection is not transmitted by the same stage of the tick that acquires it, but by the next and subsequent stages. The infection is transmitted by the *bite* of the tick. The great majority of persons with cases of Rocky Mountain spotted fever give a definite history of "tick bite" two to twelve days before onset. The percentage of ticks that contain the infectious agent is reported as small; it may be less than 1 per cent and is rarely as high as 5 per cent.

Parker (1928) states that a minority of perhaps 5 per cent of infected persons deny the possibility of having been infected by the tick bite. The reasons for this can perhaps be understood in the light of his studies. In an "exceptionally clear-cut series of tests," it was shown that the rickettsia from tick tissues: "would infect if merely dropped among the hairs on the unabraded skin of guinea pigs, also if dropped into the eyes. In another series of tests it was demonstrated, contrary to previously accepted ideas, that tick excrement is frequently infectious." Crushed tick tissues and feces might easily produce infection through abrasion but not through the unbroken skin. Crushing ticks with the fingernails can consequently be a dangerous practice.

The rickettsia survives the winter in infected nymphal or adult ticks. At the end of the winter the rickettsia in these ticks is present, according to Parker (1933), as a nonsymptom-producing and frequently immunizing form, and does not produce symptomatically recognizable infections until its level of virulence is raised, either by heat or by the ingestion of blood. It may be a matter of some hours, and not infrequently a day or more, after the tick attaches itself before reactivation occurs. If a tick that has become attached is removed within a few hours, the danger of infection is minimized materially.

The fluorescent antibody technique has permitted detailed studies on the development of *R. rickettsi* in ticks. By this means Shepard and Goldwasser (1960) detected the pathogen in individual *D. andersoni.* Burgdorfer (1963) used this technique (Fig. 18-25) to observe that the rickettsiae in *D. andersoni* females were passed through the eggs to almost all offspring, and by all infected F_1 progeny to all their offspring.

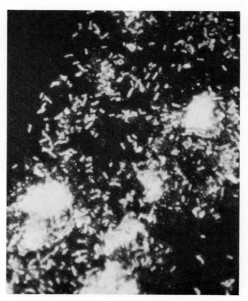

Fig. 18-25 *Rickettsia rickettsi* in smear of infected tick tissues, fluorescent antibody staining, approximately 1,000 ×. (Photograph by W. Burgdorfer, Rocky Mountain Laboratory, N.I.H.)

The rickettsiae were found in the cytoplasm around nuclei of the follicles and epithelial cells, but never in nuclei. This finding suggests endemic areas should have very high rates of infected ticks, yet only 1 to 3 per cent are naturally infected in the Bitter Root Valley (Montana, United States). Burgdorfer suggests that if immature stages are infected with a dose below a certain level, uniform infection is not produced; also most tick host animals probably experience a rather short-lived and mild infection that may be insufficient to infect ticks permanently.

A significant factor in the epidemiology of Rocky Mountain spotted fever is the interference phenomenon demonstrated by Price (1953). When guinea pigs were infected intraperitoneally with a strain of *Rickettsia rickettsi* of low virulence, the animals were protected from the highly virulent strain, provided that the concentration of the former was ten to thirty times that of the latter. Infection with the rickettsiae of Q fever, scrub typhus, endemic typhus, and epidemic typhus gave the same type of protection under the same conditions. The interference phenomenon may help to explain the contention that in certain limited localities strains of Rocky Mountain spotted fever of low and high virulence persist year after year.

Siberian Tick Typhus. First recognized in the 1930's, when virgin steppe lands began to come under extensive utilization, *Rickettsia siberica* was later established as occurring elsewhere in the Soviet Union; foci occur on islands in the Sea of Japan, the Pacific Far East (Maritime Territory), and northern and southern Siberia. The pathogen is in the Rocky Mountain spotted fever group of rickettsias (Lackman, *et al.*, 1965).

Symptoms resemble moderately severe Rocky Mountain spotted fever cases. There are fever, headache, and extensive rash. Survival is the rule, and treatment is much like that for Rocky Mountain spotted fever.

A number of ixodid ticks are implicated as vectors or reservoir. These include four species of *Dermacentor*, three species of *Haemaphysalis*, *Rhipicephalus sanguineus* from sheep and dogs in Armenia, and *Hyalomma asiaticum* from rodents (*Meriones*) in Kirgizia. Other arthropods implicated, but of uncertain epidemiologic significance, are various mites and fleas. Several species of rodents (*Citellus, Eutamias, Cricetus, Cricetulus, Rattus, Mus, Lagurus, Apodemus, Clethrionomys, Microtus, Meriones*) and a hare (*Lepus*) have yielded strains of the pathogen. Ground squirrels may start becoming infected while still in burrows in the spring (Merinov, 1962). Ticks removed from cattle, sheep, dogs, and birds have been found infected. The role of mammals as reservoir is uncertain; if infection is short lived, as with Rocky Mountain spotted fever, then ticks must serve as the main reservoir.

Transstadial and transovarial survival of *R. siberica* has been demonstrated through at least five years in *Dermacentor marginatus* (Sulzer). This type of survival has also been demonstrated in a number of other tick vectors. For main vectors implicated, Hoogstraal (1967) has summarized information on distribution and typical habitat.

Boutonneuse Fever (South African Tick Typhus, Kenya Tick Typhus, Crimean Tick Typhus, Marseilles Fever, Indian Tick Typhus). Boutonneuse fever is caused by *Rickettsia conori*, is widespread on the African continent and has also been reported from European Mediterranean regions, Israel, Turkey, Crimea, and much of Southeast Asia. Variations in virulence, along with epidemiology within diverse areas have led investigators to suspect more than one species of pathogen to be present, but most workers agree a single etiological agent is involved.

An extensive rash occurs in human cases, but is not easily detected in Africans. Mild cases are the rule in Asia. In serious cases there may be severe and persistent headache and mild delirium; full recovery may require a prolonged period. At the site of tick attachment a black buttonlike (hence *buttonneuse*) lesion develops with a central dark necrotic area; local swelling of the lymph glands draining the lesion is common. In addition to tick bite, infection may occur by contact of hands with skin or eyes after crushing ticks removed from dogs.

The reservoir of *Rickettsia conori* appears to primarily involve a variety of ticks and rodents. In the Mediterranean area lagomorphs are perhaps the most important reservoir. Birds may be part of the reservoir and can also carry ticks to other areas; dogs seemingly do not sustain infection for long, but are frequently significant because they bring ticks into close contact with humans (Heisch, *et al.*, 1962). *Rhipicephalus sanguineus* (Latreille) has been shown to be an important vector in South Africa, East Africa, Ethiopia, and around the Mediterranean and Black Seas. Other tick vectors are found in the genera *Haemaphysalis, Hyalomma, Amblyomma, Boophilus, Rhipicephalus, Ixodes,* and *Dermacentor*; in fact the general impression is that virtually any ixodid tick can serve as a host (see Hoogstraal, 1967). Wild rodents of many species have been demonstrated to harbor the rickettsia. In Malaya, Marchette (1966) showed that from a primary forest cycle wild species of rats enter scrub, where they can exchange ectoparasites with semidomestic rats that later contact rodents in close association with man; also dogs and people passing through forests may acquire infective vectors (Hoogstraal, *et al.*, 1965).

Epidemic (Louse-Borne) Typhus. Epidemic typhus has normally been considered as involving humans and the human louse only, but studies in Ethiopia discovered the pathogen, *Rickettsia prowazeki*, in ticks, large domestic animals, and possibly rodents also. Isolations from Ethiopian ticks have included *Amblyomma variegatum* (Fabricius) and *Hyalomma marginatum rufipes* Koch (Hoogstraal, 1967). Experimentally tick tissues have been shown to support development of the pathogen (Kordova and Řeháček, 1964).

Queensland Tick Typhus. The rickettsia causing Queensland tick typhus, *R. australis*, has been placed close to the rickettsialpox agent (Lackman, *et al.*, 1965), and in fact clinical symptomatology resembles the latter disease. All human cases have been reported from northern or southern Queensland, particularly from grassy savannah or secondary scrub areas. On circumstantial evidence *Ixodes holocyclus* Neumann, a tick that feeds on a great variety of warm-blooded vertebrates, is implicated as the main vector; serological evidence also suggests a number of small marsupial mammals as providing part of the biocenose.

Q Fever. The infectious agent, *Coxiella burnetti*, is worldwide in distribution, and can readily be transferred by the simplest contaminative routes such as milk or contaminated dust. This widespread occurrence obviously does not require ticks as vectors. Nonetheless, Philip and Burgdorfer (1961) note tick maintenance is more significant in natural environments, mentioning naturally infected ticks from Morocco, Queensland (Australia), western Montana (United States), and many other records. In experimental studies many species of ixodid and argasid ticks have been capable of transmission by bite and transovarial transmission, whereas others proved refractory. The rickettsial agent has been demonstrated to develop in tick tissue cultures (Kordová and Řeháček, 1965). Experimentally, the body louse has been shown to support development of this pathogen and to produce infective excreta, and this insect has been suggested as a xenodiagnostic tool (Pavilanis and Rozewicz, 1958).

Tick-Borne Rickettsias of Veterinary Importance. *Rickettsia phagocytophila*, an agent causing fever in sheep of Great Britain, can be transmitted transstadially by *Ixodes ricinus* (Foggie, 1951).

Cowdria ruminantium causes heart-water fever of ruminant stock in Africa, and can be transstadially transmitted by two species of *Amblyomma* (Neitz, 1956). This disease is recognized as enzootic in sheep, goats, and possibly camels in a 10,000 square-mile district of the Sudan, with *Amblyomma lepidum* Dönitz the likely vector (Karrar, *et al.*, 1963).

Ehrlichia bovis, E. canis, and *E. ovina,* of cattle, dogs, and sheep in Africa, are transmitted respectively, by *Hyalomma* spp., *Rhipicephalus sanguineus* (Latreille), and *R. bursa* Canestrini and Fanzango (Philip and Burgdorfer, 1961; Burgdorfer and Varma, 1967).

Rickettsia parkeri, or maculatum agent, has been isolated from *Amblyomma maculatum* Koch on cattle in three southern states (United States). Isolations have also been made from ticks on sheep. More widespread distribution probably includes the range of the Gulf Coast tick, *A. maculatum,* which encompasses coastal areas of the southeastern United States, Mexico, and to northern South America.

Other Tick-Borne Rickettsias of Minor Importance. Two nonpathogenic rickettsiae have been described from Montana, United States (Lackman, *et al.*, 1965). Eastern Montana agent, *Rickettsia montana,* has been isolated from *Dermacentor variabilis* and *D. andersoni.* An unnamed Western Montana agent has been recovered from *D. andersoni.*

Rickettsia canada is a new member of the typhus group of Rickettsiae isolated from *Haemaphysalis leporis-palustris* (Packard) ticks in Canada (McKiel, *et al.*, 1967).

BACTERIA

Most noteworthy among the bacteria transmitted by ticks are the spirochetes of relapsing fever. Tularemia is another bacterial disease in which ticks play an important role. The compilation by Dubos and Hirsch (1965) has provided a basic background for discussing these diseases, as well as have the reviews of Varma (1962), and Burgdorfer and Varma (1967).

Relapsing Fever. The causal agent of relapsing fever is a spirochete in the genus *Borrelia.* Taxonomic status of this pathogen is in question, the literature suggesting a great number of species but most authorities asserting that these are variants of the single species *Borrelia recurrentis* (Lebert) (Fig. 18-26). Characteristically such variants show marked

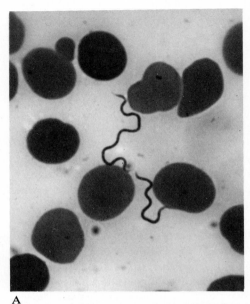

A

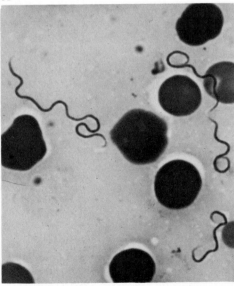

B

Fig. 18-26 Relapsing fever spirochetes in smear of mouse blood, Giemsa stain, 1,950 ×. *A. B. duttoni. B. B. hermsii.* (Photographs by W. Burgdorfer, Rocky Mountain Laboratory, N.I.H.)

'differences in their ability to develop and be transmitted by argasid ticks in the genus *Ornithodoros* and by lice. Apparently, because of the isolation caused by burrow- or den-infesting proclivities of argasid ticks in general, a single pathogen has developed strains specifically adapted to single or limited groups of arthropods. Strains are differentiated primarily on the basis of area of isolation or vector concerned with transmission, rather than biologic differences. Some tick-borne and louse-borne strains have been shown to infest the complementary vectors, and in turn to be transmissible to man. For purposes of identification, a species designation such as is often made in the literature will be used here.

The disease in man is characterized by an acute onset of fever three to ten days after infection. At this stage large numbers of organisms are present in blood, and they may be found in other body fluids. After about four days the fever declines and organisms disappear from the blood. An afebrile period of three to ten days is followed by a second attack of fever, with organisms recurring in the blood in smaller numbers. Febrile attacks may recur three to ten times. Mortality in endemic situations is 2 to 5 per cent, but may be 50 per cent or higher in epidemics. Penicillin and the tetracyclines are effective in treatment.

Human relapsing fever infections may be transmitted by arthropod vectors from man to man, from animal to animal, and from animal to man. To this must be added the fact that ticks can serve as a long-term reservoir, with transovarian passage to offspring through many generations. The percentage of transovarian transmission varies greatly between tick species (Davis, 1939, 1948). Rodents may serve as natural sources of infection for ticks. Transmission is by the bite of ticks of either sex in all active stages. Fluids of the coxal glands play an important role, inasmuch as many species produce infectious fluids from which spirochetes are introduced into the bite wound or even penetrate unbroken skin.

Relapsing fever of man is essentially world-wide in distribution except for Australia, New Zealand, and Oceania. Epidemics of the disease are normally louse-borne, endemicity is characteristic of tick-borne relapsing fever. Tick-borne endemicity is prevalent in central and south Africa, much of Asia, and the Americas.

The "species" of *Borrelia*, identified by geographic location and by their *Ornithodoros* tick vectors, have been compiled in Dubos and Hirsch (1965) as: Europe: *Borrelia hispanica* and *Ornithodoros erraticus*, *O. verrucosus*. Africa: *B. duttoni* (*crociduri*) and *O. moubata*; *B. kochi*, *B. russi*, *B. berbera*, *B. aegyptica*, and *O. erraticus*; *B. turicatae*, *B. marocana*, and *O. turicata*; *B. sogdiana* and *O. savignyi*. Middle East: *B. persica* and *O. tholozani*, *O. asperus*, *O. lahorensis*. India: *B. carteri* and *O. tholozani*, *O. crossi*, *O. lahorensis*. Soviet Union: *B. "latyshevi"* and *O. verrucosus*, *O. neerensis*, *O. tartakovskyi*, *O. tholozani*. North America: *B. novyi*, *B. turicatae*, and *O. turicata*; *B. parkerii* and *O. parkeri*; *B. hermsii* and *O. hermsi*. Central and South America: *B. dugesii* and *O. dugesi*; *B. venezuelense* and *O. venezuelensis*; *B. neotropicalis* and *O. talaje*; *B. turicatae* and *O. turicata*.

Development of *Borrelia* in their tick hosts has been well studied, though not with all tick species involved. The classical early studies were with *Ornithodoros moubata sensu lato* and *Borrelia duttoni*. Dutton and Todd (1905) and Koch (1905) proved this tick transmits relapsing fever spirochetes, and also that spirochetes are transferred to eggs and progeny. Their findings confirmed the beliefs of natives in many parts of Africa, who are reported to have dreaded tick bites. According to information cited by Walton (1962), some African tribes carried ticks on their journeys in order to retain immunity. Burgdorfer (1951) reviewed further studies on development, and through his own investigations provided a detailed picture of the progressive development of the spirochetes in the tick (Fig. 18-27). The spirochetes concentrate along the gut wall after ingestion, and may be found in the

A

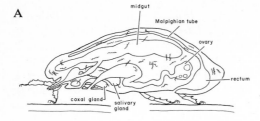

midgut

Malpighian tube

ovary

rectum

coxal gland

salivary gland

B

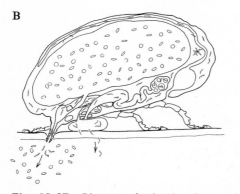

Fig. 18-27 Diagram of relapsing fever spirochetes in *Ornithodoros moubata*. *A*. Within four days after infectious blood meal the spirochetes have extensively invaded body tissues. *B*. Tick introduces spirochetes into host by salivary secretions and by infectious coxal fluid. (After Burgdorfer.)

hemocoel in as early as twenty-four hours. Multiplication ensues, with invasion of various tissues. As early as the third day spirochetes are found in salivary glands, coxal glands and central ganglion; and by the fourth day in the Malpighian tubes. Nymphs showed a prolonged heavy infection of salivary glands; in adults heavy infection of these glands was temporary. By placing clean tissues into the hemocoel in capillary tubes, it was observed that certain tissues seemed to attract spirochetes. Central ganglion and coxal glands seemed most attractive. Infection of the next generation is possible when spirochetes invade the ovaries to infect eggs at a stage in their development prior to the time they have developed an egg shell (Wagner-Jevseenko, 1958; Aeschlimann 1958).

Studies with other species of *Ornithodoros* and strains of *Borrelia* generally reveal a similar situation. One broad conclusion is that infectivity of *Borrelia* for man and other vertebrates may best be maintained under natural conditions when transmission occurs alternately between ticks and vertebrates. Under experimental conditions prolonged serial passage through ticks alone, or vertebrates alone, seems to modify infectivity, increasing it in some studies and decreasing it in others. *Borrelia duttoni* was transferred through the eggs of *Ornithodoros moubata* (prob. *O. porcinus*) for five generations but began to lose its virulence for mice by the third (Geigy and Aeschlimann, 1964). That the vector normally acquires the pathogen from a vertebrate is suggested by an investigation on *Ornithodoros hermsi* Wheeler, Herms, and Meyer (Wheeler, 1938). He found at least 20.8 per cent of this tick collected from relapsing fever foci in California to be infected, and experimental feeding on infected mice yielded up to 48 per cent tick infection, yet naturally infected female ticks of this species produced less than 2 per cent infected offspring.

Two epidemological findings on relapsing fever seem worthy of mention. In parts of Africa *Ornithodoros savignyi* (Audouin) has long been regarded an important vector, transmitting *Borrelia duttoni* in the laboratory. Naturally infected examples have not been reported, and a study of over 2,000 individuals of this species over a twelve-year period in East Africa failed to find a single infection (Heisch and Harvey, 1960). Evidence from uninhabited parts of Turkmenia showed foci of tick-borne spirochetosis can exist sixteen to thirty years, the causal agent being maintained in *Ornithodoros tholozani* (Laboulbène and Mégnin), *O. tartakovskyi* Olenev, and *O. neerensis* Pavlovskii. Foci in caves under overhanging rocks inhabited by porcupines (*Hystrix*) persisted longest (Petrischeva, 1961).

Tick-Borne Relapsing Fever in the United States. The earliest known focus of endemic (tick-borne) relapsing fever in the United States is believed to have been in Colorado, where cases were reported by Meador (1915); this focus was in the mountains near Denver. In 1921 Briggs reported two cases of relapsing fever in which the infection had been acquired at Polaris, Nevada County, California, at an elevation of 5,750 feet. It is of interest to note that prospectors and others who worked in the Sierra Nevada at altitudes of 5,000 feet and over frequently reported suffering from a malarialike disease they called "squirrel fever." In the light of our present knowledge and particularly from the experience of C. M. Wheeler, it is obvious that this infection was relapsing fever, infection having been due to contact with blood of spirochete-infected squirrels or because of tick bites not suspected.

In 1930 and 1931, cases of relapsing fever were contracted at elevations above 5,000 feet in San Bernardino, Eldorado, and Sierra counties in California. An undescribed *Ornithodoros* was collected in several areas in the Sierra Nevada, and in 1935 Wheeler, who had an attack of the disease in 1930, described this as *O. hermsi*. Proof that this species is capable of transmitting the infection to human beings was secured by Wheeler, using human subjects. From 1921 to 1944 inclusive, 283 cases of relapsing fever were reported in California, with epidemiologic evidence pointing to their origin in the Sierra Nevada at elevations of 5,000–10,000 feet. *Ornithodoros hermsi* Wheeler, Herms, and Meyer has since been taken in all endemic areas of California as high as 10,000-feet elevation, and as far north as Kamloops, British Columbia.

The largest outbreak of tick-borne relapsing fever reported to date from the Western Hemisphere involved eleven cases in March, 1968, among boy scouts camped near Spokane, Washington. All but one of these cases had occupied old rodent-infested cabins. Rodents were abundant, particularly chipmunks (*Eutamias*), and specimens of *Ornithodoros hermsi* infected with *Borrelia hermsii* were collected

from rodent nesting material and rotting wood in one cabin (unpublished communication from Dr. R. S. Thompson, Washington State Department of Health).

Ornithodoros hermsi (Fig. 18-19) transmits the infection by the *bite* of both male and female ticks and in all stages of development. The strain of *Borrelia hermsii* appears to be specific for this tick, a finding confirmed by Pavlovskii and Skrynnik (1959).

Weller and Graham (1930) reported infected *O. turicata* (Dugès) from central Texas; they found a cave in the Colorado River Valley of central Texas that was "literally alive with ticks, a handful of sand yielding thirty or forty of different sizes." The cave was reported to be "frequented by goats and sheep, also probably wild animals such as bats, foxes, skunks and rabbits." Some of the ticks were applied to three rabbits, allowed to feed for fifteen minutes, and then crushed and rubbed into abrasions. Spirochetes were later observed in the blood of the rabbits.

The control of tick-borne relapsing fever is best accomplished by measures designed to reduce the vectors. For a general discussion of such measures consult Chapter 6.

Avian Spirochetosis. A very destructive disease of poultry, known as "fowl spirochetosis," is traceable to *Borrelia anserina* (Sakharoff) Bergey, *et al.* (=*gallinarum* Blanchard), occurring in India, Australia, Brazil, Egypt, and Persia, and is no doubt very widely distributed. The disease attacks chickens, geese, turkeys, guinea fowls, and other birds.

Argas persicus sensu lato was proved to be a vector of this spirochete by Marchoux and Salimbeni, Balfour, Nuttal, and others. The pathogens are transmitted by fecal contamination; the tick is said to be infective six months or more. The infection is carried over from one generation of ticks to the next through the egg. It seems highly likely that other species of bird-infesting argasids could transmit the pathogen and serve as reservoir. The incubation period in the fowl is four to nine days.

Recovery from the disease is followed by immunity.

Tularemia. The causal agent of tularemia has commonly been known as *Pasteurella tularensis* (McCoy and Chapin), but the currently accepted name of *Francisella tularensis* (McCoy and Chapin) is based on the study of Philip and Owen, 1961. The disease in man follows a history of skinning rabbits or rodents, or the bite of a tick or deer fly. Symptoms include an influenzalike attack with initial severe fever, temporary remission and a further fever period of two weeks followed by a local lesion, possible conjunctivitis, and enlarged and tender lymph nodes. Streptomycin and broad-spectrum antibiotics provide effective treatment. Historical aspects of the discovery of this disease are treated in Chapter 12.

Ixodid ticks have been shown to be infected with tularemia in nature. Parker (1924) states that tularemia infection in ticks was suspected in numerous instances during the seasons of 1922 and 1923 because of the characteristic lesions at death in guinea pigs into which such ticks had been injected. Confirmation was made by cultivation of the pathogen from guinea pigs in which the tick strain had been propagated. *Dermacentor andersoni* collected from nature proved infective; also, experimentally, infection acquired by immature ticks was passed on to subsequent stages of the same generation. Later, Parker and Spencer (1926) demonstrated transovarial transmission. This is believed to be the first record of transovarial transmission of a known bacterial infection. Several species of ticks are able to transmit the infection; among them are *Dermacentor andersoni, D. occidentalis, D. variabilis, Rhipicephalus sanguineus, Amblyomma americanum,* and *Haemaphysalis leporispalustris.* These ticks are largely responsible for the maintenace of the infection in nature. *Pasteurella tularensis* has been recovered in Montana from the tick *Haemaphysalis chordeilis* (Packard) taken from infected sage hens. Davis and Kohls (1937) discovered evidence

indicating that *Ixodes pacificus* Cooley and Kohls may also be a carrier of tularemia to human beings.

The persistence of tularemia as a zoonosis is indicated from a study of the Great Salt Lake desert region, United States, covering the period 1951–64. A number of isolations were made from *Dermacentor parumapertus* Neumann on jack rabbits (*Lepus*), and a single isolation from *Dermacentor andersoni* Stiles on sheep. Further isolations included *Ixodes kingi* Bishopp, a flea, and a louse; all from small rodents (Thorpe, *et al.,* 1965). In Virginia (United States) during a nine-year period ending in 1958, 393 cases of tularemia were reported, with one quarter of these in a small south central part of the state. Many cases undoubtedly were acquired by the skinning of rabbits, but *Haemaphysalis leporispalustris* (Packard) is an important vector of the pathogen to rabbits and to meadow mice (*Microtus*) (Spencer, 1961).

Tularemia is known from Alaska (Philip, *et al.,* 1962), Canada, Venezuela, Mexico, and Japan. Since 1926 epizootics have spread from Siberia to Turkey, Iran, Israel, and over most of Europe, with cases also reported from Africa (Gelman, 1961).

PIROPLASMAS
TRANSMITTED BY TICKS

Ticks are the vectors of several important protozoan blood parasites of domestic and wild animals. The life cycle and identity of these blood parasites is still often not completely settled, nor is the function of tick vectors certain in all cases. For the role of ticks in these diseases, reviews by Riek (1966) and Arthur (1966) have proved useful. For an understanding of the developmental cycle of *Babesia* and *Theileria* in the vertebrate host, the reader is referred to Riek (1966). Texas cattle fever can serve as an introduction to the piroplasms, particularly from the historical viewpoint.

Texas Cattle Fever. Bovine piroplasmosis (babesiosis, splenic fever, bloody murrain, Mexican fever, red water, and so forth) is a widely distributed disease of cattle, endemic in southern Europe, Central and South America, parts of Africa, the Philippines, Mexico, and formerly in the southern United States, where it was known for more than a century, having been introduced into this country probably from Europe. Eradication of the tick vectors of the causal organism, *Babesia bigemina* (Smith and Kilbourne), a haemosporidian protozoon (Fig. 18-28), eliminated the disease from the United States; constant vigilance prevents its reintroduction from countries where it is still prevalent. No bovine babesiosis has become established in the United States since 1939.

The disease was named Texas fever in the United States because large herds driven northward from Texas passed a certain disease in some mysterious manner to northern cattle. In 1889 Smith made his epoch-making discovery of the intracorpuscular protozoon parasite inhabiting blood of the diseased cattle. Smith and Kilbourne, on suggestion of Salmon, who studied the disease earlier, proved the disease to be tick-borne. Previously infection was variously attributed to saliva, urine, or feces. The work of Smith and Kilbourne (1893) marks a most important milestone in studying protozoon disease and in the history of preventive medicine. It made possible the elimination of Texas cattle fever from the United States.

The disease may be acute during the summer months, and chronic during autumn and early winter. Vast numbers of red corpuscles are destroyed by the parasites, accounting for the reddish color of the urine through the elimination of hemoglobin by the kidneys. It is believed hyperactivity of the liver in attempting to transform the excess of destroyed corpuscles into bile causes this organ to malfunction, and eventually may result in fatal termination. Mortality in the acute form ranges from 50 to 75 per cent. The chronic form of the disease, according to Mohler (1930), shows milder symptoms resembling the acute type.

The tick responsible for transmission of the protozoon causing Texas cattle fever in the United States was the cattle tick, *Boophilus annulatus* (Say). Other tick vectors are *B. microplus* (Canestrini) and *B. decoloratus* (Koch) within their range—for the former, Mexico, Central America, southern Florida, South America, the Oriental region, Australia, and parts of Africa; and for the latter, Africa. *Haemaphysalis punctata* Canestrini and Fanzango is the chief vector in Europe, and species of *Rhipicephalus* are vectors in Africa (Richardson and Kendall, 1957). Piroplasmas other than Texas cattle fever occur in one form or another in most domestic animals.

Equine Piroplasmosis. At least two types of piroplasmosis are found in horses, mules, and donkeys, namely, true equine piroplasmosis, traceable to *Babesia caballi* (Nuttal), occurring in Africa, and the Soviet Union, and, second, a similar though distinct disease traceable to *Babesia equi* Laveran occurring in Transcaucasia, Italy, Africa, India, and South America (Brazil). *Babesia caballi* is transmitted by three species of *Dermacentor,* one of *Anocentor,* four of *Hyalomma,* and two of *Rhipicephalus*; and *Babesia equi* is transmitted by two species of *Dermacentor,* one of *Anocentor,* four of *Hyalomma,* and three of *Rhipicephalus.*

Anocentor (Dermacentor) nitens (Neumann), the tropical horse tick, was first described in the United States from southern Texas in about 1908. Surveys in 1960–63 showed it well established in the southern half of Florida, and it was also collected in Georgia. In a two-year period ending in September, 1963, 141 cases of equine piroplasmosis were registered from Florida (Strickland and Gerrish, 1964). By fluorescent antibody technique it was established that both species of equine *Babesia* (=*Piroplasma*) were present in Florida (Ristic,

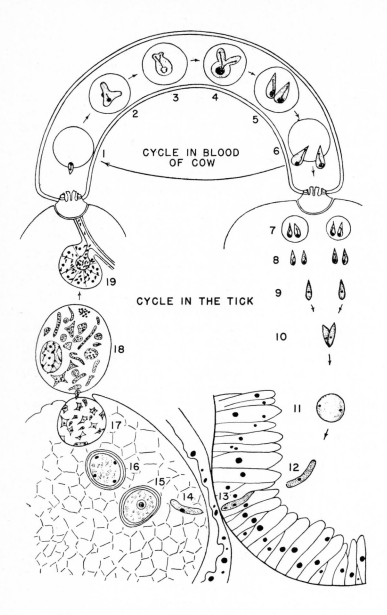

Fig. 18-28 A schematic diagram of the life cycle of *Babesia bigemina*. (*1–6*) The cycle in the bovine host, showing binary fission; (*7*) parasite just taken into the gut of the tick; (*8*) freed trophozoites in the gut of the tick; (*9*) vermicule-like isogametes; (*10*) beginning of syngamy, association of the gametes in pairs; (*11*) completion of syngamy; (*12*) motile zoite or ookinete; (*13–14*) ookinete passing through wall of gut of tick, through the oviduct, and entering the ovum; (*15*) sporont formed by the rounding-up and growth of the ookinete; (*16–17*) formation of sporoblasts; (*18*) sporokinetes in one of the large cells which are destined to form part of a salivary acinus; (*19*) sporozoites in a salivary gland (a single acinus shown) of the larva of the tick, whence they are transferred into the blood of a new host. (After Dennis.). Some investigators believe there is no evidence of a sexual cycle in the pathogen.

et al., 1964), and hereditary transmission of *B. caballi* by *Anocentor nitens* was demonstrated (Roby, *et al.,* 1964).

Canine babesiosis (piroplasmosis), also known as "malignant jaundice" of dogs is prevalent in southern Europe, Asia, South Africa, and the United States. The causal organism is *Babesia canis* (Piana and Galli-Valerio). *Rhipicephalus sanguineus* is a vector in many parts of the world; *Hyalomma marginatum* Koch and *H. plumbeum* (Panzer) in Russia; *Haemaphysalis leachi* (Audouin) in South Africa; *Dermacentor reticulatus* (Fabricius), *D. marginatus* (Sulzer), and *Ixodes ricinus* (Linnaeus) in southern Europe. Brumpt and Larousse (1922) demonstrated *Dermacentor andersoni* can carry the disease. The infection is transovarian in the tick, but transmission to the dog is effected by the bite of the adults, not by the bite of larvae or nymphs, according to Brumpt (1919). The incubation period is ten to twenty days. Sanders (1937) reported that *R. sanguineus* is by far the most common species encountered in kennels and on animals affected with canine babesiosis in Florida.

The developmental cycle of piroplasmas is still a matter of some controversy. As studied by Dennis (1932) and illustrated in Figure 18-28, sexual stages involving gametes of equal size were thought to be present. However, Riek (1966), citing his own studies on *Babesia bigemina* and *B. bovis* in the tick *Boophilus microplus,* and other investigators with different species of *Babesia* and various tick vectors, states that there is no irrefutable evidence for a sexual cycle. Arthur (1966) cites various investigations that suggest babesias of domestic animals and higher animals may have a reservoir in rodents.

East Coast fever is a highly fatal disease of cattle in eastern, central, and southern Africa. The mortality may run over 90 per cent and may, in endemic areas, take 80 per cent of the cattle crop annually. The disease is caused by the protozoon, *Theileria parva* (Theiler), family Theileridae. Unlike red water, it is not readily transmitted by means of blood inoculations, nor accompanied by jaundice or hemoglobinuria. A very characteristic symptom is swelling of the superficial lymphatic glands.

The disease is transmitted by several species of ticks as reported by Lounsbury as early as 1906. The adult brown tick, *Rhipicephalus appendiculatus* Neumann, is the most important vector, but the disease is also transmitted by the Cape brown tick, *R. capensis* Koch, and the red tick, *R. evertsi* Neumann. Robson, *et al.* (1961), suggest local epizootics of East Coast fever in Tanzania are determined mainly by taller grass cover (providing improved survival of ticks) resulting from lower stocking rates. The cyclic development of *Theileria parva* has been followed in *Rhipicephalus appendiculatus* Neumann by Martin, *et al.* (1964), who found that only developmental stages in the salivary glands and ducts could be said a part of the normal life cycle. Multiplication in this site was by multiple fission, with no sexual stages discovered. The parasites died before their tick hosts, which became noninfective thirty-four to forty weeks after becoming adults.

Henning (1932) states that, unlike red water, East Coast fever is not transmitted from the adult female tick to the larvae through the egg, but only by an adult tick that became infected during its nymphal stage or by a nymph that became infected during the larval stage. A single tick can transmit the infection only once, and that during the stage following the one in which it had the infectious meal.

Another *Theileria, T. mutans,* has been associated with cattle in the United States (Splitter, 1950), and is transmitted to cattle in Hokkaido, Japan by *Hemaphysalis bispinosa* Neumann (Namba, 1963). Theileriosis of deer is also known, though the taxonomic status of the pathogens involved is uncertain (Ristic, 1966).

Bovine Anaplasmosis. Anaplasmosis is an important and virtually worldwide infection of cattle caused by minute punctiform blood parasites, described by Theiler in 1910 as

Anaplasma marginale with the organism at or near the periphery of the red cells, and *A. centrale*, a somewhat smaller body, located approximately in the center of the infected corpuscle. The latter species is relatively benign.

Anaplasmosis is an acute, subacute, or chronic, febrile, infectious, protozoan disease. The average mortality ranges from 30–50 per cent in the animals affected. Mechanical transmission of the infection by several species of tabanid flies has been reported, and Stiles (1939) records seventeen species of ticks incriminated by various investigators; among them *Boophilus annulatus* (Say), *B. decoloratus* (Koch), *B. microplus* (Canestrini), *Rhipicephalus simus* Koch, *R. bursa* Canestrini and Fanzango, *Ixodes ricinus* (Linnaeus), *Hyalomma lusitanicum* (Koch), *Rhipicephalus sanguineus* (Latreille), *Dermacentor variabilis* (Say), *D. andersoni* (Stiles), and *D. occidentalis* Neumann. Transovarian transmission has been demonstrated.

That black-tailed deer, *Odocoileus hemionus columbianus* (Richardson), and mule deer, *O. hemionus hemionus* (Rafinesque), may serve as reservoirs for anaplasmosis was proved by Boynton and Woods in 1933.

TICK PARALYSIS

A paralysis of sheep and calves attributable to ticks has been known in Australia according to Henning (1932) since 1843. Paralysis reported as "acute ascending paralysis" associated with tick bite was described by Temple (1912) in Oregon. The case reported was that of a child in which paralysis of the motor and sensory nerves extending to the knees caused inability to stand in the morning after the child had retired in apparently good health. On the third day the paralysis had ascended to where the child was unable to swallow or speak. Upon removal of two fully engorged ticks from the occipital region, recovery was complete within a week. The ticks were not positively identified, but were presumably *Dermacentor andersoni*. Hadwen (1913) re-

ported paralysis in sheep following the bite of *Dermacentor andersoni* (*D. venustus* Banks). He also cites from letters by physicians in British Columbia (*Canada Med. Assoc. J.*, 1912, p. 686) indicating frequent paralysis in children following tick bites. The ticks were commonly removed from the nape of the neck. Hadwen and Nuttal (1913) produced paralysis like that of sheep in the dog by means of *D. andersoni*.

On a weight basis man appears to be more sensitive to tick paralysis than any other mammal (Gregson, 1958). Gregson has shown that, among North American wild mammals, none of the larger species, except the bison, *Bison b. bison* (Linnaeus), is known to be paralyzed; moose, bighorn sheep, Rocky Mountain goats, and bears do not seem to be susceptible. Deer were originally believed to be insusceptible to tick paralysis, but paralysis of these animals has been observed (Wilkinson, 1965; Brunetti; 1965). On the other hand, domestic cattle, horses, domestic sheep, and dogs may be paralyzed or killed by one or a small number of ticks. Gregson has shown that the yellow-bellied marmot, *Marmota flaviventris avara* (Bangs), and the Columbian ground squirrel, *Citellus c. columbianus* (Ord), are readily paralyzed, a fact confirmed by Hughes and Philip (1958), and additionally the hamster and the bushy-tailed wood rat *Neotoma cinerea* (Ord). The hamster is a convenient experimental animal for studying this disease.

In man, tick paralysis is characterized by flaccid ascending paralysis that, in fatal cases, causes death by respiratory failure. Unlike poliomyelitis, with which it may be confused, in its early stages it is painless and without fever, or relatively so. It is most frequently observed in children under two years of age. In North America, it occurs chiefly in the Pacific Northwest (Rose, 1954) but has become more common (or better recognized) in the eastern United States.

The disease is not caused by a pathogenic organism, but rather by a toxin produced during the feeding of some female ticks. The nature of the toxin is not yet understood, but that of *D. andersoni* produces a blockage of the neuromuscular junctions and probably some of the synapses of the spinal cord (Murnaghan, 1958); other specific types of neuromuscular activity may be affected. The *andersoni* toxin apparently is produced, in sufficient quantities to cause paralysis, only by some females five to nine days after attachment. The toxin either decomposes or is excreted rapidly, as removal of the tick before the paralysis has proceeded too far leads to rapid and complete recovery. The reason some ticks may produce paralysis, and others of the same sex and species do not is not known; a hereditary factor may be involved, as *D. andersoni* from British Columbia cause paralysis more frequently than the same tick from Montana (Hughes and Philip, 1958).

A valuable account of the disease, its etiology, diagnosis, and treatment, and a detailed description of a typical case history, has been given by Costa (1952). Although the disease is rare, accurate and rapid diagnosis is essential to save human lives. Rose (1954) lists 332 cases from the Pacific Northwest, 39 fatal, all of which almost certainly could have been saved had the tick been removed in time.

Livestock are at times seriously involved. Herds of cattle in Montana have become paralyzed and died, either from the paralysis itself or from predators taking advantage of the helpless animals. Hearle (1938), speaking of conditions in Canada, states:

Cases in sheep have been particularly numerous, and many deaths have resulted. Cattle are usually less susceptible, but trouble from tick paralysis has been noted from time to time, and in the spring of 1930 a serious outbreak in steers was investigated; over 100 paralysis cases, sixty of them fatal, being noted in one herd. We know of only one equine case. In sheep districts where this trouble is prevalent, flock masters are obliged to examine their animals frequently for the purpose of removing the offending ticks from sheep showing symptoms of weakness or staggers.

Gregson (1966) reports on 189 outbreaks of tick paralysis of livestock by *D. andersoni* in British Columbia, Canada, involving over 2,010 cattle, 1,849 sheep, and a few horses and dogs. Most of the economic losses from this disease, now that herders are thoroughly familiar with it, result from the extra manpower needed to care for affected animals, from unthrifty animals, and from avoiding otherwise valuable pasture.

In the eastern and southern United States, *Dermacentor variabilis, Amblyomma americanum,* and *A. maculatum* Koch produce tick paralysis in man and dogs. Most tick paralysis in the United States, however, is associated with *Dermacentor andersoni.*

Tick paralysis is also known from other parts of the world. In South Australia *Ixodes holocyclus* Neumann, or perhaps any of five closely related species, is held responsible for paralysis of calves, foals, sheep, dogs, and cats (Roberts, 1961). Paralysis of young chickens in Bulgaria has been attributed to nymphs of *Haemaphysalis punctata* Canestrini and Fanzango (Pavlov, 1963). A review of tick paralysis from the Karoo areas of South Africa (Stampa, 1959) attributes human cases of localized and general paralysis to *Rhipicephalus simus* Koch, *Hyalomma truncatum* Koch, and *Ixodes rubicundus* Neumann. This same account relates paralysis of sheep, goats, cattle, dogs (exceptionally), and some antelopes to adult female *Ixodes rubicundus,* with up to 15 per cent of stock lost on some farms in 1951; cases in most of South Africa of calves, lambs, and adult sheep paralyzed by *Rhipicephalus evertsi* Neumann; leg weakness of geese and ducks, with low recovery rate, by *Argas persicus* (Oken) in several parts of South Africa.

19

MITES AND MITE-BORNE DISEASES

Characteristics. In the mites, as in the ticks, the abdomen is broadly joined to the cephalothorax with little or no evidence of segmentation. All but a few species are minute, i.e., barely visible to the unaided eye. Mites, like other arachnids, have with a few exceptions—such as certain animal parasites where the number may be reduced, and plant-feeding Eriophyidae—four pairs of legs as adults but only three pairs in the larval stage. The mouth parts are quite varied but follow the general pattern of the ticks. A hypostome is lacking in many mites, but in Mesostigmata it is well developed, though not as a holdfast organ with rows of teeth as in the ticks. The chelicerae of the parasitic species are rasping or piercing structures. Eyes are absent, or one or more pairs of simple eyes may occur. The respiratory system is in most species similar to that of the ticks, i.e., tracheal, whereas others absorb oxygen through the soft general body surface. Nearly all species deposit eggs; however, a few are ovoviviparous, e.g., *Pyemotes ventricosus* (Newport). From the egg there emerges the hexapod larva, which usually soon molts, becoming the nymph and acquiring its fourth pair of legs. The life cycle of many species requires less than four weeks; in some it is as short as eight days.

Mites may be of medical or veterinary importance in any of three ways: (1) through transmission of pathogenic agents either as vectors or as intermediate hosts; (2) by causing dermatitis or other tissue damage directly; (3) through loss of blood or other tissue fluids. An infestation of mites is called *acariasis*. Although mites are commonly thought of as external parasites, some mites may cause damage in the inner and middle ear, the respiratory passages and lungs, lymphatic tissues, and nasal passages.

Although Baker and Wharton (1952) recognize more than 200 families of mites, only a few contain species that affect man and domestic animals. The identification of mites, even the few species of medical importance, is difficult, but the student is referred to Baker and Wharton's *An Introduction to Acarology*; to Baker, Camin, Cunliffe, Wooley, and Yunker's *Guide to the Families of Mites* (1958), to Baker, Evans, Gould, Hull, and Keegan's *A Manual of Parasitic Mites* (1956), to Pratt's *Mites of Public Health Importance and Their Control* (1963), to Strandtmann and Wharton's *Manual of Mesostigmatid Mites Parasitic on Vertebrates* (1958), to Wharton and Fuller's *A Manual of the Chiggers* (1952), and to Brennan and Jones' "Key to the Chiggers of North America" (1959). Radford (1943) has published a very helpful list of "Genera and Species of Parasitic Mites," which gives the authority, year of validity, and where possible the original host. Oudemans' (1937) monumental work is a standard reference source for acarologists; see also Vitzthum (1943) for an important foundation work.

Further general information may be obtained from *Terrestrial Acari of the British Isles* (Evans, *et al.* 1961); *A Review of the Phylogeny of Mites* (Woolley, 1961); *Current Trends in the Systematics of Acarines Endoparasitic in Vertebrates* (Hyland, 1963); and *The Laboratory Rearing of Parasitic Acarina* (Audy and Lavoipierre, 1964).

Taxonomy. Mites, along with the ticks, constitute the order Acarina of the Arachnida, but acarologists are not in agreement as to where the division into suborders should be made. Baker and Wharton divide the order into five suborders: Onychopalpida, Mesostigmata, Trombidiiformes, Ixodides, and Sarcoptiformes. Many specialists prefer to unite, on morphologic grounds, the Mesostigmata and Ixodides into a single suborder, the Parasitiformes. However, for the sake of simplicity, it seems better for the purpose of this work to accept the Baker and Wharton classification, even though this will not show

the phylogenetic relationships between ticks and the mesostigmatid mites. See Evans, *et al.* (1961), for a different division of the order Acari.

The following key will aid in separating the suborders of mites. One must remember, however, that some structures, particularly the spiracles and associated peritremes, are difficult or impossible to see unless the specimen has been properly cleared and mounted. Figure 19-1 illustrates various features used in identification. In many cases the use of a phase contrast compound microscope and properly prepared specimens on slide mounts is practically a necessity to determine fine details, especially when species determinations are attempted.

KEY TO THE SUBORDERS OF MITES

1. Stigmata present laterad to the legs and usually ventrally located; peritreme (a sclerotized tube or depression extending forward from the spiracle) usually present; no rodlike sensory setae on tarsi I 2
Stigmata absent, or, if present, not lateral in position; peritremes sometimes present; rodlike sensory setae usually present on tarsi I 3
2. Two pairs of stigmata present; coxae of pedipalp not fused dorsally . . . .*Onychopalpida*
One pair of stigmata present, located usually behind and laterad of the third coxa; coxae of pedipalpi fused dorsally so that the base of the gnathosoma (fused ventral parts of three segments enclosing mouth and bearing chelicerae and pedipalps) forms a tube that encloses the mouth parts . . . .*Mesostigmata*
3. Stigmata usually present and located on or near the gnathosoma; chelicerae usually modified into stylets for piercing; pedipalpi usually free and highly developed; anal suckers never present . . . . *Trombidiiformes*
Stigmata absent, or if present not on or near the gnathosoma; chelicerae pincer-

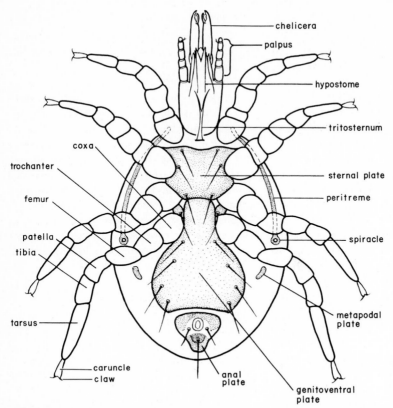

Fig. 19-1 General structure of a mite, ventral view. (Courtesy of U.S. Public Health Service.)

like, for tearing; pedipalpi simple; anal suckers frequently present . . . . *Sarcoptiformes*

THE MESOSTIGMATID MITES

Most mesostigmatids of recognized medical and veterinary importance belong to the families Dermanyssidae and Macronyssidae. A few others, however, deserve mention.

The Haemogamasidae are medium-sized, oval mites, heavily clothed with setae that give the body, both dorsally and ventrally, a furry appearance. They are parasitic on small mammals all over the world. *Haemogamasus pontiger* (Berlese) was suspected of causing dermatitis on soldiers who slept on straw-filled

mattresses in England during World War II (Baker, *et al.*, 1956). *Haemogamasus ambulans* (Thorell) (=*nidi* Michael), the lelapid *Andro-laelaps fahrenholzi* (Berlese), and the lelapid *Hirstionyssus isabellinus* (Oudemans) (=*arvicolae* Zemska), taken from small mammal nests and burrows (*Microtus, Apodemus, Sorex*), were shown to harbor the etiologic agent of hemorrhagic nephrosonephritis (epidemic hemorrhagic fever) of the Far East (Chumakov, 1957). The close association of haemogamasid mites with small mammals suggests that they may have some bearing on the transmission of plague, typhus, tularemia, and perhaps other diseases (Baker and Wharton, 1952).

Several mesostigmatid mites are internal parasites on domestic animals. The canary lung mite, *Sternostoma tracheacolum* Lawrence (family Rhinonyssidae), which invades the trachea, air sacs, bronchi, and parenchyma of the lungs of canaries, may cause illness and even death. *Pneumonyssoides caninum* (Chandler and Ruhe) (Family Halarachnidae) attacks the sinuses and nasal passages of dogs, usually with benign results, and a related species, *Pneumonyssus simicola* Banks, inhabits the lungs of monkeys. Human pulmonary acariasis is apparently due not to halarachnids but rather to free-living species (Baker and Wharton, 1952).

The house fly mite, *Macrocheles muscaedomesticae* (Scopoli) (Family Macrochelidae), is of interest because the nymph and adult prey upon the eggs and first-stage larvae of the house fly.

The cattle ear mite, *Raillietia auris* (Leidy): family Raillietidae, is often common and has been reported from the United States, Europe, and India. It is not considered to be parasitic but rather is believed to feed on ear wax and sloughed epidermal cells.

Families Dermanyssidae and Macronyssidae. An important group of mesostigmatid mites includes the tropical rat mite, *Ornithonyssus bacoti* (Hirst); the northern fowl mite, *O. sylviarum* (Canestrini and Fanzago); the tropical fowl mite, *O. bursa* (Berlese); the chicken mite, *Dermanyssus gallinae* (De Geer); the house mouse mite, *Liponyssoides* (=*Allodermanyssus*) *sanguineus* (Hirst); and others. Baker and Wharton (1952) discussed this complex (as the family Dermanyssidae):

Dermanyssids are medium-sized mites. The dorsal plate is either undivided in the female or is divided so that the anterior plate is large and the posterior one extremely small. The ventral plates of the female are typical of the sub-order except that they are somewhat reduced. The sternal plate has three pairs of setae, while the metasternal plates are reduced and lateral to the genital plate. The genito-ventral plate is drop-shaped posteriorly. The anal plate has three characteristic setae. In the Dermanyssidae the chelicerae may be extremely elongated and terminate in a minute shear so that they appear to be a pair of needle-like structures, or they may be more normal with merely reduced chelae. Tritosternum is present. All legs have pretarsi, caruncles, and claws.

Radovsky (1967) has separated out the Macronyssidae as *Ornithonyssus* and its relatives, and the Dermanyssidae as *Dermanyssus* and *Liponyssoides* (=*Allodermanyssus*), but we are following Baker and his coworkers in grouping all these together.

The genus *Ornithonyssus* (=*Liponyssus* of Authors, *Bdellonyssus* Fonseca) includes a homogeneous group of mostly tropical species, according to the diagnosis of Strandtmann and Wharton (1958). This genus has been further characterized by Furman and Radovsky (1963).

The tropical rat mite, *Ornithonyssus bacoti* (Hirst) (Fig. 19-2) was first recorded from rats (*Rattus norvegicus*) in Egypt by Hirst (1913) and described in the genus *Leiognathus*. This mite is now reported from many parts of the world as irritating to man; it occurs on all continents and in temperate as well as tropical regions. Bishopp (1923) states: "The bite is distinctly painful at the time the mouth parts are inserted. A sharp itching pain is usually experienced. Usually there is more or less irritation and itching at the site of the bite for several hours along with the development of a small haemorrhagic area." Whether or not a severe dermatitis results depends on the sensitivity of the host.

The tropical rat mite has not been incriminated in the natural transmission of any human disease. Dove and Shelmire (1932)

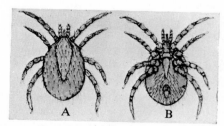

Fig. 19-2 The tropical rat mite, *Ornithonyssus bacoti. A.* Dorsal view. *B.* Ventral view. (After Dove and Shelmire.)

reported having experimentally transmitted the Texas strain of endemic typhus through the bite of this mite from guinea pig to guinea pig. Hopla (1951) found that infections of the tularemia bacillus acquired by immature mites during feeding can be passed to subsequent stages and their progeny, but their bite is noninfectious; Yamada (1932) obtained experimental transmission of plague with this mite. Philip and Hughes (1948) found it an experimental vector of rickettsialpox. Williams and Brown (1945) and Bertram, *et al.* (1946), have demonstrated that *O. bacoti* acts as an intermediate host of a filariid worm, *Litomosoides carinii* (Trav.), a parasite of the cotton rat, *Sigmodon hispidus* Say and Ord.

Life Cycle. Strandtman and Wharton (1958) summarized the life cycle of the tropical rat mite, based upon the studies of various investigators. There are five developmental stages: adult male and female, egg, nonfeeding larva, bloodsucking protonymph, and nonfeeding deutonymph. Engorgement by the protonymph and the adults of both sexes completes the life cycle. Unfertilized females may produce males only. The life cycle from egg to adult requires seven to sixteen days at room temperatures if food is available for the protonymph, with a minimum of thirteen days from egg to egg. Unfed protonymphs have survived forty-three days. Adult females live an average of sixty-one days and produce eggs after each feeding for a total of about 100 per female. Nymphs and adults readily leave nests and harborages of the host and travel for some distance to attack persons in situations where rats abound or have been recently.

Poultry Mites. *The tropical fowl mite, Ornithonyssus bursa* (Berlese), is a poultry pest in tropical and subtropical areas on all continents, including the warmer parts of the United States. It appears to be a widespread parasite of the English sparrow, *Passer domesticus*, as well as of the domestic fowl. Other bird species may be attacked. Although man is frequently bitten by this mite, only a slight irritation is reported. Because the mite

cannot exist for more than ten days apart from its avian host, annoyance to man is temporary.

The northern fowl mite, Ornithonyssus sylviarum (Canestrini and Fanzago), closely resembles the tropical fowl mite. It is a widespread parasite of poultry in the north temperate region and has been recorded from New Zealand and Australia. It will at times cause itching of man by its bite and by crawling over the skin, being especially bothersome in the absence of bird hosts, or severely affecting persons collecting and processing eggs from heavily infested flocks. Survival up to six weeks in the absence of avian hosts is known (communication from Furman to Harwood).

The chicken mite, Dermanyssus gallinae (De Geer) (Fig. 19-3), (red chicken mite or roost mite) is a pest of chickens throughout the world. Other poultry such as turkeys, as well as pigeons, English sparrows, and other birds, may be infested. Though man is commonly annoyed by crawling mites, instances of actual biting appear rare. In daytime, the mites hide in crevices of henhouses and roosts, under boards and debris. In these hiding places they deposit their eggs. At night mites leave their hiding places and attack the birds on the roosts. Damage is considerable and may be summarized as follows: Egg production is

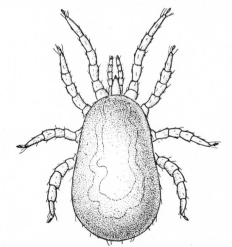

Fig. 19-3 The chicken mite, *Dernamyssus gallinae.*

greatly reduced or entirely prevented; setting hens often leave their nests or perish; newly hatched chicks die when attacked by a large number of these mites; chickens are unthrifty and unprofitable for marketing; loss of blood and reduced vitality cause increased susceptibility to disease. The chicken mite is quite resistant to starvation, surviving in laboratory tests for as long as thirty-four weeks without a blood meal (Kirkwood, 1963).

The Role of Bird Mites in the Epidemiology of Arthropod-Borne Encephalitides. In 1942 Hammon, *et al.* (1942), demonstrated that a large percentage of wild birds as well as domestic fowl possess neutralizing antibodies for western equine and St. Louis encephalitis. Discoveries that *Dermanyssus gallinae* and *Ornithonyssus sylviarum* could harbor encephalitis viruses and could transmit them experimentally led to the theory that, in the transmission of encephalitis, two bloodsucking vectors may be involved: one, a chicken mite, in which the virus is maintained in nature by transovarian passage, and the other, a *mosquito*, which transmits the infection from birds to other vertebrates, including man. Critical field and laboratory studies by Reeves, *et al.* (1955), Chamberlain and Sikes (1955), Sulkin, *et al.* (1955), and Chamberlain, *et al.* (1957), failed to indicate any definite relationship between the infection of a mite with the viruses of St. Louis or western (equine) encephalitis and their transmission. It now appears mite transmission of these viruses is of little importance. Recovery of the viruses from mites probably means they had fed recently upon viremic birds.

The House Mouse Mite. *Liponyssoides* (=*Allodermanyssus*) *sanguineus* (Hirst) (Fig. 19-4) is known to occur in northern Africa, Asia, Europe, and the United States. The house mouse, *Mus musculus*, is the preferred host, but the mite will feed on rats and other rodents and will readily attack man. This mite is important because of its transmission of rickettsialpox to man.

Ewing (1929) describes *L. sanguineus* as follows:

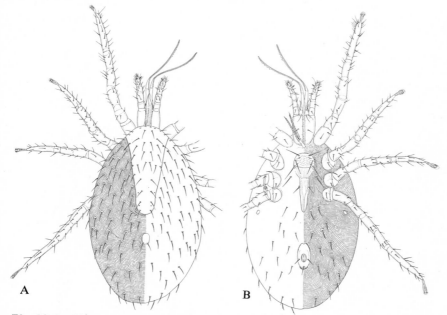

A   B

Fig. 19-4 *Liponyssoides sanguineus,* the house mouse mite. *A.* Dorsal view of male. *B.* Ventral view of female. (From Baker *et al., A Manual of Parasitic Mites of Medical or Economic Importance,* 1956; courtesy of National Pest Control Association.)

Palpi slender, reaching to the tips of anterior femora; chelicerae showing plainly the needle-like elements representing both arms. Dorsal shield divided; anterior shield broadest at the shoulders, lateral margins behind the shoulders concave; posterior shield circular, minute. Sternal plate squarish, lying entirely between the second coxae, with three pairs of subequal marginal setae. Anal plate egg-shaped in outline, anterior margin broadly rounded; anus situated centrally, rim very thin in front and on the sides, but enormously thickened behind; paired setae situated at the level of the center of the anus; median seta situated about two-thirds its length behind anus; caudal area reaching about halfway to the base of median seta. Legs very long and slender. Length, 0.91 mm; width, 0.46 mm.

Life History. As in most dermanyssid mites, there are five developmental stages; unlike the tropical rat mite, both nymphal instars take a blood meal. Adult females feed often, each feeding being followed by oviposition. The total period from deposition of the egg to emergence of the adult is seventeen to twenty-three days. Unfed females have lived as long as fifty-one days, and a female that had fed and oviposited twice lived nine weeks. Engorged nymphs and adults may be found, sometimes in great numbers, in buildings, in the vicinity of rodent nests and runways. A good summary of the life history of this mite is given by Baker, *et al.* (1956).

Identification of Dermanyssid Mites. For the identification of the dermanyssid mites, the student is referred to the works of Baker, *et al.* (1956), Strandtmann and Wharton (1958), Evans and Till (1966), and Radovsky (1967).

THE HOLOTHYRIDAE

SUBORDER ONCHOPALPIDA

The Family Holothyridae includes the largest known mites, some of which reach a length of 7 mm. One species, *Holothyrus coccinella* Gervais, is of some medical importance. On the island of Mauritius this mite is said to cause the death of ducks and chickens that swallow it, due to a toxic secretion it produces. Children are also affected through handling the mites and then touching their mouths with their fingers.

THE ITCH, MANGE, AND SCABIES MITES

SUBORDER SARCOPTIFORMES

Characteristics. Two groups of mites make up the Sarcoptiformes: the Acaridiae and the Oribatei. These, according to Baker and Wharton, have coxae forming characteristic plates (apodemes) beneath the skin on the venter of the body; chelicerae usually pincer-like or scissorslike, fitted for chewing; palpi simple.

Oribatei may serve as intermediate hosts of tapeworms including *Moniezia expansa* Rudolphi, a common parasite of ruminants (Allred, 1954). The vertebrate host ingests free-living oribatid mites that are common in pastures and may harbor the tapeworm cysticercoid. It has been suggested that some measure of control of tapeworm acquisition could be achieved by restricting the period of grazing to times when the host mites were less numerous in vegetation, but a study in the state of Kentucky showed one oribatid host to be common in vegetation at a steady density throughout the day (Wallwork and Rodriguez, 1961).

The integument of oribatids is leathery or strongly sclerotized; tarsi have one to three claws but lack caruncles (delicate, transparent suckerlike structures between the claws); sexes similar; respiratory system consisting of a complex of tracheae opening through stigmata or porous areas in many regions of the body. (Fig. 19-5.)

The Acaridiae are Sarcoptiformes of greater medical importance. These are weak-skinned, without tracheae and stigmata; caruncles usually present on tarsi; sexual dimorphism often well marked with males frequently having copulatory suckers on tarsi or anal region. Acaridiae of medical importance include the

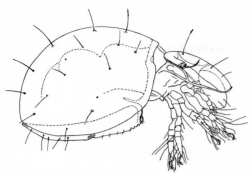

Fig. 19-5 An oribatid mite, *Pseudotritia ardua*, lateral view of female. (From Baker *et al.*, *A Manual of Parasitic Mites of Medical or Economic Importance*, 1956; courtesy of National Pest Control Association.)

families Acaridae, Glycyphagidae, Epidermoptidae, and Sarcoptidae. The family Psoroptidae is of considerable veterinary importance.

Family Acaridae (=Tyroglyphidae). A sizable group of very tiny mites, ordinarily about 0.5 mm or less in length. Several species consume grain, flour, meal, dried meat, hams, dried fruits, insect collections and so forth. Development is so rapid that literally millions of them may appear in a stored product in a few days. Persons handling stored products of various kinds, cereal, flour, or meal, may experience a severe dermatitis. It is uncertain whether the reaction is caused by the bites or simple allergy.

The metamorphosis of this group involves a peculiar stage known as the *hypopus*, appearing in a number of species between the two nymphal stages, very unlike either of these and very different from the adult. This is a phoretic stage in which the mites attach themselves, nonparasitically, to flies and other insects, which disseminate them.

Acarus siro Linnaeus is the grain mite or cheese mite, found in grain, stored products, and cheese; this mite causes a rash known as "vanillism" in vanilla pod handlers. *Tyrophagus castellanii* (Hirst) causes "copra itch" among workers handling copra; dermatitis caused by this mite also affects dock workers

who handle cheese. The exact cause of the dermatitis is not known but it is likely an allergic condition.

Baker, *et al.* (1956), have summarized reports of mites involved in human pulmonary, urinary, and intestinal acariasis. *Tyrophagus longior* (Gervais), a free-living form, has been reported from both the digestive and urinary tract. Acarids, as well as representatives of other sarcoptiform families, have been recovered from the sputum of patients suffering from lung disorders.

Family Glycyphagidae. *Glycyphagus domesticus* (De Geer), often found in dried fruits and in such organic matter as skin and feathers, causes "grocers' itch" when highly infested material is handled. It has been reported as an intermediate host of the rodent tapeworm *Catenotaenia pusilla* (Goeze).

Family Epidermoptidae. Very small mites, 0.17–0.39 mm in length, short-oval to nearly circular in shape, and flattened; integument soft and striated; tarsi end in caruncles. This family has been thoroughly reviewed by Fain (1966). *Epidermoptes bilobatus* Rivolta causes a generalized dermatitis in fowl. The genus *Dermatophagoides* has been moved by Fain (1967) from this family to the Psoroptidae.

Family Sarcoptidae. Members of the family Sarcoptidae are commonly known as the sarcoptic itch mites or scabies mites. They are very small (at limit of human visibility), somewhat hemispherical, and whitish. They are skin parasites of warm-blooded animals. Propodosoma (part of the body bearing the two fore pairs of legs) not separated from hysterosoma (posterior body) by a suture; frequently bearing a propodosomal shield, always bearing a pair of vertical setae. In other areas the skin bears fine striae that may be interrupted by scaly areas or areas bearing small points or spines. Legs very short; claws or caruncles present or absent.

The Sarcoptidae include three important genera, *Sarcoptes*, *Notoedres*, and *Knemidokoptes* (=*Cnemidocoptes*), each producing a particular type of acariasis. Several other genera are of no medical or veterinary importance.

Sarcoptes. Mange or itch mites belong to the genus *Sarcoptes*: very short legs, the posterior pair not extending beyond the margin of the nearly circular body; caruncles with nonsegmented pedicels present on first and second pairs of legs. Sarcoptic mites burrow in the skin, forming definite burrows in which the females deposit eggs. Entry into the skin may be rapid, the adult mite holding on by means of suckers on the anterior legs, raising the hind end of its body on bristles of the posterior legs until nearly perpendicular, cutting in and completely disappearing into the skin in two and a half minutes (Taylor and Murray, 1946).

The forms of *Sarcoptes* inhabiting the skin of mammals are ordinarily regarded as varieties of *Sarcoptes scabiei* (De Geer) (Fig. 19-6). They differ very slightly from one another and many exchange hosts to a certain degree, e.g., *S. scabiei* var. *suis* Gerlach is parasitic on swine and may temporarily parasitize man (Fig. 19-7).; *S. scabiei* var. *equi* Gerlach of horses, mules, and asses causes a transitory itch of man. The forms, properly physiologic races, appropriate to a given host,

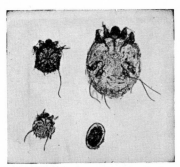

Fig. 19-7 Life history and general characteristics of a typical sarcoptid mite, *Sarcoptes scabiei* var. *suis*, the itch mite of swine: (*lower right*) egg; (*lower left*) larva; (*upper left*) adult male; (*upper right*) adult female. × 57.

however, ordinarily survive only briefly on a different host species.

Human Scabies or Itch. *Sarcoptes scabiei* (De Geer), typical form =var. *hominis* (Hering), causes "scabies," "seven-year itch," or "Norwegian itch" of man. The mite is universal in distribution. The female measures 330–450 microns in length and 250–350 microns in breadth; the male slightly more than half as large. Skin between the fingers, the bend of the knee and elbow, the penis, the breasts, and the shoulder blades are preferred, although any part of the body is attacked. Apparently newly infested persons do not experience any itching so that infestation may progress extensively before noticed. A rash appears in about a month in the neighborhood of the burrows, and an intense itching is felt. The itching, caused by toxic secretions and excretions, is associated directly with the burrowing. The sinuous burrows the mite makes in the epidermis may reach 3 cm in length (Warburton, 1920), and tiny vesicles and papules form on the surface. Scratching may cause secondary infection and result in weeping and bleeding that favor the spread of the mites. Infestation is usually effected by the adult fertilized female mite due to intimate personal contact, usually through sleeping in the same bed with an infested person. By tracing a mite burrow to its end with a hand lens,

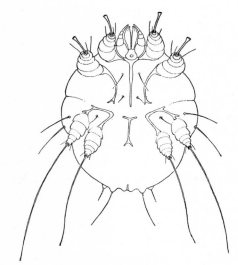

Fig. 19-6 The itch mite, *Sarcoptes scabiei.*

the female mite can usually be removed with a needle or scapel and, after treatment with potassium hydroxide on a glass slide, can be readily seen under a microscope. Long-standing chronic cases show few parasites.

Life History of the Itch Mite. The gravid female mite deposits her rather large oval eggs (150 × 100 microns) at intervals in the tortuous tunnel that she makes in the epidermis. Usually she remains in the burrow for her lifetime, depositing eggs at two- to three-day intervals for a period of about two months. The hexapod larva hatches in three to five days. Larvae move freely over the skin, and they and nymphs are frequently found in hair follicles. Within four to six days after the egg hatches, the nymph transforms into a male (which is rarely seen) or an immature female; the female makes a temporary gallery in the skin before mating. Maturity is reached in ten to fourteen days after hatching of the egg.

Sarcoptic Mange of Domestic Animals. Mange of swine is caused by *Sarcoptes scabiei* var. *suis* Gerlach (Fig. 19-7). Mange affects swine commonly about the top of the neck, shoulder, ears, and withers, and along the back to the root of the tail. A microscopic examination of deeper tissue from beneath scabs usually reveals the mites. Sucking pigs and young shoats suffer most. Animals that scratch and rub vigorously and that have the skin cracked and thickly encrusted with heavy scabs, should be examined for scab mites.

Sarcoptic acariasis in horses, mules, and asses is caused by *Sarcoptes scabiei* var. *equi* Gerlach. This species is also transmissible to man and is said to be the chief cause of a transitory itch in individuals who handle horses extensively.

Sarcoptic acariasis, or mange, of cattle caused by *Sarcoptes scabiei* var. *bovis* Robin is not so common as the psoroptic form (scabies) but is far more difficult to cure. It usually occurs where hair is short, namely on the brisket and around base of tail.

Common mange of dogs, caused by *Sarcoptes scabiei* var. *canis* Gerlach, closely re-sembles the swine parasite. Dog mange appears first on the muzzle, around the eyes, on ears, and breast, and later spreads to back, abdomen, and elsewhere.

Sarcoptes scabiei var. *ovis* Mégnin of sheep occurs primarily on the face and causes "black muzzle." In more severe cases the limbs and rarely the body, but not the woolly parts, may be affected. *S. scabiei* var. *caprae* Furstenburg of goats may be fatal.

Notoedric Mange. Mange of cats is caused by *Notoedres cati* Hering, smaller and more circular than *Sarcoptes* but otherwise quite similar; it will attack dogs and certain rodents, but apparently not man. Notoedric mange of cats begins at the tips of the ears and gradually spreads over the face and head. *Notoedres cati* var. *cuniculi* Gerlach causes a severe mange of rabbits, beginning at the muzzle and in severe cases spreading over the whole body.

Scaly Leg of Poultry. The legs of domestic fowls (chickens, turkeys, pheasants, and so forth) are frequently attacked by a microscopic burrowing mite, *Knemidokoptes mutans* (Robin and Lanquetin) (Fig. 19-8), which causes a lifting of the scales and a swollen condition of the shank with deformity and encrustation. The mites burrow and live in the skin, depositing their eggs in channels as do mange mites. Scaly leg is easily transmitted from fowl to fowl; hence, segregation is important in effecting control.

The depluming mite, *Knemidokoptes laevis* var. *gallinae* (Raillet), closely related to the scaly leg mite, attacks the skin near the bases of feathers. Intense itching caused by the mites impels the host to pluck its feathers.

Knemidokoptes pilae Lavoipierre and Griffiths has been found to cause mange of budgerigars (parakeets, *Melopsittacus*) in the United States. Information on these mites—symptoms caused, and chemical control—is in the paper of Wichmann and Vincent (1958).

Family Analgesidae, the Feather Mites. *Megninia* species have been reported as infesting domestic fowl, pigeons, and parakeets (Baker, *et al.*, 1956). *M. ginglymura* (Mégnin)

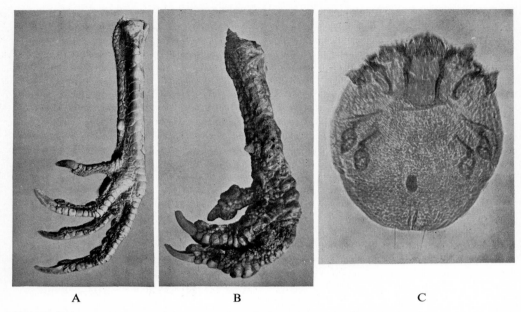

A   B   C

Fig. 19-8 *A.* Normal leg and claw of a fowl. *B.* A leg and claw affected with the scaly leg mite, *Knemidokoptes mutans*, causing scaly leg. *C.* The causal mite.

(Fig. 19-9) is suspected of causing feather picking in pullets, and in Madras (India) was related to plumage loss (Alwar, *et al.,* 1958). *M. cubitalis* (Mégnin) is reported to cause a depluming itch in poultry.

Psoroptid Mites. Mites of the family Psoroptidae attack domestic animals in a variety of ways. These mites are distinguished from the sarcoptids by propodosoma lacking vertical setae, though a dorsal shield may be present. The important genus *Psoroptes* may be distinguished from *Sarcoptes* (as well as from other genera of Psoroptidae) in that the tarsal suckers (caruncles) are borne on long, segmented stalks. Legs of Psoroptidae are longer than those of the Sarcoptidae.

Chorioptic or Symbiotic Mange. Mites of the genus *Chorioptes* produce a mange restricted to certain parts of the body such as the feet, tail, and neck. The question has arisen as to whether a number of separate species of *Chorioptes* are present, or whether there is mere physiological adaptation to specific hosts. In a careful life history study, in which

Chorioptes were raised in vials on epidermal scrapings of various hosts, Sweatman (1957) concluded that practically all previously described species are synonymous. He believes domestic cattle to be the important host species that is probably responsible for the cosmopolitan distribution of *Chorioptes bovis* (Hering) (Fig. 19-10). Synonyms are *C. equi* of horses, *C. caprae* of goats, *C. ovis* of sheep, and *C. cuniculi* of rabbits. In vial rearings it was observed that this mite fed on debris and not hair; the presence of eggs from one female attracted others to lay so that communal groups were formed. Important sites of infestation are the feet and lower hind legs of cattle and horses. A survey of forty flocks of sheep in eight widely separated states in the United States showed *C. bovis* to be present in all, and in more than half the flocks it was the commonest arthropod parasite; yet mange characterized by skin lesions was evident in only two animals (Roberts, *et al.,* 1964).

Psoroptic Mange Mites. Psoroptic mange mites (Fig. 19-11) are distinguishable from

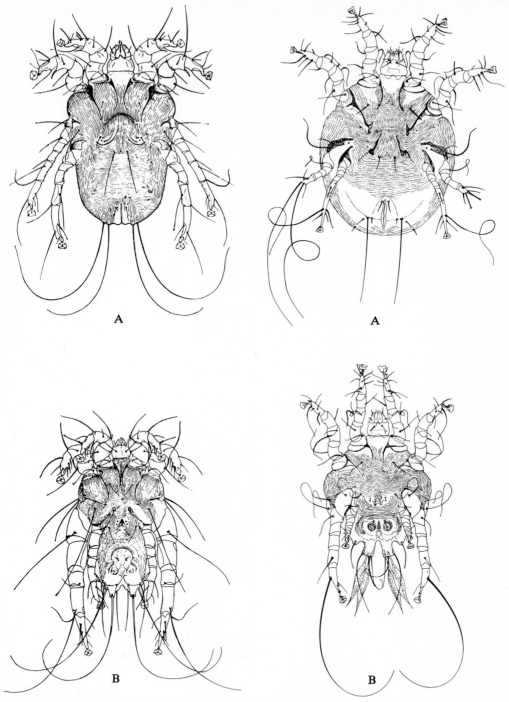

Fig. 19-9 *Megninia giglymura. A.* Ventral view of female. *B.* Ventral view of male. (From Baker *et al., A Manual of Parasitic Mites of Medical or Economic Importance,* 1956; courtesy of National Pest Control Association.)

Fig. 19-10 *Chorioptes bovis. A.* Ventral view of female. *B.* Ventral view of male. (From Baker *et al., A Manual of Parasitic Mites of Medical or Economic Importance,* 1956; courtesy of National Pest Control Association.)

Sarcoptes in that all four pairs of legs are long and slender and extend beyond the margin of the body, which is elongate; pedicel of the suckers (caruncles) segmented; chelicerae styliform, serrate near tip. Psoroptic mites do not burrow, as do sarcoptic mites, but live at the base of hairs of the host, piercing the skin and causing inflammation. An exudate follows that partially hardens, forming a scab. As mites multiply, bites and itching increase; more serum oozes out to form a loose humid crust. The parasitized areas increase and the skin becomes hardened and thickened, a condition known as *scab*. Owing to the looseness of the scabs and hardiness of the mites, this form of acariasis is quickly and easily spread from animal to animal by contact and by rubbing against fences, trees, and the like.

The taxonomic status of *Psoroptes* mange mites has been in a state of flux. In a comprehensive review of the situation Sweatman (1958) concludes that *Psoroptes caprae* (Delafond) of goats, and *P. hippotis* are synonyms of *P. cuniculi* of the rabbit. *P. bovis* (Gerlach) is a synonym of *P. ovis* (Hering), a cosmopolitan body mite of sheep, cattle, and horses. *P.*

natalensis occurs on domestic cattle, zebu, Indian water buffalo and horse, and is known from South Africa, Uruguay, Brazil, New Zealand, and probably France. *P. equi* (Hering) is a body mite of the horse and probably other equines, arbitrarily restricted to specimens from England. Although *P. cervinus* Ward is stated by Sweatman to be a distinct ear mite of bighorn sheep (*Ovis canadensis*), it was later found in scrapings from the skin of elk (*Cervus canadensis*) (Hepworth and Thomas, 1963). Unlike the sarcoptic mange mite, the scab mite on sheep infests parts of the body most thickly covered with wool. Scabies is indicated by a "tagging" of the wool; the coat becomes rough, ragged, and matted at the points affected. Tags of wool are torn away by the sheep or rubbed off at posts and other objects. There are scratching and other signs of intense itching. Contact with infested sheep spreads the infection.

Auricular Mites (*Otoacariasis*). A comparatively common infestation of cats, dogs, ferrets, and foxes, known as *otoacariasis* or *parasitic otitis*, is traceable to *Otodectes cynotis* (Hering), which resembles *Psoroptes*

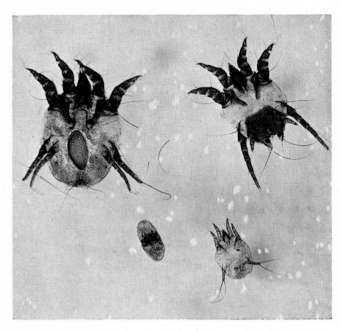

Fig. 19-11 Showing life history and general characteristics of the scab mite, *Psoroptes equi.* (*Lower left*) Egg; (*lower right*) larva; (*upper left*) adult female; (*upper right*) adult male. × 85.

very closely (Fig. 19-12). These mites literally swarm in the ears of the host causing much discomfort, tenderness of the ears, auricular catarrh, loss of appetite, wasting, twisting of the neck, "fits," and so forth. Varietal names of this species, related to the host on which collected, have been proved synonyms because these mites are biologically and morphologically identical, and will interbreed (Sweatman, 1958). *O. cynotis* occurs also on the head and other parts of the body and on hair.

Dermatophagoides saitoi Sasa, placed in the Psoroptidae by Fain (1967), has been associated with lung disorders. *Dermatophagoides scheremetewskyi* Bogdanow attacks bats, rodents, and sparrows in the eastern United States (Fig. 19-13); several human cases of infestation have been reported, sometimes accompanied by severe and persistent dermatitis. Baker, *et al.*, (1956), have summarized human infestations known prior to 1956, and Traver (1951) published a detailed account of two cases.

Family Audycoptidae. The family Audycoptidae has been described by Lavoipierre (1964) from specimens parasitic in the hair follicles of primates. The paper with these descriptions is of additional interest because it reviews the literature on other mite parasites of primates.

KEY TO SOME IMPORTANT GENERA OF ACARIDIAE

1. Free-living; tarsi terminating in clawlike empodia, which are sometimes minute; female genital openings longitudinal, with flaplike plates and two pairs of internal genital suckers 2
    Parasitic; tarsi terminating in caruncles that lack clawlike empodia; female genital openings transverse, without genital suckers 3
2. Caruncles not stalked, the clawlike empodia large; propodosoma separated from the hysterosoma by a suture (Acaridae)
    . . . . *Acarus*

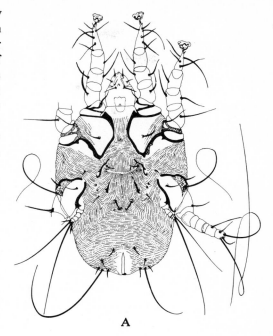

A

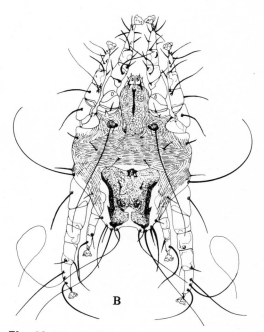

B

Fig. 19-12 *Otodectes cynotis. A.* Ventral view of female. *B.* Dorsal view of male. (From Baker *et al., A Manual of Parasitic Mites of Medical or Economic Importance,* 1956; courtesy of National Pest Control Association.)

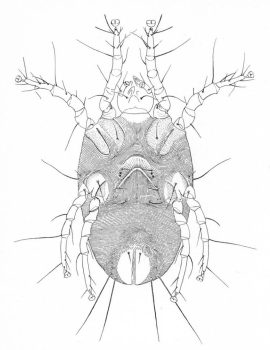

Fig. 19-13 *Dermatophagoides scheremetew-skyi.* Ventral view of female. (From Baker *et al., A Manual of Parasitic Mites of Medical or Economic Importance,* 1956; courtesy of National Pest Control Association.)

Caruncles stalked, the empodial claws minute; propodosoma not separated from the hysterosoma by a suture (Glycyphagidae)....................*Glycyphagus*

3. Propodosoma with a pair of vertical setae (except in *Knemidokoptes*); stalks of caruncles not segmented; female without genital apodemes (Sarcoptidae).......4
   Propodosoma without a pair of vertical setae; stalks of caruncles segmented or not; female with genital apodemes (Psoroptidae)..........................6

4. Dorsal striae interrupted by strong spine-like serrations; tarsi I and II of female with long-stalked caruncles.....*Sarcoptes*
   Dorsal Striae not interrupted by strong spinelike serrations..................5

5. Anus dorsal; tarsi I and II of female with long-stalked caruncles........*Notoedres*
   Anus terminal; caruncles of tarsi of female not stalked..............*Knemidokoptes*

6. All tarsi with short-stalked caruncles; all legs of equal size......*Dermatophagoides* Caruncles of tarsi III of female not stalked, those of I, II, and sometimes IV long- or short-stalked; legs of unequal size................................7

7. Stalks of caruncles long, segmented......
   ....*Psoroptes*
   Stalks of caruncles short, not segmented.8

8. Tarsi I, II, and IV of female with short-stalked caruncles, tarsus III with a pair of long terminal setae; leg IV of female not smaller than leg III...........*Chorioptes* Tarsi I and II of female with short-stalked caruncles, tarsi III and IV each with a pair of long terminal setae; leg IV the smallest in both sexes................*Otodectes*

THE CHIGGER MITES, FOLLICLE MITES, AND RELATIVES

SUBORDER TROMBIDIFORMES

Characteristics. Trombidiform mites form a large and diverse group of mites of different habits. Many are aquatic, mostly fresh-water, but some marine; some terrestrial forms are parasitic, and some free-living forms are parasitic in the larval stage. The classification as accepted by Baker, *et al.* (1958), is rather complicated, but the suborder includes the wormlike, four-legged Tetrapodili, composing the plant-feeding family Eriophyidae; the water-inhabiting Hydrachnellae; and many others. Families of demonstrated medical importance are the Pyemotidae, the Demodicidae, the Tetranychidae, and particularly the Trombiculidae.

Pyemotidae are soft-bodied mites with greatly reduced mouth parts; chelicerae tiny, styletlike, and palpi reduced, lying close to the rostrum. Females with prominent clavate organ of uncertain use between the first and second pairs of legs. The third and fourth pairs of legs separated from the first and second by a long interspace. Sexual dimorphism usually marked.

Pyemotes ventricosus (Newport) (Fig. 19-14) is a widely distributed predaceous mite that attacks the larvae of a number of insects such as the Angoumois grain moth, *Sitotroga cerealella* (Olivier); the wheat strawworm *Harmolita grandis* (Riley); the peach twig borer, *Anarsia lineatella* Zeller; the boll weevil, *Anthonomus grandis* Boheman; the bean weevil, *Acanthoscelides obtectus* (Say); the pea weevil, *Bruchus pisorum* (Linnaeus); and others. It is therefore normally beneficial, but unfortunately it also attacks man, producing a very disagreeable dermatitis known as straw, hay, or grain itch.

The male mite is very tiny, barely visible to the naked eye; the female when gravid becomes enormously swollen, measuring nearly a millimeter in length, the abdomen presenting a globular appearance and resembling a tiny pearl.

Within the enlarged abdomen of the female may be found rather large eggs that hatch internally, and the young mites develop to maturity within the body of the mother before being extruded. The number of offspring per female is 200–300. Males emerge first and remain clustered around the genital opening of the mother, fertilizing young females as they emerge.

Many epidemics of dermatitis have been traced to these mites, and because of the temporary nature of the dermatitis, many cases have probably never been reported to doctors. Infestation is brought about by sleeping on straw mattresses, laboring in grain fields at harvest time, or otherwise coming in contact with or handling grains, straw, hay, grasses, or even beans, peas, cottonseed, or other materials infested with larvae that these mites attack. The dermatitis has been confused with hives, scabies, and even chickenpox; the neck, chest, back, arms, and legs—in fact, the whole body—may be involved, and the itching is intense. Wheals caused by the bites of the mites vary with individuals, but they surround a vesicle marking the site of puncture; if the vesicle is ruptured, secondary infection may arise. The eruption, appearing in twelve to sixteen hours after attack, is commonly accompanied by some fever. In more severe cases, headache, anorexia, nausea, vomiting, mild diarrhea, and pains in the joints may occur. As many as a thousand bites have been reported for a single person.

Family Cheyletidae. Mites of the family Cheyletidae include fur mites and itch mites; gnathosoma usually conspicuous, palpi usually well developed; stigma opening at base of chelicerae.

Cheyletiella parasitivorax (Mégnin), the rabbit fur mite, is found in the fur of rabbits, occasionally of cats and dogs (Fig. 19-15). The role of this mite is uncertain, but it is generally thought to be predaceous on other mites in the fur. An outbreak of dermatitis in people associated with kennels where dogs, cats, and rabbits had been kept was believed to be caused by this mite biting man in the absence of small mites on which it normally feeds (Hart and Malone, 1958).

Psorergates ovis Womersley is known as the itch mite of sheep. In a study of its life history

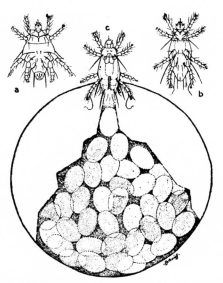

Fig. 19-14 *Pyemotes ventricosus. a.* Adult male. *b.* Adult female. *c.* Gravid female, showing developing eggs.

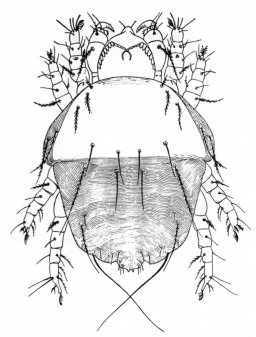

Fig. 19-15 *Cheyletiella parasitivorax.* Dorsal view of female. (From Baker *et al., A Manual of Parasitic Mites of Medical or Economic Importance,* 1956; courtesy of National Pest Control Association.)

in New South Wales, Australia (Murray, 1961), it was found that the adult mite is the only mobile stage and is responsible for spread of the infestation, chiefly from sheep to sheep. Spread is generally very slow. The mite is very susceptible to desiccation, which explains the decline reported after shearing and in summer. *P. ovis* has been found in the United States, Australia, New Zealand, and South Africa. A related species, *Psorergates simplex* Tyrell, causes skin injury to laboratory mice. *Psorergates bos* has been described as a parasite of cattle in the state of New Mexico (Johnston, 1964).

Family Demodicidae. The follicle mites; very minute (0.1–0.4 mm) with an elongated (vermiform) transversely striated abdomen and four pairs of stubby, five-segmented legs located close together on the anterior part of the body; parasitize the skin of mammals. All

stages of the life history are often present together in a follicle. Smith (1961), has reviewed the morphology, bionomics, world distribution, prevalence, and pathogenicity of *Demodex* infesting large domestic animals.

The follicle mite of man, *Demodex folliculorum* Simon (Fig. 19-16), inhabits the hair follicles and sebaceous glands, particularly around the nose and eyelids, but sometimes on other parts of the body, including the scalp. It has been thought responsible for certain skin diseases, but there is no proof of this. It is considered of no importance to man but may, under certain conditions, produce cystic lesions or acnelike conditions; though it probably is not the cause of "blackheads." The mite is, nevertheless, very common; probably most humans harbor it in all parts of the world.

Demodectic infestation may be quite serious in certain domestic animals, particularly in dogs. The species involved in red mange or demodectic mange of dogs is *Demodex canis* Leydig (Fig. 19-17) typically found in association with a bacterium, *Staphylococcus pyogenes albus* or some allied form, which seems to be the real cause of hair loss. The lesions occur chiefly around the muzzle and eyes and on the forefeet. The disease can terminate fatally. It has been contended that almost all

Fig. 19-16 The follicle mite of man, *Demodex folliculorum.* × 101.

Fig. 19-17 *Demodex canis.* Ventral view of female. (From Baker *et al., A Manual of Parasitic Mites of Medical or Economic Importance,* 1956; courtesy of National Pest Control Association.)

dogs harbor this mite, as seems borne out by an investigation where it was found in the skin of the flank in fifteen of seventeen dogs examined in the United States (Greve and Gaafar, 1964).

Demodex bovis Stiles parasitizes cattle. The mites produce swellings that may be as large as a hen's egg, and that are filled with a cheesy or fluid substance containing the mites. The nodules may produce holes in the hide, thus lessening its value. *Demodex phylloides* Csokor produces pustules in swine; *D. caprae* Railliet, may form pustules in goats; *D. equi* Railliet causes a mild mange of horses, as does *D. cati* Mégnin in cats.

Spider Mites. To the family Tetranychidae belong the spider mites or "red spiders," web-spinning mites most commonly infesting vegetation and destructive to fruit trees and other plants. Persons employed in picking hops and harvesting almonds, and other crops, often complain of itching caused by the "red spider," but this soon disappears.

In the fall with the advent of cold weather, the clover mite, *Bryobia praetiosa* (Koch) complex, will invade homes, sometimes in great numbers. Its presence is not any threat to the homeowner or his property, but may be a source of great annoyance, especially to the housewife.

Chigger Mites, Family Trombiculidae. The larvae of chigger mites are characterized by Baker and Wharton (1952) as follows:

The chelicerae have two segments; the basal segment is stout and muscular while the distal segment is a sclerotized, curved blade with or without projections called teeth. The palps have five segments; the basal segments are fused along the midline and have a median, anterior, laminar projection that extends beyond the basal segment of the chelicerae and a pair of lateral wings or galeae that curl dorsal about the chelicerae and bear a seta on each side; each basal segment also bears a seta posterior to the junction with the palpal femur. The second palpal segment or femur bears a single seta; the third or genu bears a single seta; the fourth, or tibia, has three setae; one is dorsal, one lateral, one ventral, and there is a terminal palpal claw. The fifth, or tarsus, articulates ventrally with the tibia and opposes the palpal claw in thumblike fashion. It bears several setae (usually eight), the basal one of which is a striated sensory seta. The body is usually red but may be almost colorless; it bears a dorsal plate or scutum at the level of the anterior two pairs of legs, usually two pairs of eyes that flank the scutum, several rows of dorsal setae, several rows of ventral setae, occasionally a posterior plate or a posterior group of specialized setae, a ventral anus, three pairs of legs, an urstigma or sclerotized pit associated with the posterior distal angle of coxa I, and at times a pair of tracheal trunks that open through stigmata in the region of the gnathosoma. The scutum bears from three to six marginal scutal setae or infrequently more, and a pair of pseudo-stigmata from which the sensillae or pseudo-stigmatic organs arise. The legs are composed of six segments if the femur is undivided and of seven if the femur consists of a basifemur and telofemur.

Adults are about 1 mm long, oval or, more usually figure-eight-shaped; clothed with filiform, densely pilose setae, giving a velvety appearance. The color is often bright red.

Generalized Chigger Life Cycle. The generalized developmental cycle of chiggers (Fig. 19-18) has been reviewed by Sasa (1961), who has extensively cited the findings of a number of investigators. Eggs of chiggers are globular; in about a week the egg shell splits, exposing the maturing larva or *deutovum*. The larval stage is six-legged and it is the only parasitic stage. Larvae may not be very host specific, attaching to any of a great variety of vertebrates, or some species are very specific (a few exceptional species feed on arthropods). When engorged with tissue fluid, a larva leaves the host and passes a quiescent *nymphochrysalis*, or prenymph, stage. Nymphs and adults are eight-legged and free living. A nymph passes a quiescent *imagochrysalis*, or preadult, stage before molting to become an adult. Nymphs and adults of some chiggers have been successfully reared on insect eggs as food, but their normal food habits are unknown. Females are inseminated by means of stalked spermatophores deposited by males on the substrate; there is no evidence of parthenogenesis.

Developmental time may be greatly affected by temperature and food supply. Under laboratory conditions at 28° C *Trombicula*

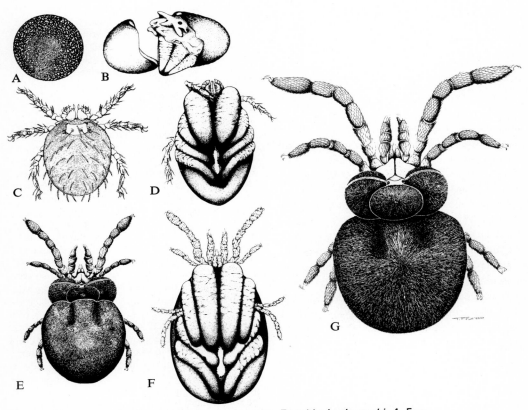

Fig. 19-18 Life cycle of scrub typhus chigger mite, *Trombicula akamushi. A.* Egg. *B.* Deutovum with ruptured shell exposing developing larva. *C.* Larva, the stage parasitic on vertebrates. *D.* Prenymph, ventral view, showing remnants of larval legs. *E.* Nymph. *F.* Preadult, ventral view, showing remnants of nymphal appendages and developing legs of adult. *G.* Adult. (From Neal and Barnett, *Ann. Entom. Soc. Amer.,* **54**: 196-203, 1961).

akamushi took about seventy-five days to complete the life cycle; at "favorable" laboratory conditions *Eutrombicula indica* took about sixty days, *Trombicula deliensis* forty days, the common North American chiggers required fifty to seventy days. The number of generations per year also varies with species and local climate. Most chiggers in the temperate zone seem to have one annual generation. *Trombicula alfreddugesi* (Oudemans), in North America, has one or two annual generations in Ohio, three generations in North Carolina, and continuous development in Florida.

Typical host-seeking behavior for several species of larval chiggers consists of congregating in a shaded niche near the top of various objects in close contact to the earth. Here they remain quiescent, but are activated by an air current bearing carbon dioxide, as would be characteristic in the approach of a vertebrate host.

Wharton and Fuller (1952) divide the Trombiculidae into four subfamilies, of which most chiggers belong to the Trombiculinae. These authors characterize this subfamily as follows: "Trombiculids whose larvae have a median, scutal seta, lack submedian scutal setae, have seven segments in all legs, at least four sternal setae, no median, anterior projection on the scutum, and no stigmata or tracheal trunks." Identification based on larvae is more pertinent than that based on nymphs or adults, because the larval form is of medical importance, and is more frequently submitted for study.

The taxonomy of the chiggers presents some difficult problems, as pointed out by Fuller (1956). Chief among these is the fact that many chigger mites have been described from the larval stage only, and adults and nymphs are either unknown or uncorrelated with larvae; also, the taxonomist is faced with the problem of evaluating the statistical and biological significance of variation.

Literature pertaining to the Trombiculidae, their taxonomy and medical importance, has grown enormously during recent years. The bibliography published by Williams (1946) consisted of 375 references, and Wharton and Fuller's *Manual of the Chiggers* (1952) contains nearly 700. For identification and taxonomic studies of the family, the student should start with the manual of Wharton and Fuller that carries these mites through keys only to genera and subgenera, although detailed bibliographic, distributional, and host information is given for the species. Fuller (1956) cites a number of references to taxonomic papers in the Pacific area and Asia. Vercammen-Grandjean (1963) has reviewed taxonomic characters of the Trombiculidae and included correlations between larvae and nymphs. For determination to species, the student is referred to the keys of Brennan and Jones (1959), to the studies of Jenkins (1949) and Brennan and Wharton (1950), respectively, for the North American species of the subgenera *Eutrombicula* and *Neotrombicula* of the medically important genus *Trombicula*, and to Farrell (1956) for the genus *Euschoengastia*. For a regional treatment, consult the study of the chiggers of Kansas by Loomis (1956) and that of the chiggers of California by Gould (1956).

Chigger Dermatitis. In many parts of the world, particularly warmer portions and late summer months in temperate climates, persons who have walked among tall weeds and grass, brambles, and low scrub often suffer an intolerable itching, beginning three to six hours after exposure and followed by a severe dermatitis consisting of pustules and wheals. When, after a trip through tall weeds or grass or berry brambles, itching begins around the ankles, knees, and wrist, a careful examination will most surely reveal at least one (there will be others) minute, bright-red mite, either traveling fast or about to attach itself to the skin.

Chiggers do not burrow into the skin as commonly believed. Ewing (1921) observed and studied daily twenty-six chiggers on his own skin; twenty-one attached to the smooth surface of the skin, five at the bases of hairs, each having the capitulum thrust into the mouth of the hair follicle, but not one penetrating a pore or hair follicle. The chigger does not suck blood; when firmly attached, it injects a digestive fluid that causes a disintegration of the contents of cells with which it comes in contact, the result being a disorganized cytoplasm and fragmented nuclei (Jones, 1950). The resulting material is utilized as food by the chigger. The skin of the host becomes hardened, and a tube (stylostome) forms in which the mouth parts remain until the mite is replete; then it retreats and drops to the ground. According to Michener and Michener (1947), it is presumably the action of the digestive fluid that causes the "bite" to itch after a few hours. Williams (1945) points out that histologic preparations of chigger bites on rabbit ears show that the epidermis is completely penetrated. A tube lined with stratum germinativum is formed that extends to the derma and subcutis. This tube appears to represent a combined reaction of the host to the secretion of the chigger and the secretory material itself (see Chapter 3); its inner layer of cells is necrotic and gives evidence of digestion.

Fig. 19-19 *Trombicula autumnalis.* Dorsal and ventral view of larva ; details of chelicera and palp, and scutum. (From Baker *et al., A Manual of Parasitic Mites of Medical or Economic Importance,* 1956 ; courtesy of National Pest Control Association.)

Important Species of Dermatitis-Causing Chiggers. Among the chigger mites that cause a severe dermatitis is the European species *Trombicula (Neotrombicula) autumnalis* (Shaw) (Fig. 19-19) known as the harvest mite, aoutat, or *lepte automnal.* It differs from American chiggers of the subgenus *Eutrombicula* in that its larvae have trifid, rather than bifid, claws.

Trombicula (Eutrombicula) alfreddugesi (Oudemans) (*Leptus irritans* of much of the earlier literature) is the common chigger (Fig. 19-20) of the United States, ranging from the Gulf states and including similar ecological situations in New England and eastern Canada to Nebraska, west to California; Texas and south into Mexico, Central America, and South America. It is known by a wide range of names, including *tlalzahuatl, bicho colorado,*

and *bete rouge.* It is abundant in second-growth cut-over areas, especially wild blackberry patches, forest edges, and river valleys. Its hosts include man, a wide range of domestic and wild animals, birds, reptiles, and even a few amphibians.

Trombicula (Eutrombicula) splendens Ewing [=*masoni* (Ewing)] is distributed along the Atlantic Coast from Florida to Massachusetts and along the Gulf Coast to Texas, then northward to westward in suitable habitats to Ontario, Michigan, and Minnesota. It is the most abundant species in Florida and parts of Georgia. It seems to occur in moister habitats than does *alfreddugesi,* such as swamps, bogs, rotten logs, and stumps, and although *splendens* and *alfreddugesi* may occur in the same region, seasonal incidences of the two are independent.

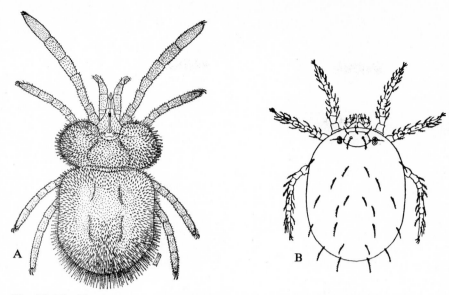

Fig. 19-20   The common chigger or harvest mite, *Trombicula alfreddugesi*. A. Adult. B. Larva. (From Ewing's *Manual of External Parasites*. Courtesy of Charles C Thomas, Publishers.)

Trombicula (Eutrombicula) batatas (Linnaeus) is a tropical species in the United States from Florida, Georgia, Alabama, Kansas, and California. It seldom attacks man in the United States, but commonly does so in Panama and other tropical areas.

Wharton and Fuller (1952) report additional species as attacking man and producing dermatitis. These include the genera *Trombicula, Euschoengastia, Schoengastia, Apolonia*, and *Acomatacarus* from an area including the Americas, Pacific Islands, Australia, and Indonesia.

Chiggers may unfavorably affect vertebrate hosts other than man. Species such as *Neoschoengastia americana* cause losses to turkey poults, and quail, and probably other birds as well. This same species causes downgrading of market turkeys due to lesions in the skin and adjacent tissues, particularly in the southeastern United States. The species *Euschoengastia latchmani* Brennan and Yunker was observed to cause mangelike dermatitis lesions on horses recently imported into the state of California from Washington, as well as lesions

on hares (*Lepus californicus*) and a golden-crowned sparrow (*Zonotrichia coronata*) (Brennan and Yunker, 1964).

Life Cycle of Vectors of the Rickettsia of Scrub Typhus.   Two closely related mites of the subgenus *Leptotrombidium*, namely *Trombicula akamushi* (Brumpt) and *T. deliensis* Walch, are proven vectors of scrub typhus. They were initially regarded as the only species involved in the transmission of this disease. The two species are differentiated from each other chiefly on the number and arrangement of the dorsal setae.

Trombicula (Leptotrombidium) akamushi (Brumpt) occurs from Japan and China southward through Indonesia to New Guinea (Fig. 19-18). It inhabits partially cultivated land that is inundated by the floods of spring and early summer, the mite reaching a peak during July and August. *Trombicula (L.) deliensis* Walsh occurs from Pakistan and India through Indonesia to New Guinea and Australia, and is more characteristically associated with forests.

The adult mites measure from 1–2 mm in

length, are generally reddish in color, often pale. In cultures they feed readily on eggs of Collembola and mosquitoes. The winter is spent as adults, except in equatorial climates where there is no hibernation. Eggs are deposited in the soil, under leaves or in damp places. The hexapod larvae, at first about 0.22 mm long, emerge in about ten to twelve days at 30° C and wait the coming of a suitable host —mammal or bird (man is an accidental host). They attack in clusters, often packed together in the ears of a field rodent. Numerous hosts are available, the chigger being habitat- rather than host-specific (Audy, 1958), but continuous propagation of the infection is dependent upon susceptible so-called reservoir animals, the first of which was demonstrated to be a vole, *Microtus montebelli*. Wartime studies as reported by Philip and Kohls (1948) indicate rats play a widespread role in the disease cycle in nature. "Six kinds of rats (among them *Rattus concolor browni* and *R. flavipectus yunanensis*) indigenous to New Guinea, Burma, or India, plus a species each of field mouse and tree shrew (*Tupaia belangeri versurae*) have been added to two murid species already demonstrated to carry natural infection in Japan and Malaya, and to others under strong indictment, in Formosa, Sumatra, and Australia." Serological studies also im- plicate birds in the natural cycle of scrub typhus.

The larval mite ("*akamushi*") remains on the host from one to ten days. It measures about 0.55 mm when fully engorged. It then drops to the ground, spends some time seeking suitable shelter, and after passing through the inactive nymphochrysalis stage, the preda- ceous nymphal stage, and the inactive imago- chrysalis stage, emerges as an adult. The life cycle, from egg to egg-laying, under laboratory conditions, is completed in "under forty days" for *T. deliensis* in Malaya and "in under seventy days" for *T. akamushi* in Japan, according to Audy (1956). Further laboratory studies on the life history may be consulted in Neal and Lipovsky, 1959, and Neal and Barnett, 1961.

Field observations on these two species of chiggers in Malaya have confirmed and further clarified their focal distribution as noted by Audy (Hubert and Baker, 1963 a, b). There is evidence that moisture rather than leaves or shade might be the requirement of *T. deliensis* supplied in forest. Foci may occupy areas of only about one square foot, each focus being supported by an individual rodent host, which may have several such foci in its home range. The same relative distribution of the population of chiggers was maintained along a transect throughout a seven-month period, though seasonal fluctuations were marked. Clusters of two to ten *T. akamushi* larvae were found a few inches above ground on dead dried grass stems in fields, sometimes remaining in place about a week; clusters of *T. deliensis* were larger, at similar heights on stems, tips, and edges of leaves in secondary forests. Larvae were stimulated by the presence of an observer to leave a cluster and move about an inch, returning to reform the cluster. Their behavior supported the idea of a fixed focus arising from larvae hatching in a particular site and waiting there for a host.

Transmission of scrub typhus is transovarial in both *T. akamushi* and *T. deliensis*. No other method would be possible in a vector that feeds on a vertebrate but once during its lifetime.

The discovery that chiggers other than the two important vectors of scrub typhus may carry the rickettsia and transmit it with more or less success has led to some interesting implications. Traub, *et al.* (1950), recovered *R. tsutsugamushi* from the chigger *Euschoen- gastia audyi* (Womersley) taken from tree squirrels. The presence of the rickettsia in different hosts, both acarine and mammalian, and under jungle conditions, led Traub and associates to the conclusion that "the natural cycle of scrub typhus in the jungle and the explosive local outbreak of the disease in man following exposure in hyperinfected areas of scrub terrain may prove to have a number of similarities to jungle and urban yellow fever." Subsequent studies by Audy (1958) and others support this theory, further complicating the epidemiology of scrub typhus. The relation of various vectors to the epidemiology of the disease is summarized by Audy when he divides mammal-infesting chiggers capable of transmitting the rickettsia into the following categories: (1) major vectors of general importance to man (*T. akamushi, T. deliensis*); (2) major vectors of local importance (apparently confined to certain palaearctic species of *Leptotrombidium*, such as *T. pallida* Nagayo, et al., and *T. scutellaris* Nagayo, et al.); (3) efficient vectors that may attack man but do not occur in sufficient numbers or in suitable habitats to infest man sufficiently, although they may be responsible for sporadic cases or rare anomalous outbreaks; and (4) species that do not attack man but promote enzootic infection.

Audy (1958) has pointed out that the tick-borne and flea-borne rickettsioses are worldwide in distribution, whereas the mite-borne rickettsiosis, scrub typhus, occurs only in eastern Asia, the East Indies, and northern Australia. He offers as an explanation the "hypothesis that scrub typhus has evolved in the broad area of evolution of both the genus *Rattus* and the chigger subgenus *Leptotrombidium*, where extensive deforestation by man has encouraged dense populations of field rats infested particularly by the major vectors." It is interesting to note, for whatever implications it may have, that one species of *Leptotrombidium*, *T. (L.) myotis* Ewing, occurs in the United States, and another, *T. (L.) mexicana* Ewing, occurs in Mexico.

MITE-ASSOCIATED DISEASES

Rickettsialpox is caused by *Rickettsia akari* transmitted by the mite *Liponyssoides* (=*Allodermanyssus*) *sanguineus* (Hirst). This mite normally parasitizes the house mouse, *Mus musculus*, and transmission to man is by more or less accidental biting. The disease was first observed in New York City in the summer of 1946 when the causal organism was isolated by Huebner, *et al.* (1946).

This is usually a mild febrile disease, commencing seven to ten days after the bite of the mite, with a vesicular rash appearing some three to four days after the onset of fever. There is an initial lesion at the site of the bite, a black scab develops, and healing is slow. Fever is accompanied by chills, sweating, backache, and muscle pains. Untreated cases recover in one to two weeks; fatalities are unknown.

Larvae of the vector mite do not feed, and transmission occurs by feeding of nymphs or adults of both sexes. Transovarial passage of the rickettsia has been shown (Kiselev and Volchanetskaya, cited in Burgdorfer and Varma, 1967), thereby making the vector an important part of the reservoir.

The epidemiology of rickettsialpox, as first studied, indicates an urban pattern in the northeastern United States. A similar relationship has been observed in the Soviet Union, but there wild commensal rodents have also been found to harbor the mite. A disease clinically and serologically resembling rickettsialpox has been described from Africa under conditions suggesting a different cycle. Evidence of independence from man is provided by the isolation of *R. akari* from a wild Korean field mouse, *Microtus fortis pelliceus* (Jackson, et al., 1957).

Scrub typhus (tsutsugamushi disease, mite-borne typhus, Japanese river fever, kedani fever, tropical or rural typhus) is an ancient disease (Blake, *et al.*, 1945) first described from Japan. It was long said that the infection is transferred to man by the "akamushi" (Japanese for "dangerous bug") from rodent reservoirs. It was not, however, until 1916 that positive experimental evidence was secured by Miyajima and Okumura (1917) in tests with monkeys. The accepted name for the causal organism is *Rickettsia tsutsugamushi* (Hayashi) Ogata (=*R. orientalis*, a name still frequently used).

The disease has an incubation period of six to twenty-one, usually ten to twelve, days. During the first five to seven days, it is characterized by Blake, *et al.* (1945), as follows:

"headache (postorbital), apathy and general malaise, fever (chills), relative bradycardia, anorexia, conjunctival congestion, lymphadenitis, often regional, and an eschar." The eschar is the primary lesion that originates at the point of chigger attack (ankle, shin, groin, waistline, or axilla) in the great majority of cases. It is a painless papule at first, usually unnoticed by the patient (and usually absent in Asians). It slowly enlarges to a diameter of 8–12 mm, the center becoming very dark and necrotic; a shallow ulcer may result eventually, leaving a scar. Between the fifth and eighth days in nearly all cases, a dull red macular or maculopapular rash appears on the trunk and may spread to the extremities, persisting for several days or disappearing within a few hours. Enlargement of the spleen, nervous disturbances, delirium, and prostration are common symptoms; in many cases there is deafness. The majority of patients recover in three to five weeks.

Mortality rates in epidemics have varied from 0.6–35.3 per cent, in some instances as high as 60 per cent, depending on localities and populations. Death results approximately equally from secondary bacterial pneumonia, encephalitis, or circulatory failure, at about the end of the second week. Scrub typhus is now effectively treated with broad-spectrum antibiotics such as chloramphenicol or tetracycline; as a consequence mortality under treatment is essentially zero.

Although the greatest number of cases occur at low elevations (sandy bottom land overgrown with grasses and scrub), infections occur at elevations of 2,000 to 3,000 ft. and, in Taiwan, as high as 6,500 ft. The chigger mites have been reported as high as 8,000 ft. in India. Scrub typhus is endemic in many parts of southeastern Asia and adjacent islands in the Indian Ocean and southwest Pacific (Ceylon, Japan, Philippines, Indonesia, Taiwan) and the coastal area of North Queensland, Australia.

The importance of scrub typhus as a "medical casualty producer in some areas during the Asiatic-Pacific operation, 1941–45," according to Philip (1948), "was second only to malaria and was more dreaded by the men." Interference with actual combat operations was greatest, Philip states, on the Assam-Burma front where:

... 18 per cent of a single battalion got scrub typhus in two months and in that time 5 per cent of the total strength had died of it.

American Task Force operations in the Schouten Islands resulted in a thousand cases in the first two months on Owi and Biak, reaching a total of 1,469 casualties in six months time, while at Sansapor beach head the curve for weekly admissions on a thousand-per-year basis shot up to over 900 at the end of the second week, a rate higher for an individual episode than any yearly rate for all causes in the entire American Army in all theatres.... These two disasters alone provided a potential estimated loss of over 150,000 man days to the American Sixth Army.

The epidemiology of scrub typhus has been further clarified in more recent investigations. Analyses of Audy (1961) and Kitaoka and associates (1962) are helpful. The most fundamentally important fact is that only larval chiggers feed on vertebrates, therefore those infective to man or rodent hosts have received the pathogen transovarially from the female parent. Limited foci of the disease, though they differ markedly in superficial appearance, are characterized by a suitable rodent population, adequate ground moisture for the specific mite vectors, and the etiological agent in the mites. Larger mammals and birds help to disperse infected mites. Occurrence of the disease in man varies by region, being year round in Malaya and during the six-month monsoon period in Burma.

Species of chiggers other than the known vectors, *Trombicula akamushi* (Brumpt) and *T. deliensis* Walsh, are recognized. In Japan *T. scutellaris* Nagayo, *et al.*, and *T. pallida* Nagayo, *et al.*, have also been demonstrated as vectors in limited situations (Kitaoka, *et al.*, 1962); in that country *T. tosa* Sasa and Kawashima is believed to be a vector in certain circumstances.

Epidemic Hemorrhagic Fever (Hemorrhagic Nephrosonephritis, Far Eastern Hemorrhagic Fever, Nephropathia Epidemica). Epidemic hemorrhagic fever is reviewed in Horsfall and Tamm (1965). The name refers to a febrile condition with prominent vascular damage and bleeding. It has been reported from the area of the Amur River separating Manchuria and eastern Siberia, and probably the same disease was involved in United Nations forces in Korea. The causal agent is filterable, therefore presumably a virus, but characterization has been hampered by a lack of susceptible laboratory animals. The etiological agent is

believed to occur in wild rodents and to be transmitted to man by mites (see introductory discussion, mesostigmatid mites). At any rate adoption of rodent and mite control measures in Korea sharply reduced military cases. In Korea the highest incidence was among troops in rural areas, with a peak in the spring and the fall.

Argentine Hemorrhagic Fever (Junin Virus). The causal agent of Argentine hemorrhagic fever has been isolated from *Laelaps (Echinolaelaps) echidninus* (Berlese), a mite associated with rodents (Horsfall and Tamm, 1965). However, this pathogen may be isolated from urine and feces of rodents, and it is generally believed that simple contamination between rodents and from rodents to humans is sufficient to achieve normal transfer.

20

VENOMS, DEFENSE SECRETIONS, AND ALLERGENS OF ARTHROPODS

The importance of envenomization by arthropods has been, at least in temperate areas, exaggerated in the public mind. Many persons are unjustifiably afraid of spiders, centipedes, millipedes, and in fact, many arthropods that are completely powerless to harm one. However, the danger from venomous arthropods is greater than most entomologists have realized. A report based on examination of death certificates from all parts of the United States (Parish, 1963) showed that deaths resulting from arthropod bites and stings, over the period 1950–59, far outnumbered those resulting from snake bite. Of 460 deaths caused by venomous animals,

30 per cent were attributed to venomous snakes; 1.7 per cent to scorpions; 14 per cent to spiders; and 50 per cent to hymenopterous insects, especially bees and wasps. Nearly three times as many males as females were involved in these cases, a reflection of the greater outdoor exposure of men and boys. It is noteworthy that centipedes, tarantulas, and, of course, millipedes, are absent from the list. Accurate statistics are for the most part lacking for the tropics, though the general impression is that all types of envenomization are more commonplace than in temperate regions. In 1941, deaths in Mexico for all venomous animals were listed as snakes 219, scorpions 1,802, spiders 19, and others 170 (Tay and Biagi, 1961).

Chemicals possessed by arthropods may cause a variety of medical complications of vertebrates. These chemicals are often complex multicomponent systems; variable with respect to amount introduced and route of entry. Chemical variability, coupled with variability in the reactivity of vertebrates, makes for differences in the severity of response. For purposes of classification chemicals may be divided on the basis of function into (1) venoms that cause immediate responses, and that are introduced beneath the skin of vertebrates by mouthparts or stinging apparatus; (2) irritating defense secretions that are received by a vertebrate in the act of contact, or that may be projected with some accuracy before bodily contact occurs; (3) allergens to which prior exposure may result in anaphylaxis, or in milder allergic symptoms. In addition to the chemicals listed, urticating hairs much like glass fibers are possessed by some insects, notably caterpillars. Such hairs may be accompanied by chemical irritants.

Clear-cut classification may be impossible because allergic reactions frequently accompany envenomization and contact with defense secretions. Furthermore, venoms and the apparatus for their disbursement may perform dual functions, namely the subduing of prey and effective self defense.

Arthropod Venoms. One characteristic of most arthropod venoms is the relative rapidity with which they act. There is usually a painful immediate response to venomous bites or stings that may be followed by complications. Beard (1963) has reviewed the characteristics of insect venoms. A further treatment by Shulman (1967) is directed toward allergic responses to insects but also includes such useful information as improved methods of venom collection.

For accurate chemical, pharmacological, and allergenic characterization it is necessary to obtain venom that is as pure as possible. A method of electric shocking has proved suitable for individual Hymenoptera (O'Connor, *et al.*, 1963), spiders (Grothaus and Howell, 1967), and centipedes (Stahnke and Larson, 1968), and has been modified for collecting large amounts of venom from honey bees (Benton, *et al.*, 1963). Nonetheless, for many arthropods it may be necessary to dissect out the venom reservoir of the stinging or biting apparatus, as Cavill and Robertson (1965) found in studying the Australian bull ant *Myrmecia*.

How the Venom Is Introduced. Arthropod venoms are introduced into the body of man

and other animals by: (1) *bite*, the thrust of piercing mouth parts, as in the conenoses, penetration of the chelicerae of spiders, or the maxillipeds of centipedes; (2) *sting*, as in the ants, bees, and wasps (aculeate Hymenoptera), and the scorpions; (3) *contact* of an essentially passive nature, e.g., by means of urticarial hairs of certain caterpillars, such as the brown-tail moth, producing a condition similar to nettling, or with vesicating fluids of the blister beetles (Meloidae), resulting in a *vesicular dermatitis*, or through wind-blown parts of insect bodies, such as cast mayfly skins, resulting in allergic reactions; (4) by *active projection* as occurs in arthropods that use their secretions as a means of defense, found in some predatory Hemiptera, some ants, and in whipscorpions.

Arthropod Defense Secretions. Defense secretions of arthropods are comprised of unpleasant fluids or gases that may have a strong smell and may be irritating to vertebrates on contact. These compounds are poured onto the body surface, or they may be forcefully ejected. Characteristically, defensive fluids are produced by glandular cells, are stored in reservoirs, and may have a specific apparatus for their expulsion. They may be expelled by blood pressure, by tracheal air pressure, or through muscular contraction of the reservoir.

Defense secretions are not normally of major medical consequence to vertebrates, for the most part being disagreeable but temporary in their effects. The very complexity of these secretions, when considered for all arthropods, increases the likelihood that lasting complications can occur, particularly if allergic responses are elicited.

The whole subject of chemical defenses of arthropods has been reviewed by Roth and Eisner (1962). They discuss the associated glands, discharge mechanisms, and medical complications, as well as provide a tabular listing of chemicals found.

Arthropod Allergens. The body constituents of arthropods cause allergic reactions of humans. The nature of insect allergens, and human allergic responses, has been reviewed by Perlman (1967), Shulman (1967), and Feingold, *et al.* (1968). Shulman logically criticizes earlier studies on insect allergens as being deficient in modern preparative techniques. The gravity of the allergic reaction, as he points out, is dependent on individual susceptibility (including hereditary predisposition), amount of previous exposure, and method of exposure. Deaths are usually due to anaphylaxis and generally require prior rapid exposure to allergens by sting. Less severe hypersensitivity may be indicated by hives or asthma and may be caused by sting or by exposure to arthropod particles. Chronic allergic reactions, such as hay fever, urticaria, and eczema can be caused by stings but are more characteristic of respiratory or skin contact with arthropod parts (Fig. 20-1). Allergy has been reported from rather commonplace household sources such as cockroaches (Bernton and Brown, 1964) and the mite *Dermatophagoides pteronyssinus* (Troussart) as the allergenic component of "house dust" (Fain, 1967; Spieksma and Spieksma-Boezeman, 1967).

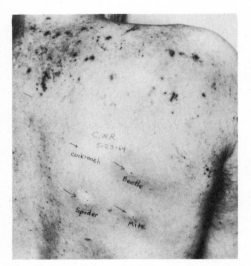

Fig. 20-1 Eruptions in a patient showing strong reactions to scratch tests of arthropod extracts. (From Perlman and Criep, 1967, by permission of W. B. Saunders Co.)

Much of what is discussed hereafter under stinging, urticaria, and irritation, really includes allergic responses; particularly if long-lasting effects are noted. In final analysis it must be admitted that serious consequences of arthropod venoms may be due to their essentially toxic nature alone, but that to an often unknown degree allergic complications also are present.

STINGING INSECTS

Stinging insects of the order Hymenoptera include the ants, bees, and wasps, in which females are usually provided with a specialized ovipositor known as a sting, more or less well adapted for piercing the skin of higher animals or of other insects. The sting is used either for defense or offense; in the latter case to procure food for the young. The venom apparatus of the so-called "aculeate," or stinging Hymenoptera, such as bees, wasps, hornets, and bumble bees, does not vary greatly in structure.

The principal aculeate Hymenoptera, according to the classification followed by Borror and DeLong (1954), are divided into the following seven superfamilies, all of which, except the first, contain representatives that can be dangerous or annoying: (1) Chrysidoidea, the cuckoo wasps and their relatives; (2) Bethyloidea, the bethyloid wasps; (3) Scolioidea, the scoliid wasps, velvet ants, and their relatives; (4) Formicoidea, the ants; (5) Vespoidea, the hornets, yellow jackets, spider wasps, and their relatives; (6) Sphecoidea, the sphecoid wasps; (7) Apoidea, the bees.

Morphology of the Honey Bee Sting. The sting of the worker bee, regarded as a specialized ovipositor, originates from the seventh and eighth abdominal segments and lies between the ovipositor and the rectum. The darts of the sting follow the ventral line of the abdomen and are held in place by the sheath situated above, the barbs of the darts point downward and outward. In the space above the sheath lie fleshy palpi (Fig. 20-2). The delicate attachment between the sting and the organs of the abdomen, as well as the barbs of the darts, account for the ease with which the sting of the honey bee is torn from the abdomen after the darts are thrust into the skin. The sting can easily be removed from a bee either by separating the segments of the abdomen from it by means of dissecting needles, or by squeezing the live bee between forceps, which causes it to protrude the sting. The sting can be grasped with other forceps and drawn out. After extraction the sting can be conveniently examined when the parts are floated out in a few drops of glycerin.

Operation of the Sting. The sting may be observed in operation by confining a bee on its back, then prodding until its sting is thrust in and out. This process shows (1) that the sharp-pointed sheath always appears first when the thrust is made; (2) that the darts inside the sheath work back and forth alternately and independently of the sheath or of one another; and (3) that the poison exudes in droplets from the tip of the sting between the darts.

The sheath opens the wound, serves as the dorsal wall of the poison canal, and holds the stylets in position. The sheath does not wholly enclose the darts; rather it forms the dorsal wall of the canal that is formed when the two concave surfaces of the darts are brought together. Two delicate, but strong, sclerotized, tracks or "rails" of the sheath dovetail into a corresponding groove in each dart, thus permitting only parallel movement.

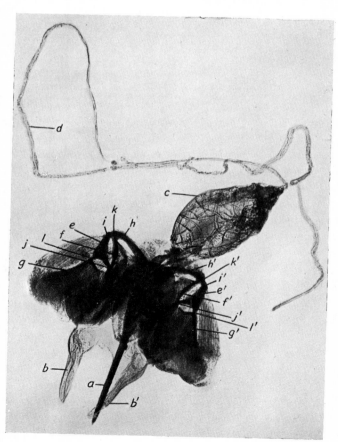

Fig. 20-2 Sting of a honey bee, *Apis mellifera:* (*a*) the two serrated darts; (*b, b′*) sting palpi; (*c*) venom (poison) sac; (*d*) venom gland; (*e, e′*) triangular plates or levers; (*f, f′*) semilunar plates or levers; (*g, g′*) lateral plates or levers; (*h, h′*) Y-shaped darts; (*i, i′*) points of attachment for darts to levers; (*j, j′*, also *e, e′*) points around which levers rotate; (*k, k′*) points of attachment for lever (*f, f′*). × 17.5.

By a series of short, quick thrusts, the sting can be driven in its full length.

The three pairs of plates composing the lateral appendages function as levers. Powerful muscles attached to the plates drive the sheath and darts into the flesh of the victim. The two components of the venom then mingle and flow down the canal formed by the sheath and the darts. The rapid series of movements is reflexive, being governed by the fifth abdominal ganglion and its radiating nerves, explaining why the severed abdomen of a bee may sting for some time after separation from the rest of the body.

The Stinging Hymenoptera. Superfamily Apoidea (honey bees and bumble bees) are readily distinguished from the wasps by the presence, especially on the bee thorax, of hairs, which under the microscope are distinctly plumose. Many bees live in solitary or subsocial existence, that is, each female develops her own nest, lays eggs, and provides for her brood without the aid of a worker caste. Many such bees possess stings. Serious cases of bee-sting envenomization, however, are usually due to bumble bees or honey bees.

Both bumble bees, *Bombus* spp., and the honey bee, *Apis mellifera* Linnaeus, are social bees, with a worker caste in addition to the fertile males and females. Bumble bees form temporary colonies with only the fertilized young queen surviving the winter. In the spring the queen searches for a place to found her colony. Her nest is generally associated with the ground, often in a deserted rodent burrow, but may be in buildings or other structures with suitable soft materials. A person working or hiking in a field where bumble bees are nesting may unwarily step into a nest and be stung severely.

Bees of the genus *Apis*, known as honey bees, form permanent colonies that may survive from year to year indefinitely. There are five well-known species: *Apis mellifera* Linnaeus, the cosmopolitan honey bee of commerce that is the cause of most bee stings and many deaths; the giant bee, *A. dorsata*

Fabricius, of Asia, vicious when aroused and with painful stings; the Indian bee, *A. indica* Fabricius, smaller and more gentle than *mellifera* and with less painful stings; the little bee, *A. florea* Fabricius, with sting comparable to a simple "needle-prick"; the Japanese or Chinese bee, *A. cerana* Fabricius, somewhat less aggressive than *mellifera*.

The common honey bee *Apis mellifera* is itself separated into about a dozen named races in European, Asian, and African groups, characterized by differences in aggressiveness. The four best-known economic races are the dark bee, *A. m. mellifera* Linnaeus, generally nervous and often aggressive; the Italian bee, *A. m. ligustica* Spinola, the major commercial stock, variably aggressive; the Carniolan bee, *A. m. carnica* Pollmann, commercial bee of much of eastern Europe and the most gentle; the Caucasian bee, *A. m. caucasica* Pollmann, usually considered the most gentle in the United States. Two African races are noted for their viciousness, a coastal variety, *A. m. litorea* Smith, and a plateau variety, *A. m. adansonii* Latreille. The latter has accidentally spread through half of Brazil and at least two neighboring countries, and severe stingings and deaths have been reported.

The cause of attack by many members of a honey bee colony is of some interest. There are sting gland "alarm odors," variously referred to by authors as iso-pentyl or iso-amyl acetate, plus unidentified components, that incite attack by other bees after one sting. Morse and Benton (1967) found iso-amyl acetate to be a sting gland alarm odor in four species of *Apis*.

The properties of bee venom, sting reactions, and treatment have been reviewed by Lehnert (1967). The venom is a water-clear liquid with a sharp, bitter taste, specific gravity of 1.1313, easily water- and acid-soluble but nearly insoluble in alcohol. It may incur neurotoxic, hemorrhagic, and hemolytic damage. At least eight biologically active components are present plus several inactive components. Melittin, a protein with a molecular weight of

33,000–35,000 is thought responsible for general local toxicity and can cause hemolysis. There is hyaluronidase (a "spreading factor" that breaks down cell-cementing substance), and phospholipase A that causes hemolysis through indirect action on the unsaturated fatty acids of red blood cells. Histamine, a powerful depressant that reduces blood pressure, is present but is not a major pharmacological component of bee venom.

Severe reactions to bee stings are considered to be due to sensitivity to bee protein, not venom. About 2 per cent of persons develop sensitivity after one sting, and a few individuals appear to have a death-dealing inborn sensitivity.

Treatment as reviewed by Lehnert (1967), is comprised of (1) combating anaphylaxis with epinephrine injected intramuscularly or deeply subcutaneously; (2) later treatment with another sympathomimetic agent, such as Metaraminol (m-hydroxynorephedrine) in isotonic saline delivered intravenously, a tourniquet if practical, intramuscular antihistamine, and corticosteroids; (3) long-term care through immunization with appropriate antigen. For some persons injection of stinging extract of one species of hymenopteran will protect against several others, other persons require mixed extracts to achieve protection. When reactions other than local swelling or irritation occur, a physician should be consulted for immediate treatment and long-term desensitization.

FAMILY VESPIDAE, SUPERFAMILY VESPOIDEA

(*Yellow Jackets and Hornets*)

Representative members of the Vespidae are the European hornet, *Vespa crabro* Linnaeus; the giant hornet of Europe and eastern North America, *Vespa crabro germana* (Christ); the bald-faced hornet of North America, *Vespula maculata* (Linnaeus) (Fig. 20-3); the North American *Vespula pennsylvanica* (Saussure) (Fig. 20-4); and the wide-

Fig. 20-3 The bald-faced hornet, *Vespula maculata*. (Courtesy of U.S. Public Health Service.)

spread Holarctic *Vespula vulgaris* (Linnaeus). Consult Miller (1961) for the taxonomy and distribution of nearctic *Vespula*. All of these species build nests (Fig. 20-5) of pulp made by masticating wood fiber. Nests are built in hollow trees (e.g., *Vespa crabro*); among the branches of trees, under eaves of houses, (e.g., *Vespula maculata*); or in holes in or near the ground (e.g., *Vespula pennsylvanica*, *V*.

Fig. 20-4 A common yellow jacket, *Vespula pennsylvanica*. (Courtesy of U.S. Public Health Service.)

Fig. 20-5 (*Top, left*) Aerial nest of yellow jacket; (*top, center, and right*) side and top view of the insect, *Vespula diabolica;* and (*bottom*) longitudinal section of nest.

vulgaris). Aerial nests are somewhat elongated and may reach 9 to 10 inches in diameter. Old colonies die out in the summer or fall, and young fertilized queens hibernate and start a new nest in the spring.

Species of *Polistes* likewise form paper dwellings; but these nests are not as massive as those of *Vespa* and *Vespula*, and are not enclosed in a paper envelope. Each consists of a single horizontal comb of hexagonal cells attached to a support by a pedicel. In cold climates the queens, which are difficult to distinguish from the workers, hibernate. They may enter houses and become quite troublesome toward spring when starting to emerge from hibernation.

Persons are rarely stung by other members of the superfamily Vespoidea, although Bromley (1933) describes pain and swelling, involving the entire hand and forearm, which he, an admittedly susceptible individual, experienced from a sting by the tarantula wasp, *Pepsis formosa* (Say) (Family Pompilidae).

Mud daubers or *thread-waisted wasps* (superfamily Sphecoidea), such as *Chalybion californicum* (Saussure) (=*C. caeruleum* Johannson and Linnaeus), make their nests, usually quite small, of mud, and provision them with insects and spiders to serve as food for the larvae. These nests are frequently found in attics and outbuildings.

Ants belong to the family Formicidae, superfamily Formicoidea. Many ants cannot sting, but on the other hand, some sting viciously. Parrish (1963) lists four human deaths in the United States, during the period of 1950–59, caused by ant stings.

The more primitive subfamilies of ants show affiliations with other stinging Hymenoptera in possessing a stinging apparatus and venom (Fig. 20-6). Proteinaceous venoms are characteristic of Myrmicinae, Ponerinae, Dorylinae,

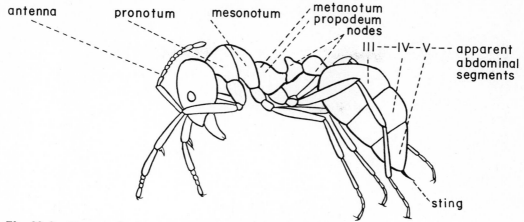

Fig. 20-6 Diagram of a fire ant. (Courtesy of U.S. Public Health Service.)

and Pseudomyrmecinae. The most detailed study of ant venoms has been undertaken with Australian bull ants of the genus *Myrmecia*; large ants, up to 2 cm long, that excavate nests in dry stony ground in areas of tree roots and large rocks (Cavill and Robertson, 1965). Venom of the red bull ant, *Myrmecia gulosa*, has histamine, hyaluronidase (spreading factor), kininlike activity (but no kinin identified), and hemolytic protein that may correspond to the toxic protein mellitin in honey bee venom.

The subfamily Myrmicinae includes several formidable stinging groups of pugnacious nature. Because of their numbers, a mass attack may be serious. Some of the more dangerous species belong to the following two groups:

1. The fire ants, genus *Solenopsis*, are so-called because of the sharp, fiery pain of their sting. Of special importance is the imported fire ant, *Solenopsis saevissima richteri* Forel, which was introduced probably as a cargo stowaway into the United States some time prior to 1930, and which has become a scourge throughout the southeastern states (anon., 1954; Arant, *et al.*, 1958). It builds large hard-crusted earthen mounds (Fig. 20-7). It first sinks its powerful mandibles into the flesh for leverage and then drives its sting into the victim. This ant not only attacks crops but

also kills and devours newly hatched quail and poultry, or enters pipped eggs to reach the unhatched chicks; it will also attack young pigs, newborn calves, and so forth. The death of large numbers of bluegill sunfish (*Lepomus* sp.) in Mississippi and Alabama is attributed to fire ants, which these fish would not readily eat in the laboratory but which on introduction into the stomach caused poisoning symptoms and death (Green and Hutchins, 1960). About 300 people at Fort Benning, Georgia (United States) were treated for imported fire ant stings in 1957. The pattern of invasion and dispersion in that locality indicated cars played an important role in spread of the insects (Olive, 1960). Persons may be stung extensively and show severe symptoms (Fig. 20-8).

The human response to a fire ant sting is an immediate flare and wheal at the site followed within twenty-four hours by an umbilicated pustule that is surrounded by a red halo or edematous painful area. Necrosis may follow. Some people show febrile and allergic symptoms, and fatalities have been reported. The venom is water-insoluble, soluble in most organic solvents, and strongly alkaline (Blum and Callahan, 1960). It has been called *solenamine*, has necrotoxic and hemolytic properties, and is composed of two closely related components: (1) 2-methyl-3-hexadecyl-

Fig. 20-7 Mounds of the imported fire ant. (U.S.D.A. photograph.)

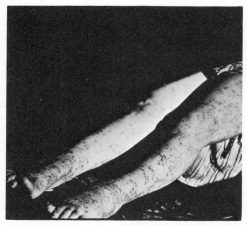

Fig. 20-8 A case of extensive and severe stinging by fire ants. (Courtesy of Dr. V. J. Derbes, Tulane University School of Medicine.)

pyrrolidine and (2) 2-methyl-3-hexadecyl-Δ^3-pyrroline (Adrouny, 1966).

Other fire ants of some importance in the United States are the common fire ant, *Solenopsis geminata* (Fabricius), and the southern fire ant, *S. xyloni* McCook. In the latter Blum, *et al.* (1961), found an amine in the venom.

2. The genus *Pogonomyrmex* (harvester ants of the Americas) have a vicious sting and readily attack man and animals (Weber, 1959). They are of concern in agricultural entomology because their low, bare mounds, and their destruction of adjacent vegetation, can waste land. The red harvester ant, *Pogonomyrmex barbatus* (F. Smith), occurs at lower altitudes from Kansas and Louisiana to Utah and

California, and into Mexico; the California harvester ant, *P. californicus* (Buckley), occurs from Texas and Utah to California and Mexico; the western harvester ant, *P. occidentalis* (Cresson), is widespread, from North Dakota and British Columbia southward to Arizona and Oklahoma; and the Florida harvester ant, *P. badius* (Latreille), the only species known from east of the Mississippi, occurs in the southeastern states. These ants will readily attack man and small animals. Young pigs may be killed by their stings.

Ants are further mentioned here as playing a very minor role in the dissemination of pathogenic organisms. Smith (1951) has pointed out that *Solenopsis* workers may carry viable dysentery germs on their bodies for at least twenty-four hours, and Donisthorpe (1945) recorded mechanical transmission of smallpox by ants in a hospital in Egypt. In Germany Pharaoh's ant, *Monomorium pharaonis* (Linnaeus), imported from the subtropics, shows a marked predilection for hospitals where it is suspected of contaminating surgical instruments and other aseptic items (Eichler, 1964). Krull and Mapes (1952) recorded *Formica fusca* (Linnaeus) as being an intermediate host of the little liver fluke of sheep, *Dicrocoelium dendriticum* (Rudolphi), and O'Rourke (1956) cites the role of ants as important intermediate hosts of cestodes affecting poultry and wild gallinaceous birds.

Mutillid Wasps (velvet ants, woolly ants, cow killers, mule killers). Among the less-known stinging insects are wasps belonging to the family Mutillidae, superfamily Scolioidea. Most mutillids are covered with a velvety pubescence (Fig. 20-9); many are brightly colored with orange or red or yellow. The females are apterous, good runners, and may inflict a painful sting. They are parasites of bees and other wasps (Mickel, 1928). There are many species, some of the commoner forms measuring from 1/2 to 1 inch in length. *Dasymutilla occidentalis* (Linnaeus), a very common rather large black species clothed largely with scarlet hairs dorsally, causes

Fig. 20-9 A velvet ant, family Mutillidae, also known as a "cow killer." × 2.2.

barefoot bathers much distress on the beach sands of Lake Erie (United States).

The bethylid wasps, Superfamily Bethyloidea, are, so far as known, parasitic on hymenopterous, lepidopterous, and coleopterous larvae, although comparatively little is known of their bionomics. Three genera, *Cephalonomia, Scleroderma,* and *Epyris* have been reported as stinging man. Cariaso (1962) has provided some details on the morphology and biology of *Scleroderma domesticum* Latreille. These small wasplike insects may become abundant in houses as a result of a persistent infestation by one of their hosts.

Guiglia (1958) describes two cases of bethylid sting that occurred in Genoa, Italy, and gives considerable general information concerning the stinging propensities of these insects. A woman, stung in many places on her body by *Scleroderma domesticum* Latreille, showed localized results, general symptoms of the anaphylactic type, and other complications such as malaise, nausea, and headaches. A second case involved multiple stings of three members of a family by a species of *Cephalonomia*. Muesebeck and Walkley (1951) state that there are many reports of the North American *C. gallicola* (Ashmead) stinging man.

In 1927 von Geldern reported a tiny wasp from Yolo County, California, identified as a species of *Epyris*, to inflict a sharp pricking sting followed, in susceptible individuals, by numbness, itching, diarrhea and cramps, weakness, and sweating. Essig (1932) reported a number of instances, in the same county, of stings by *Epyris californicus* (Ashmead), which is barely over 5 mm in length and is black in color.

Reaction to Bee and Wasp Stings. The painful effect of the stings of bees and wasps is not caused by the simple thrusts of the sting, but more particularly by the introduced venom. The severity is greatly increased by multiple stings. Pawlowsky, according to Martini (1932), estimates 500 bee stings within a short time as a lethal dose for man. Tolerance to bee stings appears to be developed in bee-keepers, long exposed to stings; however, this tolerance seems to be lost when exposure to stings is discontinued.

A sting in a nonsensitized person produces local pain, swelling, and redness, which pass harmlessly within a few hours. In susceptible individuals, however, it is quite a different matter. Mueller (1959), on the basis of a study involving eighty-four patients who showed allergic reactions to insect stings, groups susceptible individuals into four classes, according to the severity of the reaction. (1) In those with a slight general reaction (twelve patients), general urticaria, malaise, and anxiety develop on an average of twenty-four minutes (range two to sixty) after the occurrence of the sting. (2) In those with a general reaction (thirty-six patients), in addition to the above, the signs and symptoms include two or more of the following: generalized edema; chest constriction; wheezing; abdominal pain, nausea, and vomiting; and dizziness. (3) In severe cases (twenty-three patients), two or more of the following are added to the above: dyspnea; dysphagia; hoarseness and thickened speech; confusion; and feeling of impending disaster. (4) Finally, in patients with a shock reaction (thirteen patients), at least two of the following may be added to any of the above signs or symptoms: cyanosis; fall in blood pressure;

collapse; incontinence; and unconsciousness. The onset of the symptoms becomes progressively more rapid with the increasing severity of the case, ranging from two to fifteen minutes in cases involving shock.

It must be emphasized that to some persons a single bee or wasp sting may be very dangerous (Miller, 1956). If a person shows severe allergic reactions to insect stings it is practically mandatory that he undergo a course of desensitization. If the insect causing the reaction is known *accurately and specifically*, desensitization using the extract of that particular insect alone may be safe. If the offending insect is not known, or if there is a possibility of sensitivity to other stinging insects, desensitization with a combined antigen, including at least bee, wasp, yellow jacket, and hornet extracts, would seem advisable (Foubert and Stier, 1958).

If no antigenic complications are present, the application of an ice-pack followed by a paste of bicarbonate of soda and water to the area of the sting is soothing.

BITING (PIERCING) INSECTS

Insects that pierce the skin with their mouth parts are normally bloodsuckers, and the act of biting or piercing is simply a part of the act of obtaining food. There are noteworthy exceptions, as later explained. The pain caused by the mechanical insertion of such tiny mouth parts would be, no doubt, relatively benign, particularly if only one or a few individual insects were concerned in the attack; however, in perhaps every instance an irritating salivary enzyme is introduced. This enzyme differs among various insects, as shown by the resulting reactions, local and systemic, that are generally specific enough so that one who is experienced may be able to determine whether the offender was a bed bug, a flea, a mosquito, a black fly or other. Progress has been realized in collecting pure oral secretions of biting insects to study their chemical and antigenic characteristics (Benjamini, *et al.*, 1963).

To understand the operation of the blood-sucking mechanism of various insects one should consult Chapter 3 on mouth parts and the other chapters appropriate to the subject. The student will profit much by a careful study of *Zoonosen der Haut in warmeren Landern* by Martini (1932).

Some individuals apparently suffer no ill effects from insect bites, not even a swelling at the site of the bite; others react violently to even one bite. These differences in tolerance to a given species are not fully understood, but doubtless allergic responses play a role.

Various studies indicate the cause of the allergic response to insect bites. In studying the response of guinea pigs to flea bites (Benjamini, *et al.*, 1963a, 1963b; Michaeli, *et al.*, 1965) it was found that substances causing hypersensitivity were haptenic in nature, and gel filtration showed allergenic activity in a fraction of high molecular weight (4,000–10,000) as well as a fluorescing aromatic fraction of molecular weight probably below 1,000. It was suggested the skin of the host plays an essential role in inducing hypersensitivity by the conjugation of hapten with skin collagen. Likewise the oral secretions of the mosquito *Aedes aegypti* caused allergic reactions when injected into guinea pigs. Animals bitten for the first time did not react, but an allergic response followed on the next challenge (McKiel, 1959). Hudson, *et al.* (1960) succeeded in cutting the salivary duct of mosquitoes, demonstrating that such insects caused no wheal on humans, but their bite was more painful.

Some allergic responses to the bites of vectors are thought caused by sensitivity to the pathogens they introduce. *Chrysops* transmitting infective larvae of *Loa* of human or simian origin may cause severe immediate reactions after previous sensitization (Crewe and Gordon, 1959). On the other hand, experiments with various triatomid bugs show that

bi- or unilateral palpebral edema, considered an early symptom of Chagas' disease, is caused by uninfected bugs in sensitized persons (Lumbreras, *et al.*, 1959).

Arthropods that inflict a very painful bite, such as the stable fly and most salt-marsh mosquitoes, e.g., *Aedes dorsalis* (Meigen), are apparently seldom vectors of disease; species with benign bites, such as *Anopheles maculipennis* Meigen, are commonly potent vectors. It seems successful adaptation to feeding upon a given host, to the extent that the arthropod may become a successful vector of disease, is dependent upon a modification of the severity of the bite. At least for trombiculid mites, the severity of reaction does not appear to be related to whether natural or unnatural hosts are involved; rather histological findings indicate degree of response is related to intensity and duration of infestation (Hoeppli and Schumacher, 1962).

True bugs (Order Hemiptera) have already been discussed in Chapter 8. The assassin bugs, aside from the Triatominae, attack species of insects, particularly soft-bodied forms from which they suck the body fluids. Attacks upon man are made principally, if not wholly, in self defense. Persons picking up boards, sticks, or stones may accidentally pick up one of these insects; likewise, in plucking a leaf or flower from a tree or other plant, the fingers may close upon the insect as well, with the result that a very painful bite may be suffered. The predaceous reduviid, *Platymeris rhadamanthus* Gerstaecker, from East Africa and Zanzibar, injects its salivary secretions into prey, but also ejects saliva forcibly as a defense against vertebrates. The saliva contains at least six proteins, and has trypsinlike activity, strong hyaluronidase (spreading factor) and weak phospholipase activity; and causes intense local pain, vasodilation, and edema around eye and nose membranes (Edwards, 1961).

A number of aquatic forms of Hemiptera include biting species; among these are the families Belostomatidae and Notonectidae.

The giant water bugs *Lethocerus, Belostoma,* and *Benacus,* belonging to the family Belostomatidae, are among the largest of bugs, the larger species measuring 2½ inches or more in length and possessing formidable beaks. They feed on other aquatic insects, also young frogs, fish, and so forth and because they are winged and readily attracted to light, they are commonly known as electric light bugs. They have been known to attack birds, fatally in at least one instance. Ewing (1928) describes the bite of *Benacus griseus* (Say) as causing a burning sensation with some swelling, but no very lasting effects. Back swimmers belonging to the family Notonectidae may also inflict a painful bite. These predaceous bugs swim on their backs, hence the common name "back swimmers." The bite may be nearly as severe as a bee sting.

Numerous instances of bloodsucking among phytophagous Hemiptera have been reported. Much information concerning these cases has been assembled by Usinger (1934). Among the species exhibiting this fortuitous bloodsucking behavior are members of the families Membracidae (treehoppers), Cicadellidae (leafhoppers and sharpshooters), Miridae, Coreidae and Tingidae.

Thrips Biting Man. Thrips (Order Thysanoptera) are minute, mostly plant-feeding (sapsucking) insects; however, there have been numerous reports of their attacking man and of their ability to suck blood. Bailey (1936) states that while working in experimental plots, the onion thrips, *Thrips tabaci* Lindeman, caused slight pricks on his arm, face, and neck, both when perspiring and when not. He had similar experiences with the pear thrips, *Taeniothrips inconsequens* (Uzel).

According to personal communication (to James) from Stanley F. Bailey, *Chirothrips aculeatus* Bagnall and *Limothrips cerealium* (Haliday) (species, which normally breed in the heads of oats, rye, foxtail grass, and similar plants) often annoy man. Reports of annoyance have come from many areas in Europe and the United States. Military installations, commercial plants, and populated areas in the wake of thrips migrations from drying cereals may suffer serious annoyance. The insects are so small that they pass through ordinary window screen.

Several other species of thrips have been reported in a similar connection, e.g., *Heliothrips* sp., recorded as *indicus* Bagnall, but probably either *H. fumipennis* Bagnall and Cameron or *H. sudanensis* Bagnall and Cameron, in the Sudan; *Thrips imaginis* Bagnall, reported from Australia; *Limothrips denticornis* (Haliday), for Germany; *Gynaitkothrips ficorum* (Marchal), for Algiers; and other species. Apparently this behaviour is not restricted to one or two species.

Urticarial Hairs. The caterpillars, or larvae, of many species of Lepidoptera (at least ten families and more than fifty species) possess urticating hairs (Fig. 20-10). These hairs are hollow and may contain a toxin, though in some instances irritation seems largely due to a mechanical effect similar to glass fibers. Entrance of urticating hairs into the eye proper can cause blindness (Corkey, 1955).

Among the families that have urticating larvae is the Saturniidae of which the genus *Hemileuca* is especially offensive (Fig. 20-11). *Hemileuca oliviae* Cockerell, the range caterpillar, was reported to be a menace to cattlemen in New Mexico (Caffrey, 1918). In 1967 some 470,000 acres of rangeland were treated for control of the range caterpillar in this state. Cattle strictly avoided heavily infested areas, but they received blisters on the mouth through accidental contact in lightly infested areas or where forced to feed in heavily infested areas through lack of suitable grazing lands (J. G. Watts, communication to Harwood).

The io moth, *Automeris io* (Fabricius) (Fig. 20-12), produces a sharp, stinging dermatitis similar to that produced by some species of nettles. A rash known as "brown-tail rash" is traceable to the caterpillar of the brown-tail moth, *Nygmia phaeorrhoea* (Donovan) (Family

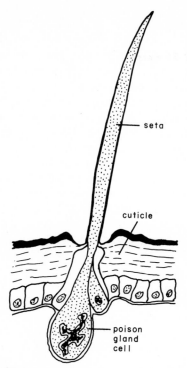

seta

cuticle

poison gland cell

Fig. 20-10 Urticating hair of a caterpillar showing sharp seta and associated poison glands. (Redrawn from Gilmer, P. M.: *Ann. Ent. Soc. Amer.*, **18**: 203-39, 1925.)

Lymantriidae), a common and very destructive shade-tree pest in Europe and in America, especially in New England. When the caterpillars of this species molt, numerous tiny barbed hairs are shed with the skin. The cocoons of the pupated caterpillars as well as the adult moths possess these hairs. Hairs are blown by the wind, and when in contact with the skin of the neck, face, hands, and other exposed parts of the body, they produce a severe dermatitis. An especially acute dermatitis is produced when the hairs come into contact with the conjunctiva of the eye. Ingestion or inhalation of the hairs may cause serious internal disturbances.

Certain flannel moths, family Megalopygidae, are among the most serious urticating forms. *Megalopyge lanata* (Stoll) is a constant cause of a painful dermatitis in the Panama

Fig. 20-11 A species of *Hemileuca* larva. (Photograph by R. L. Furniss; courtesy of U.S. Forest Service.)

Canal Zone. Randel and Doan (1956) observed eighteen cases at the Albrook Air Force Base in 1949–51; they briefly described five case histories. All cases were characterized by sudden burning at the point of contact, erythema, swelling, lymphangitis, leukocytosis, and eosinophilia. Numbness, lymphadenopathy, and vesication sometimes occurred. All cases were self-limiting. These authors point out the need for the physician to be alert to the hazard, in order to relieve the symptoms and to distinguish the condition from insect

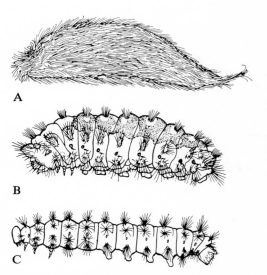

A

B

C

Fig. 20-12 Various urticating caterpillars. *A. Megalopyge. B.* The flannel moth, *Norape crenata. C.* Io moth, *Automeris io.* (Courtesy of U.S. Public Health Service.)

bites (and even snake bite), which may need more specific treatment. The caterpillar is yellow, about 5 cm long and 1 1/2 cm in diameter; the body is covered with tufts of black hairs emerging from papillae. Contact with the caterpillar, in the Canal Zone, occurs during March and April.

The puss caterpillar (Fig. 20-12), *Megalopyge opercularis* (J. E. Smith), produces a painful and sometimes serious dermatitis in the southern United States, characterized initially by an intense burning pain, followed by itching and general swelling. Paralytic symptoms, nausea, and fever (especially in young children) often ensue. This caterpillar caused 2,130 sting cases in Texas in 1958. (McGovern, *et al.*, 1961).

Students concerned with the study of urticating hairs will need to consult Weidner's work (1936), which includes a bibliography on poisonous insect hairs. Among the more recent papers that have been published on the subject are those of Kemper, particularly his report to the Tenth International Congress of Entomology (1958). Some of the more important nettling and urticating Lepidoptera are the following: **Morphoidae,** *Morpho hercules* Dalman (South America); **Arctiidae,** *Lithosia caniola* Hübner, *L. griseola* Hübner, and *Arctia caja* (Linnaeus), Europe, and *Euchaetias egle* (Drury) and *Halisidota caryae* (Harris), the hickory tussock moth, North America; **Lymantriidae,** *Nygmia phaeorrhoea* (Donovan), the brown-tail moth, *Stilpnotia salicis* (Linnaeus), the satin moth, and *Porthetria dispar* (Linnaeus) the gypsy moth, Europe and the United States; *Lymantria monacha* (Linnaeus), the nun moth, *Euproctis similis* (Fueszly), and *Dasychira pudibunda* (Linnaeus), Europe, *Hemerocampa leucostigma* (J. E. Smith), the white-marked tussock moth, United States, and *Euproctis flava* (Bremer), China; **Thaumetopoeidae,** *Thaumetopoea processionea* (Linnaeus), the processionary caterpillar, *T. pinivora* Treitschke, and *Anaphe infracta* Walsingham, Europe; **Lasiocampidae,** *Macrothylacia rubi* (Linnaeus), *Dendrolimnus pini*

(Linnaeus), *Lasiocampa quercus* (Linnaeus), and *Gastropacha quercifolia* (Linnaeus), Europe; **Noctuidae,** *Acronicta lepusculina* Guénée, *A. oblinata* (J. E. Smith), and *Catocala* spp., United States; **Nymphalidae,** *Nymphalis antiopa* (Linnaeus), the mourning-cloak butterfly, North America and Europe, and *Nymphalis io* (Linnaeus), Europe; **Saturniidae,** *Automeris io* (Fabricius), the io moth, *Hemileuca oliviae* Cockerell, the range caterpillar, *H. maia* (Drury), the buck moth, *H. nevadensis* Stretch, *H. lucina* Edwards, *Coloradia* spp., *Pseudohazis eglanterina* (Boisduval), and *P. hera* (Harris), United States, and probably many other species, including other species of *Automeris* and *Hemileuca*; **Megalopygidae,** *Lagoa crispata* Packard, the white moth, *Megalopyge opercularis* (J. E. Smith), the puss moth, *Lagoa pyxidifera* (J. E. Smith), and *Norape crenata* (Grote) (Fig. 20-12), United States, and *Megalopyge lanata* (Stoll), tropical America; **Limacodidae,** *Sibine stimulea* (Clemens) (Fig. 20-13), *Adoneta spinuloides* (Herrich-Schaeffer), *Parasa chloris* (Herrich-Schaeffer), *Parasa indetermina* (Boisduval), *Phobetron pithecium* (J. E. Smith), and others, United States, *Parasa hilarata* (Staudinger), east Asia, and *Parasa latistriga* (Walker), South Africa. Undoubtedly many Saturniidae, Megalopygidae, and others should be added to the list.

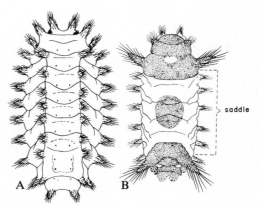

Fig. 20-13 *A.* A slug caterpillar, *Euclea chloris. B.* The saddleback caterpillar, *Sibine stimulea.* (Courtesy of U.S. Public Health Service.)

On the other hand, some of the species listed, such as those of Noctuidae, are very mild in their nettling effects and would have no effect at all on any but the most highly sensitized individuals.

The severity and peculiarity of circumstances surrounding urticaria may be puzzling. In Israel 600 of 3,000 soldiers encamped in a pine grove developed rash and severe irritation. No living larvae were found, but dead larvae and old cocoons of *Thaumetopoea wilkinsoni* Tams were present and these caused typical reactions on volunteers' arms (Ziprkowski, *et al.*, 1959). In 1960 in Serra do Navio, Amapá Territory, Brazil, nearly 40 per cent of the population was affected by dermatitis caused by *Hylesia*.

Lepidoptera larvae can cause allergic reactions, as is the case with a great many arthropods, by other than urticating hairs. In Bulgaria eczema, dermatitis, and pruritus of women shelling and cleaning walnuts was associated with reaction to the larvae and larval excreta of a stored products pest, the Indian meal moth *Plodia interpunctella* (Hb.).

Blister beetles (family Meloidae, order Coleoptera) are so designated because of their vesicating properties, i.e., the application of the pulverized bodies or even simple contact with the insect may produce a blistering of the skin. The family is comprised of medium to large beetles with comparatively soft body; head broad, held vertically, and abruptly narrowed to a neck; prothorax narrower than the soft and flexible wing covers; legs long and slender, hind tarsi four-jointed, middle and fore tarsi five-jointed (Fig. 20-14).

Adult blister beetles are plant feeders that deposit their eggs on the ground; the larvae are active, and some species feed on the eggs of grasshoppers and in nests of solitary bees, whereas others are predaceous. They undergo a number of changes not usual to insects, in that there is a multiplicity of larval stages which differ structurally and in habits from one another; this development is termed "hypermetamorphosis."

The Spanish fly, *Lytta vesicatoria* (Linnaeus), is a European blister beetle found most abundantly during early summer in Spain, southern France, and other parts of Europe (Fig. 20-15). It is golden green or bluish in color, from 1/2 to 3/4 inch in length. It appears quite suddenly in early summer, when it may be collected by the hundreds, clinging principally to such vegetation as ash, privet, and lilac. Their sudden appearance and equally sudden disappearance, owing to short adult life, give rise to the belief that they are migrating forms.

Cantharidin, a crystalline anhydrid of

 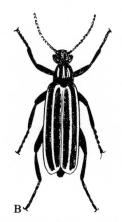 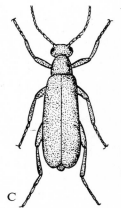

Fig. 20-14 Common North American blister beetles. *A.* Margined blister beetle, *Epicauta pestifera. B.* Striped blister beetle, *E. vittata. C.* Ash-gray blister beetle, *E. fabrici.* (Courtesy of U.S. Public Health Service.)

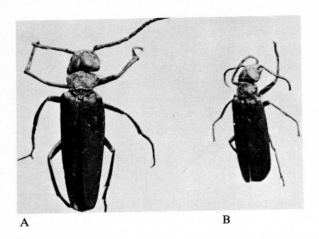

Fig. 20-15 The Spanish fly, *Lytta vesicatoria. A.* Female. *B.* Male.

A   B

cantharidic acid, isolated by Robiquet in 1812 from the Spanish fly, penetrates the epidermis quite readily and produces, even in very small quantities (0.1 mg), violent superficial irritation, resulting in vesication (blistering) in a few hours. Even when applied to the skin, cantharidin irritates the kidneys so that it should never be used where kidney ailments occur. Formerly used as an aphrodisiac, its effects may be dangerous to life; hence, its use for that purpose has been largely discontinued.

The collection and preparation of beetles, for medical purposes, require special precautions owing to their vesicating properties. The best quality of cantharidin produced from the pulverized beetles results from special care in the drying, which must be gradual.

Other blister beetles, causing severe vesicular dermatitis in Africa, are *Zonabris nubica* (de Marseul), *Epicauta tomentosa* Maeklin, and *E. sapphirina* Maeklin, according to Chalmers and King (1917).

Other Vesicating Beetles. At least two species, *Sessinia collaris* (Sharp) and *S. decolor* Fairmaire, belonging to the family Oedemeridae, cause severe blistering on some of the mid-Pacific islands where they are called coconut beetles (Herms, 1925). These beetles fairly swarm about the newly opened male flowers of the coconut where they feed on pollen. They are readily attracted to light.

Contact with one of these beetles causes a sharp momentary pain, like a burn from hot oil, but the large blister that forms in a few hours causes little pain.

In Puerto Rico an oedemerid, *Oxicopis vittata* (Fabricius), is a cause of vesication (communication to Harwood from Dr. T. Lawrence Fleisher, Dermatology Section, Department of Medicine, University of Puerto Rico). The beetle must be crushed while on the skin, resulting in a few minutes in stinging followed by a vesicle. The vesicle is replaced by a crust and the lesions heal without scarring.

At least thirty species of staphylinid beetles in the genus *Paederus* produce dermatitis and ophthalmic lesions in animals (Pavan, 1959). Agricultural workers in Paraguay suffer from the secretions of these beetles (Dallas, 1938). *Paederus fuscipes* Curt is a problem in Thailand; on one occasion large numbers of these beetles caused numerous cases of dermatitis and ocular involvement in the Bangkok area (Papasarathorn, *et al.*, 1961). In Southwest Africa a widespread outbreak of vesicular dermatitis was reported with essentially painless lesions caused by contact with crushed adults of *Paederus sabaeus* Erichs (Deneys and Zumpt, 1963). In Uganda this species was found to breed in large numbers in damp leaf litter and humus. It is strongly attracted to light. The term "Nairobi eye" applies to conjunctivitis caused when juices of crushed beetles are rubbed in the eye. The vesicating toxin in the hemolymph was thought to be cantharidin, but gas chromatographic analysis suggests this is not so (McCrae and Visser, 1963). Pavan and Bo (1953) obtained a crystalline toxic principle they termed *pederin* from *Paederus fuscipes* Curt. Pederin, as well as derivatives called pseudopederin and pederone, have been chemically analyzed by Cardani, *et al.* (1965).

Tenebrionid beetles of the genus *Blaps* produce a fluid that causes blisters, and that probably contains quinones (Roth and Eisner, 1962). *B. judaeorum* Miller is common in certain dune areas of Palestine (Howells, 1957); caustic effects of the secretion of *B. nitens* Cast. have been described in detail (Laurent, 1939).

SPIDERS

CLASS *ARACHNIDA,*
ORDER *ARANEIDA*

General Characteristics. Spiders are arachnids in which the prosoma is uniform, bearing not more than eight eyes, and joined to the opisthosoma by a pedicel. The opisthosoma is usually unsegmented and bears not more than four, usually three, pairs of spinnerets. There is no telson. The chelicerae are two-segmented, moderately large, and unchelate, and contain (or are connected with) a poison gland. The pedipalps are six-segmented, leg-like, and tactile in function. In some forms they are so large they might be mistaken for an extra pair of legs. Legs consist each of seven segments; tarsi have two or three claws. Respiration is by book lungs or tracheae or, normally, both. The pedipalps of the male are modified as intromittent organs (see Savory, 1935, p. 95). A good account of spider anatomy is given by Snodgrass (1952).

Although spiders are universally feared, no doubt because of the knowledge that they are able to kill insects and other small animals by introducing a venom with the bite, neverthe-

less, of the more than 2,000 genera in more than sixty families only a very few species are known to be dangerous to man.

TARANTULAS

The term "tarantula" was first applied to a European species, *Lycosa tarentula* (Linnaeus), a member of the family Lycosidae (wolf spiders). It is of interest to note that the American tarantulas belong to an entirely different group of spiders, and that the arachnid that goes by the generic name *Tarantula* is not a spider at all, but a tailless whip-scorpion (Order Phrynichida). In Italy in the vicinity of Taranto, there occurred a spider scare during the seventeenth century, which gave rise to a condition known as "tarantism," resulting from the bite of the European tarantula, *Lycosa tarentula*. To rid the body of the venom those bitten engaged in a frenzied dance known as the "tarantella" (Thorp and Woodson, 1945). Tarantism is further discussed in Chapter 1.

In the United States the term "tarantula" is applied to the very large spiders belonging to the family Theraphosidae, also known as "bird spiders," as *carangueigeiras* or "crab spiders" (in Brazil), or as *aranas de caballo* or *matacaballos* (in Central America). Many of these spiders measure 6 or 7 inches in the spread of legs. About thirty species live within the limits of the United States, mostly in the Southwest (Gertsch, 1949), and many others occur in the New World tropics. They are greatly feared and are erroneously supposed to have prodigious jumping power.

The supposedly venomous nature of American tarantulas has been investigated at length by Baerg, whose studies, involving thirty-five years of research and numerous publications, have been summarized in an interesting and very readable little book entitled *The Tarantula* (Baerg, 1958). Baerg tested the effects of the venom on guinea pigs, white rats, rabbits, and himself. He concludes that most species from Mexico, Central America, and Trinidad, as well as all from the United States, so far as has been determined, are harmless to man. The bite "is as painful as a couple of pin stabs and has essentially the same effect." The Arkansas tarantula, *Dugesiella hentzi* (Girard), can kill rats; but usually, after a rat is bitten, it "runs about excitedly, and in a jumping and jerking manner. Then it becomes more quiet and appears to have considerable pain in the wounded leg. For much of the time the eyes are closed. In about four or five hours the rat shows evidence of recovery and in another hour it is normal" (Baerg, 1929).

On the other hand, some tropical tarantulas, such as the southern Mexican species *Aphonopelma emilia* (White), may be poisonous to man. *Aphonopelma* venom and *Centruroides* scorpion venom have similar biological and electrophoretic properties (Stahnke and Johnson, 1967). The large black tarantula of Panama and the Canal Zone, *Sericopelma communis* Cambridge, is definitely poisonous to man, but the effects of its bite, though severe, are local, not general. Baerg allowed a spider of this species to bite him on the finger with just one fang. The finger felt numb in a few minutes, and in ten minutes the pain was quite severe. There followed considerable swelling of the finger, hand, and wrist. After two hours Baerg put his hand in hot water for thirty minutes, and the pain and swelling subsided. A lame feeling in the small and third fingers remained for several days.

BLACK WIDOWS *(LATRODECTUS)*

Dangerous spiders belonging to the genus *Latrodectus* are found throughout the world. The genus belongs to the family Theridiidae, the combfooted spiders. They have eight eyes and three tarsal claws; the hind pair of legs is comb-footed. They spin irregular webs in which the female spiders hang belly upward.

Arachnologists do not agree as to the classification of the spiders of this genus. Even in local areas there may be real difficulties (Abalos and Baez, 1967). Levi (1958, 1959) recognizes only six species in the world; *Latrodectus mactans* (Fabricius), the black widow, widespread from the southern United States, through much of tropical America, and through the tropical and warmer temperate regions of all continents; *L. curacaviensis* Müller, widespread from southern Canada and the northern United States through the lesser Antilles southward in America to Chile and Argentina; *L. geometricus* Koch, the brown widow, widespread in the tropics, particularly in Africa, but occurring in the United States only in Florida; *L. pallidus* Cambridge, occurring from the Turkmen Soviet Republic through Iran and Asia Minor to Libya and Tripolitania in North Africa; *L. hystrix* Simon, known only from Yemen; and *L. dahli* Levi, from Iran and the island of Sokotra. If this classification is accepted, one must consider the black widow of Canada and most of the northern United States as distinct from the predominant species in the South (although both may coexist in the same area); also, one must consider *L. mactans* as occurring throughout the tropics and as being the important venomous member of the genus in the Old World as well as the new. Arachnologists who do not accept this synonymy consider the following as important venomous species: *L. bishopi* Kaston, from Florida; *L. tredecimguttatus* Rossi, from the Mediterranean region and the European and Asiatic steppes, *L. cinctus* Blackwell (=*L. indistinctus* Cambridge), the *Knoppiespinnekop* or "shoe-button spider" of South Africa; *L. hasselti* Thorell, occurring from Australia and New Zealand northward to India; and *L. menavodi* Vinson, from Madagascar.

Maretić (1965) provides a map of the species and subspecies of *Latrodectus*. He states that *Latrodectus mactans tredecimguttatus* is the only dangerous poisonous spider in Europe. In Yugoslavia this subspecies occurs only in the dry sunny fields and scrub. Of 176 cases in man in that country between 1948–65, no biting was recorded indoors.

The Black Widow Spider, *Latrodectus mactans* (Fabricius) (here including *L. curacaviensis* of Levi). In the United States, in addition to "black widow," the names "hourglass spider" and "shoe-button spider" have been used. "Pokomoo" was a name used by the California Indians, who referred to this species as "a small black spider with a red spot under his belly."

The adult female is glossy black to sepia and densely clothed with short, almost microscopic hairs, which gives it a naked appearance. As it occurs in the United States, it is usually wholly black dorsally, although an irregular red (or rarely white) stripe or pattern is sometimes present. The characteristic crimson hourglass marking on the underside of the abdomen (Fig. 20-16), rarely altogether absent, varies among individuals from the distinct hourglass marking to a design comprising two or more distinct triangles or blotches or sometimes only an irregular longitudinal area. The abdomen is globose and often likened to a shoe button. The average width of the abdomen is 6 mm, or $\frac{1}{4}$ inch; and the length overall (legs extended) is about 40 mm, or 1.5 inches. The abdomen of gravid females often measures 9 to 13 mm.

The color pattern of the adult male (Fig. 20-17), although exhibiting considerable variation, approaches that of the immature female spider. Occasionally mature males are almost black but retain some of the abdominal markings of the immature form. The terminal segment of each palpus is shaped like a knob (black) at the front of the head and contains the ejaculatory sexual apparatus, a portion of which resembles a coiled watch spring. The abdomen measures about 3 mm ($\frac{1}{8}$ inch) in diameter, and the length overall is about 30 mm (about $1\frac{1}{8}$ inches).

Distribution and Habitat. *Latrodectus mactans* (including *L. curacaviensis* as interpreted by Levi) is known to occur in virtually every state in the continental United States, with the exception of Alaska, and in southern Canada. It has been recorded at an altitude of 8,000 feet in Colorado. In her natural habitat the female spider is found with her web and egg sacs in protected places, such as, vacant rodent burrows, under stones, logs

Fig. 20-16 The black widow, *Latrodectus mactans;* (*upper left*) mature female with egg sac; (*upper right*) eggs and first instars; (*lower left*) second and third instars; (*lower right*) fourth instar.

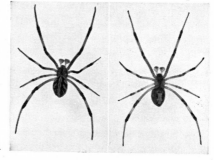

A   B

Fig. 20-17 Male black widow spider, *Latrodectus mactans. A.* Dorsal view. *B.* Ventral view.

and long grass, in hollow stumps, and in brush piles. Convenient abode is found in darker corners of barns, stables, privies, pump houses, garages, fruit-drying sheds, piles of boxes and crates, wood piles, stone piles, and so forth.

As a rule the females are not aggressive unless agitated or hungry. When guarding the egg sac, the female is particularly prone to bite. Once a web is established in a suitable location, the female spends the rest of her life feeding on the prey ensnared in this crude but effective web and guarding such eggs as she may deposit.

Feeding Habits. The coarse, permanent web is not particularly viscid in nature, but inadvertent insect visitors become temporarily entangled and in struggling to free themselves inform the owner of their presence. The spider approaches the victim backward, extending a freshly spun strand of viscid silk with either or both hind legs, and attempts to tie down the thrashing insect. If the captured prey appears particularly obstreperous, the spider ejects from the spinnerets large viscous droplets which dry quickly, and if the victim becomes entangled by these jets, escape is impossible. At about this point, a lethal bite is usually administered. After being bitten, the victim struggles violently and, in the course of a few minutes of progressively weaker tremors, dies. The body fluids are sucked from the trussed-up victim at leisure. After the meal is finished, all points of attachment between the remains of the prey and the web are severed, allowing it to drop from the web.

Life History. There seems to be variation in regard to the stage in which the black widow hibernates. The studies of Lawson (1933) and of Herms, *et al.* (1935), indicate that the adult female hibernates, but Baerg (1959) cites Frank R. Smith as saying that in Pennsylvania the black widow winters in the immature stage. The life history of the black widow spider from egg to maturity requires about four months under laboratory conditions with ample food.

The number of molts of the black widow varies, and the length of the intervening periods is even less constant, seemingly conditioned by the season and the amount of food assimilated. The average number of skins cast by the male is five. At optimum temperatures and with plenty of food this number is often reduced to three; under less favorable conditions, resulting in slower growth, a series of six or seven skins may be shed. The sexes may be distinguished by the palpi, which in the male are swollen or knoblike and in the female are slender. Subsequent to acquiring this secondary character, the male molts once (sometimes twice) before attaining maturity, at which time the web is abandoned, and his search for a mate begins.

The female takes longer to mature with an average of seven molts (six to nine range). When preparing to molt, she eats nothing for several days. The old skin splits around the margin of the carapace, slips off the abdomen, and the spider then gradually pulls its legs free from its old sheaths, leaving the "ghost" of itself on or near the web. The entire process requires about an hour. The newly molted spider is rather delicate and usually remains at rest for a day or so after molting.

The Immature Stages: First Instar. The abdomen of the newly hatched spiderling is opalescent white with no markings. The cephalothorax and appendages are white to pale yellow; short hair covers the body, becoming dark at the tips of the legs. The tarsi, or last segment of the legs, have each notched claws and a supplementary third between. Eight simple eyes are on the anterior margin of the cephalothorax in two rows of four, and the anterior medians are comparatively dark.

Second Instar. All eyes become darker, and a black band extends down the center and around the margin of the carapace. Also the mouth parts and the appendages become darker as well as the margin of the sternum of the cephalothorax. A double row of black dots extends down the midregion of the dorsum of the abdomen, which remains whitish. On the underside of the abdomen the white area takes on a broad hourglass design outlined by a dark-brown border.

Third Instar. From the third instar to maturity a wide variety in color pattern occurs. Distinct lateral stripes begin to appear on the dorsum of the abdomen, in the region of the dots of the second instar. Intervening areas take on a pale greenish-yellow cast, and the legs acquire four black bands, one at each end of the patella, one near the center of the tibia, and one at the junction of the tibia and the metatarsus. The longitudinal white areas on the underside of the abdomen become tinged with crimson.

Fourth Instar. Dark stripes or bands become distinct and faintly bordered with buff. The spinnerets take on a mottled appearance. Black bands at the leg joints become more distinct.

Fifth Instar. The center dorsal white stripe on the abdomen tends to be constricted at intervals and acquires a reddish tinge near the tip. All white areas become lightly colored with brown. Males usually mature at this point.

Sixth and Seventh Instars. Usually only the females go through the sixth and seventh instars. All coloration is much darker, and the more variable remaining white areas become more and more restricted. Often a series of reddish spots is formed along the mid-dorsal region of the abdomen.

Eighth Instar. Only the females pass through the final stage, which is often difficult to distinguish from the mature form. They are usually all black or sepia with the exception of the characteristic crimson markings and an occasional white band on the anterior margin of the abdomen.

Longevity. The length of life of individual spiders, as one might expect, depends on food supply, natural enemies, including man, and other factors. Under optimum conditions of food, temperature, humidity, and protection, the complete life cycle from egg to maturity requires at least four months. Activity on the part of both the spiders and the insect prey is greatly reduced during the winter months, which largely accounts for retardation in development.

In late spring or early summer hatchings, the females generally reach maturity before cold weather sets in, but egg-laying is held over until the following spring; hence, the life cycle is extended over a complete year. Mature males have not been found overwintering. Under laboratory conditions a few females have lived through the second and third summers, giving a life span of nearly two years.

Arachnidism (Black Widow). The chain of symptoms resulting from the bite of the black widow spider is so striking that once recognized there is little danger of confusing it with that of other venomous forms or with abdominal conditions. Cases suggest numerous acute abdominal conditions such as a ruptured peptic ulcer, acute appendicitis, renal colic, enteritis, food poisoning, and similar conditions.

The bite itself (similar to a pinprick) is not always felt, and often there is but little evidence of a lesion. However, a slight local swelling and two tiny red spots may occur, with local redness usually evident at the point of attack.

Clinical case records published by Baerg (1923), Herms, *et al.* (1935), Sampayo (1942), Tinkham (1956, for *L. bishopi*), and others are characterized by severe muscular pain, a rigid "boardlike" abdomen, tightness in the chest, difficulty in breathing and speech (usually), and nausea generally accompanied by profuse sweating. The condition is self-limiting, and in most cases symptoms wane without treatment after two to three days. Treatment is directed toward the relief of pain in which calcium gluconate intravenously has proved effective.

Of thirty-seven persons with cases of arachnidism treated at the Woodland, California, Clinic during a period of ten years, about one half were bitten on the genitalia while using a privy (Halter and Kuzell, 1943). Four of the patients were females and the remainder males, the majority of whom were laborers and farmers between the ages of twenty and fifty years. Five schoolchildren were among those treated. Spider bite cases were admitted to this hospital every month in the year except December and January, with the greater number during June, July, and August. There was no correlation between the time of day and the bites. The spider was seen in eleven cases. None of the patients reported after effects on follow-up inquiry.

Mortality from black widow spider bite is usually considered as 4–5 per cent. Of the thirty-seven Woodland cases, two terminated fatally; one of these was a 78-year-old male with heart complications. Thorp and Woodson (1945) list 1,291 cases of black widow spider bite in the United States from 1726 to 1943, with fifty-five fatalities, or 4.26 per cent; these figures have led several authors to conclude that the death rate of 4 to 5 per cent is too high, on the assumption that all deaths, but not all cases, of arachnidism have been reported. However, Parrish (1963) lists sixty-four deaths from spider bite in the United States in the period 1950–59. It is not reasonable to suppose that more people died from arachnidism in this period than did during the entire previous history of our country. Apparently many cases of black widow poisoning have been misdiagnosed and the death rate is higher than Thorp and Woodson's figures indicate.

The death rate of black widow bite is exaggerated in the public mind, however. The spider is ordinarily shy and retiring. She does not bite without provocation but will defend her eggs and bite when cornered. If one attempts to put on a shoe in which a spider is concealed, or if one grasps a spider while picking tomatoes, or comes into contact with a spider trapped in the bed sheets, one is apt to be bitten. Spiders may be very abundant in a field and never attack a person. Most bites occur in open toilets, the spider apparently

responding to the vibration in the web caused by the presence of a foreign object. Spider bites decrease in areas where outdoor privies have been eliminated.

Venom Apparatus. The venom apparatus of *Latrodectus mactans* consists of poison sacs, each with an attached duct leading into the heavily sclerotized chelicerae (horny fangs) from which the poison is expelled at the time of biting (Fig. 20-18). This apparatus is present in both males and females. In the male the venom is primarily of use in the immature stages, as the mature male does not attack its prey, and the poison apparatus appears to become inactive with maturity and remains small in size. In the female spider, the venom apparatus increases in size and strength with maturity. The large quantity of the venom present in the poison glands of the female black widow spider makes her presence perilous. The poison glands of the mature female average about 0.40 mm in diameter and 2.70 mm in length, and in the mature male they average 0.16 mm in diameter and 0.66 mm in length.

Nature of the Venom. There is good evidence that the poison glands are not exclusively glandular in nature but also function as absorptive organs that take up the poisonous constituents from the body fluid of the spider. Proteolytic or hemolytic substances variously known as *epeiralysin, arachnotoxin, arachnolysin,* and *epeiratoxin,* have been found in the eggs, newly hatched spiderlings, and gravid females (Kaston, 1948), as well as the venom of the adult female.

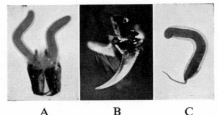

A   B   C

Fig. 20-18 *A.* Chelicerae and venom gland of female black widow spider, *Latrodectus mactans. B.* Separated chelicerae. *C.* A freed gland. (Photograph by Charles Ladenheim.)

The venom in the poison glands is a neurotoxin. It is composed of seven protein and three nonprotein fractions, one of the protein fractions having mammalian toxicity (McCrone and Hatala, 1967). Severe muscular pain and rigidity following the bite of the spider are caused by excessive heightening of the muscular tonus and by contraction of the intercostal muscles. Death results from asphyxia by respiratory paralysis. The venom of the black widow spider is far more potent than that of the prairie rattlesnake (about fifteen times as potent, on the basis of dry weight), but the amount of venom injected into a wound, even when the spider injects the full contents of her poison glands into the bite, is relatively very small. Consequently, the mortality resulting from spider bite is far less than that from rattlesnake bite. The effect on infants and small children is much more serious than that on older persons, presumably because the amount of poison is large in comparison with their small bodies or low resistance. Differences in susceptibility of vertebrates, however, are not solely related to body weight, as Maretić (1965) points out that horses are highly susceptible, whereas rabbits are comparatively resistant.

Treatment. Even though arachnidism of this type is usually self-limiting, the intense suffering of the victim justifies considerations of therapy. When bitten by the black widow spider, the patient should be treated with local antiseptics, such as alcohol or hydrogen peroxide, at the point of injury to prevent secondary bacterial infection, and should be kept as quiet as possible; a physician should be summoned at once. Since, among other properties, the venom appears to be neurotoxic and its effects little short of instantaneous, first-aid measures for snake bite are of little value; in fact the use of a tourniquet, incision and scarification at the site of the bite, and the use of suction and corrosive chemicals such as potassium permanganate only tend to increase local necrosis and add to the patient's discomfort.

Treatment of latrodectism (black widow arachnidism) is discussed concisely by Bogen (1956), and the following account is taken mainly from his discussion. Gilbert and Stewart (1935) had pointed out that, since the toxin stimulates the myoneural junctions or acts on the nerve endings, calcium salts, which apparently depress the neuromuscular junctions, would have a desirable therapeutic effect. Calcium gluconate was used instead of calcium chloride because of the necrotic effect of the latter on tissue outside a vein, particularly in the case of children. Bogen states that the value of the use of intravenous injection of calcium gluconate has been "abundantly confirmed" and relief is rapid.

The use of depressant drugs is usually not indicated. Analgesics and sedatives such as opiates and barbiturates are usually not sufficient to overcome the muscular pain. Hydrotherapy in the form of warm baths or applications may aid in lessening the pain resulting from muscular spasms and some of the undesirable after effects.

An antiserum is available against the venom of the black widow, and in some areas it is being used widely. In South Africa, the *L. cinctus* (=*indistinctus*) antiserum has been shown to be equally effective against the venom of *L. geometricus* (Finlayson, 1956). Experimentally, the results obtained with the use of *L. mactans* antiserum are impressive, and clinically the antiserum is useful, but the results are not so dramatic as those obtained from the intravenous injections of calcium salts.

The brown widow, *Latrodectus geometricus* Koch is a little smaller than *L. mactans.* In color it varies from gray to light brown to almost black. The dorsal abdominal pattern is rather intricate and variable, and the hourglass on the venter is brownish yellow. The spider occurs in most of the tropical areas of the world, particularly in Africa, where it is supposedly endemic. It occurs in the United States only in Florida.

The brown widow is much less aggressive

than the black widow, and records of its biting man are rare. Baerg (1959) describes two cases, one involving himself while studying this spider in Jamaica and the other involving a visiting scientist in his laboratory. The spider was very reluctant to bite, but when finally induced to do so, it produced a definite syndrome of arachnidism. The pain was restricted to the hand, in one case, and to the arm in the other, but was sufficiently sharp to make sleep impossible without sedation for two or three subsequent nights. In South Africa, *L. geometricus* poisoning, according to Finlayson, occurs among workers in vineyards in the Western Cape Province. Workmen are bitten while harvesting grapes. No fatal cases have been reported.

THE GENUS LOXOSCELES

At least two species of *Loxosceles* are of medical importance, one in the United States and one in Central and South America. The genus *Loxosceles*, family Scytodidae (sometimes placed in Loxoscelidae), contains spiders of medium size, the body 10–15 mm in length, and yellow to brown in color. The carapace is flattened, with six eyes (most spiders have eight) in a strongly curved row; legs are long and lack unpaired claws on all tarsi. The genus in North, Central, and South America, and the West Indies has been reviewed by Gertsch (1958, 1967).

Loxosceles reclusa Gertsch and Mulaik, the brown recluse spider, or violin spider (Fig. 20-19), has been responsible for a number of cases of necrotic spider poisoning in Arkansas and Missouri. According to Wingo (1964) this spider is commonest in Missouri, Arkansas, and eastern Kansas, and is found in the southern United States from Texas to northwestern Georgia and north to Indiana and southern Illinois (see also Gorham, 1968). It has also been reported from Tucson, Arizona, and Los Angeles County, California. It is found outdoors under rocks and rubble in its southern range, and predominantly in

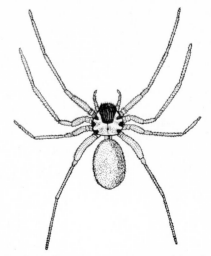

Fig. 20-19 The brown recluse spider, *Loxosceles reclusa*. Note dark violin-shaped marking on cephalothorax. (Courtesy of U.S. Public Health Service.)

and around homes in its northern range. Hite, *et al.* (1966), indicate that within homes this spider is most frequently in boxes, and outdoors it is usually under rocks.

Unlike the bite of the black widow, that of *L. reclusa* is localized, but it produces considerable local necrosis that may ultimately produce an unsightly scar. Atkins, *et al.* (1958), who have studied the bite of this spider in Missouri, describe the pathology.

A thick wheal usually forms with necrosis of tissue at the immediate site of the punctures made by the chelicerae. The necrotic area soon turns violaceous, then black and dry. The area sloughs in a few days or a week, leaving a deep sharply defined granular area surrounded by the raised edge of healthy tissue. The sloughed area, frequently quite large, may persist for several weeks, and healing takes place very slowly. In a few patients, systemic disturbances of a general nature have been indicated by a rash resembling that of scarlet fever.

Baerg cites one case in which the wound failed to heal and in which a skin graft was ultimately necessary. In another case, the patient became very ill, but the patient herself suggested that the illness might have been psychosomatic. At least two fatal cases involving *L. reclusa* have been reported (Parrish, 1963). Treatment with corticosteroids has proved useful (Dillaha, *et al.*, 1967).

South American Loxoscelism. Numerous cases of arachnidism in Peru and Chile (also Argentina and Uruguay) have been attributed to *Loxosceles,* chiefly *L. laeta* (Nicolet), although another species, erroneously referred to as *L. rufipes* (Lucas), apparently was the spider involved in a fatal case authentically reported from Argentina (Schenone, 1959). Gertsch (1967) has reviewed the genus *Loxosceles* in South America. *Loxosceles laeta,* known as the *arana de los rincones, arana de detras de cuadros* ("spider of the corners," "spider of behind the pictures"), is similar in size and appearance to *L. reclusa,* and is found on walls, especially in the corners, behind pictures, in cracks, and sometimes in clothing that has been hung on the walls. Most cases of spider bite occcur in homes, while the victims are sleeping or dressing themselves. Case histories indicate a much higher incidence of spider bite among women than among men. Levi and Spielman (1964) found *L. laeta* infesting a museum in Massachusetts, possibly introduced in shipments. *L. rufescens* Dufour was introduced and became widely established along the East Coast and Gulf states of the United States (Gertsch, 1958).

Two forms of loxoscelism occur: a *cutaneous* form, localized and benign, involving local necrosis (*mancha gangrenosa,* skin gangrene) similar to that usually produced by *L. reclusa*; and a *cutaneovisceral* form, generalized and often fatal. The latter is fortunately uncommon; in it the kidneys and liver are involved; symptoms are general, and there is considerable passage of hemoglobin and albumin in the urine. Death results, in the fatal cases, within a few days as a result of internal hemorrhages and renal blockage due to the accumulation of hemoglobin in the renal tubules. If general symptoms (fever, jaundice, hematuria) do not appear within the first twenty-four hours, the prognosis is good (Schenone, 1953 and 1959).

Schenone (1959) has presented a valuable summary of twenty-seven cases, twenty-five cutaneous and two cutaneovisceral (one fatal), occurring in Chile. Subcutaneous or intramuscular administration of the antihistamine drug chlorprophenpyramidine (Chlor-Trimeton) decreased local pain and edema almost immediately and apparently effected a milder development of the gangrenous spot.

Other Venomous Spiders. A dangerous spider in southern Brazil is *Phoneutria fera* (Perty) (Family Ctenidae) (Bücherl, 1956). Several hundred accidents involving this spider occur annually in the state of São Paulo alone; occasionally in young children fatalities occur. The venom acts on both the central and peripheral nervous systems. An antiserum is available and should be used in cases of disturbance of cardiac output, vision, and respiration, even in adults. Symptomatic treatment with analgesics and antihistamines may be sufficient if general symptoms do not occur during the first three to twelve hours after the accident.

Atrax formidabilis Cambridge and *A. robustus* Cambridge are cited by Thorp and Woodson (1945) as dangerous spiders in Australia. The bite may cause severe symptoms, and death may result. They are funnel-web spiders of fairly large size, up to $1\frac{1}{2}$ inches in length excluding the legs. The fore part of the body is glossy ebony black, the black abdomen is covered with a velvety pile, and the undersurface bears tufts and brushes of red hair.

In Peru, the *pododora* or "pruning spider" is popularly supposed to be dangerous, but Gertsch (1949) points out that supposed poisoning by this spider is probably a case of mistaken identity. At least three species of *Chiracanthium,* family Clubionidae, are venomous. *Chiracanthium inclusum* (Hentz), a widespread species in the United States, has been known to bite man, producing a temporarily painful localized effect, and *C. diversum* Koch, in Hawaii, has on a number of occasions bitten persons in the Honolulu area, in some cases requiring hospitalization and supportive treatment with calcium gluconate (Hardy, cited by Baerg, 1959).

Eye inflammation related to spiders is reported from Japan (Kawashima, 1961). *Araneus ventricosus* causes conjunctivitis, *Tegenaria domestica* causes keratitis, and *Nephila clavata* causes conjunctivitis with hemorrhage. Inflammation may be caused by these spiders or their webs and is thought to be the effect of quinones.

SCORPIONS

CLASS *ARACHNIDA,*
ORDER *SCORPIONIDA*

General Characteristics. Scorpions are easily recognized by their more-or-less crablike appearance, but particularly by the long fleshy five-segmented taillike postabdomen terminating in a bulbous sac and prominent sting (Fig. 20-20). The pedipalps are greatly enlarged, and the last two segments form strong chelae or pincers. The true jaws, chelicerae, are small and partly concealed from above by the front edge of the carapace. There are four pairs of terminally clawed legs.

The cephalothorax bears a pair of conspicuous eyes near the middorsal line (median eyes) and several smaller ocelli in groups of from two to five on the lateral margins (lateral eyes); some species are eyeless. Scorpions breathe by means of book lungs. They are ovoviviparous, and when young are born, they are carried attached by their pincers to the body of the mother. Although the sexes are very similar in appearance, the males have a longer cauda and broader chelae. An excellent account of the morphology as well as characters used in classification of scorpions is given by Moreno (1940) in *Scorpiologia Cubana.*

Scorpions are most common in warmer climates. They are nocturnal, remaining hidden during the day beneath loose stones,

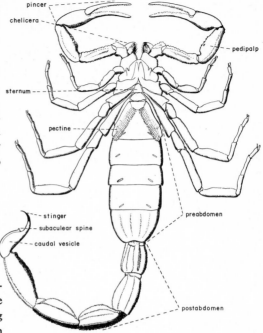

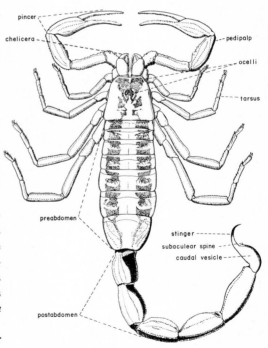

Fig. 20-20 Anatomy of a scorpion. (Courtesy of U.S. Public Health Service.)

loose bark of fallen trees, boards, piles of lumber, floors of outbuildings, and debris; some bury themselves in sand or loose earth. They feed upon insects, spiders, millipedes, and even small rodents (Vachon, 1953); they seize prey with their chelae and strike with the powerful sting, which is thrust forward in a characteristic fashion over the scorpion's head.

Scorpion Sting. The aculeus or sting of the scorpion is situated terminally on the final bulbous segment. This segment contains a pair of venom glands, which are separated by a muscular septum. From the glands are given off fine efferent ducts opening at the apex of the sting (Pawlowsky, 1924). The sting curves upward when the "tail" is extended but downward when the scorpion poises for attack or defense, the entire taillike postabdomen being curved dorsally and forward. The victim is struck quickly and repeatedly, the thrust being made forward over the scorpion's carapace.

Although published information is not consistent on the nature and effect of scorpion venom, it seems there are two general types: one is local in effect and comparatively harmless to man; the other is a neurotoxin and can be fatal (Cloudsley-Thompson, 1958). Scorpions such as the highly venomous *Androctonus australis*, as well as the dangerous American species of *Centruroides*, are of the latter type. It is of interest to note, however, that very closely related species may differ markedly in the effectiveness of their venom; for example, Stahnke (1956) has shown that *Centruroides pantheriensis* Stahnke, which he first confused with the dangerous *C. sculpturatus* Ewing, produces a local effect only. Pozo (1956) believes that, in spite of the differences in toxicity, the actions of all scorpion venoms are similar, variations in toxicity being due to the variable content of several active chemical components. The toxicity of *Centruroides sculpturatus* venom seems dependent on the presence of sulfhydryl groups (McIntosh and Watt, 1967).

Scorpion stings are especially dangerous to children. Baerg (1929) records 1,608 deaths due to the sting of the Durango scorpion, *Centruroides suffusus* Pocock, in the state of Durango, Mexico, from 1890 to 1926, with an additional forty deaths recorded for 1927 and seventeen for 1928. For all of Mexico, Mazzotti and Bravo-Becherelle (1963) state that annual deaths from scorpion stings range from 1,100 to 1,900. According to Balozet (1956), scorpions account for many more deaths in French North Africa than does snake bite. Waterman (1938), in discussing the scorpion problem in Trinidad, says that "in children under five years of age the sting frequently causes death." Waterman states that the "diagnosis is generally easy if a history of the sting is obtained, a slow full pulse easily compressible, with rapid respirations, a pulse respiration of 3:1, 2:1, or 1:1; salivation, vomiting, glycosuria and epigastric pain and tenderness—a characteristic picture of scorpion sting." The puncture made by the sting may be visible.

The symptoms produced by the sting of the Durango scorpion, *Centruroides suffusus,* are described by Baerg (1959) as follows:

Immediately following the sharp pain produced by the sting is a feeling of numbness or drowsiness, then there is an itching sensation in the nose, mouth, and throat that makes the victim distort the face, rub nose and mouth, and sneeze. There is at first an excessive production of saliva; this and a curious feeling that is described as the sensation of a ball of hair in the throat, induce the victim to swallow as rapidly as possible. The tongue is sluggish, so that communication is often by signs. The muscles of the lower jaw are contracted so that it is difficult, or impossible, to give medicine through the mouth. There is a disorder of movements in arms and legs. The temperature rises rapidly to 104° or 104.8° F., the salivary secretion now diminishes and there is a scarcity of urine. The senses of touch and sight are affected, objects appear large on touching them, hair feels rigid, face feels bulky, a veil seems to be interposed between the eyes and various objects, strong light is unpleasant to patients. Luminous objects, such as a candle, are surrounded by a red circle. Frequently there is a pronounced strabismus. There may be a hemorrhage of the stomach, intestine, and lungs. The convulsions come in waves and increase in severity for an hour and a half to two hours, or in severe cases until a fatal result. When the case ends in death, respiration stops a full minute before the pulse ceases to beat. When the patient survives for three hours he is usually considered out of danger; yet death may occur six to eight hours after the patient was stung. It is then probably due to nervous exhaustion following the long periods of convulsions.

Stahnke (1956), characterizing the effects of the sting of the two dangerous species of scorpions that occur in Arizona, *Centruroides sculpturatus* and *C. gertschi*, emphasizes the fact that the venom does not produce a swelling or discoloration at the site of the sting; the spot may become quite painful, however, and is hypersensitive so that bumping it will cause additional tingling sensations. On the other hand, the sting of the less venomous species of *Centruroides* and some species of *Vejovis, Diplocentrus, Hadrurus,* and others may produce local swellings, with or without discoloration. These swellings, if a person is bitten on the hand or fingers, may extend up the arm and even to the axilla, but with little or no systemic reaction, and, unless there are anaphylactic reactions, there is no danger of death. Consequently, the *lack of swelling* following scorpion sting in areas where dangerous *Centruroides* species may occur should be taken as a warning indication of possibly serious or even fatal poisoning.

Stahnke's bulletin entitled *Scorpions* (1956) is of inestimable value to persons living in areas where dangerous *Centruroides* species might occur and who might be in danger of coming in contact with these animals. This bulletin is available through the Poisonous Animals Research Laboratory, Arizona State University, Tempe.

If at all in doubt, one should take the victim of scorpion sting to a physician, preferably one who has had experience with the problem,

particularly if the victim is under five years of age, has a heart ailment, has been stung on a number of widely distributed places, or has been stung on the face, back of the neck, or genitalia. Antiscorpion serum is available for most dangerous scorpions, and, when administered early and in sufficient quantities, saves many lives. Failure of antiserum results, according to Balozet (1956), from (1) delay in administration, (2) rapid development of bulbar intoxication, or (3) sudden relapse following the disappearance of symptoms and discontinuation of treatment.

After applying a tight tourniquet as close as possible beyond the site of the sting, scorpion stings may be given first-aid treatment according to Stahnke (1944) as follows:

A piece of ice should be applied as soon as possible against the site of the sting; then more ice should be finely crushed and placed in water, using more ice than water. With a piece of ice against the site of the sting place the hand in the ice mixture.... Where a large dose of venom has been received the hand should be kept in this mixture for about two hours ... a large ice pack of finely crushed ice in a thin cloth may be placed over the site of the sting.

Hypothermia decreases absorption or localizes the venom; it has no effect on the venom itself. The patient should be kept cool and as calm as possible, but morphine or Demerol should not be used to relieve the pain as these increase the killing power of the venom. It is useless to make incisions at the site of the sting; bleeding will probably not eliminate the small amount of venom injected into the wound, and complications may result from the incision wound.

The **order Scorpionida** is divided into six families (some authorities recognize seven); these are the Scorpionidae, Buthidae, Vejovidae, Chactidae, Bothriuridae, and Diplocentridae. Stahnke (1967) has provided a simple key with illustrations for identifying families of scorpions, as well as general information on them. Of the more than 600 species of scorpions in about 70 genera, approximately 40 species are found in the United States, and according to Stahnke only two are dangerously virulent to man.

Family Buthidae. The most important venomous scorpions of the world all belong to the family Buthidae. The dangerous scorpions of Mexico and the southwestern United States belong to the genus *Centruroides* (Fig. 20-21). The Durango scorpion, *C. suffusus* Pocock, is the common scorpion of the State of Durango, Mexico. Its sting is frequently fatal to children, particularly those under seven years of age. At least four other Mexican species are dangerous, including *C. limpidus* Karsch and *C. norius* Hoffmann; the latter is reported to be about six times as venomous as *C. suffusus*.

Centruroides sculpturatus Ewing, believed to be confined to Arizona, is a small species, about 2½ inches in length; it is generally of a solid yellow-straw color. It is dangerously

virulent and is reported to be abundant. *Centruroides gertschi* Stahnke, so far as is known, is also confined to Arizona, but is much less abundant than *C. sculpturatus*. It is about the same size as the latter but has two irregular black stripes down its entire back; its basic color is yellow. This is also a dangerous species.

Centruroides vittatus (Say), the common striped scorpion of the United States, is widely distributed, having been reported from Georgia, Florida, Kansas, Texas, Arkansas, Louisiana, New Mexico, and South Carolina. Ewing (1928) reports the sting of this species to cause a sharp pain followed by a wheal that soon disappears with no complications. Stahnke also regards this species as relatively harmless.

Buthus quinquestriatus Hemprish and Ehrenberg is a common Egyptian and North African species, more especially in upper Egypt, according to Wilson (1904) who states that it is of a sandy-yellow color tending to

Fig. 20-21 Three *Centruroides scorpions*. (*Left to right*) *C. sculpturatus, C. gertschi,* and *C. vittatus*. (Reprinted with permission from Stahnke, Herbert L.: *Scorpions*, Figure 6, page 16, 1956; through courtesy of Dr. Stahnke and the Poisonous Animals Research Laboratory, Tempe, Arizona.)

brown and that it measures about 10 cm in length. He also states that it is undoubtedly the commonest species in that region and is generally believed to be the most dangerous; it is frequently found in houses, and is the species, in all probability, giving rise to the numerous cases of scorpion sting said to be most commonly fatal in upper Egypt. Shulov (1939) traced four fatal cases in children between the ages of six and thirteen years in Palestine.

Androctonus australis (Linnaeus) is the most important of several venomous species (genera *Androctonus, Buthus,* and *Buthacus*) occurring in North Africa west of Egypt. Balozet (1956), citing the work of Sergent, says this scorpion was responsible for 142 of 183 stings in which the guilty scorpion was identified. It is widespread in Algeria, Morocco, and Tunisia. In the Near East, *Prionurus crassicauda* (Oliver) is the most dangerous species.

Tityus serratulus Lutz and *T. bahiensis* Perty are dangerous species in Brazil. In South Africa certain species of *Parabuthus* are dangerous.

WHIPSCORPIONS

CLASS *ARACHNIDA,*
ORDER *PEDIPALPIDA*

Characteristics of the Pedipalpida. The Pedipalpida (also known as the Uropygi or Thelyphonida) are widespread through the tropics and subtropics, although very unevenly distributed. They are scorpionlike in appearance but differ in the form of the pedipalps, the antennalike first legs, and the whip-bearing abdomen. Whipscorpions feed chiefly on insects, worms, and slugs, which they seize quickly with their sharp pedipalps. They are nocturnal, and in the daytime they may be found under stones, in burrows, and in other protected places. They protect themselves by means of their pedipalps and an acid, which they eject from near the base of the tail.

The giant whipscorpion, *Mastigoproctus giganteus* (Lucas) (Fig. 20-22) (known as the vinegarone, vinegaroon, grampus, or mule killer), occurs commonly in Florida, Texas, other parts of the South and westward to California. The term vinegaroon is apt, inasmuch as the secretions of this species contain acetic acid as well as caprylic acid. Forcible ejection of the spray may extend to 80 cm, though discharge is in response to direct body stimulation only (Roth and Eisner, 1962). This whipscorpion feeds on almost all larger insects and other arthropods, if not too hard or active; it has been known to kill small frogs and toads (Cloudsley-Thompson, 1958).

Fig. 20-22 Whipscorpion, *Mastigoproctus giganteus.* × 0.8.

Although it is greatly feared, there seems to be little justification for this.

Flower (cited by Cloudsley-Thompson) described the scorpionlike behavior of *Thelyphonus skimkewitchii* Tarnani in Thailand and the resulting "sting" that pained him for several hours and that required medication. If the irritating fluid secreted by the whipscorpion should come into contact with a prick or scratch on a person's hand, possibly one made by the chelicerae or pedipalps of the arachnid, it is quite possible that a smarting sensation that might be mistaken for the result of a sting may occur. Cloudsley-Thompson also cites one case of a blacksmith experiencing blisters as the result of a vinegarone being crushed on his chest.

SOLPUGIDS

ORDER *ARACHNIDA,*
CLASS *SOLPUGIDA*

General Characteristics. The solpugids (Fig. 20-23), commonly known as "sun spiders" and "wind scorpions," are in general appearance largely spiderlike, although there is no pedicel; they are rather hairy, occurring mainly in the desert, tropical, and subtropical regions. The chelicerae are large and powerful and are two-segmented. The second segment is movable and articulates in such fashion as to work in a more or less vertical plane. Food is crushed to a pulp, the fluid is swallowed, and the hard parts are usually ejected. The first pair of legs is long and rather feeble and used as tactile organs. Respiration is tracheate.

Solpugids are commonly but erroneously regarded as exceedingly venomous. There is not the slightest foundation for the suggestion that any animal drinking from a water trough in which a solpugid was present would die. The question as to the venomous nature of these animals cannot be dismissed summarily, however. Cloudsley-Thompson (1958) has given a concise account of the subject. No poison glands associated with the jaws have been found, but it has been suggested that poisoning might result from toxic excretions through the setal pores that could be traced along the tips of the jaws. Apparently authentic cases of aftereffects resulting from solpugid bite have been recorded, some of them even fatal. Cloudsley-Thompson concludes, however, that "on the few occasions that poisoning does occur, it is most probably due to infection of the wound."

The solpugids of the United States have been monographed by Muma (1951), who

A   B

Fig. 20-23 *A.* A solpugid, commonly called "sun spider." *B.* Eggs.

recognizes about seventy-five species (in addition to several of uncertain status) distributed through two families, four subfamilies, and ten genera. Most species are found in the southwest, from Texas to California, but *Ammotrechella stimpsoni* (Putnam) inhabits Florida, and *Eremobates pallipes* (Say) is widespread throughout the western half of the United States.

VENOMOUS TICKS

CLASS *ARACHNIDA,*
ORDER *ACARINA*

Ticks belonging to both families, Ixodidae and Argasidae, may cause local as well as systemic disturbances by their bites (see Chapter 18).

Ordinarily little or no injury results from the mere bite of an ixodine tick; *Dermacentor occidentalis* Neumann and *D. variabilis* (Say) have been known to remain attached to a person for days without causing any great inconvenience and occasionally are quite unobserved by the host. However, Nuttall, *et al.* (1908–11), record a number of cases cited by other authors in which the bite of *Ixodes ricinus* (Linnaeus) has caused serious consequences, notably a case described by Johannessen of a "boy where the tick's body was removed but the capitulum remained embedded in the skin at the back of the head. Swelling followed at the point of injury, accompanied by headache, stiffening and cramps in the muscles of one side, partial loss of memory and polyuria; the pupils became dilated, etc. The boy made a slow recovery." The bite of *Ixodes pacificus* commonly results in more or less marked systemic disturbances.

A number of studies in conjunction with toxic effects of tick bites, or inquiries into the causal effects of tick paralysis, have uncovered the presence of toxins in various ticks, particularly their eggs. Thus Riek (1957) des-

cribed a toxin in the eggs of *Amblyomma.* Toxins extracted from eggs and young larvae of *Boophilus microplus* from Australia, as characterized by electrophoresis, revealed three toxic fractions in eggs and only one in larvae (Riek, 1959).

Quite a number of species belonging to the family Argasidae are known to cause more or less serious consequences by their bites alone, notably *Ornithodoros moubata* (Murray), *O. coriaceus* Koch, *O. talaje* (Guérin-Ménéville), and *O. turicata* (Dugès).

Ornithodoros moubata has been reported repeatedly as causing marked disturbances by its bite. Wellman, as quoted by Nuttall, *et al.* (1908–11, p. 98), "states that the bite is very painful, the swelling and irritation (especially in Europeans) not subsiding for days. The wheals are hard, raised and swell most disagreeably if scratched, and this even a week after being bitten. The bite of young ticks (nymphae) is said by the natives to be more severe than that of the adults."

Ornithodoros coriaceus Koch (Fig. 20-24) occurs commonly in the more mountainous coastal counties of California, having been first described from Mexico where it is known as the "tlalaja." In California it is known as the "pajaroello."

Many harrowing tales are told regarding the loss of an arm or leg, even death resulting from the bite of the pajaroello. Much of this, of course, is gross exaggeration. However, a University of California student some years ago, in July, experienced sharp pain on the left arm, and upon rolling up his sleeve discovered a large tick, partly engorged, attached to the upper arm in front. He dislodged the tick and sucked the lesion that, when first discovered, showed a small dark-purple ring surrounding a bright-red spot, the point of attachment. The discoloration disappeared in a short time, but the arm was severely irritated for two or three days and at the point of attachment of the tick a minute, clear scab formed. The tick proved to be a pajaroello. A

Fig. 20-24 Showing *Ornithodoros coriaceus* just backing away from her eggs recently deposited in the sand. Note protective coloration of the tick.

second bite took place two weeks later, with even more serious reactions suggesting allergic sensitization.

Life History of Ornithodoros coriaceus. The pajaroello deposits large plum-colored spherical eggs (Fig. 20-24). There are commonly four to seven layings at intervals during the months of May to July, inclusive, and the female is known to deposit eggs for at least two successive seasons. The greatest number of eggs observed at one laying was 802, with a total of 1,158 for one season. The incubation period at 24°–26° C was 19–29 days, with an average of about 22 days.

The larvae (Fig. 20-25) are very active, scattering quickly and attaching to a host,

Fig. 20-25 Eggs of *Ornithodoros coriaceus*; larvae in the act of emerging; and two fully emerged individuals. × 14.

particularly the ears of rabbits in the laboratory. Experimentally man may also serve as a larval host. The larva remains attached to the host for a period of about seven days; the larval stage lasts ten to twelve days. Smith (1944) reports that reared females begin ovipositing four to six months after the first feeding. He records the adult longevity of reared, fed ticks as eight months to more than three years and seven months for males, and thirteen months to more than five years for a female.

CENTIPEDES

CLASS *CHILOPODA*

Centipedes are wormlike in form, with a distinct head that possesses a pair of antennae, and with many fairly similar body segments, each with one pair of segmented appendages. Like the insects, they are tracheated and, for the most part, terrestrial. The individual body segments are somewhat flattened so that a cross section through one of them is oval. The legs are at least moderately conspicuous; in number from 15 pairs to more than 100 pairs. Notwithstanding the confusing number of walking appendages, centipedes crawl very rapidly.

Most centipedes are predaceous, feeding mainly on insects. They are provided with powerful poison claws, the maxillipeds, located immediately ventral to the mouth and connected by means of a hollow tube to large poison glands. These maxillipeds are the appendages of the first body segment behind the head. Large insects are quickly killed when the poison claws of a large centipede close upon them. Centipedes have been reported as feeding on flesh of living toads and small snakes and as killing mice, small birds, and geckoes (Cloudsley-Thompson, 1958).

The larger centipedes (Fig. 20-26) are commonly regarded as venomous and are generally much feared. Much of this fear is

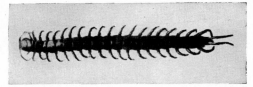

Fig. 20-26 A centipede, *Scolopendra heros.* × 0.66.

without justification, although it is true that the larger species of *Scolopendra*, some of which reach a length of 8 to 10 inches or more, and even the smaller house centipede, *Scutigera cleopatra* (Linnaeus) =*S. forceps* (Rafinesque), are able to pierce the skin and cause severe pain with some swelling at the site of the bite. Accounts of centipede bites in the literature are somewhat confusing, but it would seem that the worst a centipede can be expected to do is to produce severe local pain, which, like the sting of a hornet, will gradually disappear. Bücherl (1946), experimenting with five of the largest and commonest Brazilian species, with mice, guinea pigs, and pigeons as experimental animals, concluded that the poison was too feeble to endanger the life of man, even of young children. Remington (1950) has reviewed the literature on centipede bites, and, coupling his studies with personal experience, states that "the soundest conclusion from the published records appears to be that no centipede bites are potentially deadly to man and that the immediate pain diminishes rapidly, much like the sting of a honey bee." There is only one record, he points out, of centipede bite fatal to man, and that was a seven-year-old child bitten on the hand, who died twenty-nine hours later.

Remington makes one interesting observation in respect to treatment of centipede bite. A medical aid man in the Philippine Islands conceived the idea of treating the symptoms by injecting local anesthetics, such as used by dentists, in the vicinity of the bite. Many suffering from centipede bite received prompt relief from this treatment.

MILLIPEDES

CLASS *DIPLOPODA*

Millipedes differ from centipedes in that most apparent body segments possess two pairs of appendages instead of one (Fig. 20-27). Millipedes are vegetarians and lack poison fangs characteristic of centipedes. In most species the body is cylindrical, and the numerous legs, as well as the antennae, are relatively short and inconspicuous.

The Diplopoda are commonly separated into two groups depending upon the presence or absence of repugnatorial glands. In the *Chilognatha*, to which all North American genera except one, *Polyxenus*, belong (Chamberlin and Hoffman, 1958), these glands are present and are capable of producing irritating effects (Burt, 1947). Certain species squirt irritating fluids a distance of several inches; the Haitian species *Rhinocrichus latespargor*

Fig. 20-27   A millipede. Note two pairs of legs per apparent segment. (Courtesy of U.S. Public Health Service.)

Loomis is reported as discharging its secretion a distance of 28 to 33 inches. This fluid is dangerous to the eyes and is responsible for occasional blindness in poultry in the West Indies and elsewhere. Halstead and Ryckman (1949) report a conclusively proven case of vesicular dermatitis in Montemorelos, Nuevo Leon, Mexico, caused by a diplopod of the genus *Orthoporus*. Roth and Eisner (1962) tabulate the defense secretion components of various species of millipedes as hydrogen cyanide, benzoquinone and its derivatives, and undetermined mixed components.

REFERENCES

Abalos, J. W., and E. C. Baez. 1967. The spider genus *Latrodectus* in Santiago del Estro, Argentina, *in Animal Toxins*. New York, Pergammon Press, pp. 59–74.

Abalos, J. W., and P. Wygodzinsky. 1951. Las Triatominae Argentinas (Reduviidae, Hemiptera). Univ. Nac. (Tucumán) Inst. Med. Regional, Pub. 601, Mon. 2. 179 pp.

Adams, T. S., and D. R. Nelson. 1968. Bioassay of crude extracts for the factor that prevents second matings in female *Musca domestica. Ann. Entom. Soc. Amer.* **61**:112–116.

Adler, S., and O. Theodor. 1957. Transmission of disease agents by phlebotomine sand flies. *Ann. Rev. Entom.*, **2**:203–226.

Adrouny, G. A. 1966. The fire ant's fire. *Bull. Tulane Univ. Med. Fac.*, **25**:67–72.

Aeschlimann, A. 1958. Développement embryonnaire d'*Ornithodorus moubata* (Murray) et transmission transovarienne de *Borrelia duttoni. Acta Trop.*, **15**:15–64.

Aguilar, F. J. 1958. Enfermedad de Robles (Estado actual de la oncocercosis en Guatemala). *Proc. Sixth Internat. Congr. Trop. Med. Malaria*, **2**:287–296.

Aidem, H. P., and V. F. Garagusi. 1961. Japanese B. encephalitis. A case report from New York and a brief review of the literature. *Ann. Intern. Med.*, **55**:324–327.

Aitken, T. H. G., W. G. Downs, C. R. Anderson, and L. Spence. 1960. Mayaro virus isolated from a Trinidadian mosquito, *Mansonia venezuelensis. Science*, **131**:986.

Aitken, T. H. G., and H. Trapido. 1961. Replacement phenomenon observed amongst Sardinian Anopheline mosquitoes following eradication measures, *in* Kuenen, D. J. (ed.) *Symposium. The Ecological Effects of Biological and Chemical Control of Undesirable Plants and Animals*. 8th tech. Meeting, I.U.C.N., Warsaw 15–24, VII, 1960, pp. 106–114.

Allison, A. C. 1961. The distribution of the sickle-cell gene. *Ann. NY Acad. Sci.*, **91**:710–715.

Allred, D. M. 1954. Mites as intermediate hosts of tapeworms. *Proc. Utah Arts, Sci.*, Letters, **31**:44–51.

Alvarado, C. A. 1963. The epidemiology of malaria under the impact of eradication attack. *Proc. 7th Int. Cong. Trop. Med. Malaria.*

Alwar, V. S., C. M. Lalitha, and H. N. Achuthan. 1958. Depluming itch in fowls caused by the feather mite *Megninia ginglymura* (Megnin)—a preliminary note. *Indian Vet. J.*, **35**:621–623.

Anastos, G. 1957. The ticks, or ixodides, of the U.S.S.R.: A review of the literature. *Pub. Hlth. Serv. Publ.*, 548, 397 pp.

Anderson, A. W., and R. F. Harwood. 1966. Cold tolerance in adult female *Culex tarsalis* (Coquillett). *Mosquito News*, **26**:1–7.

Anderson, C. R. 1963. Recent advances in arthropod-borne virus research in India. *Bull. Nat. Inst. Sci. India*, **24**:205–216.

Anderson, C. R., L. Spence, W. G. Downs, and T. H. G. Aitken. 1961. Oropouche virus: A new human disease agent from Trinidad, West Indies. *Amer. J. Trop. Med.*, **10**:574–578.

Anderson, E. 1962. Control of *Dermatobia hominis* in America. *Vet. Rec.*, **74**:284–287.

Anderson, J. L. 1963. Cattle tick (*Boophilus microplus*) —its occurrence and attempted eradication in the Territory of Papua and New Guinea. *Papua New Guinea Agric. J.*, **15**:91–104.

Anderson, J. R. 1964. Methods for distinguishing nulliparous from parous flies and for estimating the ages of *Fannia canicularis* and some other cyclorraphous Diptera. *Ann. Entom. Soc. Amer.*, **57**:226–236.

Anderson, J. R., W. Olkowski, and J. B. Hoy. 1967. Relationships between host attack rates and CO_2-baited Malaise trap catches of certain *Symphoromyia* species. *Proc. Calif. Mosquito Control Assoc.*, **35**:77.

Anderson, J. R., D. O. Trainer, and G. R. De Foliart.

1962. Natural and experimental transmission of the waterfowl parasites, *Leucocytozoon simondi* M. & L., in Wisconsin. *Zoonos. Res.*, 1:155–164.

Anderson, L. D., E. C. Bay, and A. A. Ingram. 1964. Studies of chironomid midge control in water-spreading basins near Montebello, California. *Calif. Vector Views*, 11:13–20.

Anderson, R. C. 1957. The life cycles of dipetalone-matid nematodes (Filarioidea, Dipetalonematidae): the problem of their evolution. *J. Helminth.*, 31:203–244.

Andrewes, C. H. 1957. Factors in virus evolution. *Advances Virus Res.*, 4:1–24.

Anon. 1947. *Malaria Control on Impounded Water.* U.S. Public Health Serv. T. V. A. (available U.S. Govt. Printing Office), 422 pp.

Anon. 1954. *The Imported Fire Ant and how to Control it.* U.S. Dept. Agr. Leaflet 350, 8 pp.

Anthony, D. W. 1962. Tabanidae as disease vectors, *in* Maramorosch, K., *Biological Transmission of Disease Agents.* New York, London, Academic Press, pp. 93–107.

Arant, F. S., *et al.* 1958. Facts about the imported fire ant, *Highlights of Agr. Res. Alabama Agr. Expt. Sta.*, 5(4):1–2.

Arnaud, P. 1956. The heleid genus *Culicoides* in Japan, Korea, and Ryukyu Islands (Insecta: Diptera). *Microentomology*, 21:84–207.

Arthur, D. R. 1962. *Ticks and Disease.* New York, Pergamon, 445 pp.

Arthur, D. R. 1966. The ecology of ticks with reference to the transmission of Protozoa, *in* Soulsby, E. J. L. (Editor), *Biology of Parasites.* New York and London, Academic Press, Inc., pp. 61–84.

Ashburn, P. M., and C. F. Craig. 1907. Experimental investigations regarding the etiology of dengue fever. *J. Infect. Dis.*, 4:440–475.

Ashcroft, M. T. 1959. The Tinde experiment: a further study of the long-term cyclical transmission of *Trypanosoma rhodesiense. Ann. Trop. Med. Parasit.*, 53:137–146.

Ashcroft, M. T. 1960. A comparison between a syringe-passaged and a tsetse-fly-transmitted line of a strain of *Trypanosoma rhodesiense. Ann. Trop. Med. Parasit.*, 54:44–53.

Atkins, J. A. C., W. Wingo, W. A. Sodeman, and J. E. Flynn. 1958. Necrotic arachnidism. *Amer. J. Trop. Med.*, 7:165–184.

Atwood, E. L., and D. E. Sonenshine. 1967. Activity of the American dog tick, *Dermacentor variabilis* (Acarina: Ixodidae) in relation to solar energy changes. *Ann. Entom. Soc. Amer.*, 60:354–362.

Aubert, 1879. Les pous et les écoles: Un point d'hygiene scolaire. *Reviewed in Ann. Dermatol. Syph.*, 1880, 2 ser., 1:292–293.

Audy, J. R. 1958 (1956). The role of mite vectors in the natural history of scrub typhus. *Proc. 10th Internat. Cong. Entom.*, 3:639–649.

Audy, J. R. 1961. The ecology of scrub typhus, *in* May, J. M. (Editor), *Studies in Disease Ecology.* New York, Hafner, pp. 389–432.

Audy, J. R., and M. M. J. Lavoipierre. 1964. The laboratory rearing of parasitic Acarina. A general review. *Bull. WHO*, 31:583–586.

Axtell, R. C. 1963. Effect of Macrochelidae (Acarina: Mesostigmata) on house fly production from dairy cattle manure. *J. Econ. Entom.*, 56:317–321.

Azevedo, J. F. de, J. Tendeiro, L. T. de A. Franco, M. da C. Mourão, and J. M. de C. Salazar. 1956.

Noticia sobre a tsé-tsé de Ilha do Príncipe. *Garcia de Orta*, 4:507–522.

Bacot, A. W. 1914. A study of the bionomics of the common rat fleas and other species associated with human habitations, with special reference to the influence of temperature and humidity at various periods of the life history of the insect. *J. Hyg.* (Plague Supp.), 13:447–654.

Bacot, A. W. 1915. Further studies on the mechanism of the transmission of plague by fleas. *J. Hyg.*, 14 (Plague Supp. 4):774–776.

Bacot, A. W., and C. J. Martin. 1914. Observations on the mechanism of the transmission of plague by fleas. *J. Hyg.*, 13 (Plague Supp. 3):423–439.

Baer, J. G. 1952. *Ecology of Animal Parasites.* Urbana, University of Illinois Press, 224 pp.

Baer, W. S. 1931. The treatment of chronic osteo-myelitis with the maggot (larva of the blowfly). *J. Bone Joint Surg.*, 13:438–475.

Baerg, W. J. 1923. The effects of the bite of *Latrodectus mactans* Fabr. *J. Parasit.*, 9:161–169.

Baerg, W. J. 1929. Some poisonous arthropods of North and Central America. *Trans. 4th Internat. Cong. Entom.*, 2:418–438.

Baerg, W. J. 1958. *The Tarantula.* Lawrence, University of Kansas Press, 88 pp.

Baerg, W. J. 1959. The black widow spider and five other venomous spiders in the United States. *Univ. Ark. Exp. Sta. Bull.*, 608, 43 pp.

Bailey, S. F. 1936. Thrips attacking man. *Canad. Entom.*, 68:95–98.

Bailey, S. F., and D. C. Baerg, 1967. The flight habits of *Anopheles freeborni* Aitken. *Proc. and Papers 23rd Ann. Mtg. Amer. Mosquito Control Assoc.*, pp. 55–69.

Baker, E. W., J. H. Camin, F. Cunliffe, T. A. Woolley, and C. E. Yunker. 1958. *Guide to the Families of Mites.* College Park, Maryland, Institute of Acarology, Contributions no. 3, 242 pp.

Baker, E. W., T. M., Evans, D. J. Gould, W. B. Hull, and H. L. Keegan. 1956. *A Manual of Parasitic Mites of Medical or Economic Importance.* New York, National Pest Control Assoc., New York, 170 pp.

Baker, E. W., and G. W. Wharton. 1952. *An Introduction to Acarology.* New York, Macmillan, 465 pp.

Baker, F. C. 1935. The effect of photoporiodism on resting treehole mosquito larvae. *Canad. Entom.*, 67:149–153.

Balashov, Y. S. 1963. The effect of external factors on the number of nymphal stages in the Argasid ticks (in Russian). *Parazit. Sborn.*, 21:28–38.

Ball, H. G. 1965. Adaptation of the malarial parasite, particularly to its insect host, *in* McCauley, J. E. (Editor), *Host-Parasite Relationships.* Corvallis, Oregon State University Press, pp. 73–96.

Balozet, L. 1956. Scorpion venoms and antiscorpion serum. *In* Buckley, E. E., and N. Porges, *Venoms,* Amer. Assoc. Adv. Sci. publ., 44:141–144.

Baltazard, M. 1960. Déclin et destin d'une maladie infecteuse: la peste. *Bull. WHO*, 23:247–262.

Baltazard, M., and M. Bahmanyar. 1960. Recherches sur la peste en Inde. *Bull. WHO*, 23:169–215.

Baltazard, M., and others. 1960. (Articles reviewing the status of plague on a worldwide basis). *Bull. WHO*, 23:135–418.

Bancroft, E. 1769. *An Essay on the Natural History of Guiana in South America.* London, T. Becker and P. A. De Houdt, 402 pp.

Banez, L. F. L. 1964. Use of ordinary table salt against

breeding of mosquitoes in artificial containers. *Philip. J. Sci.*, (1963):447–481.

Bardos, V., and V. Danielova. 1959. The Tahyna virus—a virus isolated from mosquitoes in Czechoslovakia. *J. Hyg. Epidem. Praha*, 3:264–276.

Barnett, H. C. 1956. Experimental studies of concurrent infection of canaries and of the mosquito *Culex tarsalis* with *Plasmodium relictum* and western equine encephalitis virus. *Amer. J. Trop. Med.*, 5:99–109.

Barnett, H. C. 1960. The incrimination of arthropods as vectors of disease. *Proc. 11th Inter. Congr. Entom.*, 2:341–345.

Barnett, H. C. 1962. Sandflies and sandfly-borne diseases, *in* Maramarosch, K., *Biological Transmission of Disease Agents*. New York and London, Academic Press, pp. 83–91.

Barnett, S. F. 1961. The control of ticks on livestock. *FAO Agric. Stud.* No. 54, 115 pp.

Barnley, G. R., and M. A. Prentice. 1958. *Simulium neavei* in Uganda. *E. Afr. Med. J.*, 35:475–483.

Barr, A. R. 1957. The distribution of *Culex p. pipiens* and *C. p. quinquefasciatus* in North America. *Amer. J. Trop. Med.*, 6:153–165.

Barr, A. R., T. A. Smith, and M. M. Boreham. 1960. Light itensity and the attraction of mosquitoes to light traps. *J. Econ. Entom.*, 53:876–880.

Barretto, M. P. 1943. Observacoes sobre a biologia, em condições naturais, dos flebótomos do Estado de São Paulo. São Paulo; Fac. Med. Univ. São Paulo, Texe de Concurso à Docencia-Livre de Cadeira de Parasitologia. 162 pp.

Barretto, M. P. 1947. Catálogo dos flebótomos americanos. *Arq. Zool. Estado São Paulo*, 5:177–242.

Bastianelli, G., A. E. Bignami, and B. Grassi, 1898. Coltivazione delle semilune malariche dell' uomo nell' *Anopheles claviger* Fabr.: Note preliminare Atti Reale Accad. Lincei, Nov. 28, p. 313. (Cited by Nuttall.)

Bates, M. 1949. *The Natural History of Mosquitoes.* New York, The Macmillan Company, 379 pp.

Baumhover, A. H. 1966. Eradication of the screwworm fly. *J.A.M.A.*, 196:240–248.

Bay, E. C. 1966. Adaptation studies with the Argentine pearl fish, *Cynolebias bellottii*, for its introduction into California. *Copeia*, No. 4, pp. 839–846.

Bay, E. C., and L. D. Anderson. 1965. Chironomid control by carp and goldfish. *Mosquito News*, 25: 310–316.

Bay, E. C., and E. F. Legner. 1963. The prospect for the biological control of *Hippelates collusor* (Townsend) in southern California. *Proc. 31st Conf. Calif. Mosquito Control Assoc.*, 1963:76–79.

Beauperthuy, L. D. 1854. Transmission of yellow fever and other diseases by mosquito. *Gazeta Oficial de Cumanà*, May 23. (Cited by Howard, Dyar, and Knab.)

Beadle, L. D. 1966. Epidemics of mosquito-borne encephalitis in the United States, 1960–1965. *Mosquito News*, 26:483–486.

Beard, R. L. 1963. Insect toxins and venoms. *Ann. Rev. Entom.*, 8:1–18.

Beaver, P. C. 1966. Zoonoses, with particular reference to parasites of veterinary importance, *in* Soulsby, E. J. L. (Editor), *Biology of Parasites*. New York and London, Academic Press, Inc., pp. 215–227.

Beaver, P. C., and T. C. Orihel, 1965. Human infection with filariae of animals in the United States. *Amer. J. Trop. Med.*, 14:1010–1029.

Beklemischev, V. N. 1958. The identification of arthropods injurious to the health of man. (In Russian.) Gosudarstvennoe Izdatel'stvo Meditsinskoi Literatury Medgiz, Moscow.

Bellamy, R. E., and W. C. Reeves. 1963. The winter biology of *Culex tarsalis* (Diptera: Culicidae) in Kern County, California. *Ann. Entom. Soc. Amer.*, 56:314–323.

Belozerov, V. N. 1964. Diapause and the conditions for the reactivation of females of the tick *Dermacentor marginatus* Sulz. (Ixodidae) [in Russian], *Vest. Leningr. Univ.* 19(21) (Ser. Biol. pt. 4):5–11.

Benjamini, E., B. F. Feingold, and L. Kartman. 1963. The physiological and biochemical role of the host's skin in the induction of flea-bite hypersensitivity. Preliminary studies with guinea pig skin following exposure to bites of cat fleas. *Exp. Parasit.*, 14: 75–80.

Benjamini, E., B. F. Feingold, J. D. Young, L. Kartman, and M. Shimizu, 1963. Allergy to flea bites. IV. *In vitro* collection and antigenic properties of the oral secretion of the cat flea *Ctenocephalides felis felis* (Bouché). *Exp. Parasit.*, 13:143–154.

Bennet-Clark, H. C. 1963. Negative pressure produced in the pharyngeal pump of the blood-sucking bug, *Rhodnius prolixus. J. Exp. Biol.*, 40:223–229.

Benton, A. W., R. A. Morse, and J. D. Stewart. 1963. Venom collection from honey bees. *Science*, 142:228–230.

Bequaert, J. C. 1930. Tsetse flies—past and present (Diptera: Muscoidea). *Entom. News*, 41:158–164, 202–203, 227–233.

Bequaert, J. C. 1937. Notes on Hippoboscidae: 5. The American species of *Lipoptena. Bull. Brooklyn Entom. Soc.*, 32:91–101.

Bequaert, J. C. 1938. The black-flies, or Simuliidae, of the Belgian Congo. *Amer. J. Trop. Med.*, 18 (Supp.): 116–136.

Bequaert, J. C. 1946. The ticks, or Ixodoidea, of the northeastern United States and eastern Canada. *Entom. Amer.*, 25:73–120.

Bequaert, J. C. 1953–1957. The Hippoboscidae or louse-flies (Diptera) of mammals and birds. Part I. Structure, physiology, and natural history. Part II. Taxonomy, evolution, and revision of American genera and species. *Entom. Amer.*, 32(n.s.):1–209; 33(n.s.):211–422; 34(n.s.):1–232; 35(n.s.):233–416; 36(n.s.):417–611.

Bernton, H. S., and H. Brown. 1964. Insect allergy—preliminary studies of the cockroach. *J. Allerg.*, 35:506–513.

Berry, I. L., and R. A. Hoffman. 1963. Use of step-on switches for control of automatic sprayers. *J. Econ. Entom.*, 56:888–890.

Bertram, D. S., K. Unsworth, and R. M. Gordon. 1946. The biology and maintenance of *Liponyssus bacoti* Hirst, 1913, and an investigation into its role as a vector of *Litomosoides carinii* to cotton rats and white rats, together with some observations on the infection in the white rats. *Ann. Trop. Med.*, 40:228–252.

Bertram, D. S., M. G. R. Varma, and J. R. Baker. 1964. Partial suppression of malaria parasites, and of the transmission of malaria, in *Aedes aegypti* (L.) doubly infected with Semliki Forest virus and *Plasmodium gallinaceum* Brumpt. *Bull. WHO*, 31:679–697.

Beye, H. K., M. E. Getz, G. R. Coatney, H. A. Elder, and D. E. Eyles. 1961. Simian malaria in man. *Amer. J. Trop. Med.*, 10:311–316.

Bhatia, M. L., and B. L. Wattal. 1958. Tolerated density of *Culex fatigans* Wied. in transmission of bancroftian filaria. *Bull. Nat. Soc. India Malar.,* 6:117–122.

Biagi, F. J., A. M. de B. Biagi, and H. F. Beltrán. 1965. Phlebotomus flaviscutellatus, transmisor natural de Leishmania Mexicana. *Prensa Med. Mex.* 30:267–272.

Biagi, F. J., R. Lopes, and A. M. de B. Biagi. 1965. El Kala-zar en Mexico; problema cologico por estudiar. *Rev. Inst. Salubr. Enferm. Trop.,* 25:3–12.

Biagi, F., and F. Navarrete. 1961. Estado actual de nestros conocimientos sobre la enfermidad de Chagas en Mexico. I. Transmisores. *Ann. Congr. Internac. Doença Chagas,* 1961:285–289.

Bidlingmayer, W. L. 1961. Field activity studies of adult *Culicoides furens. Ann. Entom. Soc. Amer.,* 54:149–156.

Bishop, A. 1962. *In* Goodwin, L. G., and R. H. Nimmosmith (Editors), *Drugs, Parasites and Hosts.* London, Churchill.

Bishopp, F. C. 1921. *Solenopotes capillatus,* a sucking louse of cattle not heretofore known in the United States. *J. Agric. Res.,* 21:797–801.

Bishopp, F. C. 1923. *The Rat Mite Attacking Man.* U.S. Dept. Agr. Dept. Circular 294, 4 pp.

Bishopp, F. C. 1929. The pigeon fly, an important pest of pigeons in the United States. *J. Econ. Entom.,* 22:974–980.

Bishopp, F. C. 1939. The stable fly; how to prevent its annoyance and its losses to livestock. *U.S. Dept. Agr. Farmer's Bull.,* 1097, 18 pp. (revised).

Bishopp, F. C., and H. Hixson. 1936. Biology and economic importance of the Gulf Coast tick. *J. Econ. Entom.,* 29:1068–1076.

Black, R. J., and A. M. Barnes. 1958. Effect of earth cover on fly emergence from sanitary landfills. *Pub. Works Mag.,* 89:91–94.

Blacklock, D. B. 1926. Development of *Onchocerca volvulus* in *Simulium damnosum. Ann. Trop. Med., Med.,* 20:1–48, 203–218.

Blake, F. G., K. F. Maxcy, J. F. Sadusk, Jr., G. M. Kohls, and E. J. Bell. 1945. Studies on tsutsuga-mushi disease (scrub typhus, mite-borne typhus) in New Guinea and adjacent islands. Epidemiological, clinical observations and etiology in the Dobadura area. *Amer. J. Hyg.,* 41:243–373.

Blue, S. 1910. Rodents in relation to the transmission of bubonic plague. The rat and its relation to the public health. Washington, D.C., U.S. Public Health and Marine Hospital Serv., 254 pp.

Blum, M. S., and P. S. Callahan. 1960. Chemical and biological properties of the venom of the imported fire ant (*Solenopsis saevissima* var. *richteri* Forel) and the isolation of the insecticidal component. *Proc. 11th Intern. Congr. Entom.,* 3(symp. 4):290–293.

Blum, M. S., J. E. Roberts, Jr., and A. F. Novak. 1961. Chemical and biological characterization of venom of the ant *Solenopsis xyloni* McCook. *Psyche,* 68:73–74.

Bogen, E. 1956. The treatment of spider bite poisoning, *in* Buckley and Porges, *op. cit.,* pp. 101–105.

Boger, N., B. Rightblat, R. Cwilich, and A. Adani, 1964. A case of *Ixodes* tick in man, *Refuah Vet.,* 21:30–39.

Boičev, D., and K. Rizvanov. 1960. Relation of *Botrytis cinerea* Pers. to ixodid ticks (in Russian). *Zool. Zhur.* 39:462.

Bond, J. O., D. T. Quick, J. J. Witte, and H. C.

Oard. 1965. The 1962 epidemic of St. Louis encephalitis in Florida. I. Epidemiologic observations. *Amer. J. Epidem.,* 81:392–404.

Boorman, J. P. T. 1961. Observations on the habits of mosquitoes of. Plateau Province, Northern Nigeria, with particular reference to *Aedes (Stegomyia) vittatus (Bigot). Bull. Entom. Res.,* 52:709–725.

Bořkovec, A. B. 1966. *Insect Chemosterilants.* Adv. Pest Control. Res. 7. New York, Wiley, 143 pp.

Borror, D. J., and D. M. DeLong. 1954. *An Introduction to the Study of Insects.* New York, Reinhard, 1030 pp.

Boshell-Manrique, J. 1959. Outline history of yellow fever epidemic in Middle America—1948–1957. *Proc. 6th Int. Cong. Trop. Med. and Malariol.,* 5:62–87.

Boyd, C. E., and D. E. Ferguson. 1964. Susceptibility and resistance of mosquito fish to several insecticides. *J. Econ. Entom.,* 57:430–431.

Boyd, M. F. 1941. An historical sketch of the prevalence of malaria in North America. *Amer. J. Trop. Med.,* 21:223–244.

Boyd, M. F. 1950. *Malariology.* Philadelphia, Saunders, 2 vols. 1,643 pp.

Boyd, M. F., and S. F. Kitcher. 1936. The comparative susceptibility of *Anopheles quadrimaculatus* and *Anopheles punctipennis* to *Plasmodium vivax* and *Plasmodium falciparum. Amer. J. Trop. Med.,* 16:67–71.

Boynton, W. H., and G. M. Woods. 1933. Deer as carriers of anaplasmosis. *Science,* 78:559–560.

Bram, R. A. 1967. Contributions to the mosquito fauna of Southeast Asia. II. The genus *Culex* in Thailand (Diptera-Culicidae). *Contrib. Amer. Entom. Inst.,* 2:1–296.

Bray, R. S., and P. C. C. Garnham. 1964. *Anopheles* as vectors of animal malaria parasites. *Bull. WHO,* 31:143–147.

Breed, R. S., E. G. D. Murray, and N. R. Smith. 1957. *Bergey's Manual of Determinative Bacteriology,* 7th ed. Baltimore, Williams and Wilkins, 1,094 pp.

Breeland, S. G., and E. Pickard. 1965. The Malaise trap: an efficient and unbiased mosquito collecting device. *Mosquito News,* 25:19–21.

Breeland, S. G., and E. Pickard. 1967. Field observations on twenty-eight broods of floodwater mosquitoes resulting from controlled floodings of a natural habitat in the Tennessee valley. *Mosquito News,* 27:343–358.

Breland, O. P. 1957. Some factors that might influence the reintroduction of yellow fever into the United States. *Texas J. Sci.,* 9:262–266.

Breland, O. P. 1958. A report on *Haemogogus* mosquitoes in the United States with notes on identification (Diptera: Culicidae). *Ann. Entom. Soc. Amer.,* 51:217–221.

Bremner, K. C. 1959. Observations on the biology of *Haemaphysalis bispinosa* Neumann (Acarina: Ixodidae) with particular reference to its mode of reproduction by parthenogenesis. *Australian J. Zool.,* 7:7–12.

Brennan, J. M. 1935. The Pangoniinae of Nearatic America, Diptera: Tabanidae. *Univ. Kansas Sci. Bull.,* 22:249–402.

Brennan, J. M., and E. K. Jones. 1959. Keys to the chiggers of North America with synonymic notes and descriptions of two new genera (Acarina; Trombiculidae). *Ann. Entom. Soc. Amer.,* 52:7–16.

Brennan, J. M., and G. W. Wharton. 1950. Studies on North American chiggers no. 3. The subgenus Neotrombicula. *Amer. Midland Naturalist,* **44**: 153–197.

Brennan, J. M., and C. E. Yunker. 1964. A new species of *Euschoengastia* of potential veterinary importance (Acarina: Trombiculidae). *J. Parasit.,* **50**:311–312.

Briggs, J. D. 1960. Reduction of adult housefly emergence by the effects of *Bacillus* spp. on the development of immature forms. *J. Ins. Path.,* **2**:418–432.

Bromley, S. W. 1933. The sting of a tarantula wasp. *Bull. Brooklyn Entom. Soc.,* **28**:192.

Brown, A. W. A. 1958. *Insecticide Resistance in Arthropods.* Geneva, WHO, Mon. Ser. No. 38, 240 pp.

Brown, A. W. A. 1966. The attraction of mosquitoes to hosts. *J.A.M.A.,* **196**:249–252.

Brown, A. W. A. 1967. Genetics of insecticide resistance in insect vectors, *in* Wright, J. W., and R. Pal. *Genetics of Insect Vectors of Disease.* New York, Elsevier, pp. 505–552.

Brown, A. W. A. 1968. Insecticide resistance comes of age. *Bull. Entom. Soc. Amer.,* **14**:3–9.

Brown, A. W. A., and P. E. Morrison. 1955. Control of adult tabanids by aereal spraying. *J. Econ. Entom.,* **48**:125–129.

Brown, H. W. 1945. Current problems in filariasis. *Amer. J. Public Health,* **35**:607–613.

Bruce, D. 1895. *Tsetse-fly Disease or Nagana in Zululand: Preliminary Report.* Durban, Bennett and Davis. (Cited by Nuttall.)

Bruce, D., and D. Nabarro. 1903. Progress Report on Sleeping Sickness in Uganda. Rept. *Sleeping Sickness Comm. Roy. Soc. London.* no. 1.

Bruce, W. N. 1952. Automatic sprayer for control of biting flies on cattle. Biol Notes No. 27, *Nat. Hist. Surv.,* Urbana, Ill.

Bruce-Chwatt, L. J. 1965. Paleo-genesis and paleoepidemiology of primate malaria. *Bull. WHO,* **32**: 263–287.

Brues, C. T., A. L. Melander, and F. M. Carpenter. 1954. Classification of insects. *Bull. Museum Comp. Zool.,* 108, 917 pp.

Brumpt. E., 1912. La *Trypanosoma cruzi* evolue chez *Conorhinus megistus, Cimex lectularius, Cimex boueti* et *Ornithodorus moubata,* cycle evolutiv de ce parasite. *Bull. Soc. Path. Exot.,* **5**:360.

Brumpt, E. 1914. Le xénodiagnostic application au diagnostic de quelques infections parasitaires et en particulier a la Trypanosome de Chagas. *Bull. Soc. Path. Exot.,* **7**:706–710.

Brumpt, E. 1919. Transmission de la piroplasmose canine tunisienne par le *Rhipicephalus sanguineus. Bull. Soc. Path. Exot.,* **12**:757–764.

Brumpt, E., and F. Larousse. 1922. Transmission de la piroplasmose canine francaise par le *Dermacentor venustus. Bull. Soc. Path. Exot.,* **15**:540–545.

Brunetti, O. A. 1965. Tick paralysis in California deer. *Calif. Fish and Game,* **51**:208–210.

Bücherl, W. 1946. Acção do veneno dos escolopendromorfos do Brasil sobre algunas animais de laboratorio. *Mem. Inst. Butantan,* São Paulo, **19**:181–187.

Bücherl, W. 1956. Studies on dried venom of *Phoneutria fera* Perty, 1833, *in* Buckley and Porges, *op. cit.,* pp. 95–97.

Buckley, E. E., and N. Porges (eds.). 1956. *Venoms.* Amer. Assoc. Adv. Sci. Publ. 44, 467 pp.

Buckley, J. J. C. 1933. A note on the development of

Filaria ozzardi in *Culicoides furens* Poey. *J. Helminth.,* **11**:257–258.

Buckley, J. J. C. 1960. On *Brugia* gen. nov. for *Wuchereria* spp. of the *"malayi"* group; i.e., *W. malayi* (Brug, 1927), *W. pahangi* Buckley and Edeson, 1956, and *W. patei* Buckley, Nelson and Heisch, 1958. *Ann. Trop. Med. Parasit.,* **53**:75–77.

Bullock, H. R., W. P. Murdoch, H. W. Fowler, and H. R. Brazzel, 1959. Notes on the overwintering of *Culex tritaeniorhynchus* Giles in Japan. *Mosquito News,* **19**:184–188.

Burdick, D. J., and E. H. Kardos. 1963. The age structure of fall, winter, and spring populations of *Culex tarsalis* in Kern County, California. *Ann. Entom. Soc. Amer.,* **56**:527–535.

Burgdorfer, W. 1951. Analyse des Infektionsverlaufes bei *Ornithodorus moubata* (Murray) und der naturlichen Übertragung von *Spirochaeta duttoni. Acta Trop.,* **8**:193–262.

Burgdorfer, W. 1957. Artificial feeding of ixodid ticks for studies on the transmission of disease agents. *J. Infect. Dis.,* **100**:212–214.

Burgdorfer, W. 1963. Investigation of "transovarial transmission" of *Rickettsia rickettsii* in the wood tick, *Dermacentor andersoni. Exp. Parasit.,* **14**: 152–159.

Burgdorfer, W., and C. M. Eklund. 1959. Studies on the ecology of Colorado tick fever virus in western Montana. *Amer. J. Hyg.,* **69**:127–137.

Burgdorfer, W., and D. Lackman. 1960. Identification of the virus of Colorado tick fever in mouse tissues by means of fluorescent antibodies. *J. Bact.,* **80**: 131–136.

Burgdorfer, W., V. F. Newhouse, E. G. Pickens, and D. B. Lackman. 1962. Ecology of Rocky Mountain spotted fever in western Montana. I. Isolation of *Rickettsia rickettsii* from wild animals. *Amer. J. Hyg.,* **76**:293–301.

Burgdorfer, W., and M. G. R. Varma. 1967. Transstadial and transovarial development of disease agents in arthropods. *Ann. Rev. Entom.,* **12**:347–376.

Burgess, R. W. 1951. The life history and breeding habits of the eye gnat, *Hippelates pusio* Loew, in the Coachella Valley, Riverside County, California. *Amer. J. Hyg.,* **53**:164–177.

Burns, E. C., B. H. Wilson, and B. A. Tower. 1961. Effect of feeding *Bacillus thuringiensis* to caged layers for fly control. *J. Econ. Entom.,* **54**: 913–915.

Burt, E. 1947. Exudate from millipeds, with particular reference to its injurious effects. *Trop. Dis. Bull.,* **44**:7–12.

Burton, A. N., J. McLintock, and J. G. Rempel. 1966. Western equine encephalitis in Saskatchewan garter snakes and leopard frogs. *Science,* **154**:1029-1031.

Burton, G. J. 1963. Bedbugs in relation to transmission of human disease. *Public Health Rep.,* **78**:513–524.

Bushland, R. C., R. D. Radeleff, and R. O. Drummond. 1963. Development of systemic insecticides for pests of animals in the United States. *Ann. Rev. Entom.,* **8**:215–238.

Busvine, J. R., and J. Lien. 1961. Methods for measuring insecticide susceptibility levels in bedbugs, cone-nosed bugs, fleas and lice. *Bull. WHO,* **24**:509–517.

Büttiker. W. 1958. Observations on physiology of adult anophelines in Asia. *Bull. WHO,* **19**:1063–1071.

Büttiker, W. 1959. Observations on feeding habits of adult Westermanniinae (Lepid., Noctuidae) in Cambodia. *Acta Trop.*, **16**:356–361.

Büttiker. W. 1962. Notes on two species of Westermanniinae (Lepidoptera: Noctuidae) from Cambodia. *Proc. Roy. Entom. Soc. Lond.* (B), **31**:73–76.

Büttiker, W. 1964. New observations on eye-frequenting Lepidoptera from S.E. Asia. *Verh. Natur. Ges. Basel*, **75**:231–236.

Buxton, P. A. 1924. Applied entomology of Palestine, being a report to the Palestine Government. *Bull. Entom. Res.*, **14**:289–340.

Buxton, P. A. 1955. *The Natural History of Tsetse Flies.* London, H. K. Lewis & Co., xviii + 816 pp. (47 plates).

Caffrey, D. J. 1918. Notes on the poisonous urticating spines of *Hemileuca oliviae* larvae. *J. Econ. Entom.*, **11**:363–367.

Cardani, C., D. Ghiringhelli, R. Mondelli, M. Pavan, and A. Quilico. 1965. Propriétés biologiques et composition chimique de la pédérine, *Ann. Soc. Entom. Fr.* (n.s.), **1**:813–816.

Cariaso, B. L. 1962. A contribution to the knowledge of the black widow spider. *Philipp. Agric.*, **46**:160–165.

Carpenter, S. J., and W. J. LaCasse. 1955. *Mosquitoes of North America (North of Mexico).* Berkeley, University of California Press, 360 pp.

Carter, H. R. 1931. *Yellow-Fever: An Epidemiological and Historical Study of its Place and Origin*, Baltimore, Williams & Wilkins, 308 pp.

Casals, J., and L. V. Brown. 1954. Hemagglutination with arthropod-borne viruses. *J. Exp. Med.*, **99**:429–449.

Casals, J., and D. H. Clarke. 1956. Arboviruses; group A, *in* Horsfall, F. L., and I. Tamm (Editors), *Viral and Rickettsial Infections of Man*, 4th ed. Philadelphia, Lippincott, pp. 583–605.

Casals, J., and L. Whitman. 1960. A new antigenic group of arthropod-borne viruses. The Bunyamwera group. *Amer. J. Trop. Med.*, **9**:73–77.

Castellani, A. 1907. Experimental investigation on *Framboesia tropica* (Yaws). *J. Hyg.*, **7**:558–559.

Causey, O. R., C. E. Causey, O. M. Maroja, and D. G. Macedo. 1961. The isolation of arthropod-borne viruses, including members of two hitherto undescribed serological groups, in the Amazon region of Brazil. *Amer. J. Trop. Med.*, **10**:227–249.

Causey, O. R., R. E. Shope, and H. Laemmert. 1964. Report of an epizootic of encephalomyocarditis virus in Para', Brazil. *Rev. Serv. Esp. Saude Publ.*, **12**:47–50.

Causey, O. R., R. E. Shope, and M. Theiler. 1964. Isolation of St. Louis encephalitis virus from arthropods in Para', Brazil. *Amer. J. Trop. Med.*, **13**:449.

Cavill, G. W. K., and P. L. Robertson. 1965. Ant venoms, attractants, and repellents. *Science*, **149**:1337–1345.

Chabaud, A. G., M. C. Durette. 1963. Interfécondité de deux souches d'*Ornithodorus moubata* et remarques sur les phénomènes de spéciation particuliers au genre. *Ann. Parasit. Hum. Corp.*, **38**:109–112.

Chagas, C. 1909. Ueber eine neue Trypanosomiasis des Menschen. *Mem. Inst. Cruz.*, **1**:159–218.

Chalmers, A. J., and H. H. King. 1917. Blister beetles as a public nuisance. *New Orleans Med. Sci. J.*, **70**:445–455.

Chamberlain, R. and R. L. Hoffman, 1956. *Checklist of the Millipeds of North America.* U.S. National Museum Bull. 212, 236 pp.

Chamberlain, R. W., and R. K. Sikes. 1955. Laboratory investigations on the role of bird mites in the transmission of eastern and western equine encephalitis. *Amer. J. Trop. Med.*, **4**:106–118.

Chamberlain, R. W., R. K. Sikes, and W. D. Sudia. 1957. Attempted laboratory infection of bird mites with the virus of St. Louis encephalitis. *Amer. J. Trop. Med.*, **6**:1047–1053.

Chamberlain, R. W., and W. D. Sudia. 1961. Mechanism of transmission of viruses by mosquitoes. *Ann. Rev. Entom.*, **6**:371–390.

Chamberlain, R. W., W. D. Sudia, and J. D. Gillett. 1959. St. Louis encephalitis virus in mosquitoes. *Amer. J. Hyg.*, **70**:221–236.

Chamberlain, W. F. 1962. Chemical sterilization of the screw-worm. *J. Econ. Entom.*, **55**:240–248.

Chambon, L., and others. 1967. Une épidémie de fievre jaune au Sénégal en 1965. *Bull. WHO*, **36**:113:150.

Chapple, P. J., and N. D. Lewis. 1965. Myxomatosis and the rabbit flea. *Nature*, **207**:388–389.

Cheng, T., and E. M. Kesler. 1961. A three-year study on the effect of fly control on milk production by selected and randomized dairy herds. *J. Econ. Entom.*, **54**:751–757.

Cheng, T. H. 1967. Frequency of pinkeye incidence in cattle in relation to face fly abundance. *J. Econ. Entom.*, **60**:598–599.

Cheng, T. H., R. E. Patterson, B. W. Avery, and J. P. Vandenberg. 1957. An electric-eye-controlled sprayer for application of insecticides to livestock. *Penn. Agr. Exp. Sta. Bull.* 626, 14pp.

Chiang, C., and W. C. Reeves. 1962. Statistical estimation of virus infection rates in mosquito vector populations. *Amer. J. Hyg.*, **75**:377–391.

Chin, W., P. J. Contacos, G. R. Coatney, and H. R. Kimball. 1965. A naturally acquired quotidian-type malaria in man transferable to monkeys. *Science*, **149**:865.

Chorley, J. K. 1929. The bionomics of *Glossina morsitans* in the Umniati fly belt, Southern Rhodesia, 1922–23. *Bull. Entom. Res.*, **20**:279–301.

Christie, M. 1958. Predation on larvae of *Anopheles gambiae* Giles. *J. Trop. Med. Hyg.*, **61**:168–176.

Christophers, S. R. 1960. *Aedes aegypti* (L.) *the Yellow Fever mosquito: its Life History, Bionomics and Structure.* London, Cambridge University Press, 739 pp.

Christophers, S. R., and P. J. Barraud. 1931. The eggs of Indian Anopheles, with a description of the hitherto undescribed eggs of a number of species. *Records Malaria Survey India*, **2**:161–192.

Chumakov, M. P. 1957. *Etiology, Epidemiology and Prophylaxis of Hemorrhagic Fevers* Public Health Service: Public Health Monograph No. 50, pp.19–25.

Chung, H. L., and L. C. Feng. 1936. Studies on the development of *Spirochaeta recurrentis* in body louse. *Chin. Med. J.*, **50**:1181–1184.

Clay, T. 1963. A new species of *Haematomyzus* Piaget (Phthiraptera, Insecta). *Proc. Zool. Soc. London*, **141**:153–161.

Clements, A. N. 1963. *The Physiology of Mosquitoes.* Oxford, Pergamon Press, 393 pp.

Cloudesley-Thompson, J. L. 1958. *Spiders, scorpions, centipedes and mites.* New York, Pergamon Press, 228 pp.

Coatney, J. R., H. A. Elder, P. G. Contacos, M. E.

Getz, R. Greenland, R. N. Roseau, and L. H. Schmidt. 1961. Transmission of the M strain of *Plasmodium cynomolgi* to man. *Amer. J. Trop. Med.,* **10**:673–678.

Cockbill, G. F. 1960. The use of records from traffic control points in Southern Rhodesia. *Publ. Comm. Tech. Co-op. Afr. S. Sahara,* No. 41, pp. 231–234.

Colless, D. H. 1958. Recognition of individual nulliparous and parous mosquitoes. *Trans. Roy. Soc. Trop. Med. Hyg.,* **52**:187.

Connal A., and S. L. M. Connal. 1922. The development of *Loa loa* (Guyot) in *Chrysops silacea* (Austen) and in *Chrysops dimidiata* (van der Wulp). *Trans. Roy. Soc. Trop. Med. Hyg.,* **16**:64–89.

Contacos, P. G., J. S. Lunn, G. R. Coatney, J. W. Kilpatrick, and J. E. Jones. 1963. Quartan type malaria parasite of New World monkeys transmissible to man, *Science,* **142**:676.

Cook, S. F., Jr. 1967. The increasing chaoborid midge problem in California. *Calif. Vector Views,* **14**:39–44.

Cooley, R. A. 1932. *The Rocky Mountain Wood Tick. Bozeman, Montana State Coll. Agr. Exp. Sta. Bull.,* 268, 58 pp.

Cooley, R. A. 1938. The genera *Dermacentor* and *Otocentor* (Ixodidae) in the United States with studies in variation. U.S. Public Health Service, in *Nat. Inst. Health Bull.,* **171**, 89 pp.

Cooley, R. A. 1946. The genera *Boophilus, Rhipicephalus,* and *Haemaphysalis* (Ixodidae), of the new world. U.S. Public Health Service *Nat. Inst. Health Bull.,* 187, 54 pp.

Cooley, R. A., and G. M. Kohls. 1944. The genus *Amblyomma* (Ixodidae) in the United States. *J. Parasit.,* **30**:77–111.

Cooley, R. A., and G. M. Kohls, 1945. The genus *Ixodes* in North America. U.S. Public Health Service *Nat. Inst. Health Bull.,* 184. 246 pp.

Corbet, P. S. 1960. Recognition of nulliparous mosquitoes without dissection. *Nature,* **187**:525–526.

Corbet, P. S. 1964. Autogeny and oviposition in Arctic mosquitoes. *Nature,* **203**:669.

Corbet, P. S. 1964. Reproduction in mosquitoes of the high Arctic. *Proc. 12th. Inter. Cong. Entom.,* pp. 817–818.

Corbet, P. S. 1967. Facultative autogeny in Arctic mosquitoes. *Nature,* **215**:662–663.

Corbet, P. S., M. C. Williams, and J. D. Gillett. 1961. O'nyongnyong fever: an epidemic virus disease in East Africa. IV. Vector studies at epidemic sites. *Trans. Roy Soc. Trop. Med. Hyg.,* **55**:463–480.

Corkey, J. A. 1955. Ophthalmia nodosa due to caterpillar hairs. *Brit. J. Ophthal.,* **39**:301–306.

Costa, J. A. 1952. Tick paralysis on the Atlantic Seaboard. *Amer. J. Dis. Child.,* **83**:336–347.

Couch, J. N., and C. J. Umphlett. 1963. *Coelomomyces* infections, *in* Steinhaus, E. A. (Editor), *Insect Pathology. An Advanced Treatise,* Vol. 2. N.Y. and London, Academic Press, pp. 149–188.

Cova Garcia, P., and M. A. Suarez. 1959. *Estudio de los Triatominos en Venezuela.* Caracas Div. Malariol., Ministerio Sanidad Asistencia Social, Pub, 11, 209 pp.

Craig, G. B., Jr. 1967. Mosquitoes: female monogamy induced by male accessory gland substance. *Science.* **150**:1499–1501.

Craig, G. B., Jr., W. A. Hickey, and R. C. VandeHey. 1960. An inherited male-producing factor in *Aedes aegypti, Science,* **132**:1887–1889.

Crewe, W., and R. M. Gordon. 1959. The immediate reaction of the mammalian host to the bite of uninfected *Chrysops* and of *Chrysops* infected with human and with monkey Loa. *Ann. Trop. Med. Parasit.,* **53**:334–340.

Cross, H. F. 1964. Observations on the formation of the feeding tube by *Trombicula splendens* larvae. *Acaralogia,* **6**:255–261.

Curran, C. H., 1934. *The Families and Genera of North American Diptera.* New York, The Ballou Press, 512 pp.

Cushing, E. C. 1957. *History of Entomology in World War II.* Smithsonian Inst. Publ. 4294, vi + 117 pp.

Dallas, E. D. 1938. Coleópteros que originan dermatitis en la República Argentina. *Proc. 7th. Intern. Cong. Entom.,* pp. 678–682.

Dalmat, H. T. 1955. *The Black Flies (Diptera, Simuliidae) of Guatemala and their Role as Vectors of Onchocerciasis.* Smithsonian Misc. Coll. 125, no. 1, 425 pp.

Damassa, A. J. 1966. The role of *Culex tarsalis* in the transmission of fowl pox virus. *Avian Dis.,* **10**:57–66.

Dame, D. A., and H. R. Ford. 1966. Effect of the chemosterilant tepa on *Glossina morsitans* West. *Bull. Entom. Res.,* **56**:649–658.

Danilevskii, A. S. 1965. *Photoperiodism and Seasonal Development of Insects.* Edinburgh and London, Oliver & Boyd, 283 pp.

Dasgupta, B. M. 1938. Transmission of *Plasmodium inui* to man. *Proc. Nat. Inst. Sci. India.,* **4**: 241–244.

Davidson, G., and C. E. Jackson. 1962. Incipient speciation in *Anopheles gambiae* Giles. *Bull. WHO,* **27**:303–305.

Davies, D. M. 1959. The parasitism of black flies (Diptera, Simuliidae) by larval water mites mainly of the genus *Sperchon. Canad. J. Zool.,* **37**:353–369.

Davies, D. M., and B. V. Peterson. 1956. Observations on the mating, feeding, ovarian development, and oviposition by adult black flies (Simuliidae, Diptera). *Canad. J. Zool.,* **34**:615–655.

Davies, D. M., B. V. Peterson, and D. M. Wood. 1962. The black flies, (Diptera; Simuliidae) of Ontario: Part I. Adult identification and distribution, with descriptions of six new species. *Proc. Entom. Soc. Ontario,* **92**:70–154.

Davis, D. H. S. 1964. Ecology of wild rodent plague, *in* Davis, D. H. S. (Editor), *Ecological Studies in South Africa.* The Hague, W. Junk, pp. 301–314.

Davis, G. E. 1939. *Ornithodoros parkeri:* distributions and host data: spontaneous infection with relapsing fever spirochetes. *Public Health Rep.* (U.S.), **54**: 1345–1349.

Davis, G. E. 1947. A note on the larval stage of the argasid tick. *Ornithodoros moubata* (Murray) 1877. *J. Parasitol.,* **33**:495–496.

Davis, G. E. 1948. The spirochetes. *Ann. Rev. Microbiol.,* **2**:305–334.

Davis, G. E., and G. M. Kohls. 1937. *Ixodes ricinus californicus* (Banks), a possible vector of *Bacterium tularense. Public Health Rep.* (U.S.), **52**:281–282.

Davis H. G., and M. T. James. 1957. Black flies attracted to meat baits. *Proc. Entom. Soc. Wash.,* **59**:243–244.

Davis, H. G., T. P. McGovern, G. W. Eddy, T. E. Nelson, K. M. R. Bertun, M. Beroza, and J. C. Ingangi. 1968. New chemical attractants for yellow jackets (*Vespula* spp.). *J. Econ. Entom.,* **61**:459–462.

Davis, S. 1961. Soil, water and crop factors that indicate mosquito production. *Mosquito News,* 21:44–47.

Day, M. F. 1955. Mechanisms of transmission of viruses by arthropods. *Exp. Parasit.,* 4:387–418.

DeBach, P. (Editor). 1964. *Biological Control of Insect Pests and Weeds.* New York, Reinhold, 844 pp.

De Leon, R. 1961. Contribución al conocimiento de la transmision de la *Oncocerca volvulus* por los simulidos de Guatemala. Inst. Inestigaciones Cientificas Publ., 12:1–53.

De Meillon, B., D. H. S. Davis, and F. Hardy. 1961. *Plague in Southern Africa. I. The Siphonaptera (Excluding Ischnopsyllidae).* Pretoria, Govt. Printer 280 pp.

Deneys, J. B., and F. Zumpt. 1963. Rove beetle dermatitis in South West Africa. *S. Afr. Med. J.,* 37:1284–1285.

Dennis, E. W. 1932. The life-cycle of *Babesia bigemina* (Smith & Kilborne) of Texas cattle fever in the tick *Margaropus annulatus* (Say) with notes on the embryology of *Margaropus. Univ. Calif. Publ. Zool.* 36:263–298.

Depner, K. R. 1961. The effect of temperature on development and diapause of the horn fly, *Siphona irritans* (L.) (Diptera: Muscidae). *Canad. Entom.,* 93:855–859.

Depner, K. R., and R. F. Harwood. 1966. Photoperiodic responses of two latitudinally diverse groups of *Anopheles freeborni* (Diptera; Culicidae). *Ann. Entom. Soc. Amer.,* 59:7–11.

Detinova, T. S. 1962. *Age-Grouping Methods in Diptera of Medical Importance With Special Reference to Some Vectors of Malaria.* WHO Monogr. Ser. no. 47, 216 pp.

Detinova, T. S. 1968. Age structure of insect populations of medical importance. *Ann. Rev. Entom.,* 13:427–450.

Dewèvre, Doctor, 1892. Note sur le role des Pediculi dans la propogation de l'impetigo. *C.R. Soc. Biol.* (Paris), 4:232–234.

Dickerson, G., and M. M. J. Lavoipierre. 1959. Studies on the methods of feeding of blood-sucking arthropods: II. The method of feeding adopted by the bed-bug (*Cimex lectularius*) when obtaining a blood-meal from the mammalian host. *Ann. Trop. Med. Parasit.,* 53:347–357.

Dijk, W. J. O. M. van. 1960. Notes on the breeding of mosquitoes in fishponds in Netherlands New Guinea. *Tech. Inf. Circ. S. Pacif. Comm.* no. 37:3–8.

Dillaha, C. J., G. T. Jansen, and W. M. Honeycutt. 1967. North America loxoscelism, *in* Conn. H. F. (Editor), *Current Therapy,* Philadelphia, Saunders, 844 pp.

Dinulescu, G. 1966. *Fauna Republicii Socialiste România. Insecta.* Vol. XI., fasc. 8. *Diptera. Fam. Simuliidae (Mustele columbace).* Bucuresti, Editura Acad. Rep. Socialiste România, 600 pp.

Doerr, R., K. Franz, and S. Taussig. 1909. *Das Pappatacifieber.* Leipzig and Vienna, Franz Deutsche, 166 pp.

Dogiel, V. A. 1966. *General Parasitology.* N.Y. and London, Academic Press, 516 pp.

Doherty, R. L., J. G. Carley, M. J. Mackerras, and E. N. Marks. 1963. Studies of arthropod-borne virus infections in Queensland: III. Isolation and characterization of virus strains from wild-caught mosquitoes in North Queensland. *Austral. J. Exp. Biol. Med. Sci.,* 41:17–39.

Donisthorp, H. 1945. Ants as carriers of disease. *Entom. Monthly Mag.,* 81:185.

Dorman, S. C., W. C. Hale, and W. M. Hoskins. 1938. The laboratory rearing of flesh flies and the relations between temperature, diet, and egg production. *J. Econ. Entom.,* 31:44–51.

Douglas, J. R. 1943. The internal anatomy of *Dermacentor andersoni,* Stiles. *Univ. Calif. Pub. Entom.,* 7:207–272.

Dove, W. E., and B. Shelmire. 1932. Some observations on tropical rat mites and endemic typhus. *J. Parasit.,* 18:159–168.

Dow, R. P. 1959a. A dispersal of adult *Hippelates pusio,* the eye gnat. *Ann. Entom. Soc. Amer.,* 52: 372–381.

Dow, R. P. 1959b. A method of testing insect traps and attractants, and its application to studies of *Hippelates pusio* and *Culex tarsalis. J. Econ. Entom.,* 52:496–503.

Dow, R. P., J. R. Bigham, and C. W. Sabrosky. 1951. Sequel to "Hippelates (eye gnat) investigations in the Southeastern States" by John T. Bigham. *Proc. Entom. Soc. Wash.,* 53:263–271.

Downes, J. A. 1965. Adaptations of insects in the Arctic. *Ann. Rev. Entom.,* 10:257–274.

Downs, W. G. 1957. Epidemiological notes in connection with the 1954 epidemic of yellow fever in Trinidad, B. W. I., *in Yellow Fever—A Symposium in Commemoration of Carlos Juan Finlay.* Philadelphia, Jefferson Medical College, pp. 71–78.

Downs, W. G. 1963. Birds in relation to arthropod-borne viruses in Trinidad. *Proc. 13th Int. Ornithol. Cong.,* pp. 581–590.

Downs, W. G., L. Spence, and T. H. G. Aitken. 1962. Studies on the virus of Venezuelan equine encephalomyelitis in Trinidad, W.I.: III. Reisolation of virus. *Amer. J. Trop. Med.,* 11:841–843.

Dresner, E. 1949. Culture and use of entomogenous fungi for the control of insect pests. *Contr. Boyce Thompson Inst.,* 15:319–335.

Dubos, R. J., and J. G. Hirsch. 1965. *Bacterial and Mycotic Infections of Man.* Philadelphia, Lippincott, 1,025 pp.

Duggan, A. J. 1962. The occurrence of human trypanosomiasis among the Rukuba tribe of Northern Nigeria. *J. Trop. Med. Hyg.,* 65:151–163.

Duke, B. O. L. 1959. Studies on the biting habits of *Chrysops:* VI. A comparison of the biting habits, monthly biting densities and infection rates of *C. silacea* and *C. dimidiata* (Bombe form) in the rainforest at Kumba, Southern Cameroons, U.U.K.A. *Ann. Trop. Med. Parasit.,* 53:203–214.

Dunn, L. H. 1930. Rearing the larvae of *Dermatobia hominis* Linn. in man. *Psyche,* 37:327–342.

Dutton, J. E. 1902. Note on a Trypanosoma occurring in the blood of man. *Brit. Med. J.,* 2:881–884.

Dutton, J. E., and J. L. Todd. 1905. *The Nature of Human Tick Fever in the Eastern Part of the Congo Free State, With Notes on the Distribution and Bionomics of the tick.* Liverpool, School Trop. Med. Memoir no. 17, p. 18.

Dyar, H. G. 1916. New *Aedes* from the mountains of California. *Insec. Incit. Mens.,* 4:80–90.

Dyar, H. G. 1928. *The Mosquitos of the Americas.* Washington, Carnegie Inst. Publ. 387, 616 pp.

Dyer, R. E., L. F. Badger, and A. Rumreich. 1931. Rocky Mountain Spotted fever (eastern type) transmission by the American dog tick (*Dermacentor variabilis*). *Public Health Rep.,* 46:1403–1413.

Eads, R. B. 1965. Biological notes on *Culex tarsalis* in

the Lower Rio Grande Valley of Texas. *Mosquito News*, **25**:61–63.

Eads, R. B., E. G. Campos, and H. A. Trevino. 1966. Quarantine problems associated with the importation of bananas from Mexico. *J. Econ. Entom.*, **59**:896–899.

Ebeling, W. 1960. Control of the tropical rat mite. *J. Econ. Entom.*, **53**:475–476.

Eddy, G. W., A. R. Roth, and F. W. Plapp, Jr. 1962. Studies on the flight habits of some marked insects. *J. Econ. Entom.*, **55**:603–607.

Edeson, J. G. B., and T. Wilson. 1964. The epidemiology of filariasis due to *Wuchereria bancrofti* and *Brugia malayi*. *Ann. Rev. Entom.*, **9**:245–268.

Edeson, J. G. B., T. Wilson, R. H. Wharton, and A. B. G. Laing. 1960. Experimental transmission of *Brugia malayi* and *B. pahangi* to man. *Trans. Roy. Soc. Trop. Med. Hyg.*, **54**:229–234.

Edney, E. B. 1957. *The Water Relations of Terrestrial Arthropods.* Cambridge Monogr. Exptl. Biol., No. 5, Cambridge, Cambridge Univ. Press.

Edwards, J. S. 1961. The action and composition of the saliva of an assassin bug *Platymeris rhadamanthus* Gaerst (Hemiptera, Reduviidae). *J. Exp. Biol.*, **38**:61–77.

Ehrlich, S., and D. Spielberg. 1960. Alteration of the environment of *Anopheles* larvae by nutria in the Naaman swamps, Acre District, Israel. *Amer. J. Trop. Med.*, **9**:265–268.

Eichler, W. 1940. Untersuchung zur Epidemiologie der Aussenparasiten: II. Masseninvasionen von Ektoparasiten. *Arch. Wiss. Prakt. Tierheilk.*, **75**:212–221.

Eichler, W. 1964. Gesichtspunkte der Gesundheitsschädlichkeit von Insekten unter besonderer Berücksichtigung der Pharaoameise. *Wiss. Z. Humboldt. Univ. Berl. Mathnat. Reihe*, **13**(1):113–118.

Eklund, C. M., G. M. Kohls, W. L. Jellison, W. Bugdorfer, R. C. Kennedy, and L. Thomas. 1959. The clinical and ecological aspects of Colorado tick fever. *Proc. 6th Intern. Cong. Trop. Med. Mal.*, **5**:197–203.

Emerson, K. C. 1956. Mallophaga (chewing lice) occurring on the domestic chicken. *J. Kansas Entom. Soc.*, **29**:63–79.

Emerson, K. C. 1962a. Mallophaga (chewing lice) occurring on the turkey. *J. Kansas Entom. Soc.*, **35**:196–201.

Emerson, K. C. 1962b. *A Tentative List of Mallophaga for North American Birds (North of Mexico).* Dugway Utah, Digway Proving Grounds, 217 pp.

Emerson, K. C. 1962c. *A Tentative List of Mallophaga for North American Mammals (North of Mexico).* Dugway Utah, Dugway Proving Grounds, 20 pp.

Emerson, K. C. 1964. *Checklist of the Mallophaga of America (North of Mexico). Part I, Suborder Ischnocera; Part II, Suborder Amblycera.* Dugway, Utah, Dugway Proving Grounds, 171 and 104 pp.

Entomological Society of America, Committee on Common Names of Insects (C. C. Blickenstaff, Chairman. 1965. Common names of insects approved by the Entomological Society of America. *Bull. Entom. Soc. Amer.*, **11**:287–320 (periodically revised).

Eschle, J. L., and G. R. DeFoliart. 1965. Rearing and biology of *Wohlfahrtia vigil* (Diptera; Sarcophagidae). *Ann. Entom. Soc. Amer.*, **58**:849–855.

Eskey, C. R. 1938. Recent developments in our knowledge of plague transmission. *Public Health Rep.*, **53**:49–57.

Eskey, C. R., and V. H. Haas. 1940. *Plague in the Western Part of the United States.* U.S. Pub. Health Bull. 254. 83 pp.

Essig, E. O. 1932. A small insect which stings severely. *Science*, **75**:242–243.

Esten, W. N., and C. J. Mason. 1908. Sources of bacteria in milk. *Connecticut Agric. Exper. Sta. Bull.*, **51**:94–98.

Evans, G. O., J. G. Sheals, and D. Macfarlane. 1961. *The Terrestrial Acari of the British Isles. An Introduction to Their Morphology, Biology and Classification.* Vol. I. *Introduction and Biology.* London, British Museum (Natural History), 219 pp.

Evans, G. O., and W. M. Till. 1966. Studies on the British Dermanyssidae (Acari: Mesostigmata): Part II. Classification. *Bull. Brit. Mus. (Nat. Hist.) Zool.*, **14**:109–370.

Ewing, H. E. 1921. *Studies on the Biology and Control of Chiggers.* U.S. Dept. Agr. Bull. 986. 19 pp.

Ewing, H. E. 1928a. The scorpions of the western part of the United States, with note on those occurring in northern Mexico. *Proc. U.S. Nat. Museum.* **73** (Art. 9):1–24.

Ewing, H. E. 1928b. Observations on the habits and the injury caused by the bites and stings of some common North American arthropods. *Amer. J. Trop. Med.*, **8**:39–62.

Ewing, H. E. 1929. *A Manual of External Parasites.* Baltimore, C. C. Thomas, 225 pp.

Ewing, H. E. 1942. The relation of flies (*Musca domestica* Linnaeus) to the transmission of bovine mastitis. *Amer. J. Vet. Res.*, **3**:295–299.

Ewing, H. E., and I. Fox. 1943. *The Fleas of North America: Classification, Identification, and Geographic Distribution of These Injurious and Disease-Spreading Insects.* U.S. Dept. Agr. Misc. Publ. 500, 142 pp.

Faichnie, N. 1929. The etiology of enteric fever: Personal views and experiences. *J. Med. Ass. S. Africa.*, **3**:669–675.

Fain, A. 1966. *A Review of the Family Epidermoptidae Trouessart Parasitic on the Skin of Birds (Acarina: Sarcoptiformes).* Verhand, Vlaamse Acad. Wetenschappen, 27 (84), Part I, 176 pp.; Part II, 144 pp.

Fain, A. 1967. Le genre *Dermatophagoides* Bogdanov 1864, son importance dans les allergies respiratoires et cutanées chez l'homme (Psoroptidae: Sarcoptiformes). *Acarologia*, **9**:179–225.

Fairbairn, H. 1958. The penetration of *Trypanosoma rhodesiense* through the peritrophic membrane of *Glossina palpalis*. *Ann. Trop. Med. Parasit.*, **52**:18–19.

Falleroni, D. 1926. Fauna anofelica italiana e suo "habitat" (paludi, risaie, canali): Metodi di lotta contro la malaria. *Riv. di Malariol.*, **5**:553–593.

Fallis, A. M., and G. F. Bennett. 1961. Sporogony of *Leucocytozoon* and *Haemoproteus* and a revised classification of Haemosporidiida. *Canad. J. Zool.*, **39**:215–228.

Fallis, A. M., and S. M. Smith. 1964. Ether extracts from birds and CO_2 as attractants for some ornithophilic simuliids. *Canad. J. Zool.*, **42**:723–730.

Farrell, C. E. 1956. Chiggers of the genus *Euschöngastia* (Acarina: Trombiculidae) in North America. *Proc. U.S. Nat. Museum.*, **106**:85–235.

Faust, E. C., and J. A. Maxwell. 1930. The finding of the larvae of the chigoe, *Tunga penetrans*, in scrapings from human skin. *Arch. Dermat. Syph.*, **22**:94–97.

Fay, R. W., and D. A. Eliason. 1966. A preferred

oviposition site as a surveillance method for *Aedes aegypti. Mosquito News,* 26:531–535.

Feingold, B. F., E. Benjamini, and D. Michaeli. 1968. The allergic responses to insect bites. *Ann. Rev. Entom.,* 13:137–158.

Fenner, F., and F. N. Ratcliffe. 1965. *Myxomatosis.* Cambridge, Cambridge University Press, 379 pp.

Ferris, G. F. 1924. The new world Nycteribiidae (Diptera: Pupipara). *Entom. News,* 3:191–199.

Ferris, G. F. 1951. The sucking lice. *Pacific Coast Entom. Soc., Mem. 1,* 320 pp.

Fibiger, J. 1913. Ueber eine durch Nematoden (Spiroptera sp. n.) hervorgerufene papillomatose und carcinomatose Geschwulstbildung im Magen der Ratte. *Berl. Klin. Wochschr.,* 50:289–298.

Finlayson, M. H. 1956. *Arachnidism in South Africa. In* Buckley and Porges, *op. cit.,* pp. 85–87.

Florence, L. 1921. The hog louse, *Haematopinus suis* Linné: Its biology, anatomy, and histology. *Cornell Univ. Agric. Exp. Sta. Mem.,* 51:641–743.

Flügge, C. 1891. *Grundriss der Hygiene.* Leipzig, Veit & Co., x+560 pp.

Foggie, A. 1951. Studies on the infectious agent of tick-borne fever in sheep. *J. Path. Bact.,* 63:1–15.

Foggie, A. 1959. Studies on the relationship of tick-bite to tick pyaemia of lambs. *Ann. Trop. Med. Parasit.,* 53:27–34.

Fontan, R., and P. Fauran. 1961. Problèmes posés par les foyers résiduels d'*Aedes aegypti* sur le continent américain. *Bull. Soc. Path. Exot.,* 53:892–903.

Foote, R. H., and D. R. Cook. 1959. *Mosquitoes of Medical Importance.* U.S.D.A. Agric. Handbook, 152, 158 pp.

Foote, R. H., and H. D. Pratt. 1954. *The Culicoides of the Eastern United States (Diptera, Heleidae).* Pub. Health Mon. (U.S.) 18, 53 pp.

Forattini, O. P. 1957. Culicoides da região neotropical *Arq. Fac. Hig. S. Paulo,* 11:161–526.

Ford, J., J. P. Glasgow, D. L. Johns, and J. R. Welsh. 1959. Transect fly-rounds in field studies of *Glossina. Bull. Entom. Res.,* 50:275–285.

Forde, R. M. 1902. Some clinical notes on a European patient in whose blood a Trypanosoma was observed. *J. Trop. Med.,* 5:261.

Foubert, E. L., Jr., and R. A. Stier. 1958. Antigenic relationships between honeybees, wasps, yellow hornets, black hornets, and yellow jackets. *J. Allerg.,* 29:13–23.

Fox, C. 1925. *Insects and Diseases of Man.* Philadelphia, P. Blakiston's Son & Co., 349 pp.

Fox, I. 1940. *Fleas of Eastern United States.* Ames, Iowa, State College Press, 191 pp.

Fox, I. 1955. A catalogue of the bloodsucking midges of the Americas (*Culicoides, Leptoconops,* and *Lasiohelea*) with keys to the subgenera and nearctic species, a geographical index, and bibliography. *Univ. Puerto Rico J. Agric.,* 39:214–285.

Fox, I., and I. Garcia-Moll. 1961. Ants attacking fleas in Puerto Rico. *J. Econ. Entom.,* 54:1065–1066.

Francis, E. 1919. Deer fly fever or Pahvant Valley plague. *Public Health Rep.,* 34:2061–2062.

Francis, E., and B. Mayne. 1921. Experimental transmission of tularemia by flies of the species *Chrysops discalis. Public Health Rep.,* 36:1738–1746.

Franks, R. E., E. C. Burns, and N. C. England. 1964. Color preference of the horn fly, *Haematobia irritans,* on beef cattle. *J. Econ. Entom.,* 57:371–372.

Fredeen, F. J. H., and J. A. Shemanchuk. 1960. Black flies (Diptera: Simuliidae) of irrigation systems in

Saskatchewan and Alberta. *Canad. J. Zool.,* 38:723–735.

Freeborn, S. B. 1926. The mosquitoes of California. *Univ. Calif. Technical Bull. Entomol.,* 3:333–360.

Freeborn, S. B., W. M. Regan, and A. H. Folger. 1925. The relation of flies and fly sprays to milk production. *J. Econ. Entom.,* 18:779–790.

Frogatt, W. W. 1922. *Sheep-Maggot Flies.* New South Wales Dept. Agric., Farmers Bull. 144. 32 pp.

Frohne, W. C. 1957. Habitat and males of Alaskan snipe fly pests (Symphoromyia: Rhagionidae). *Mosquito News,* 17:94–96.

Fuller, H. S. 1954. Studies of rickettsialpox: III. Life cycle of the mite vector, *Allodermanyssus sanguineus. Amer. J. Hyg.,* 59:236–239.

Fuller, H. S. 1956. Veterinary and medical acarology. *Ann. Rev. Entom.,* 1:347–366.

Furman, D. P., and F. J. Radovsky. 1963. A new species of *Ornithonyssus* from the white-tailed antelope squirrel, with a rediagnosis of the genus *Ornithonyssus* (Acarina: Dermanyssidae). *Pan-Pac. Entom.,* 39:75–79.

Furman, D. P., and V. S. Stratton. 1963. Control of northern fowl mites, *Ornithonyssus sylviarum,* with sulfaquinoxaline. *J. Econ. Entom.,* 56:904–905.

Furman, D. P., R. D. Young, and E. P. Catts. 1959. *Hermetia illucens* as a factor in the natural control of *Musca domestica* Linnaeus. *J. Econ. Entom.,* 52:917–921.

Gajardo-Tobar, R., and A. Honorato. 1947. Anotaciones acerca de una epidemia de miasis humana. *Hospital de Viña del Mar, Chile,* 3:5–14.

Galindo, P. 1958. Bionomics of *Sabethes chloropterus* Humboldt, a vector of sylvan yellow fever in middle America. *Amer. J. Trop. Med.,* 7:429–440.

Galindo, P., P. H. Peralta, R. B. Mackenzie, and H. K. Beye. 1964. St. Louis encephalitis in Panama: A review and a progress report. *Amer. J. Trop. Med.,* 13:455.

Galindo, P., and E. de Rodaniche. 1964. Surveillance for sylvan yellow fever activity in Panama (1957–1961). *Amer. J. Trop. Med.,* 13:844–850.

Galloway, C. B. 1967. *Annual Report of the Gorgas Memorial Laboratory for the Fiscal Year Ended June 30, 1966.* 38:1–34.

Galun, R., Y. Avi-dor, and M. Bar-Zeev. 1963. Feeding response in *Aedes aegypti*: Stimulation by adenosine triphosphate. *Science,* 142:1674–1675.

Galun, R., and S. H. Kindler. 1965. Glutathione as an inducer of feeding on ticks. *Science,* 147:166–167.

Garcia, R. 1962. Carbon dioxide as an attractant for certain ticks (Acarina: Argasidae and Ixodidae). *Ann. Entom. Soc. Amer.,* 55:605–606.

Garcia, R., and F. J. Radovsky. 1962. Haematophagy by two non-biting muscid flies and its relationship to tabanid feeding. *Canad. Entom.,* 94:1110–1116.

Garnham, P. C. C. 1947. Exo-erythrocytic schizogony in *Plasmodium kochi* Laveran: A preliminary note. *Trans. Roy. Soc. Trop. Med. Hyg.,* 40:719–722.

Garnham, P. C. C. 1963. Distribution of simian malaria parasites in various hosts. *J. Parasit.,* 49:905–911.

Garnham, P. C. C. 1966. *Malaria Parasites and other Haemosporidia.* Oxford, England, Blackwell, Philadelphia, Davis, 1,132 pp.

Garnham, P. C. C., J. O. Harper, and R. B. Highton. 1946. The mosquitoes of the Kaimose Forest, Kenya Colony, with special reference to yellow fever. *Bull. Entom. Res.,* 36:473–496.

Garrett-Jones, C. 1962. The possibility of active long-distance migrations by *Anopheles pharoensis* Theobald. *Bull. WHO*, 27:299–302.

Garret-Jones, C., and B. Grab. 1964. The assessment of insecticidal impact on the malaria mosquito's vectorial capacity, from data on the proportion of parous females. *Bull. WHO*, 31:71–86.

Gay, F. J. 1966. Scientific and common names of insects and allied forms occurring in Australia. *Commonwealth Sci. Industrial Research Organization Bull.*, 285:1–52.

Gebauer, O. 1958. *Die Dasselfliegen des Rindes und ihre Bekämpfung.* Parasitol. Schriftenreihe. Heft. 9. 97 pp.

Geigy, R., and A. Aeschlimann. 1964. Langfristige Beobachtungen über transovarielle Ubertragung von *Borrelia duttoni* durch *Ornithodorus moubata*. *Acta Trop.*, 21:87–91.

Geldern, C. E. von. 1927. Systemic effects following the sting of a species of *Epyris*. *Science*, 65:302–303.

Gelman, A. C. 1961. The ecology of tularemia, *in* May, J. M. (Editor), *Studies in Disease Ecology*. New York, Hafner, p. 89.

Gentry, J. W., C. G. Moore, and D. E. Hayes. 1967. Preliminary report on soluble antigen fluorescent antibody technique for identification of host source of mosquito blood meals. *Mosquito News*, 27:141–143.

Gerhardt, R. W. 1956. Present knowledge concerning the relationship of blue-green algae and mosquitoes in California rice fields. *Proc. Calif. Mosquito Control Assoc.*, 24:47–50.

Gertsch, W. J. 1949. *American Spiders*. New York, Van Nostrand, 285 pp.

Gertsch, W. J. 1958. The spider genus *Loxosceles* in North America, Central America, and the West Indies. *Amer. Mus. Novitates*, 1907:1–46.

Gertsch, W. J. 1967. The spider genus *Loxosceles* in South America (Araneae, Scytodidae). *Amer. Mus. Nat. Hist. Bull.*, 136:117–174.

Gilbert, E. W., and C. M. Stewart. 1935. Effective treatment of arachnidism by calcium salts, a preliminary report. *Amer. J. Med. Sci.*, 189:532–536.

Gil Collado, J. 1961. Los chinchorros de las palomas como plaga domestica. *Med. Trop.*, 37:378–385.

Gill, C. A., and R. B. Lal. 1931. Epidemiology of cholera, with special reference to transmission: A preliminary report. *Indian J. Med. Res.*, 18:1255–1297.

Gillies, M. T. 1964. Selection for host preference in *Anopheles gambiae*. *Nature*, 203:852–854.

Gilmour, D. 1961. *The Biochemistry of Insects*. New York, Academic Press, 343 pp.

Gjullin, C. M., W. W. Yates, and H. H. Stage. 1950. Studies on *Aedes vexans* (Meig.) and *Aedes sticticus* (Meig.), floodwater mosquitoes, in the Lower Columbia River Valley. *Ann. Entom. Soc. Amer.*, 43:262–275.

Glancey, B. M., A. C. White, C. N. Husman, and J. Salmela. 1966. Low volume applications of insecticides for the control of adult mosquitoes. *Mosquito News*, 26:356–359.

Glasgow, J. P. 1963. *The Distribution and Abundance of Tsetse*. New York, London, Pergamon, 241 pp.

Glasgow, J. P. 1967. Recent fundamental work on tsetse flies. *Ann. Rev. Entom.*, 12:421–438.

Gless, E. E., and E. S. Raun. 1959. Effects of chicken body louse infestations on egg production. *J. Econ. Entom.*, 52:358–359.

Glover, P. E., J. G. LeRoux, and D. F. Parker. 1960. The extermination of *Glossina palpalis* on the Kuja-Migori river systems with the use of insecticides, *in International Scientific Committee for Trypanosomiasis Research*. Seventh meeting, Brussels, 1958. Publ. Comm. Tech. Co-op. Afr. S. Sahara no. 41, pp. 331–342.

Goldberger, J., and J. F. Anderson. 1912. The transmission of typhus fever, with reference to transmission by the head louse (*Pediculus capitis*). *Public Health* Rep., 27:297–307.

Goldblum, N. 1959. West Nile fever in the Middle East. *Proc. 6th Int. Cong. Trop. Med. Malar.* 5:112–125.

Goldfield, M., R. Altman, and R. P. Kandle. 1966. The 1964 St. Louis encephalitis outbreak. *Proc. 52nd Ann. Meeting N. J. Mosquito Exterm. Assoc.* pp. 105–110.

Goldman, L. 1947. Types of American cutaneous leishmaniasis—Dermatological aspects. *Amer. J. Trop. Med.*, 27:561–584.

Gordon, R. M., and W. H. R. Lumsden. 1939. A study of the behaviour of the mouth-parts of mosquitoes when taking up blood from living tissues; together with some observations on the ingestion of microfilariae. *Ann. Trop. Med. Parasit.*, 33:259–278.

Gorham, J. R. 1968. The geographic distribution of the brown recluse spider *Loxosceles reclusa* (Araneae, Scytodidae) and related species in the United States. *Coop. Econ. Insect. Rpt.* U.S.D.A 18:171–175.

Gotaas, H. G. 1956. *Composting: Sanitary Disposal and Reclamation of Organic Wastes*. Geneva, WHO, 205 pp.

Gouck, H. K. 1966. Protection from ticks, fleas, chiggers, and leeches. *Arch. Derm.*, 93:112–113.

Gouck, H., T. P. McGovern, and M. Beroza. 1967. Chemicals tested as space repellents against yellow-fever mosquitoes. I. Esters. *J. Econ. Entom.*, 60:1587–1590.

Gould, D. J. 1956. The larval trombiculid mites of California. *Univ. Calif. Pub. Entom.*, 11:1–116.

Gould, D. J., H. C. Barnett, and W. Suyemoto. 1962. Transmission of Japanese encephalitis virus by *Culex gelidus* Theobald. *Trans. Roy. Soc. Trop. Med. Hyg.*, 56:429–435.

Gould, D. J., and M. L. Miesse. 1954. Recovery of a rickettsia of the spotted fever group from *Microtus pennsylvanicus* from Virginia. *Proc. Soc. Exp. Biol. Med.*, 85:558–561.

Gould, G. E., and H. O. Deay. 1940. *The Biology of Six Species of Cockroaches which Inhabit Buildings*. Purdue Univ. Agric. Exp. Sta. Bull. 451, 31 pp.

Graham, H. 1902. Dengue: A study of its mode of propagation and pathology. *Med. Record*, 61:204–207.

Graham, J. E., and I. E. Bradley. 1963. Preliminary studies of the effects of organic pollution on mosquito larval populations in Salt Lake County, Utah. *Proc. 31st Conf. Calif. Mosquito Control Assoc.*, 1963. pp. 71–72.

Graham-Smith, G. S. 1930. The Oscinidae (Diptera) as vectors of conjunctivitis, and the anatomy of their mouth parts. *Parasitology*, 22:457–467.

Granett, P., and E. J. Hansens. 1957. Further observations on the effect of biting fly control on milk production on cattle. *J. Econ. Entom.*, 50:332–336.

Grashchenkov, N. I. 1964. Japanese encephalitis in the U.S.S.R. *Bull. WHO*. 30:161–172.

Grashchenkov, N. I. 1964. Tick-borne encephalitis in the U.S.S.R. *Bull. WHO*, **30**:187–196.

Grassi, B., A. E. Bignami, and G. Bastianelli. 1899. Ciclo evolutivo delle semilune nell' *Anopheles claviger* ed altri studi sulla malaria dall' ottobre 1898 al maggio 1899. *Atti Soc. Studi Malaria*, **1**:14–27. (Cited by Ross, 1910).

Graybill, H. W. 1911. *Studies on the Biology of the Texas Fever Tick.* U.S. dept. Agr. Bur. Animal Industry, Bull. No. 130, 42 pp.

Grayston, J. T., and others. 1962. Encephalitis on Taiwan, I-VI. *Amer. J. Trop. Med.*, **11**:126–161.

Green, H. B., and R. E. Hutchins. 1960. Laboratory study of toxicity of imported fire ants to bluegill fish. *J. Econ. Entom.*, **53**:1137–1138.

Greenberg, B. 1959. Persistence of bacteria in the developmental stages of the housefly. IV. Infectivity of the newly emerged adult. *Amer. J. Trop. Med.*, **8**:618–622.

Greenberg, B. 1965. Flies and disease. *Sci. Amer.*, **213**:92–99.

Greenberg, B. 1968. In press.

Greenberg, B., G. Varela, A. Bornstein, and H. Hernandez. 1963. Salmonellae from flies in a Mexican slaughterhouse. *Amer. J. Hyg.*, **77**:177–183.

Gregson, J. D. 1949. Note on the longevity of certain ticks (Ixodoidae). *Proc. Entom. Soc. Brit. Columbia*, **45**:14.

Gregson, J. D. 1956. *The Ixodoidae of Canada.* Canada Dept. Agr. Science Service Entomol. Div. Publ. 930. 92 pp.

Gregson, J. D. 1958a. Host susceptibility to paralysis by the tick *Dermacentor andersoni* Stiles (Acarina: Ixodidae). *Canad. Entom.*, **90**:421–424.

Gregson, J. D. 1958b. Tick paralysis in cattle in British Columbia in 1957. *Proc. Entom. Soc. Brit. Columbia*, **55**:6–7.

Gregson, J. D. 1960. Morphology and functioning of the mouthparts of *Dermacentor andersoni* Stiles. Acta Trop., **17**:48–79.

Gregson, J. D. 1962. Observations on the feeding of *Dermacentor andersoni* Stiles on perfused preparations. *Proc. 11th Internat. Cong. Entom.*, **2**(10): 463–466.

Gregson, J. D. 1966. Records of tick paralysis in livestock in British Columbia. *J. Entom. Soc. Brit. Columbia*, **63**:13–18.

Gresikova, M., W. C. Reeves, and R. P. Scrivani. 1964. California encephalitis virus in Kern County, California. *Amer. J. Hyg.*, **80**:229–234.

Greve, J. H., and S. M. Gaafar. 1964. Effects of hypothyroidism on canine demodicosis. *Amer. J. Vet. Res.*, **25**:520–522.

Grinnell, M. E., and I. L. Hawes. 1943. *Bibliography on Lice and Man, With Particular Reference to Wartime Conditions.* U.S. Dept. Agric., Washington D.C., Bibliographical Bull. no. 1.

Grodhaus, G. 1963. Chironomid midges as a nuisance. *Calif. Vector Views*, **10**:19-24, 27–37.

Grosdanov, A. 1959. Berufsbedingte Ekzeme und Hautentzündungen durch Raupen der *Plodia interpunctella. Berufsdermatosen*, **7**:30–35.

Grothaus, R. H., and D. E. Howell. 1967. A new technique for the recovery of spider venom. *J. Kansas Entom. Soc.*, **40**:37–41.

Guberlet, J. E. 1916. Morphology of adult and larval cestodes of poultry. *Trans. Amer. Micr. Soc.*, **35**: 23–44.

Guiglia, D. 1958. Les sclerodermines par rapport à l'homme. *Proc. 10th Internat. Cong. Entom.*, **3**:883–887.

Guilbride, P. D. L., L. Barber, and A. M. G. Kalikwani. 1959. Bovine infectious keratitis. Suspected moth-borne outbreak in Uganda. *Bull. Epiz. Dis. Afr.*, **7**:149–154.

Guimarães, J. H., and N. Papavero. 1966. A tentative annotated bibliography of *Dermatobia hominis* (Linnaeus Jr., 1781) (Diptera, Cuterebridae). *Arq. Zool.*, **14**:223–294.

Gunstream, S. E. 1965. The ecology of *Psorophora confinnis* (Diptera; Culicidae) in southern California I. The seasonal nature of hatching. *Ann. Entom. Soc. Amer.*, **58**:663–667.

Gurney, A. B. 1953. Distribution, general bionomics, and recognition characters of two cockroaches recently extablished in the United States. *Proc. U.S. Nat. Museum*, **103**:39–56.

Gutsevich, A. V. 1960. *Blood-Sucking Ceratopogonids (Culicoides and Leptoconops, Diptera, Heleidae) of the Fauna of the U.S.S.R.* Opred. Faune U.S.S.R. No. 72. 131 pp.

Hackett, L. W. 1937. *Malaria in Europe, an Ecological Study.* London, Oxford Univ. Press, Humphrey Milford, 336 pp.

Hackett, L. W., E. Martini, and A. Missiroli. 1932. The races of *A. maculipennis. Amer. J. Hyg.*, **16**:137–162.

Hackett, L. W., and A. Missiroli. 1935. The varieties of *Anopheles maculipennis* and their relation to the distribution of malaria in Europe. *Riv. Malar.*, **14**:45–109.

Haddow, A. J., C. W. Davies, and A. J. Walker. 1960. O'nyongnyong fever: An epidemic virus disease in East Africa. I. Introduction. *Trans. Roy. Soc. Trop. Med. Hyg.*, **54**:517–522.

Hadwen, S. 1913. On tick paralysis in sheep and man following bites of *Dermacentor venustus. Parasitology*, **6**:283–297.

Hadwen, S., and G. H. F. Nuttall. 1913. Experimental tick paralysis in the dog. *Parisatology*, **6**:298–301.

Hale, T. H., T. A. L. Davies, and W. K. NGCheng Hin. 1960. Flies (*Musca domestica*) in aeroplanes as vectors of faecal-borne diseases. *Trans. Roy. Soc. Trop. Med. Hyg.*, **54**:261–262.

Hall, D. G. 1932. Some studies on the breeding media, development, and stages of the eye gnat, *Hippelates pusio* Loew. *Amer. J. Hyg.*, **16**:854–864.

Hall, D. G. 1948. *The Blowflies of North America.* Thomas Say Foundation, *Entom. Soc. Amer.*, 477 pp.

Hall, M. C. 1924. Lesions due to the bite of the wheelbug, *Arilus cristatus* (Hemiptera; Reduviidae). *Arch. Intern. Med.*, **33**:513–515.

Hall, M. C., and J. T. Muir. 1913. A critical study of a case of myiasis due to *Eristalis. Arch. Intern. Med.*, **2**:193–203.

Hall, R. R., and J. A. McKiel. 1961. Occurrence of the American dog tick, *Dermacentor variabilis* (Say) in western Nova Scotia. *Canad. Entom.*, **93**:891–893.

Hall, W. T. K., and P. R. Wilkinson. 1960. Observations on survival of cattle tick, *Boophilus microplus* (Can.) in northern Queensland. *Qd. J. Agric. Sci.*, **17**:91–96.

Halstead, B. W., and R. E. Ryckman. 1949. Injurious effects from contacts with millipedes. *Med. Arts. Sci.*, **3**:16–18.

Halter, B. L., and W. C. Kuzell. 1943. Black widow spider bites in the adult male. *Milit. Surgeon*, **92**:427–432.

Hammon, W. M., H. W. Lundy, J. A. Gray, F. C.

Evans, F. Bang, and E. A. Izumi. 1942. A large-scale serum neutralization survey of certain vertebrates as part of an epidemiological study of encephalitis of western equine and St. Louis types. *J. Immun.*, **44**:75–86.

Hammon, W. McD., and W. C. Reeves. 1952. California encephalitis virus. A newly described agent. I. Evidence of natural infection in man and other animals. *Calif. Med.*, **77**:303–309.

Hammon, W. McD., W. C. Reeves, B. Brookman, E. M. Izumi, and C. M. Gjullin. 1941. Isolation of the viruses of western equine and St. Louis encephalitis from *Culex tarsalis* mosquitoes. *Science*, **94**:328–330.

Hammon, W. McD., W. C. Reeves, and G. E. Sather, 1951. Western equine and St. Louis encephalitis viruses in the blood of experimentally infected wild birds and epidemiological implications of findings. *J. Immun.*, **67**:357–367.

Hammon, W. M., G. E. Sather, and A. Rudnik. 1961. (*Identification and Serology of Dengue Viruses Especially in Philippines and Thailand*). SEATO Med. Res. Mon. 2, pp. 30–36, 45–58.

Hamon, J., and J. Mouchet. 1962. Observations sur les méthodes actuellement disponibles pour déterminer la sensibilité aux insecticides des insects d'importance médicale. *Bull. Soc. Path. Exot.*, **54**:1143–1156.

Hannoun, C., R. Panthier, J. Mouchet, and J. P. Eouzan. 1964. Isolement en France du virus West-Nile à partir de malades du vecteur *Culex modestus* Ficalbi. *Note. C. R. Acad. Sci.*, **259**:4170–4172.

Hansens, E. J. 1956. Granulated insecticides against greenhead (*Tabanus*) larvae in the salt marsh. *J. Econ. Entom.*, **49**:401–403.

Hanson, W. J. 1961. The breeding places of phlebotomus in Panama (Diptera, Psychodidae). *Ann. Entom. Soc. Amer.*, **54**:317–322.

Harden, F. W., and H. S. Chubb. 1960. Observations of *Aedes taeniorhynchus* dispersal in extreme south Florida and the Everglades National Park. *Mosquito News*, **20**:249–255.

Harley, K. L. S. 1966. Studies on the survival of the nonparasitic stages of the cattle tick *Boophilus microplus* in three climatically dissimilar districts of north Queensland. *Autral. J. Agr. Res.*, **17**:387–410.

Harris, R. L., E. D. Frazer, P. D. Grossman, and O. H. Graham. 1966. Mating habits of the stable fly. *J. Econ. Entom.*, **59**:634–636.

Harwood, R. F. 1952. The function of the pharynx in the retention of particulate material by the larvae of culicine mosquitoes. Master's thesis, Univ. Ill. 27 pp.

Harwood, R. F. 1961. A mobile trap for studying the behavior of flying bloodsucking insects. *Mosquito News*, **21**:35–39.

Harwood, R. F. 1965. Observations on distribution and biology of *Phlebotomus* sandflies from northwestern North America (Diptera: Psychodidae). *Pan-Pac. Entom.*, **41**:1–4.

Harwood, R. F., and E. Halfhill. 1964. The effect of photoperiod on fat body and ovarian development of *Culex tarsalis* (Diptera: Culicidae). *Ann. Entom. Soc. Amer.*, **57**:596–600.

Hase, A. 1934. Zur Frage der Bettwanzenbekampfung durch sogenannte biologische Verfohren. *Naturwiss.* **18**:23.

Hase, A. 1942. Über Entlausung durch Ameisen sowie uber die Wirkung der Ameisensäure auf Kleiderlause. *Z. Parasitenk*, **12**:665–677.

Hart, C. B., and J. C. Malone. 1958. The occurrence of the rabbit fur mite, *Cheyletiella parasitivorax* (Megnin, 1878) on the dog. *Vet. Rec.*, **70**:991–993.

Hartwell, W. V., S. F. Quan, K. G. Scott, and L. Kartman. 1958. Observations on flea transfer between hosts: A mechanism in the spread of bubonic plague. *Science*, **127**:814.

Haufe, W. O. 1957. Physical environment and behavior of immature stages of *Aedes communis* (Deg.) (Diptera: Culicidae) in subarctic Canada. *Canad. Entom.*, **89**:120–139.

Haufe, W. O., and L. Burgess. 1956. Development of *Aedes* at Fort Churchill, Manitoba, and prediction of dates of emergence. *Ecology*, **37**:500–519.

Haufe, W. O., and L. Burgess. 1960. Design and efficiency of mosquito traps based on visual response to patterns. *Canad. Entom.*, **92**:124–140.

Hawking, F., and M. Worms. 1961. Transmission of filarioid nematodes. *Ann. Rev. Entom.*, **6**:413–432.

Hayes, R. O., L. D. Beadle, A. D. Hess, O. Sussman, and M. J. Bonese. 1962. Entomological aspects of the 1959 outbreak of eastern encephalitis in New Jersey. *Amer. J. Trop. Med.*, **11**:115–121.

Hayes, R. O., and A. D. Hess. 1964. Climatological conditions associated with outbreaks of eastern encephalitis. *Amer. J. Trop. Med.*, **13**:851–858.

Hazard, E. I., C. S. Lofgren, D. B. Woodard, H. R. Ford, and B. M. Glancey. 1964. Resistance to the chemical sterilant apholate, in *Aedes aegypti*. *Science*, **145**:500–501.

Hearle, E. 1938. *Insects and Allied Parasites Injurious to livestock and Poultry in Canada*. Ottawa; Dept. Agr. Pub. 604, 108 pp.

Hebard, M. 1917. The Blattidae of North America north of the Mexican Boundary. *Mem. Amer. Entom. Soc.*, No. 2, 284 pp.

Heisch, R. B., W. E. Grainger, A. E. C. Harvey, and G. Lister. 1962. Feral aspects of rickettsial infections in Kenya. *Trans. Roy. Soc. Trop. Med. Hyg.*, **56**:272–282.

Heisch, R. B., and A. E. C. Harvey. 1960. Is *Ornithodoros savignyi* (Audouin) a vector of relapsing fever in Africa? *Ann. Trop. Med. Parasit.*, **54**:205–207.

Henderson, J. R., N. Karabatsos, A. T. C., Bourke, R. C. Wallis, and R. M. Taylor. 1962. A survey for arthropod-borne viruses in south-central Florida. *Amer. J. Trop. Med.*, **11**:800–810.

Henning, M. W. 1932. Animal diseases of South Africa. *South African Agriculture Series*, **11**:298–329.

Hepworth, W. G., and G. M. Thomas. 1963. Attempts to transfer psoroptic mites from elk to cattle and sheep. *J. Amer. Vet. Med. Assoc.*, **140**:689–690.

Herms, W. B. 1909. Medical Entomology. Its scope and methods. *J. Econ. Entom.*, **2**:265–268.

Herms, W. B. 1911. *The Housefly in its Relation to the Public Health*. Univ. Calif. Agric. Exper. Sta. Bull. 215, pp. 513–548.

Herms, W. B. 1917. Contribution to the life history and habits of *Ornithodoros megnini*. *J. Econ. Entom.*, **10**:407–411.

Herms, W. B. 1925a. A case of human myiasis caused by the ox-warble, *Hypoderma bovis* DeG. *J. Parasit.*, **11**:149–150.

Herms, W. B. 1925b. Entomological observations on Fanning and Washington Islands. *Pan-Pac. Entom.*, **2**:49–54.

Herms, W. B. 1929. Anopheline mosquito investigations in California. *Fourth Internat. Cong. Entom.* **2**:708–721.

Herms, W. B. 1943. Preparation for a career as a medical entomologist. *J. Econ. Entom.*, 36:18–22.

Herms, W. B., S. F. Bailey, and B. McIvor. 1935. The black widow spider. *Science*, 82:395–396.

Herms, W. B., and S. B. Freeborn. 1920. Egglaying habits of California anophelines. *J. Parasit.*, 7:69–79.

Herms, W. B., and F. M. Frost. 1932. A comparative study of the eggs of California anophelines. *J. Parasit.*, 18:240–244.

Herms, W. B., and Q. O. Gilbert. 1933. An obstinate case of intestinal myiasis. *Ann. Intern. Med.*, 6:941–945.

Herms, W. B., and Y. Nelson. 1913. The croton bug (*Ectobia germanica*) as a factor in bacterial dissemination. *Amer. J. Public Health*, 3:929–934.

Herms, W. B., and C. M. Wheeler. 1936. *Ornithodoros hermsi* Wheeler as a vector of relapsing fever in California. *J. Parasit.*, 22:276–282.

Hertig, M. 1927. A technique for artificial feeding of sandflies (*Phlebotomus*) and mosquitoes. *Science*, 65:328–329.

Hertig, M. 1942. Phlebotomus and Carrión's disease. *Amer. J. Trop. Med.*, 22(Supp.):1–81.

Hertig, M. 1948. Sand flies of the genus *Phlebotomus* —a review of their habits, disease relationships and control. *Proc. 4th Internat. Cong. Trop. Med. Malaria* (Abstracts) Washington, D.C.

Hess, A. D., C. E. Cherubin, and L. C. Lamotte. 1963. Relation of temperature to activity of western and St. Louis encephalitis viruses. *Amer. J. Trop. Med.*, 12:657–667.

Hewitt, C. G. 1910. *The Housefly*. Manchester, England. The University Press, xiii, 195 pp.

Hindle, E. 1914. *Flies in Relation to Disease: Blood-Sucking Flies*. London, Cambridge Univ. Press, 398 pp.

Hindle, E. 1935. Relapsing fever: Some recent advances. *Trop. Dis. Bull.*, 32:309–327.

Hinman, E. H. 1966. *World Eradication of Infectious Diseases*. Springfield, Ill. Thomas, 223 pp.

Hinton, H. E. 1958. The phylogeny of the panorpoid orders. *Ann. Rev. Entom.*, 3:181–206.

Hirst, L. F. 1953. *The Conquest of Plague*. Oxford, The Clarendon Press, 478 pp.

Hirst, S. 1913. On three new species of gamasid mites found on rats. *Bull. Entom. Res.*, 4:119–124.

Hitchcock, C. R., and E. T. Bell. 1952. Studies on the nematode parasite, *Gongylonema neoplasticum* (*Spiroptera neoplasticum*) and avitaminosis A in the forestomach of rats: Comparison of Fibiger's results. *J. Nat. Cancer Inst.*, 12:1345–1387.

Hite, J. M., W. J. Gladney, J. L. Lancaster, Jr., and W. H. Whitcomb. 1966. The biology of the brown recluse spider. *Univ. Arkansas Agr. Expt. Sta. Bull.*, 711, 26 pp.

Hocking, B. 1960. Northern biting flies. *Ann. Rev. Entom.*, 5:135–152.

Hodge, C. F. 1911. *In Nature and Culture*. July, 1911.

Hoeppli, R. 1963. Early references to the occurrence of *Tunga penetrans* in tropical Africa. *Acta Trop.*, 20:143–153.

Hoeppli, R., and H. H. Schumacher. 1962. Histological reactions to trombiculid mites, with special reference to "natural" and "unnatural" hosts. *Z. Tropenmed. Parasit.*, 13:419–428.

Hoeppli, R., and J. Y. C. Watt. 1933. Experiments on resistance of dipterous larvae in connection with the problem of intestinal and urinary myiasis. *Chin. Med. J.*, 47:1298–1306.

Hoffman, W. A. 1926. Resting position of Haitian Anopheles. *Amer. J. Trop. Med.*, 6:377–379.

Holland, G. P. 1949. *The Siphonaptera of Canada*. Ottawa, Canada Dept. Agric. Tech. Bull., 70, 306 pp.

Holland, G. P. 1964. Evolution, classification, and host relationships of Siphonaptera. *Ann. Rev. Entom.*, 9:123–146.

Holway, R. T., A. W. Morrill, and F. J. Santana. 1967. Mosquito control activities of the U.S. armed forces in the Republic of Vietnam. *Mosquito News*, 27:297–307.

Holway, R. T., A. W. Morrill, and F. J. Santana. 1967. Mosquito control activities of the U.S. armed forces in the Republic of Vietnam. *Proc. and Papers 23 Ann. Mtg. Amer. Mosquito Contr. Ass.*, pp. 23–29.

Hoogstraal, H. 1956. *African Ixodoidae I. Ticks of the Sudan*. Washington, D.C., Dept of the Navy, 1,101 pp.

Hoogstraal, H., and D. R. Dietlein. 1963. Ecological relationships of sandfly species and *Leishmania* infection. *Amer. J. Trop. Med.*, 12:165–174.

Hoogstraal, H., *et al.* 1964. Ticks (Ixodidae) on migrating birds in Egypt, spring and fall 1962. *Bull. WHO*, 30:355–367.

Hoogstraal, H. 1966. Ticks in relation to human diseases caused by viruses. *Ann. Rev. Entom.*, 11:261–308.

Hoogstraal, H. 1967. Ticks in relation to human diseases caused by *Rickettsia* species. *Ann. Rev. Entom.*, 12:377–420.

Hoogstraal, H., H. Trapido, and G. M. Kohls. 1965. Southeast Asia *Haemaphysalis* ticks *H.* (*Kaiseriana*) *papuana nadchatrami* sp. n. and redescription of *H.* (*K.*) *semermis* Neumann. *J. Parasit.*, 51:433–451.

Hopkins, G. H. E. 1949. The host-associations of the lice of mammals. *Proc. Zool. Soc. London*, 119:387–604.

Hopkins, G. H. E., and T. Clay. 1952. *A Check List of the Genera and Species of Mallophaga*. London, British Museum (Natural History), 362 pp.

Hopkins, G. H. E., and M. Rothschild, 1953–56, 1962. *An Illustrated Catalogue of the Rothschild Collection of Fleas,* (*Siphonaptera*) *in the British Museum* (*Natural History*). London, British Museum (Natural History), Vol. I, 361 pp., Vol. II, 445 pp., Vol. III, 500 pp.

Hopla, C. E. 1951. Experimental transmission of tularemia by the tropical rat mite. *Amer. J. Trop. Med.*, 31: 768–783.

Horsfall, F. L., and I. Tamm (eds.). 1965. *Viral and Rickettsial Infections of Man*. Philadelphia, Lippincott, 1,282 pp.

Horsfall, W. R. 1954. A migration of *Aedes vexans* Meigen. *J. Econ. Entom.*, 47:544.

Horsfall, W. R. 1955. *Mosquitoes: Their Behavior and Relation to Disease*. New York, Ronald Press, 723 pp.

Horsfall, W. R. 1956. A method for making a survey of floodwater mosquitoes. *Mosquito News*, 16:66–71.

Horsfall, W. R., and G. B. Craig, Jr. 1956. Eggs of floodwater mosquitoes IV. Species of *Aedes* common in Illinois (Diptera: Culicidae). *Ann. Entom. Soc. Amer.*, 49:368–374.

Horsfall, W. R., R. C. Miles, J. T. Sokatch. 1952. Eggs of floodwater mosquitoes. I. Species of *Psorophora* (Diptera: Culicidae). *Ann. Entom. Soc. Amer.*, 45:618–624.

Hoskins, W. M., and H. T. Gordon. 1956. Arthropod resistance to chemicals. *Ann. Rev. Entom.*, 1:89–122.

Hosoi, T. 1959. Identification of blood components which induce gorging of the mosquito. *J. Insect Physiol.*, 3:191–218.

Howard, J. E., C. Rios, I. Ekensperger, and P. Olivos. 1957. Enfermedad de Chagas congenita. *Bol. Chileno Parasit.*, 12:42–45.

Howard, L. O. 1900. A contribution to the study of the insect fauna of human excrement. *Proc. Acad. Sci.*, 2:541–604.

Howard, L. O. 1921. Sketch history of medical entomology, *in* Ravenel, M. P., *A Half Century of Public Health*. New York, Amer. Pub. Health Assn., pp. 412–438.

Howells, V. 1957. *A Naturalist in Palestine*, New York, Philosophical Library, 180 pp.

Hoy, J. B. 1966. *The Behavior of the Genus Symphoromyia Attacking Deer in Northern California (Diptera: Rhagionidae)*. University of Kansas, Ph.D. thesis, 162 pp.

Hoy, J. B., and J. R. Anderson. 1966. Snipe flies (*Symphoromyia*) attacking man and other animals in California. *Proc. Pap. 33rd Ann. Conf. Calif. Mosquito Control Assoc.*, 1966:61–64.

Hubbard, C. A. 1947. *Fleas of Western North America*. Ames, Iowa State College Press, 533 pp.

Hubert, A. A., and H. J. Baker. 1963a. Studies on the habitats and population of *Leptotrombidium* (*Leptotrombidium*) *akamushi* and *L.* (*L.*) *deliensis* in Malaya (Acarina: Trombiculidae). *Amer. J. Hyg.*, 78:131–142.

Hubert, A. A., and H. J. Baker. 1963b. The persistence of foci of *Leptotrombidium* (*Leptotrombidium*) *akamushi* along a transect in Malaya (Acarina: Trombiculidae). *Amer. J. Hyg.*, 78:143–149.

Hudson, A., L. Bowman, and C. W. M. Orr. 1960. Effects of absence of saliva on blood feeding by mosquitoes. *Science*, 131:1730–1731.

Hudson, A., and J. McLintock. 1967. A chemical factor that stimulates oviposition by *Culex tarsalis* Coquillett (Diptera, Culicidae). *Animal Behav.*, 15:336–341.

Huebner, R. J., W. L. Jellison, and C. Pomerantz. 1946. Rickettsialpox—a newly recognized rickettsial disease. IV. Isolation of a rickettsia, apparently identical with the causative agent of rickettsialpox from *Allodermanyssus sanguineus*, a rodent mite. *Public Health Rep.*, 61:1677–1682.

Huff, C. 1931. A proposed classification of disease transmission by arthropods. *Science*, 74:456–457.

Huff, C. G. 1945. A consideration of the problem of evolution of malaria parasites. *Rev. Inst. Salubr. Enferm. Trop.*, 6:253–258.

Huff, C. G., *et al.* 1948. Symposium on exoerythrocytic forms of malaia parasites, Parts I-VI. *J. Parasit.*, 34:261–320.

Hughes, J. H. 1961. Mosquito interceptions and related problems in aerial traffic arriving in the United States. *Mosquito News*, 21:93–100.

Hughes, L. E., and C. B. Philip. 1958. Experimental tick paralysis in laboratory animals and native Montana rodents. *Proc. Soc. Exp. Biol.*, 99:316–319.

Hunter, W. D., and F. C. Bishopp. 1911. *The Rocky Mountain Spotted Fever Tick*. U.S. Dept. Agr. Bur. Entom. Bull. 105, 47 pp.

Hunter, W. D., and W. A. Hooker. 1907. *Information Concerning the North American Fever Tick*. U.S. Dept. Agr. Bur. Entom. Bull., 72, 87 pp.

Hurlbut, H. S. 1965. Arthropod transmission of animal viruses. *Advances Virus Res.*, 11:277–292.

Hyland, K. E. 1963. Current trends in the systematics of acarines endoparasitic in vertebrates. *Advances. Acarology*, 1:365–373.

Hynes, H. B. N., T. R. Williams, and W. E. Kershaw. 1961. Freshwater crabs and *Simulium neavei* in East Africa. I. Preliminary observations on the slopes of Mount Elgon in December, 1960, and January, 1961. *Ann. Trop. Med. Parasit.*, 55:197–201.

Ishijima, H. 1967. Revision of the third stage larvae of synanthropic flies of Japan (Diptera: Authomyiidae, Muscidae, Calliphoridae, and Sarcophagidae). *Jap. J. Sanit. Zool.*, 18:47–100.

Iyengar, R. 1962. The bionomics of salt-water *Anopheles gambiae* in East Africa. *Bull. WHO*, 27:223–229.

Jachowski, L. A., Jr., and C. Schultz. 1948. Notes on the biology and control of mosquitoes at Umiat, Alaska. *Mosquito News*, 8:155–165.

Jackson, E. B., J. X. Danauskas, M. C. Coale, and J. E. Smadel. 1957. Recovery of *Rickettsia akari* from the Korean vole *Microtus fortis pelliceus*. *Amer. J. Hyg.*, 66:301–308.

Jacobson, M. 1965. *Insect Sex Attractants*. New York, Interscience, 154 pp.

Jacobson, M., and M. Beroza. 1963. Sex attractants of the American cockroach. *Science*, 142:1258.

Jakeman, L. A. R. 1961. The internal anatomy of the spiny rat mite, *Echinolaelaps echidninus* (Berlese). *J. Parasit.*, 47:328–349.

James, M. T. 1948. *The Flies that Cause Myiasis in Man*. U.S. Dept. Agric. Publ. 631. 175 pp. (1947).

Jamnback, H. 1965. *The Culicoides of New York State* (*Diptera: Ceratopogonidae*). New York State Mus. Sci. Serv. Bull. 399, 154 pp.

Jamnback, H. 1967. Some effects of ingested thiotepa on the development of *Plasmodium gallinaceum* in yellow fever mosquitoes and in chickens. *J. Econ. Entom.*, 60:390–393.

Jamnback, H., and H. S. Eabry. 1962. Effects of DDT, as used in black fly larval control, on stream arthropods. *J. Econ. Entom.*, 55:636–639.

Jamnback, H., and W. Wall. 1957. Control of salt Marsh *Tabanus* larvae with granulated insecticides. *J. Econ. Entom.*, 50:379–382.

Jayawardene, L. G. 1963. Larval development of *Brugia ceylonensis* Jayawardene, 1962, in *Aedes aegypti*, with a brief comparison of the infective larva with those of *Brugia* spp., *Dirofilaria repens* and *Artionema digitata*. *Ann. Trop. Med. Parasit.*, 57:359–370.

Jellison, W. L. 1950. Geographical distribution of "deer-fly fever" and the biting fly *Chrysops discalis* Williston. *Public Health Rep.*, 65:1321–1329.

Jellison, W. L. 1959. Fleas and disease. *Ann. Rev. Entom.*, 4:389–414.

Jellison, W. L. and L. Glesne. 1967. *Index to the Literature of Siphonaptera of North America.* Supplement 2, 1951–1960. Mimeo. manuscript, 356 pp. Hamilton, Montana, Rocky Mountain Laboratory, USPHS.

Jellison, W. L., and N. E. Good. 1942. *Index to the Literature of Siphonaptera of North America.* Washington, D.C., USPHS, *in* Nat. Inst. Health Bull. 178, 193 pp.

Jellison, W. L., and G. M. Kohls. 1938. Tick-host anemia: A secondary anemia induced by *Dermacentor andersoni* Stiles. *J. Parasit.*, 24:143–154.

Jellison, W. L., B. Locker, and R. Bacon. 1953.

Index to the Literature of Siphonaptera of North America. Supplement 1, 1939–1950. Mimeo. manuscript, 246 pp. Hamilton, Montana, Rocky Mountain Laboratory, USPHS.

Jenkins, D. W. 1949. Trombiculid mites affecting man. IV. Revision of *Eutrombicula* in the American hemisphere. *Ann. Entom. Soc. Amer.*, **42**:289–318.

Jenkins, D. W. 1962. Radioisotopes in ecological and biological studies of agricultural insects, *in Radioisotopes and Radiation in Entomology.* Vienna, Int. Atomic Energy Agency, pp. 3–20.

Jenkins, D. W. 1964. Pathogens, parasites, and predators of medically important arthropods. Annotated list and bibliography. *Bull. WHO*, Supplement to Vol. 30. 150 pp.

Jenkins, D. W., and K. L. Knight. 1950. Ecological survey of the mosquitoes of Great Whale River. Quebec (Diptera, Culicidae). *Proc. Entom. Soc. Wash.*, **52**:209–223.

Jobling, B. 1925. A contribution to the biology of *Ornithodorus moubata* Murray. *Bull. Entom. Res.*, **15**:271–279.

Jobling, B. 1926. A comparative study of the structure of the head and mouth parts in the Hippoboscidae (Diptera, Pupipara). *Parasitology*, **18**:319–349.

Johannsen, O. A. 1933–37. *Aquatic Diptera, Parts 1–3.* Cornell Univ. Agric. Exper. Sta. Mem. nos. 164, 177, and 205.

Johnston, D. E. 1964. *Psorergates bos, a New Mite Parasite of Domestic Cattle (Acari, Psorergatidae).* Ohio Agric. Exp. Sta. Circ. 129, 7 pp.

Jones, B. M. 1950. The penetration of the host tissue by the harvest mite, *Trombicula autumnalis* Shaw. *Parasitology*, **40**:247–260.

Jones, R. H. 1961. Equipment for blood feeding and holding large numbers of *Culicoides* in experiments with sheep. *J. Econ. Entom.*, **54**:816–818.

Jones, C. M., and D. W. Anthony. 1964. *The Tabanidae (Diptera) of Florida.* U.S.D.A. Tech. Bull. 1295. 85 pp.

Jordan, A. M., F. Lee-Jones, and B. Weitz. 1962. The natural hosts of tsetse flies in northern Nigeria. *Ann. Trop. Med. Parasit.*, **56**:430–442.

Jordan, K. 1932. A new *Xenopsylla* from Hawaii. *Novitates Zoologicae*, **38**:264–266.

Jorge, R. 1928. *Les Faunes Regionales des Rongeurs et des puces dans leurs Rapports avec la Peste*, Paris, Masson et Cie, 306 pp.

Joseph, C., M. A. U. Menom, K. R. Unnithan, and S. Raman. 1963. Studies on the comparative hospitability of *Salvinia auriculata* Aubet and *Pistia stratiotes* Linn., to *Mansoniodes annulifera* (Theobald) in Kerala. *Indian J. Malar.*, **17**:311–332.

Joyce, C. R., and P. Y. Nakagawa. 1964. New immigrant mosquito in Hawaii. *Public Health Rep.*, **79**:24.

Judson, C. L., Y. Kokama, and A. D. Bray. 1962. The effects of various chemicals on eggs of the yellow-fever mosquito, *Aedes aegypti. J. Econ. Entom.*, **55**:805–807.

Jurgenson, I. A., and V. C. Teplyh. 1960. On the parasite of fleas, *Bairamlia fuscipes* Waterston (Hymenoptera, Pteromalidae). (in Russian) *Zool. Zh.*, **39**:1879–1880.

Kamal, A. S. 1958. Comparative studies of thirteen species of sarcosaprophagous Calliphoridae and Sarcophagidae (Diptera). I. Bionomics. *Ann. Entom. Soc. Amer.*, **51**:261–271.

Kamal, A. S. 1959. Comparative studies of thirteen species of sarcosaprophagous Calliphoridae and Sarcophagidae (Diptera). II. Digestive enzymology. *Ann. Entom. Soc. Amer.*, **52**:167–173.

Kappus, K. D., and C. E. Venard. 1967. The effects of photoperiod and temperature on the induction of diapause in *Aedes triseriatus* (Say). *J. Insect Physiol.*, **13**:1007–1019.

Karrar, G., M. N. Kaiser, and H. Hoogstraal. 1963. Ecology and host-relationships of ticks (Ixodoidea) infecting domestic animals in Kassala Province, Sudan, with special reference to *Amblyomma lepidum* Dönitz. *Bull. Entom. Res.*, **54**:509–522.

Kartman, L. 1957. The concept of vector efficiency in experimental studies of plague. *Exp. Parasit.*, **6**:599–609.

Kartman, L. 1958. An insecticide-bait-box method for the control of sylvatic plague vectors. *J. Hyg.*, **56**:455–465.

Kartman, L. 1960. The role of rabbits in sulvatic plague epidemiology, with special attention to human cases in New Mexico and use of the fluorescent antibody technique for detection of *Pasteurella pestis* in field specimens. *Zoonoses Res.*, **1**:1–27.

Kartman, L., F. M. Prince, and S. F. Quan. 1958. Studies on *Pasteurella pestis* in fleas. VII. The plague-vector efficiency of *Hystrichopsylla linsdalei* compared with *Xenopsylla cheopis* under experimental conditions. *Amer. J. Trop. Med.*, **7**:317–322.

Kartman, L., and S. F. Quan. 1964. Notes on the fate of avirulent *Pasteurella pestis* in fleas. *Trans. Roy. Soc. Trop. Med. Hyg.*, **58**:363–365.

Kartman, and others. 1958. Ecological studies of wild rodent plague in the San Francisco Bay area of California. I, II, *Amer. J. Trop. Med.*, **7**:112–124, 411–415.

Kartman, L., and others. 1960. Ecological studies of wild rodent plague in the San Francisco Bay area of California. III, IV, V. *Amer. J. Trop. Med.*, **9**:85–100.

Kashin, P. 1966. Electronic recording of the mosquito bite. *J. Insect Physiol.*, **12**:281–286.

Kaston, B. J. 1948. *Spiders of Connecticut.* State of Connecticut, State Geol. and Nat. Hist. Survey Bull. 70. 874 pp.

Kawashima. 1961. Spiders, spider web toxin, and ophthalmitis. (in Japanese) *Ganka Rinsho I-Ho*, **55**:40–48.

Keh, B. 1956. Cone-nosed bugs of California. *Calif. Vector Views*, **3**:47–50.

Kelser, R. A. 1933. Mosquitoes as vectors of the virus of equine encephalomyelitis. *Amer. J. Vet. Med. Ass.*, 82, n.s. **35**:767–771.

Kemper, H. 1958. Experimentelle untersuchungen über die Wirkung von Raupenhaaren auf die Menschliche Haut. *Proc. 10th Int. Cong. Entom. Montreal*, **3**:719–723.

Kenaga, E. E. 1966. Commercial and experimental organic insecticides. (1966 revision) *Bull. Entom. Soc. Amer.*, **12**:161–217.

Kerdel-vegas, F., and M. Goihmann-yahr. 1966. *Paederus* dermatitis. *Arch. Derm.*, **94**:175–185.

Kerr, R. W. 1946. Control of fleas: Laboratory experiments with DDT and certain other insecticides. *J. Council Sci. Indust. Res.*, **19**:233–240.

Kershaw, W. E., T. R. Williams, S. Frost, and H. B. N. Hynes. 1965. Selective effect of particulate insecticides on *Simulium* among stream fauna. *Nature*, **208**:199.

Kessel, E. L. 1939. *The Embryology of Fleas.* Smithsonian Misc. Coll. Vol. 98, no. 3; Smithsonian Inst. Pub. No. 3527. 69 pp.

Kessel, J. F. 1957. An effective programme for the control of filariasis in Tahiti. *Bull. WHO*, **16**: 609–632.

Kessel, J. F. 1967. Diethylcarbamazine in filariasis control. *Proc. and Papers 23rd Ann. Mtg. Amer. Mosquito Control. Ass.*, pp. 17–22.

Kessel, Q. C. 1925. A synopsis of the Streblidae of the world. *J. NY Entom. Soc.*, **33**:11–34.

Kettle, D. S. 1965. Biting ceratopogonids as vectors of human and animal diseases. *Acta Trop.*, **22**: 356–362.

Khelevin, N. V. 1959. The seasonal character of hatching and the embryonic diapause in *Aedes caspius dorsalis* Mg. (Diptera, Culicidae). *Entom. Rev.*, **38**:355–365.

Kilpatrick, J. W., and C. T. Adams, Sr. 1967. Emergency measures employed in the control of St. Louis encephalitis epidemics in Dallas and Corpus Christi, Texas, 1966. *Proc. and Papers 23rd Ann. Mtg. Amer. Mosquito Control Ass.*, p. 53.

King, W. V. 1917. The effect of cold upon malaria parasites in the mosquito-host. *J. Exp. Med.*, **25**: 495–498.

Kinghorn, A., and W. Yorke. 1912. On the transmission of human trypanosomes by *Glossina morsitans* Westw., and on the occurrence of human trypanosomes in game. *Ann. Trop. Med.*, **6**:1–23.

Kirkwood, A. 1963. Longevity of the mites *Dermanyssus gallinae* and *Liponyssus sylviarum*. *Exp. Parasit.*, **14**:358–366.

Kitaoka and others. 1962. (Scrub typhus in Japan, epidemology and vectors.) *Jap. J. Med. Sci. Biol.*, **15**:281–308.

Kleine, F. K. 1909. Positive Infectionversuche mit *Trypanosoma brucei* durch *Glossina palpalis*. *Deutsch. Med. Wschr.*, **35**:469–470.

Kliewer, J. W., T. Miura, R. C. Husbands, and C. H. Hurst. 1966. Sex pheromones and mating behavior of *Culiseta inornata* (Diptera: Culicidae). *Ann. Entomol. Soc. Amer.*, **59**:530–533.

Knapp, F. W., and H. Knutson. 1958. Reproductive potential and longevity of two relatively isolated field populations of insecticide-susceptible house flies. *J. Econ. Entom.*, **51**:43–45.

Knapp, S. E., G. M. Padilla, and F. M. Philips. 1955. An apparent human case of myiasis by the horn fly, *Siphona irritans*. *Parasitology*, **41**:324.

Knight, K. L. 1964. Qualitative methods for mosquito larval surveys. *J. Med. Entom.*, **1**:109–115.

Knight, K. L., and D. E. Bryan. 1963. Induced removal of embedded *Amblyomma americanum* (L.) ticks. *Iowa State J. Sci.*, **37**:399–416.

Knipling, E. F. 1964. *The Potential Role of the Sterility Method for Insect Population Control with Special Reference to Combining this Method With Conventional Methods*. USDA, ARS-33-98, 54 pp.

Knipling, E. F. 1966. Some basic principles of insect population suppression. *Bull. Entom. Soc. Amer.*, **12**:7–16.

Knowles, R., and B. C. Basu. 1943. Laboratory studies on the infectivity of *Anopheles stephensi*. *J. Malaria Inst. India*, **5**:1–30.

Koch, R. 1905. Vorläufige Mitteilungen über die Ergebnisse einer Forschungsreise nach Ostafrika. *Deutsch. Med. Wschr.*, **47**:1866.

Kohls, G. M., H. Hoogstraal, and C. M. Clifford. 1961. Observations on the subgenus *Argas* (Ixodoidae, Argasidae, *Argas*). 5. Study of *A. brevipes* Banks, 1908, from birds in Arizona and California,

U.S.A. and Baja, California, Mexico. *Ann. Entom. Soc. Amer.*, **54**:869–877.

Kokernot, R. H., K. C. Smithburn, H. E. Paterson, and B. M. McIntosh. 1960. Isolation of Germiston virus, a hitherto unknown agent, from Culicine mosquitoes, and a report of infection in two laboratory workers. *Amer. J. Trop. Med., Hyg.*, **9**:62–69.

Komp, W. H. W. 1942. A technique for staining, dissecting, and mounting the male terminalia of mosquitoes. *Public Health Rep.*, **57**:1327–1333.

Königsmann, E. 1960. Zur Phylogenie der Parametabola unter besonderer Berücksichtigung der Phthiraptera. *Beitr. Entom.*, **10**:705–744.

Kordova, N., and J. Rehacek. 1965. Development of *Coxiella burneti* from their ultrafilterable particles in ticks *in vivo*, their organs *in vitro* and in tick tissue culture. *Proc. XII Internat. Congress Entom.*, p. 777.

Kosminskii, R. B. 1960. The method of determining the age of the fleas *Leptopsylla segnis* Schönh. 1811 and *L. taschenbergi* Wagn. 1898, (Suctoria-Aphaniptera) and an experiment on the age analysis of a population of *L. segnis*. (in Russian) *Med. Parazit.* (Moskva), **29**:590–594.

Kramer, J. P. 1963. Pathogens of vertebrates and plants as pathogens of their acarine and insect vectors, in E. A. Steinhaus (Editor), *Insect Pathology, an Advanced Treatise*. Vol. 1, pp. 251–272.

Kriggsman, B. J., and G. L. Windred. 1933. *Investigations on the Buffalo Fly, Lyperosia exigua de Meij*. Commonwealth of Australia: Council Sc. Ind. Research Pamph. 43. 40 pp.

Kröber, O. 1925. Tabanidae. *In* Lindner, E., *Die Fliegen der Palaearktischen Region*. **19**:1–146.

Krull, W. H., and C. R. Mapes. 1952. Studies on the biology of *Dicrocoelium dendriticum* (Rudolphi, 1819) Loos 1899 (Trematoda: Dicrocoeliidae) including its relationships to the intermediate host, *Cionella lubrica* (Müllu). VII. The second intermediate host of *Dicrocoelium dendriticum*. *Cornell Veterinarian*, **42**:603–604.

Kumm, H. W. 1935. The natural infection of *Hippelates pallipes* Loew with spirochaetes of yaws. *Trans. Roy. Soc. Trop. Med. Hyg.*, **29**:265–272.

Kumm, H. W., and T. B. Turner. 1936. The transmission of yaws from man to rabbits by an insect vector, *Hippelates pallipes* Loew. *Amer. J. Trop. Med.*, **16**:245–262.

Kumm, H. W., T. B. Turner, and A. A. Peat. 1935. The duration of motility of the spirochaetes of yaws in a small West India fly, *Hippelates pallipes* Loew. *Amer. J. Trop. Med.*, **15**:209–223.

Kunin and others. 1957. An outbreak of St. Louis encephalitis in the Lower Rio Grande Valley of Texas in 1954. *Public Health Rep.*, **72**:510–535.

Kusel'tan, I. V. 1964. On the penetration of adults of the tick *Hyalomma asiaticum* into the skin of lambs and its consequences. (In Russian) *Zool. Zh.*, **43**:138–139.

Laake, E. W. 1936. Economic studies of screwworm flies, *Cochliomyia* species (Diptera, Calliphorinae), with special reference to the prevention of myiasis of domestic animals. *Iowa State Coll. J. Sci.*, **10**: 345–359.

LaBrecque, G. C., and C. N. Smith. 1967. *Principles of Insect Chemosterilization*. New York, Appleton-Century-Crofts, 352 pp.

Lackman, D. B., E. J. Bell, H. G. Stoenner, and E. G. Pickens. 1965. The Rocky Mountain spotted fever group of rickettsias. *Health Lab. Sci.*, **2**:135–141.

Laing, A. B. G. 1961. Influence of the animal host on the microfilarial periodicity of *Brugia malayi*. *Trans. Roy. Soc. Trop. Med., Hyg.*, **55**:558.

Laing, A. B. G., J. F. B. Edeson, and R. H. Wharton. 1961. Studies of filariasis in Malaya, further experiments on the transmission of *Brugia malayi* and *Wucherehia bancrofti*. *Ann. Trop. Med. Parasit.*, **55**:86–92.

Laird, M. 1959. Fungal parasites of mosquito larvae from the Oriental and Australian regions, with a key to the genus *Coelomomyces* (Blastocladiales: Coelomomycetaceae). *Canad. J. Zool.*, **37**:781–791.

Laird, M. 1966. A coral island experiment. *WHO Chronicle*, **21**:18–26.

Langridge, W. P. 1961. Scent attractants for tsetse flies. *Intern. Sci. Comm. Trypanosomiasis Res. 8th Mtg.*, pp. 235–241.

Larousse, F., A. G. King, and S. B. Wolbach. 1928. The overwintering in Massachusetts of *Ixodiphagus caucurtei*. *Science*, **67**:351–353.

Laurent, P. 1939. Auto-observation: Effets de la sécrétion toxique du ténébrionide *Blaps nitens* Cast. *Bull. Soc. Zool. France*, **64**:20–23.

Laven, H. 1953. Reziprok unterschiedliche Kreuzbarkeit von Stechmucken (Culicidae) und ihre Deutung als plasmatische Vererbung. *Z. Indukt. Abstam. Vererbungslehre*, **85**:118–136.

Laven, H. 1967. Eradication of *Culex pipiens fatigans* through cytoplasmic incompatibility. *Nature*, **216**:383–384.

Laveran, A. 1880. Note sur un nouveau parasite trouvé dans le sang de plusieres malades atteints de fievre palustre. *Bull. Acad. Méd. Paris*, **9**:1235.

Lavoipierre, M. M. J. 1958a. Studies on the host-parasite relationships of filarial nematodes and their arthropod hosts. I. The sites of development and the migration of *Loa loa* in *Chrysops silacea*, the escape of the infective forms from the head of the fly, and the effect of the worm on its insect host. *Ann. Trop. Med. Parasit.*, **52**:103–121.

Lavoipierre, M. M. J. 1958b. Studies on the host-parasite relations of filarial nematodes and their arthropod hosts. II. The arthropod as a host to the nematode; a brief appraisal of our present knowledge, based on a study of the more important literature from 1878 to 1957. *Ann. Trop. Med. Parasit.*, **52**:326–345.

Lavoipierre, M. M. J. 1964. A new family of acarines belonging to the suborder Sarcoptiformes parasitic in the hair follicle of primates. *Ann. Natal Museum*, **16**:191–208.

Lavoipierre, M. M. J. 1965. Feeding mechanism of bloodsucking arthropods. *Nature*, **208**:302–303.

Lavoipierre, M. M. J. 1967. Feeding mechanism of *Haematopinus suis*, on the transilluminated mouse ear. *Exp. Parasit.*, **20**:303–311.

Lavoipierre, M. M. J., and A. J. Beck. 1967. Feeding mechanism of *Chiroptonyssus robustipes* on the transilluminated bat wing. *Exp. Parasit.*, **20**:312–320.

Lavoipierre, M. M. J., G. Dickerson, and R. M. Gordon. 1959. Studies on the methods of feeding of blood-sucking arthropods. I. The manner in which Triatomine bugs obtain their blood-meal, as observed in the tissues of the living rodent, with some remarks on the effects of the bite on human volunteers. *Ann. Trop. Med. Parasit.*, **53**:235–250.

Lavoipierre, M. M. J., and M. Hamachi. 1961. An apparatus for observations on the feeding mechanism of the flea. *Nature*, **192**:998–999.

Lavoipierre, M. M. J., and B. C. Ho. 1966. Studies on filariasis. I. The migration of the infective larvae of *Brugia pahangi* in *Aedes togoi* and their loss from the mosquito under experimental conditions. *J. Helminth.*, **40**:343–362.

Lavoipierre, M. M. J., and M. Lavoipierre. 1966. An arthropod intermediate host of a pentatomid. *Nature*, **210**:845–846.

Lavoipierre, M. M. J., C. Rajamanickam, and P. Ward. 1967. Host-parasite relationships of acarine parasites and their vertebrate hosts. I. The lesions produced by *Bakerocoptes cynopteris* in the skin of *Cynopterus brachyotis*. *Acta Trop.*, **24**:1–18.

Lavoipierre, M. M. J., and R. F. Riek. 1955. Observations on the feeding habits of argasid ticks and on the effect of their bites on laboratory animals, together with a note on the production of coxal fluid by several of the species studied. *Ann. Trop. Med. Parasit.*, **49**:96–113.

Lawson, P. B. 1933. Notes on the life history of the hourglass spider. *Ann. Entom. Soc. Amer.*, **26**:568–574.

LeBrun, A. J. 1964. The African *Aedes aegypti*. *Mosquito News*, **24**:389–393.

Lechleitner, R. R., and others. 1962. Die-off of a Gunnison's prairie dog colony in central Colorado. I,II. *Zoonoses Res.*, **1**:185–224.

Leclercq, M. 1952. Introduction à l'etude des tabanides et revision des espèces de Belgique. *Inst. Roy. des Sci. Nat. Belgique, Mem.*, 123. 79 pp.

Leclercq, M. 1960. Revision systématique et biogéographique des Tabanidae (Diptera) paléarctiques. Vol. I. Pangoniinae et Chrysopinae. *Institut Roy. des Sci. Nat. de Belgique, Mem.*, 2e Ser., fasc. 63, 77 pp.

Lee, D. J. 1968. Human myiasis in Australia. *Med. J. Aust.*, **1**:170–173.

Lee, D. J., F. Fenner, and J. J. Lawrence. 1958. Mosquitoes and fowl pox in the Sydney area. *Aust. Vet. J.*, **34**:230–237.

Lee, R. D. 1955. The biology of the Mexican chicken bug, *Haematosiphon inodorus* (Dugès). *Pan-Pac. Entom.*, **31**:47–61.

Lees, A. D. 1956. The physiology and biochemistry of diapause. *Ann. Rev. Entom.*, **1**:1–16.

Lees, A. D., and J. W. L. Beament. 1948. An egg-waxing organ in ticks. *Quart. J. Micros. Sci.*, **89**:291–332.

Leeson, H. S. 1941. The effect of temperature upon the hatching of the eggs of *Pediculus humanus corporis* DeGeer. *Parasitology*, **33**:243.

Legner, E. F., and E. C. Bay. 1964. Natural exposure of *Hippelates* eye gnats to field parasitization and the discovery of one pupal and two larval parasites. *Ann. Entom. Soc. Amer.*, **57**:767–769.

Lehnert, T. 1967. *Hymenopterous Insect Stings*. U.S.D.A. Agric. Handbook 335, pp. 105–106.

Leiper, R. R. 1913. Metamorphosis of *Filaria loa*. *Lancet*, **1**:51.

Leonard, M. D. 1930. A revision of the dipterous family Rhagionidae (Leptidae) in the United States and Canada. *Amer. Entom. Soc. Mem.* 7, 181 pp.

Le Prince, J. A., and A. J. Orenstein. 1916. *Mosquito Control in Panama: the Eradication of Malaria and Yellow Fever in Cuba and Panama*. New York, G. P. Putnam's Sons, 355 pp.

Levi, H. W., and A. Spielman. 1964. The biology and control of the South American brown spider, *Loxosceles laeta* (Nicolet), in a North American focus. *Amer. J. Trop. Med. Hyg.*, **13**:132–136.

Levi, H. W. 1958. Number of species of black-widow spiders (Theridiidae: Latrodectus). *Science*, 127: 1055.

Levi, H. W. 1959. The spider genus *Latrodectus* (Araneae, Theridiidae). *Trans. Amer. Micr. Soc.*, 78:7–43.

Lewis, D. J. 1934. The behavior of the larvae of the tsetse flies before pupation. *Bull. Entom. Res.*, 25:195–199.

Lewis, D. J. 1957. A method of recognizing individual nulliparous and parous mosquitoes. *Trans. Roy. Soc. Trop. Med. Hyg.*, 57:561.

Lienert, R. M., and W. Thorsell. 1955. Untersuchungen über die Aktivität von Autolysaten aus Wanderlarven (*Hypoderma bovis*) auf Elemente des Bindegewebes. *Exp. Parasit.*, 4:117–122.

Lillie, R. D., and E. Francis. 1936. *Pathology of Tularaemia*. U.S. Public Health Service, Nat. Inst. Health Bull. 167. 217 pp.

Lindner, E. 1949. *Die Fliegen der Palaearktischen Region, Handbuch*. Stuttgart, E. Schweizerbart'sche Verlagsbuchhandlung, 422 pp.

Lindsay, D. R., and H. I. Scudder. 1956. Nonbiting flies and disease. *Ann. Rev. Entom.*, 1:323–346.

Link, V. B. 1955. *A History of Plague in the United States*. U.S. Publ. Health Ser. Pub. Health Monograph 26. 120 pp.

Lipke, H., and C. W. Kearns. 1960. DDT-dehydrochlorinase. *Adv. Pest Control Res.*, 3:253–388.

Liston, W. G. 1905. Plague, rats and fleas. *J. Bombay Nat. Hist. Soc.*, 16:253–273.

Little, D. A. 1963. The effect of cattle tick infestation on the growth rate of cattle. *Austral. Vet. J.*, 39:6–10.

Little, J. W., J. Tay, and F. Biagi. 1966. A study of the susceptibility of triatomid bugs to some Mexican strains of *Trypanosoma cruzi*. *J. Med. Entom.*, 3:252–255.

Liu, C., S. Chang, Y. Cheng, and Y. Wang. 1959. Studies on vectors of Japanese B encephalitis virus in Peking. II. Studies on the blood feeding habits of common species of mosquitoes in Peking (in Chinese). *Acta Entom. Sin.*, 9:51–56.

Lloyd, J. E., and J. G. Matthysse. 1966. Polymer-insecticide systems for use as livestock feed additives. *J. Econ. Entom.*, 59:363–367.

Logathetis, C., and H. H. Schwardt. 1948. Biological studies on the horse flies of New York. *J. Econ. Entom.*, 41:335–336.

Loomis, R. B. 1956. *The Chigger Mites of Kansas (Acarina, Trombiculidae)*. Univ. Kansas Sci. Bull. 37 (part 2):1195–1443.

Love, G. J., and J. G. Whelchel. 1955. Photoperiodism and the development of *Aedes triseriatus* (Diptera, Culicidae). *Ecology*, 36:340–342.

Lumbreras, H., W. Flores, and A. Escallón. 1959. Allergische Reaktionen auf Stiche von Reduviiden und ihre Bedeutung bei der Chagaskrankheit. *Z. Tropenmed. Parasit.*, 10:6–19.

Lumsden, L. L. 1958. St. Louis encephalitis in 1933: Observations on epidemiological features. *Public Health Rep.*, 73:340–353.

Lumsden, W. H. R. 1958. A trap for insects biting small vertebrates. *Nature*, 181:819–820.

Lupaşcu, G., A. Bossie, M. Smolinski, E. Ballif, P. Constantinesco, T. Isfan, D. Petrea, V. Mazilu, and V. Roman. 1963. Le problème des infections à *P. malariae* et les programmes d'éradication du paludisme. *Arch. Roum. Path. Exptl. Microbiol.*, 22:333–348.

MacDonald, G. 1957. *The Epidemiology and Control of Malaria*. London, Oxford University Press, 201 pp.

Macdonald, W. W. 1967a. Host feeding preferences. *WHO Bull.*, 36:597–599.

Macdonald, W. W. 1967b. The influence of genetic and other factors on vector susceptibility to parasites, *in* Wright, J. W., and R. Pal. *Genetics of Insect Vectors of Disease*. New York, Elsevier, pp. 567–586.

Mackerras, I. M. 1954–55. The classification and distribution of Tabanidae. *Australian J. Zool.*, 2:431–454; 3:439–511, 583–633.

Mackerras, I. M. 1956, 1960, 1961. The Tabanidae of Australia. *Australian J. Zool.*, 4:376–443; 8:1–152; 9:827–905.

Mackerras, J. 1965–1966. Australian Blattidae (Blattodea). Parts I–VI. *Australian J. Zool.*, 13:841–882, 883–902, 903–927; 14:305–334, 335–363, 593–618.

Mackie, F. P. 1907. The part played by *Pediculus corporis* in the transmission of relapsing fever. *Brit. Med. J.*, 2:1706–1709.

Magoon, E. H. 1935. A portable stable trap for capturing mosquitoes. *Bull. Entom. Res.*, 26:363–369.

Mahfouz, M. S. 1963. Host preference of *A. pharoensis* females under laboratory conditions. *J. Egypt. Pub. Health Assoc.*, 38:193–198.

Manson, P. 1878. On the development of *Filaria sanguinis hominis*, and on the mosquito considered as a nurse. *J. Linn. Soc. Zool. London*, 14:304–311.

Manwell, R. D. 1955. Some evolutionary possibilities in the history of malaria parasites. *Indian J. Malar.*, 9:247–253.

Marchand, W. 1920. *The Early Stages of Tabanidae (Horseflies)*. Rockefeller Institute for Medical Research, in Monograph no. 13. 203 pp.

Marchette, N. J. 1966. Rickettsioses (tick typhus, Q fever, urban typhus) in Malaya. *J. Med. Entom.*, 2:339–371.

Marchoux, E., and A. Salimbeni. 1903. La spirillose des poules. *Ann. Inst. Pasteur*, 17:569–580.

Maretić, Z. 1965. *Latrodectus* und Latrodectismus. *Natur. Mus.*, 95:124–232.

Marshall, A. L. 1965. State reports (Indiana). *In 1964 Annual summary Communicable Disease Center Encephalitis Surveillance*, pp. 15–17.

Marston, N. 1965. Recent modifications in the design of Malaise insect traps with a summary of the insects represented in collections. *J. Kans. Entom. Soc.*, 38:154–162.

Martin, H. M., S. F. Barnett, and B. O. Vidler. 1964. Cyclic development and longevity of *Theileria parva* in the tick *Rhipicephalus appendiculatus*. *Exp. Parasit.*, 15:527–555.

Martini, E. 1932. *Zoönosen der Haut in wärmeren Ländern. In Handbuch der Haut- und Geschlechtskrankheiten*. Berlin, Springer, 133 pp.

Mason, J. and P. Cavalie. 1965. Malaria epidemic in Haiti following a hurricane. *Amer. J. Trop. Med.*, 14:533–539.

Mattingly, P. F. 1957. Genetical aspects of the *Aedes aegypti* problem. I. Taxonomy and bionomics. *Ann. Trop. Med. Parasit.*, 51:392–408.

Mattingly, P. F. 1958. Genetical aspects of the *Aedes aegypti* problem II. Disease relationships, genetics and control. *Ann. Trop. Med. Parasit.*, 52:5–17.

Mattingly, P. F. 1962. Population increases in *Culex pipiens fatigans* Wiedemann. A review of present knowledge. *Bull. WHO*, 27:579–584.

Mattingly, P. F. 1964. The *Anopheles gambiae* complex. Some introductory notes. *Riv. Malar.*, **43**:165–166.

Mattingly, P. F. 1965. The evolution of parasite-arthropod vector systems. *Evolution of Parasites*; Third Symposium of the British Society for Parasitology, pp. 29–45.

Mattingly, P. F., L. E. Rozeboom, K. L. Knight, H. Laven, F. H. Drummond, S. R. Christophers, and P. G. Shute. 1951. The *Culex pipiens* complex. *Trans. Roy. Entom. Soc. London*, **102**:331–382.

May, J. M. (ed.) 1961. *Studies in Disease Ecology.* New York, Hafner, 688 pp.

Mayer, M. S., and C. W. Thaggard. 1966. Investigations of an olfactory attractant specific for males of the house fly, *Musca domestica* L. (Diptera: Muscidae). *J. Insect Physiol.*, **12**:891–897.

Mazzotti, L., and M. A. Bravo-Becherelle. 1963. Scorpionism in the Mexican Republic, *in* Keegan, H., and W. V. Macfarlane. *Venomous and Poisonous Animals and Noxious Plants of the Pacific Region.* New York, Macmillan, pp. 119–131.

McCoy, G. W. 1910. Bubonic plague in ground squirrels. *N.Y. Med. J.*, **92**:652–665.

McCrae, A. W. R., and S. A. Visser. 1963. Recent "Nairobi eye" beetle (*Paederus sabaeus* Er.) outbreaks in Uganda, and studies on the vesicating toxin. *Biochem. J.*, **89**:79.

McCrone, J. D., and R. J. Hatala. 1967. Isolation and characterization of a lethal component from the venom of *Latrodectus mactans mactans*, *in* Russell, F. E., and P. R. Saunders. *Animal Toxins.* New York, Pergamon, pp. 29–34.

McGovern, J. P., G. B. Barkin, T. R. McElhenney, and R. Wende. 1961. *Megalopyge opercularis.* Observations of its life history, natural history of its sting in man, and report of an epidemic. *J.A.M.A.*, **175**:1155–1158.

McGovern, T. P., M. Beroza, and H. Gouck. 1967. Chemicals tested as space repellents for yellow-fever mosquitoes. II. Carbanilates, benzamides, aliphatic amides, and imides. *J. Econ. Entomol.*, **60**:1591–1594.

McIntosh, B. M., R. M. Harwin, H. E. Paterson, and M. L. Westwater. 1963. An epidemic of chikungunya in south-eastern Southern Rhodesia. *Cent. Afr. J. Med.*, **9**:351–359.

McIntosh, M. E., and D. D. Watt. 1967. Biochemical-immunochemical aspects of the venom from the scorpion *Centruroides sculpturatus*. *In* F. E. Russell and P. R. Saunders, *Animal Toxins.* New York, Pergamon, pp. 47–58.

McKiel, J. A. 1959. Sensitization to mosquito bites. *Canad. J. Zool.*, **37**:341–351.

McKiel, J. A., E. J. Bell, and D. B. Lackman. 1967. *Rickettsia canada*: A new member of the typhus group of rickettsiae isolated from *Haemaphysalis leporispalustris* ticks in Canada. *Canad. J. Microbiol.*, **13**:503–510.

McKittrick, F. A. 1964. *Evolutionary Study of Cockroaches.* Cornell Univ. Agr. Exp. Sta. Mem. 389, 197 pp.

McLintock, J., and K. R. Depner. 1954. A review of the life history and habits of the horn fly, *Siphona irritans* (L.) (Diptera, Muscidae). *Canad. Entom.*, **86**:20–33.

McMahon, J. P., R. B. Highton, and H. Goiny. 1958. The eradication of *Simulium neavei* from Kenya. *Bull. WHO*, **19**:75–107.

Mead-Briggs, A. R. 1964. Observations on the rabbit

flea—a vector of myxomatosis. *Ann. Appl. Biol.*, **51**:338–342.

Meador, C. N. 1915. Five cases of relapsing fever originating in Colorado, with positive blood findings in two. *Colorado Med.*, **12**:365–368.

Meifert, D. W., G. C. LaBrecque, C. N. Smith, and P. B. Morgan. 1967. Control of house flies on some West Indies islands with metepa, apholate, and trichlorfon baits. *J. Econ. Entom.*, **60**:480–485.

Mellanby, K. 1933. The influence of temperature and humidity on the pupation of *Xenopsylla cheopis*. *Bull. Entom. Res.*, **24**:197–202.

Melnick, J. L., and R. M. McCombs. 1966. Classification and nomenclature of animal viruses, 1966. *Progr. Med. Virol.*, **8**:400–409.

Melnikoff, H. 1869. Ueber die Jugendzustände der *Taenia cucmerina*. *Arch. Naturgesch.*, **25**:62–69.

Mercurialis (Hieronymus). 1577. De pestes in universum, praesertim vero de Veneta et Patavina. Item de morbis cutaneis, et omnibus humani corporis excrementis. (Not available to the authors.)

Merinov, V. A. 1962. The significance of the immature stages of *Dermacentor nuttalli* in the epizootology of north-Asian rickettsiosis (in Russian). *Med. Parazit.* Moskva, **31**:393–398.

Metcalf, C. L., W. P. Flint, and R. L. Metcalf. 1962. *Destructive and Useful Insects.* New York, McGraw-Hill, 1,087 pp.

Meyer, K. F. 1955. The modern outlook on plague in California. *Calif. Vector Views*, **2**:41–43.

Meyer, K. F., C. M. Haring, and B. Howitt. 1931. Newer knowledge of the neutotropic virus infection of the horse. *J. Amer. Vet. Med. Assn.* n.s., **32**:376–389.

Michaeli, D., E. Benjamini, J. D. Young, and B. F. Feingold. 1965. Biochemical studies on hypersensitivity to flea bites. *Proc. XXI Inter. Cong. Ento.* p. 832.

Michener, M. H., and C. D. Michener. 1947. Chiggers! *Natural History*, **56**:231–235.

Mickel, C. E. 1928. *Biological and Taxonomic Investigations on the Mutillid Wasps.* Bull. U.S. Nat. Museum, No. 143. 352 pp.

Miles, J. A. R. 1960. Epidemiology of the arthropod-borne encephalitides. *Bull. WHO*, **22**:339–371.

Miles, V. I., A. R. Kinney, and H. E. Stark. 1957. Flea host relationships of associated *Rattus* and native wild rodents in the San Francisco Bay Area of California, with special reference to plague. *Amer. J. Trop. Med.*, **6**:752–760.

Miller, C. D. F. 1961. Taxonomy and distribution of nearctic *Vespula*. *Canad. Entom. Suppl.*, 22, 52 pp.

Miller, D. G. 1956. Massive anaphylaxis from insect stings. *In* Buckley and Porges *op. cit.*, pp. 44, 121.

Miller, N. C. E. 1956. *The Biology of the Heteroptera.* London, Leonard Hill (books) Ltd., 162 pp.

Milne, A. 1948. The ecology of the sheep tick *Ixodes ricinus* L. *Parasitology*, **39**:167–197 (2 papers).

Milner, K. C., W. L. Jellison, and B. Smith. 1957. The role of lice in transmission of *Salmonella. J. Infect. Dis.*, **101**:181–192.

Mitzmain, M. B. 1913a. The bionomics of *Stomoxys calcitrans* (Linnaeus); a preliminary account. *Philip. J. Sci.*, **8** (ser. B):29–48.

Mitzmain, M. B. 1913b. The mechanical transmission of surra by *Tabanus striatus* Fabr. *Philip. J. Sci.*, **8** (ser. B):223–229.

Mitzmain, M. B. 1914. Summary of experiments in the transmission of anthrax by biting flies. *U.S. Public Health Bull.*, **94**, pp. 41–48.

Mitzmain, M. B. 1916. An attempt to determine the number of persons one mosquito can effect with malaria. *Public Health Rep.*, **31**:2325–2335.

Mohler, J. R. 1930. *Tick Fever.* U.S. Dept. Agr. Farmer's Bull. No. 1625.

Montfils, A. J. 1776. D'une maladie fréquente connue en Bourgogne sous le nom de Puce maligne. *J. Méd.*, **45**:500. (Cited by Nuttall.)

Moore, W. 1918. An interesting reaction to louse bites. *J.A.M.A.*, **71**:1481–1482.

Mooser, H. 1932. Essai sur l'histoire naturelle du typhus exanthématique. *Arch. Inst. Pasteur Tunis*, **21**:1–19.

Morel, P. C., and G. Vassiliades. 1962. Les *Rhipicephalus* du groupe *sanguineus:* Espèces africaines (Acariens: Ixodoidea). *Rev. Élev.*, **15**:343–386.

Moreno, A. 1940. *Scorpiologia Cubana.* Rev. Univ. Habana, nos. 23, 26, 27. 75 pp.

Morikawa, T. 1958. Studies on myiasis. I. A revision of human myiasis reported in Japan. *Ochanomizu Egaku Zasshi*, **6**:1451–1466 (in Japanese, with English Summary).

Morris, K. R. S. 1961. Effectiveness of traps in tsetse surveys in the Liberian rain forest. *Amer. J. Trop. Med.*, **10**:905–913.

Morris, R. F. 1960. Sampling insect populations. *Ann. Rev. Entom.*, **5**:243–264.

Morse, R. A., D. A. Shearer, R. Boch, and A. W. Benton. 1967. Observations on alarm substances in the genus *Apis. J. Apicultural Res.*, **6**:113–118.

Mortensen, E. W., and J. D. Walsh. 1963. Review of the *Triatoma protracta* problem in the Sierra Nevada foothills of California. *Proc. Calif. Mosquito Control Ass.*, **31**:44–45.

Mueller, H. L. 1959. Further experiences with severe allergic reactions to insect stings. *New Eng. J. Med.*, **261**:374–377.

Muesebeck, C. F. W. 1961. A new Japanese *Trichopria* parasitic on the house fly (Hymenoptera: Diapriidae). *Mushi, Fukuoka*, **35**:1–2.

Muesebeck, C. F. W., and L. M. Walkley. 1951. Bethyloidea, *in* Musebeck, Krombein, and Towns, *Hymenoptera of America North of Mexico—Synoptic Catalog.* U.S. Dept. Agric. Mon. No. 2.

Mulla, M. S. 1958. Recent developments in the biology and control of *Hippelates* eye gnats. *Proc. Papers Calif. Mosquito Control Ass.*, **26**:78–82.

Mulla, M. S. 1959. Some important aspects of *Hippelates* gnats, with a brief presentation of current research findings. *Proc. Papers Calif. Mosquito Control Ass.*, **27**:48–52.

Mulla, M. S. 1965. Biology and control of *Hippelates* eye gnats. *Proc. 33rd. Annual Conf. Calif. Mosquito Control Ass.*, pp. 26–28.

Mulla, M. S., R. W. Dorner, G. P. Georghiou, and M. J. Garber. 1960. Olfactometer and procedure for testing baits and chemical attractants against *Hippelates* eye gnats. *Ann. Entom. Soc. Amer.*, **53**:529–537.

Mulla, M. S., G. P. Georghiou, and R. W. Dorner. 1960. Effect of aging and concentration on the attractancy of proteinaceous materials to *Hippelates* gnats. *Ann. Entom. Soc. Amer.*, **53**: 835–841.

Mulla, M. S., and R. B. March. 1959. Flight range, dispersal patterns and population density of the eye gnat *Hippelates collusor* (Townsend). *Ann. Entom. Soc. Amer.*, **52**:641–646.

Müller-Kögler, E. 1965. *Pilzkrankheiten bei Insekten. Anwendung zur biologischen Schädlingsbekämpfung und Grundlagen der Insektenmykologie.* Berlin, Paul Parey, 444 pp.

Muma, M. H. 1951. The arachnid order Solpugida in the United States. *Bull. Amer. Mus. Nat. Hist.*, **97**:35–141.

Municipal Refuse Disposal. 1966. Chicago, Pub. Admin, Serv., 528 pp.

Murnaghan, M. F. 1958. Tick paralysis in the dog: A neurophysiological study. *Proc. 10th Internat. Cong. Entom.*, **3**:841–847.

Murray, K. F. 1957. An ecological appraisal of host-ectoparasite relationship in a zone of epizootic plague in central California. *Amer. J. Trop., Med.* **6**:1068–1086.

Murray, M. D. 1961. The life cycle of *Psorergates ovis* Womersley, the itch mite of sheep. *Austral. J. Agr. Res.*, **12**:965–973.

Mussgay, M. 1964. Growth cycle of arboviruses in vertebrate and arthropod cells. *Progr. Med. Virol.*, **6**:193–267.

Myers, R. M., and D. E. Carey. 1967. Concurrent isolation from a patient of two arboviruses, chikungunya and dengue type 2. *Science*, **157**:1307–1308.

Nakagawa, P. Y. 1963. Status of *Toxorhynchites* in Hawaii. *Proc. Hawaiian Entom. Soc.*, **18**:291–293.

Namba, N. 1963. Researches on the distribution of the ticks and their habitat in pasture in Hokkaido (in Japanese). *Res. Bull. Hokkaido Nat. Agric. Exp. Sta.*, **80**: 103–114.

Nash, T. A. M. 1939. The ecology of the puparium of *Glossina* in northern Nigeria. *Bull. Entom. Res.*, **30**:259–284.

Neal, T. J., and H. C. Barnett. 1961. The life cycle of the scrub typhus chigger mite, *Trombicula akamushi. Ann. Entom. Soc. Amer.*, **54**:196–203.

Neal, T. J., and L. J. Lipovsky. 1959. Techniques for rearing the chigger mite. *Trombicula akamushi* (Brumpt). *J. Econ. Entom.*, **52**:824–826.

Negi, P. S. 1933. The small red ant *Solenopsis geminata* sub. sp. *rufa*, Jerdon, and its usefulness to man. *J. Bombay Nat. Hist. Soc.*, **36**:1018–1021.

Neitz, W. O. 1956a. Classification, transmission and biology of piroplasma of domestic animals. *Ann. N.Y. Acad. Sci.*, **64**:56–111.

Neitz, W. O. 1956b. A consolidation of our knowledge of the transmission of tick-borne diseases. *Onderstpoort J. Vet. Res.*, **27**:115–163.

Neiva, A., and H. Lent. 1941. Sinopse dos triatomideos. *Rev. Entom.*, **12**:61–92.

Nelson, G. S., R. B. Heisch, and M. Furlong. 1962. Studies in filariasis in East Africa II. Filarial infections in man, animals and mosquitoes on the Kenya coast. *Trans. Roy. Soc. Trop. Med. Hyg.*, **56**:202–217.

Nelson, R. L. 1964. Parity in winter populations of *Culex tarsalis* Coquillett in Kern County, California. *Amer. J. Hyg.*, **80**:242–253.

Nelson, W. A. 1962. Development in sheep of resistance to the ked *Melophagus ovinus* (L.). *Exp. Parasit.*, **12**:41–51.

Newhouse, V. F., W. Burgdorfer, J. A. McKeil, and J. D. Gregson. 1963. California encephalitis virus. Serologic survey of small wild mammals in northern United States and southern Canada, and isolation of additional strains. *Amer. J. Hyg.*, **78**:123–129.

Newson, H. D., and T. E. Blakeslee. 1957. Observations of a laboratory colony of the mosquito *Culex tritaeniorhynchus* Giles. *Mosquito News*, **17**:308–311.

Nicoll, William. 1911. On the part played by flies in the dispersal of the eggs of parasitic worms, *in* Reports to the Local Government Board on Public Health and Medical Subjects, London n.s. no. 53, further reports (No. 4) on flies as carriers of infection.

Nicolle, C., C. Comte, and E. Conseil. 1909. Transmission experimentals du typhus exanthimatique par le pou du corps. *Compt. Rend. Acad. Sci.*, **149**:486–489.

Nielsen, E. T., and J. S. Haeger. 1960. Swarming and mating in mosquitoes. *Misc. Publ. Entom. Soc. Amer.*, **1**:71–95.

Noguchi, H., R. C. Shannon, E. B. Tilden, and J. R. Tyler. 1929. Etiology of Oroyo fever: The insect vectors of Carrion's disease. *J. Exp. Med.*, **49**:993–1008.

Norman, M. J. T. 1957. Weight responses to tick control and phosphate supplementation in beef cattle at Katherine, N.T. *J. Austral. Inst. Agr. Sci.*, **23**:344–345.

Norris, K. R. 1966. Notes on the ecology of the bush-fly, *Musca vetustissima* Walk. (Diptera: Muscidae) in the Canberra district, *Australian J. Zool.*, **14**:1139–1156.

Norris, K. R., and M. D. Murray. 1964. *Notes on the Screw-worm fly, Chrysomya bezziana (Diptera: Calliphoridae) as a Pest of Cattle in New Guinea.* Commonwealth Sci. Industrial Res. Organization Tech. Paper 6. 26 pp.

Nott, J. C. 1848. On the origin of yellow fever. *New Orleans Med. Sci. J.*, **4**:563–601.

Nuorteva, P. 1959. Studies on the significance of flies in the transmission of poliomyelitis. I. *Ann. Entom. Fennici*, **25**:1–14.

Nuttall, G. H. F. 1899. On the role of insects, arachnids, and myriapods as carriers in the spread of bacterial and parasitic disease of man and animals. A critical and historical study. *John Hopkins Hospital Reports*, **8**:1–154.

Nuttall, G. H. F. 1917. The biology of *Pediculus humanus*. *Parasitology*, **10**:80–185.

Nuttall, G. H. F. 1918. The biology of *Pthirus pubis*. *Parasitology*, **10**:383–405.

Nuttall, G. H. F., and C. Warburton. 1908. *Ticks, a Monograph of the Ixodoidea. Part I, Argasidae.* 104 + 35 pp. Part II, *Ixodidae*. xix + 105 + 348 pp. London, Cambridge University Press.

O'Brien, R. D., and L. S. Wolfe. 1964. *Radiation, Radioactivity and Insects.* New York, Academic Press, 211 pp.

O'Connor, R., W. Rosenbrook, Jr., and R. Erickson, 1963. Hymenoptera: Pure venom from bees, wasps and hornets. *Science*, **139**:420.

Ogata, M. 1897. Ueber die Pestepidemie in Formosa. *Centrabl. Bakteriol.*, **21**:769–777.

O'Gower, A. K. 1960. Townsville culicines as possible vectors of dengue and allied viruses among local feral fauna. *Austral. J. Exp. Biol. Med. Sci.*, **38**:1–9.

Oldroyd, H. 1954–1957. *The Horse Flies (Diptera) of the Ethiopian Region, I–III.* London, British Mus. (Nat. Hist.).

Oldroyd, H. 1964. *The Natural History of Flies.* New York, W. W. Norton & Co. Inc., xiv + 324 pp.

Olive, A. T. 1960. Infestation of the imported fire ant, *Solenopsis saevissima* v. *richteri*, at Fort Benning, Georgia. *J. Econ. Entom.*, **53**:646–648.

O'Roke, E. C. 1934. *A Malaria-like Disease of Ducks caused by Leucocytozoon anatis Wickware.* Univ. Michigan School of Forestry, Bull. 4, 44 pp.

O'Rourke, F. J. 1956. The medical and veterinary importance of the Formicidae. *Insectes Sociaux*, **3**:107–118.

Oudemans, A. C. 1937. *Kritisch historisch overzicht der akarologie. Tydschrift voor Entomologie intzegeven door de Nederlandsche Vereeniging*, Jan. 1926. (850 v.c. tot 1758), Vol. G. (1805–1850), Leiden, E. J. Brill, 3,379 pp.

Pampana, E. 1963. *A Textbook of Malaria Eradication.* New York, Oxford, 508 pp.

Pantheir, R., C. Lucasse, and C. Hannoun. 1962. Petite épidémie de fièvre jaune en Afrique centrale, en 1958 (district de Gemena, province de l'Equateur, Congo— Léopoldville). *Ann. Soc. Belge. Med. Trop.*, **42**:65–84.

Papasarathorn, T., S. Areekul, S. Chermsirivatana, and S. Pinichpongse. 1961. A study of the rove beetle (*Paederus fuscipes* Curt.) causing vesicular dermatitis in Thailand (in Thai). *J. Med. Assn. Thailand*, **44**:60–81.

Paramonov, S. J. 1962. A review of the Australian Leptidae. *Australian J. Zool.*, **10**:113–169.

Parker, R. R. 1924. Tularaemia. XI. Tularaemia infection in ticks of the species *Dermacentor andersoni* Stiles in the Bitter Root Valley, Montana. *Public Health Rep.*, **39**:1057–1073.

Parker, R. R. 1928. Rocky Mountain spotted fever. *Montana State Board of Entom. Biennial Rep.*, **7**:39–62.

Parker, R. R. 1933. Certain phases of the problem of Rocky Mountain spotted fever. *Arch. Path.*, **15**:398–429.

Parker, R. R. 1937. Recent studies of tick-borne diseases made at the U.S. Public Health Service laboratory at Hamilton, Montana. *Proc. Fifth Pacific Sci. Cong.*, pp. 3,367–3,374.

Parker, R. R., and G. M. Kohls. 1943. American Q fever. The occurrence of *Rickettsia diaporica* in *Amblyomma americanum* in eastern Texas. *Public Health Rep.*, **54**:1510–1511.

Parker, R. R., G. M. Kohls, and E. A. Steinhaus. 1943. Rocky Mountain spotted fever, spontaneous infection in the tick, *Amblyomma americanum*. *Public Health Rep.*, **58**:721–729.

Parker, R. R., C. B. Philip, G. E. Davis, and R. A. Cooley. 1937. Ticks of the United States in relation to disease in man. *J. Econ. Entom.*, **30**:51–69.

Parker, R. R., and R. R. Spencer. 1926. Hereditary transmission of tularaemia infection by the wood tick, *Dermacentor andersoni* Stiles. *Public Health Rep.*, **41**:1403–1407.

Parman, D. C. 1923. Biological notes on the hen flea, *Echidnophaga gallinacea*. *J. Agr. Res.*, **23**:1007–1009.

Parrish, H. M. 1963. Analysis of 460 fatalities from venomous animals in the United States. *Amer. J. Med. Sci.*, **245**:129–141.

Patterson, R. S., C. S. Lofgren, and M. D. Boston. 1967. Resistance in *Aedes aegypti* to chemosterilants: Effect of apholate selection on resistance to apholate, tepa, and metepa. *J. Econ. Entom.*, **60**:1673–1678.

Pausch, R. D., and G. Fraenkel. 1966. The nutrition of the larva of the oriental rat flea *Xenopsylla cheopis* (Rothschild). *Physiol. Zool.*, **39**:202–222.

Pavan, M. 1959. Biochemical aspects of insect poisons. *4th Intern. Congr. Biochem.*, **12**:15–36.

Pavan, M., and G. Bo. 1953. Pederin, toxic principle obtained in the crystalline state from the beetle *Paederus fuscipes* Curt. *Physiol. Comp. Oecol.*, **3**:307–312.

Pavilanis, V., and M. Rozewicz. 1958. Culture de *Coxiella burneti* chez le pou. Isolement de *Coxiella burneti* des produits pathologiques par l'inoculation aux poux. *Rev. Canad. Biol.*, **17**:503–511.

Pavlov, P. 1963. Recherches sur la "tick paralysis" observée chez des poulets en Bulgarie et provoquée par des nymphes d'*Haemaphysalis punctata* Can. et Fanz. *Ann. Parasit. Hum. Comp.*, **38**:459–461.

Pavlovskii, E. N., and A. N. Skrynnik. 1959. Laboratory observations on the tick *Ornithodorus hermsi* Wheeler, 1935 (in Russian). *Dokl. Akad. Nauk SSSR*, **128**:863–864.

Pawlowsky, E. N. 1924. Studies on the organization and development of scorpions. *Quart. J. Micr. Sci.*, **68**:615–640.

Pechuman, L. L., and W. W. Wirth. 1961. A new record of Ceratopogonidae (Diptera) feeding on frogs. *J. Parasit.*, **47**:600.

Perlman, F. 1967. Arthropod sensitivity, *in* Criep, L. H. (Editor), *Dermatologic Allergy: Immunology, Diagnosis, Management*. Philadelphia, Saunders, 605 pp.

Perry, A. S., and R. W. Fay. 1967. Correlation of chemical constitution and physical properties of fatty acid esters with oviposition response of *Aedes aegypti*. *Mosquito News*, **27**:175–183.

Peterson, B. V. 1960. Notes on some natural enemies of Utah black flies (Diptera: Simuliidae). *Canad. Entom.*, **92**:266–274.

Peterson, B. V., and D. M. Davies. 1960. Observations on some insect predators of black flies (Diptera: Simuliidae) of Algonquin Park, Ontario. *Canad. J. Zool.*, **38**:9–18.

Petrishcheva, P. A. 1961. The duration of existence of natural foci of tick-borne spirochaetosis (in Russian). *Med. Parasit.*, **30**:439–442.

Phelps, R. J., and G. R. De Foliart. 1964. *Nematode Parasitism of Simuliidae*. Univ. Wisc. Res. Bull. 245. 78 pp.

Philip, C. B. 1931. *The Tabanidae (Horseflies) of Minnesota, With Special Reference to Their Biologies and Taxonomy*. Univ. Minn. Tech. Bull. 80. 132 pp.

Philip, C. B. 1948. Tsutsugamushi disease (scrub typhus) in World War II. *J. Parasit.*, **34**:169–191.

Philip, C. B. 1961. Arthropod vectors in relation to the reservoir mechanism of microbial agents of animal diseases. *Acta Trop.*, **18**:257–262.

Philip, C. B. 1962. Transmission of yellow fever virus by aged *Aedes aegypti* and comments on some other mosquito-virus relationships. *Amer. J. Trop. Med.*, **11**:697–701.

Philip, C. B. 1963. Ticks as purveyors of animal ailments: a review of pertinent data and of recent contributions. *Adv. Acarology*, **1**:285–325.

Philip, C. B., J. F. Bell, and C. L. Larson. 1955. Evidence of infectious diseases and parasites in a peak population of black-tailed jack rabbits in Nevada. *J. Wildlife Management*, **19**:225–233.

Philip, C. B., and W. Burgdorfer. 1961. Arthropod vectors as reservoirs of microbial disease agents. *Ann. Rev. Entom.*, **6**:391–412.

Philip, C. B., and L. E. Hughes. 1948. The tropical rat mite, *Liponyssus bacoti* as an experimental vector of rickettsial pox. *Amer. J. Trop. Med.*, **28**:697–705.

Philip, C. B., L. E. Hughes, and D. I. Darrow. 1958. Experimental transmission of yellow fever virus by oriental mosquitoes. *Proc. X Int. Cong. Entom.*, **3**:587–592.

Philip, C. B., and G. M. Kohls. 1948. Mites and scrub typhus. *Proc. 4th Internat. Cong. Trop. Med. Malaria* (Abstracts), Washington, D.C.

Philip, C. B., and G. M. Kohls. 1952. Elk, winter ticks and Rocky Mountain spotted fever; a query. *Public Health Rep.*, **66**:1672–1675.

Philip, C. B., and C. R. Owen. 1961. Comments on the nomenclature of the causative agent of tularemia. *Internat. Bull. Bact. Nomenclature*, **11**:67.

Philip, R. N., B. Huntly, D. B. Lackman, and G. W. Comstock. 1962. Serologic and skin test evidence of tularemia infection among Alaskan Eskimos, Indians and Aleuts. *J. Infect. Dis.*, **110**:220–230.

Phillips, N. R. 1960. Experimental studies on the quantitative transmission of *Trypanosoma cruzi*: Aspects of the rearing, maintenance and testing of vector material, and of the origin and course of infection in the vector. *Ann. Trop. Med. Parasit.*, **54**:397–414.

Pimentel, D., and R. Al-Hafidh. 1965. Ecological control of a parasite population by genetic evolution in the parasite-host system. *Ann. Entom. Soc. Amer.*, **58**:1–6.

Pipkin, A. C. 1949. Experimental studies on the role of filth flies in the transmission of *Endamoeba histolytica*. *Amer. J. Hyg.*, **49**:255–275.

Plath, O. E. 1919. A muscid larva of the San Francisco Bay region which sucks the blood of nestling birds. *Univ. Calif. Pub. Zool.*, **19**:191–200.

Plyater-Plokhotskaya, V. N. 1962. Age changes in the ovaries of females of the German cockroach (in Russian). *Med. Parazit.*, **31**:79–82.

Pollitzer, R. 1954. *Plague*. Geneva, World Health Org., Monograph series No. 22. 698 pp.

Pollitzer, R. 1966. *Plague and Plague Control in the Soviet Union*. Bronx, N.Y., Fordham University, Institute of Contemporary Russian Studies, 478 pp.

Pomerantz, C. 1959. Arthropods and psychic disturbances. *Bull. Entom. Soc. Amer.*, **5**:65–67.

Portschinsky, I. A. 1916. *Wohlfahrtia magnifica Schin. Sa Biologie et son Rapport à l'Homme et aux Animaux Domestiques*. Bur. Entomol. Sci. Com. Min. Agr. Mem. 11(9), 108 pp. (In Russian).

Potts, S. F. 1958. *Concentrated Spray Equipment, Mixtures and Application Methods*. Caldwell, N.J., Dorland, 598 pp.

Pozo, E. C. del. 1956. Mechanisms of pharmacological action of scorpion venom, *in* Buckley and Porges, *op. cit.*, pp. 123–129.

Pratt, H. D. 1963. *Mites of Public Health Importance and their Control*. U.S. Pub. Hlth. Serv. Pub. No. 772.

Pratt, H. D., H. O. Lobeland, and R. L. Kaiser. 1967. Malaria and *Anopheles* are still important. *Mosquito News*, **27**:295–296.

Price, R. D. 1956. The multiplication of *Pasteurella tularensis* in human body lice. *Amer. J. Hyg.*, **63**:186–197.

Price, W. H. 1953. Interference phenomenon in animal infections with rickettsiae of Rocky Mountain spotted fever. *Proc. Soc. Exp. Biol. and Med.*, **82**:180–184.

Price, W. H. 1953. The epidemiology of Rocky Mountain spotted fever. I. The characterization of strain virulence of *Rickettsia rickettsii*. *Amer. J. Hyg.*, **58**:248–268.

Pringle, G. 1965. A count of the sporozoites in an oocyst of *Plasmodium falciparum*. *Trans. Roy. Soc. Trop. Med. Hyg.*, **59**:289–290.

Provost, M. W. 1959. The influence of moonlight on light-trap catches of mosquitoes. *Ann. Entom. Soc. Amer.*, **52**:261–271.

Quarterman, K. D. 1960. Test methods for establishing levels of susceptibility and detecting the development of resistance in insects of public health importance, *in Research Progress on Insect Resistance*. Misc. Pub. Entom. Soc. Amer. 2, No. 1, pp. 95–102.

Quate, L. W. 1955. A revision of the Psychodidae (Diptera) in America north of Mexico. *Univ. Calif. Pub. Entom.*, **10**:103–273.

Radford, C. D. 1943. Genera and species of parasitic mites (Acarina). *Parasitology*, **35**:58–81.

Radovsky, F. J. 1967. The Macronyssidae and Laelapidae (Acarina: Mesostigmata) parasitic on bats. *Univ. Calif. Publ. Entom.*, **46**, 288 pp.

Raffaele, G., and A. Coluzzi. 1949. Malaria relationships in the province of Frosinore during the years 1945–1948. The malaria epidemic of Cassino (in Italian). *Riv. Malar.*, **28**:3–48.

Raghavan, N. G. S. 1957. Epidemiology of filariasis in India. *Bull. WHO*, **16**:553–579.

Rahman, M. H. 1957. Observations on the mode of infection of the hump of cattle by *Stephanofilaria assamensis* in East Pakistan. *J. Parasit.*, **43**:434–435.

Rai, K. S. 1966. *Feasibility Study on the Application of the Sterile Male Technique for Control of the Filariasis Vector.* Report to the government of Ceylon. Internat. Atomic Energy Agency, T.A. Report No. 283, 24 pp.

Raimbert, A. 1869. Recherches experimentales sur la transmission du charbon par les mouches. *Compt. Rend. Acad. Sci.* **69**:805–812. (Cited by Nuttall.)

Randel, H. W., and C̆. B. Doan. 1956. Caterpillar urticaria in the Panama Canal Zone: Report of five cases. *In* Buckley and Porges, *op. cit.*, pp. 111–116.

Rau, P. 1924. Biology of the roach. *Trans. Acad. Sci. St. Louis*, **25**:57–79.

Razumova, I. V. 1962. Determination of the physiological age and composition of a natural population of *Dermacentor pictus* Herm. (in Russian). *Med. Parazit.*, **31**:55–61.

Readio, P. A. 1926. Studies on the eggs of some Reduviidae (Heteroptera). *Univ. Kansas Sci. Bull.*, **16**:157–179.

Readio, P. A. 1927. Studies on the biology of the Reduviidae of America North of Mexico. *Univ. Kansas Sci. Bull.*, **17**:1–289.

Reed, A. C. 1937. Ultimate prognosis of hookworm disease, malaria, and amebiasis. *Proc. 27th Annual Meet. Med. Sci. Amer. Life Convention*, pp. 176–206.

Reeves, W. C. 1953. Quantitative studies on a carbon dioxide chemotropism of mosquitoes. *Amer. J. Trop. Med.*, **2**:325–331.

Reeves, W. C. 1965. Ecology of mosquitoes in relation to arboviruses. *Ann. Rev. Entom.*, **10**:25–46.

Reeves, W. C., R. E. Bellamy, A. F. Geib, and R. P. Scrivani. 1964. Analysis of the circumstances leading to abortion of a western equine encephalitis epidemic. *Amer. J. Hyg.*, **80**:205–220.

Reeves, W. C., R. E. Bellamy, and R. P. Scrivani. 1961. Differentiation of encephalitis virus infection rates from transmission rates in mosquito vector populations. *Amer. J. Hyg.*, **73**:303–315.

Reeves, W. C., B. Brookman, and W. M. Hammon. 1948. Studies in the flight range of certain *Culex* mosquitoes, using a fluorescent-dye marker, with note on *Culiseta* and *Anopheles*. *Mosquito News*, **8**:61–69.

Reeves, W. C., W. M. Hammon, W. H. Doetschman, H. E. McClure, and G. Sather. 1955. Studies on mites as vectors of western equine and St. Louis encephalitis viruses in California. *Amer. J. Trop. Med.*, **4**:90–105.

Reeves, W. C., W. M., Hammon, D. P. Furman, H. E. McClure, and B. Brookman. 1947. Recovery of western equine encephalomyelitis virus from wild bird mites (*Lyponyssus sylviarum*) in Kern County, California. *Science*, **105**:411–412.

Reeves, W. C., W. M. Hammon, W. A. Longshore, Jr., H. E. McClure, and A. F. Geib. 1962. *Epidemiology of the Arthropod-Borne Viral Encephalitides in Kern County California 1943–52.* Univ. Calif. Publ. Public Hlth. 4, 257 pp.

Řeháček, J. 1962. Transovarial transmission of tick-borne encephalitis virus by ticks. *Acta Virol.*, **6**:220–226.

Řeháček, J. 1964. Relation between viruses and tick tissues *in vitro*. *Proc. XIIth Internat. Cong. Entom.*, pp. 774–775.

Rehn, J. A. G. 1945. Man's uninvited fellow traveler—the cockroach. *Sci. Monthly*, **61**:265–276.

Rehn, J. W. H. 1950. A key to the genera of North American Blattaria, including established adventives. *Entom. News*, **61**:64–67.

Reid, W. M., J. E. Ackert, and A. A. Case. 1938. Studies on the life history and biology of the fowl tapeworm, *Raillietina cesticillus* (Molin). *Trans. Amer. Micr. Soc.*, **57**:65–76.

Reiss-Gutfreund, R. J. 1956. Un nouveau réservoir de virus pour *Rickettsia prowazeki:* Les animaux domestiques et leur tiques. *Bull. Soc. Path. Exot.*, **49**:946–1051.

Remington, C. L. 1950. The bite and habits of a giant centipede (*Scolopendra subspinipes*) in the Philippine Islands. *Amer. J. Trop. Med.*, **30**:453–455.

Rich, G. B. 1957. The ear tick, *Otobius megnini* (Dugès) (Acarina: Argasidae), and its record in British Columbia. *Canad. J. Comp. Med.*, **21**:415–418.

Richardson, U. F., and S. B. Kendall. 1957. *Veterinary Protozoology*, 2nd ed. Edinburgh and London, Oliver and Boyd. 260 pp.

Ricketts, H. T. 1906. The transmission of Rocky Mountain spotted fever by the bite of the wood tick (*Dermacentor occidentalis*). *J.A.M.A.*, **57**:358.

Ricketts, H. T. 1911. *Contribution to Medical Science.* Chicago, University of Chicago Press. 497 pp. (See pp. 278–450.)

Ricketts, H. T., and R. M. Wilder. 1910a. The transmission of the typhus fever of Mexico (tabardillo) by means of the louse (*Pediculus vestimenti*). *J.A.M.A.*, **54**:1304–1307.

Ricketts, H. T., and R. M. Wilder. 1910b. Further investigation regarding the etiology of tabardillo, Mexican typhus fever. *J.A.M.A.*, **55**:309–311.

Riek, R. F. 1957. Studies on the reactions of animals to infestation with ticks. II. Toxins. *Austral. J. Agr. Res.*, **8**:215–223.

Riek, R. F. 1959. Studies on the reactions of animals to infestation with ticks. IV. The protein components of tick extracts. *Austral. J. Agr. Res.*, **10**:604–613.

Riek, R. F. 1962. Studies on the reactions of animals to infestation with ticks. VI. Resistance of cattle to infestation with the tick *Boophilus microplus* (Canenstrini). *Aust. J. Agr. Res.*, **13**:532–550.

Riek, R. F. 1966. The development of *Babesia* and *Theileria* spp. in ticks with special reference to those occurring in cattle, *in* Soulsby, E. J. L. *Biology of Parasites*, New York, Academic Press, pp. 15–32.

Riley, W. A. 1939. The possibility of intestinal myiasis in man. *J. Econ. Entom.*, **32**:875–876.

Ristic, M. 1966. The vertebrate developmental cycle of *Babesia* and *Theileria*, *in* Soulsby, E. J. L. *op. cit.*, pp. 127–141. New York, Academic Press.

Ristic, M., J. Oppermann, S. Sibinovic, and T. N. Phillips. 1964. Equine piroplasmosis—a mixed strain of *Piroplasma caballi* and *Piroplasma equi* isolated in Florida and studied by the fluorescent-antibody technique. *Amer. J. Vet. Res.*, **104**:15–23.

Robbins, W. E., M. J. Thompson, R. T. Yamamoto, and T. J. Shortino. 1965. Feeding stimulants for the female house fly, *Musca domestica* Linnaeus. *Science*, **147**:628–630.

Roberts, I. H., G. J. Hanosh, and S. A. Apodaca. 1964. Observations on the incidence of chorioptic acariasis of sheep in the United States. *Amer. J. Vet. Res.*, **25**:478–482.

Roberts, F. H. S. 1961. Tick paralysis in South Australia. *Austral. Vet. J.*, **37**:440.

Robertson, M. 1913. Notes on the life history of *Trypanosoma gambiense*, with a brief reference to the cycles of *Trypanosoma nanum* and *Trypanosoma pecorum* in *Glossina palpalis*. *Phil. Trans. Roy. Soc. London* (Ser. B.), **203**:161–184.

Robson, J., G. H. Yeoman, and J. P. J. Ross. 1961. *Rhipicephalus appendiculatus* and East Coast fever in Tanganyika. *E. African Med. J.*, **38**:206–214.

Roby, T. O., D. W. Anthony, C. W. Thornton, Jr., and A. A. Holbrook. 1964. The hereditary transmission of *Babesia caballi* in the tropical horse tick, *Dermacentor nitens* Neumann. *Amer. J. Vet. Res.*, **25**:494–499.

Rocha-Lima, H. da. 1916. Untersuchungen über Fleckfieber. *München. Med. Wschr.*, **63**:1381–1384.

Rodaniche, E. de, P. Galindo, and C. M. Johnson. 1959. Further studies on the experimental transmission of yellow fever by *Sabethes chloropterus*. *Amer. J. Trop. Med.*, **8**:190–194.

Rodeck, H. G. 1932. Arthropod designs on prehistoric Mimbres pottery. *Ann. Entom. Soc. Amer.*, **25**:688–693.

Rodhain, J. 1948. Susceptibility of the chimpanzee to *P. malariae* of human origin. *Amer. J. Trop. Med.*, **28**:629–631.

Rodriguez, J. L., Jr., and L. A. Riehl. 1959. Results with cockerels for house fly control in poultry droppings. *J. Econ. Entom.*, **52**:542–543.

Rodriguez, J. L., Jr., and L. A. Riehl. 1960. Control of northern fowl mite in community wire cages with malathion in special dust-bath boxes. *J. Econ. Entom.*, **53**:701–704.

Rogers, A. J. 1962. Effects of impounding and filling on the production of sand flies (*Culicoides*) in Florida salt marshes. *J. Econ. Entom.*, **55**:521–527.

Rogoff, W. M., A. D. Beltz, J. O. Johnsen, and F. W. Plapp, Jr. 1964. A sex pheromone in the housefly, *Musca domestica* L. *J. Insect Physiol.*, **10**:239–246.

Rogoff, W. M., and A. L. Moxon. 1952. Cable type back rubbers for horn fly control on cattle. *J. Econ. Entom.*, **45**:329–334.

Rohdendorf, B. B. (Editor). 1962. *Foundations of Paleontology. Arthropods, Tracheates and Chelicerates.* (In Russian) Publications of the Academy of Science, Moscow, 560 pp.

Rollo, I. M. 1965. Drugs used in the Chemotherapy of malaria, *in* Goodman, L. S., and A. Gilman (Editors), *The Pharmacological Basis of Therapeutics*. New York, Macmillan, pp. 1,087–1,117.

Romaña, C. 1947. Miocarditis cronica equizo tropanosica. *An. Inst. Med. Regional*, Univ. Nacional de Tucumán, Argentina, **2**:1–39.

Root, F. M. 1921. Experiments on the carriage of intestinal protozoa of man by flies. *Amer. J. Hyg.*, **1**:131–153.

Rose, I. 1954. A review of tick paralysis. *J. Canad. Med. Ass.*, **70**:175–176.

Rosen, L. 1958a. Dengue antibodies in residents of the Society Islands, French Oceania. *Amer. J. Trop. Med.*, **7**:403–405.

Rosen, L. 1958b. Observations on the epidemiology of dengue in Panama. *Amer. J. Hyg.*, **68**:45–48.

Ross, E. S., and H. R. Roberts. 1943. *Mosquito Atlas: Part I. The Nearctic Anopheles Important Malaria Vectors of the Americas, and Aedes aegypti, Culex quinquefasciatus.* 44 pp. *Part II. Eighteen Old World Anophelines Important to Malaria.* Philadelphia, Amer. Entom. Soc., 44 pp.

Ross, H. H. 1940. The Rocky Mountain "black fly", *Symphoromyia atripes*, *Ann. Entom. Soc. Amer.*, **33**:254–257.

Ross, H. H. 1964. The colonization of temperate North America by mosquitoes and man. *Mosquito News*, **24**:103–118.

Ross, R. 1897. On some peculiar pigmented cells found in two mosquitoes fed on malaria blood. *Brit. Med. J.*, **2**:1786–1788.

Ross, R. 1910. *The Prevention of Malaria*. New York, E. P. Dutton & Co., 669 pp.

Roth, L. M. 1948. A study of mosquito behavior. An experimental laboratory study of the sexual behavior of *Aedes aegypti* (Linnaeus). *Amer. Midland Naturalist*, **40**:265–352.

Roth, L. M. 1967. Water changes in cockroach oöthecae in relation to the evolution of ovoviviparity and viviparity. *Ann. Entom. Soc. Amer.*, **60**:928–946.

Roth, L. M. 1968. Oöthecae of the Blattaria. *Ann. Entom. Soc. Amer.*, **61**:83–111.

Roth, L. M., and T. Eisner. 1962. Chemical defenses of arthropods. *Ann. Rev. Entom.*, **7**:107–136.

Roth, L. M., and E. R. Willis. 1954. *The Reproduction of Cockroaches*. Smithsonian Misc. Coll., Vol. 122. No. 12. 49 pp.

Roth, L. M., and E. R. Willis. 1957. *The Medical and Veterinary Importance of Cockroaches*. Smithsonian Misc. Coll., Vol. 134, No. 10. 147 pp.

Roth, L. M., and E. R. Willis. 1958. An analysis of oviparity and viviparity in the Blattaria. *Trans. Amer. Entom. Soc.*, **83**:221–238.

Rothschild, M. 1965. Fleas. *Sci. Amer.*, **213**:44–53.

Rothschild, M., and B. Ford. 1964. Maturation and egglaying of the rabbit flea (*Spilopsyllus cuniculi* Dale) induced by the external application of hydrocortisone. *Nature*, **203**:210–211.

Rothschild, M., and B. Ford. 1965. Observations on gravid rabbit fleas (*Spilopsyllus cuniculi* (Dale)) parasitising the hare (*Lepus europaeus* Pallas), together with further speculations concerning the course of myxomatosis at Ashton, Northants. *Proc. Roy. Entom. Soc. London*, (A) **40**:109–117.

Roubaud, E. 1918. Le rôle des mouches dans la dispersion des amibes dysentriques et autre protozoaires intestinaux. *Bull. Soc. Path. Exot.*, **11**:166–171.

Roy, D. N. 1928. Report on investigation into aetiology and prevention of Naga sore in Assam. *Indian Med. Gaz.*, **63**:673–687.

Rozeboom, L. E. 1936. The life cycle of laboratory-bred *Anopheles albimanus* Wiedemann. *Ann. Entom. Soc. Amer.*, **29**:480–489.

Rozeboom, L. E., and R. W. Burgess. 1962. Dry-season survival of some plant-cavity breeding mosquitoes in Liberia. *Ann. Ent. Soc. Amer.*, **55**:521–524.

Rubtsov, I. A. 1964. Simuliidae (Melusinidae), *in* Lindner, *Die Fliegen der Palaearktischen Region*, Band III, 4:1–689.

Rudnick, A., and W. M. Hammon. 1960. Newly recognized *Aedes aegypti* problems in Manila and Bangkok. *Mosquito News*, **20**:247–249.

Rush, W. A., J. M. Brennan, and C. M. Eklund. 1958. A natural hibernation site of the mosquito *Culex tarsalis* Coquillett in the Columbia River Basin, Washington. *Mosquito News*, **18**:288–293.

Rush, W. A., R. C. Kennedy, and C. M. Eklund. 1963. Evidence against winter carryover of western equine encephalomyelitis virus by *Culex tarsalis*. *Mosquito News*, **23**:285–286.

Russell, P. F. 1932. The control of *Anopheles minimus* mosquito larvae in the Philippines by stranding and flushing. *Philippine J. Sci.*, **47**:439–445.

Russell, P. F. 1958. Malaria in the world today. *Amer. J. Public Health*, **47**:414–420.

Russell, P. F. 1959. Insects and the epidemiology of malaria. *Ann. Rev. Entom.*, **4**:415–434.

Russell, P. F., L. E. Rozeboom, and A. Stone. 1943. *Keys to the Anopheline Mosquitoes of the World With Notes on Their Identification, Distribution, Biology*, and *Relation to Malaria*. Philadelphia, *Amer. Entom. Soc.*, 152 pp.

Russell, P. F., L. S. West, R. D. Manwell, and G. MacDonald. 1963. *Practical Malariology*. New York, Oxford, 750 pp.

Ryckman, R. E. 1951. Recent observations of cannibalism in *Triatoma* (Hemiptera : Reduviidae). *J. Parasit.*, **37**:433–434.

Ryckman, R. E. 1967. Why kissing bug research at Loma Linda University? *Loma Linda Univ. Mag.*, **53**:28–30.

Ryckman, R. E., D. L. Folkes, L. E. Olsen, P. L. Robb, and A. E. Ryckman. 1965. Epizootology of *Trypanosoma cruzi* in southwestern North America. Parts I–VII. *J. Med. Entom.*, **2**:87–108.

Sabrosky, C. W. 1941. The *Hippelates* flies or eye gnats : Preliminary notes. *Canad. Entom.*, **73**:23–27.

Sabrosky, C. W. 1949. The North American heleomyzid genus *Lutomyia*, with descriptions of a new species. *Occas. Papers Mich. Univ. Mus. Zool.*, **517**:1–6.

Sabrosky, C. W. 1951. Nomenclature of the eye gnats (*Hippelates* spp.). *Amer. J. Trop. Med.*, **31**:257–258.

Sabrosky, C. W. 1959. Recognition of species of Musca. *Coop. Econ. Insect Rept.*, **9**:988.

Salt, R. W. 1961. Principles of insect cold hardiness. *Ann. Rev. Entom.*, **6**:55–74.

Samarawickrema, W. A. 1962. Follicular relics in wild-caught *Culex pipiens fatigans* Wiedemann in Ceylon. *Bull. WHO*, **27**:637–640.

Sambon, L. W. 1910. Progress report of investigations of pellagra, *J. Trop. Med.*, **13**:271–287, 305–319.

Sambon, L. W., and G. Low. 1900. The malaria experiments in the Campagna. *Brit. Med. J.*, **2**:1679–1682.

Sampayo, R. L. 1942. *Latrodectus mactans y Latrodectismo*. Inst. Fisiol. Faculdad Ciencias Medicas, Buenos Aires.

Sanders, D. A. 1937. Observations on canine babesiasis (piroplasmosis). *J. Amer. Vet. Med. Ass.*, **90**, n.s. 43, 27–40.

Sanders, D. A. 1940a. A *Musca domestica* and *Hippelates* flies, vectors of bovine mastitis. *Science*, **92**:286.

Sanders, D. A. 1940b. *Musca domestica* a vector of bovine mastitis (preliminary report). *J.A.M.A.*, **97**:120–122.

Sasa, M. 1961. Biology of chiggers. *Ann. Rev. Entom.*, **6**:221–244.

Sasa, M. 1964. Sensory physiology of parasitic mites with special reference to stimulants and attractants of chiggers. *Acarologia*, **6**:233–234.

Sasa, M., T. Kurihara, O. Dhamvanij, and C. Harinasuta. 1964. *Observations on a Mosquito-Eating Fish (Lebistes reticulatus) Breeding in Polluted Waters in Bankok*. WHO, Vector Control, 99.64, 22 pp.

Satchell, G. H., and R. A. Harrison. 1953. Experimental observations on the possibility of transmission of yaws by wound-feeding diptera, in western Samoa. *Trans. Roy. Soc. Trop. Med. Hyg.*, **47**: 148–153.

Sather, G. E., and W. M. Hammon. 1967. Antigenic patterns within the California-encephalitis-virus group. *Amer. J. Trop. Med.*, **16**:548–557.

Saunders, D. S. 1961. Laboratory studies on the biology of *Syntomosphyrum albiclavus* Kerrich (Hym., Eulophidae), a parasite of tsetse flies. *Bull. Entom. Res.*, **52**:413–429.

Saunders, D. S. 1964. Age-changes in the ovaries of the sheep ked, *Melophagus ovinus* (L.) (Diptera : Hippoboscidae). *Proc. Roy. Entom. Soc. London*, (A.) **39**(4–6):68–72.

Savory, T. H. 1935. *The Arachnida*. London, Edward Arnold & Co. 218 pp.

Sawyer, W. A., and W. B. Herms. 1913. Attempts to transmit poliomyelitis by means of the stable fly (*Stomoxys calcitrans*). *J.A.M.A.*, **41**:461–466.

Schenone, H. 1953. Mordeduras de arañas. *Bol. Chileno Parasit.*, **8**:35–37.

Schenone, H. 1959. Estudio de 27 casos de loxoscelismo. *Bol. Chileno Parasit.*, **14**:7–13.

Scherer, W. F., and others. 1959. Ecologic studies of Japanese encephalitis virus in Japan. I–VIII. *Amer. J. Trop. Med.*, **8**:644–718.

Schmidt, J. R., and M. I. Said. 1964. Isolation of West Nile virus from the African bird argasid, *Argas reflexus hermanni*, in Egypt. *J. Med. Entom.*, **1**:83–86.

Schomberg, O., and D. E. Howell. 1955. Biological notes on *Tabanus abactor* Phil. and *aequalis* Hine. *J. Econ. Entom.*, **48**:618–619.

Schoof, H. F., and R. E. Siverly. 1954. Multiple release studies on the dispersion of *Musca domestica* at Phoenix, Ariz. *J. Econ. Entom.*, **47**:830–888.

Schumacher, H. H., and R. Hoeppli. 1963. Histochemical reactions to Trombiculid mites, with special reference to the structure and function of the "stylostome." *Z. Tropenmed. Parasit.*, **14**:192–208.

Schwardt, H. A. 1936. *Horseflies of Arkansas*. Univ. Arkansas Agric. Exper. Sta. Bull. 332. 66 pp.

Scott, H. G. 1964. Human myiasis in North America (1952–1962 inclusive). *Fla. Entom.*, **47**:255–261.

Scott, H. G., and K. S. Littig. 1962. *Flies of Public Health Importance and Their Control*. Public Health Service Publ. No. 779. pp. 1–40.

Scott, H. G., J. S. Wiseman, and C. J. Stojanovich. 1962. Collembola infesting man. *Ann. Entom. Soc. Amer.*, **55**:428–430.

Scovel, R. E. 1958. The Dano method of refuse disposal. *Calif. Vector Views*, **5**:5–9.

Scudder, H. I. 1947. A new technique for sampling the density of housefly populations. *Public Health Rep.*, **62**:681–686.

Seal, S. C. 1960. Epidemiological studies of plague in India. 2. The changing pattern of rodents and fleas in Calcutta and other cities. *Bull. WHO*, **23**:293–300.

Seal, S. C., and L. M. Bhattacharji. 1961. Epidemiological studies on plague in Calcutta. Part I. Bionomics of two species of rat fleas and distribution, densities and resistance of rodents in relation to the epidemiology of plague in Calcutta. *Indian J. Med. Res.*, **49**:974–1007.

Seamans, L., and L. C. Woodruff. 1939. Some factors influencing the number of molts of the German roach. *J. Kansas Entom. Soc.*, **12**:73–76.

Sellers, R. F., G. H. Bergold, O. M. Suárez, and A. Morales. 1965. Investigations during Venezuelan equine encephalitis outbreaks in Venezuela 1962–1964. *Amer. J. Trop. Med.*, **14**:460–469.

Sérié, C., L. Andral, A. Lindrec, and P. Neri. 1964. Epidémie de fievre jaune en Éthiopie (1960–1962): Observations préliminaires. *Bull. WHO*, **30**:299–319.

Service, M. W. 1966. The replacement of *Culex nebulosus* Theo. by *Culex pipiens fatigans* Wied. (Diptera, Culicidae) in towns in Nigeria. *Bull. Entom. Res.*, **56**:407–415.

Shah, K. V., H. N. Johnson, T. R. Rao, P. K. Rajogopalan, and B. S. Lamba. 1960. Isolation of five strains of Sindbis Virus in India. *Indian J. Med. Res.*, **48**:300–308.

Sharif, M. 1935. On the presence of wing buds in the pupa of Aphaniptera. *Parasitology*, **27**:461–464.

Shemanchuk, J. A., and J. Weintraub. 1961. Observations on the biting and swarming of snipe flies (Diptera: *Symphoromyia*) in the foothills of southern Alberta. *Mosquito News*, **21**:238–243.

Shepard, C. C., and R. A. Goldwasser. 1960. Fluorescent antibody staining as a means of detecting Rocky Mountain spotted fever infection in individual ticks. *Amer. J. Hyg.*, **72**:120–129.

Shewell, G. E. 1955. Identity of the black fly that attacks ducklings and goslings in Canada (Diptera: Simuliidae). *Canad. Entom.*, **87**:345–349.

Shipitsina, N. K. 1959. Effect of the shortening of daylight on the onset of diapause in *Anopheles maculipennis* Mg. (in Russian). *Med. Parazit.*, **28**:4–17.

Shortt, H. E., N. H. Fairley, G. Govell, P. G. Shute, and P. C. C. Garnham. 1951. The pre-erythrocytic stages of *Plasmodium falciparum*. *Trans. Roy. Soc. Trop. Med. Hyg.*, **44**:405–419.

Shortt, H. E., and P. C. C. Garnham. 1948. The pre-erythrocytic development of *Plasmodium cynomolgi* and *Plasmodium vivax*. *Trans. Roy. Soc. Trop. Med. Hyg.*, **41**:785–795.

Shtakelberg, A. A. 1956. *Synanthropic Flies of the Fauna of the U.S.S.R.* (in Russian). Moscow, Academy of Sciences of the U.S.S.R., 164 pp.

Shulman, S. 1967. Allergic responses to insects. *Ann. Rev. Entom.*, **12**:323–346.

Shulov, A. 1939. The venom of the scorpion *Buthus quinquestriatus* and the preparation of an antiserum. *Trans. Roy. Soc. Trop. Med. Hyg.*, **33**:253–256.

Shute, P. G., and M. Maryon. 1951a. Studies in the transmission of *Plasmodium malariae* by *Anopheles* mosquitoes. *Parasitology*, **41**:292–300.

Shute, P. G., and M. Maryon. 1951b. A study of gametocytes in a West African strain of *Plasmodium falciparum*. *Trans. Roy. Soc. Trop. Med. Hyg.*, **45**:421–438.

Shute, P. G., M. E. Maryon, and G. Pringle. 1965. A method for estimating the number of sporozoites in the salivary glands of a mosquito. *Trans. Roy. Soc. Trop. Med. Hyg.*, **59**:285–288.

Sikorowski, P. P., and C. H. Madison. 1967. *Diseases of the Clear Lake Gnat (Chaoborus astictopus).* *Mosquito News*, **28**:180–187.

Simmonds, H. W. 1958. The housefly problem in Fiji and Samoa. *Quart. Bull. S. Pacif. Comm.*, **8**:29–30, 47.

Simmons, P. 1927. *The Cheese Skipper as a pest in Cured Meats.* U.S. Dept. Agric. Bull. 1453. 5 pp.

Simmons, J. S., J. H. St. John, and F. H. K. Reynolds. 1931. Experimental studies of dengue. *Manila Bur. of Science Mon.*, **29**:19–77, 112–146, 189–247.

Simmons, S. W. (Editor). 1959. *The Insecticide Dichlorodiphenyltrichloroethane and its Significance.* II. *Human and Veterinary medicine.* Lehrb. Monogr. Geb. exakt. Wiss., chem. Reihe 10. Basle and Stuttgart, Birkhaüser Verlag, 570 pp.

Simond, P. L. 1898. La propagation de la peste. *Ann. Inst. Pasteur*, **12**:625.

Siniscal, Arthur A. 1955. The trachoma story. *Public Health Rep.*, **70**:497–507.

Sippell, W. L., and A. W. A. Brown. 1953. Studies on the responses of the female *Aedes* mosquito: V. The role of visual factors. *Bull. Entom. Res.*, **43**:567–574.

Skidmore, L. V. 1932. *Leucocytozoon smithi* infection in turkeys and its transmission by *Simulium occidentale* Townsend. *Zbl. Bakt.*, **125**:329–335.

Skuf'in, K. V. 1949. Contribution to the ecology of tabanids in the Province of Voronezh. *Zool. Zhur.*, **28**:145–156. In Russian. (Abstract). *Rev. Appl. Entom.*, B **41**:18.

Smart, J. 1934. On the biology of the black fly, *Simulium ornatum* Mg. (Diptera, Simuliidae). *Proc. Roy. Physical Soc.*, **22**:217–238.

Smart, J. 1945. The classification of the Simuliidae (Diptera). *Trans. Roy. Entom. Soc. London*, **95**:217–238.

Smart, J. 1965. *A Handbook for the Identification of Insects of Medical Importance.* London, British Museum (Natural History), 303 pp.

Smit, F. G. A. M. 1954. Identification of fleas, *in* Pollitzer, R., *Plague.* WHO Monogr. Ser. No. 22, pp. 648–682.

Smit, F. G. A. M. 1958. A preliminary note on the occurrence of *Pulex irritans* L. and *Pulex simulans* Baker in North America. *J. Parasit.*, **44**:523–536.

Smith, A. 1961. Resting habits of *Anopheles gambiae* and *Anopheles pharoensis* in salt bush and in crevices in the ground. *Nature*, **190**:1220–1221.

Smith, A. C. 1956. Fly prevention in dairy operations. *Calif. Vector Views*, **3**:57, 59–60.

Smith, C. E. G., M. G. R. Varma, and D. McMahon. 1964. Isolation of louping ill virus from small mammals in Ayrshire, Scotland. *Nature*, **203**:992–993.

Smith, C. N. (Editor). 1966. *Insect Colonization and Mass Production.* New York, Academic Press, 618 pp.

Smith, C. N., and others. 1963. *Factors Affecting the Protection Period of Mosquito Repellents.* Tech. Bull. U.S.D.A. No. 1285, 36 pp.

Smith, C. N., M. M. Cole, and H. K. Gouck. 1946. *Biology and Control of the American Dog Tick.* U.S. Dept. Agr. Tech. Bull. 905. 74 pp.

Smith, H. J. 1961. *Demodicidiosis in Large Domestic Animals. A Review.* Health Anim. Dir., Canad. Agr., Ottawa. 56 pp.

Smith, L. M., and H. Lowe. 1948. The black gnats of California. *Hilgardia* (Calif. Agric. Exper. Sta.), **18**:157–183.

Smith, M. R. 1951. Formicidae, *in* Musebeck, Krombein and Townes, *Hymenoptera of America North of Mexico—Synoptic catalog,* U.S. Dept. Agr. monograph No. 2, p. 812.

Smith, T., and F. L. Kilbourne. 1893. *Investigations into the Nature, Causation, and Prevention of Texas or Southern Cattle Fever.* U.S. Dept. Agric. Bur. Animal. Indust. Bull. 1. 301 pp.

Smith, T. A., and D. D. Linsdale. 1967. First supplement to an annotated bibliography of the face fly, *Musca authumnalis* De Geer, in North America. *Calif. Vector Views*, **14**:74–76.

Smith, T. A., D. D. Linsdale, and D. J. Burdick. 1966. An annotated bibliography of the face fly, *Musca autumnalis* DeGeer, in North America. *Calif. Vector Views*, **13**:43–54.

Smith, W. W. 1957. Populations of the most abundant ectoparasites as related to prevalence of typhus antibodies of farm rats in an endemic murine typhus region. *Amer. J. Trop. Med.*, **6**:581–589.

Smith, W. W., and V. G. Perry. 1967. Intersexes in *Culicoides* spp. caused by mermithid parasitism in Florida. *J. Econ. Entom.*, **60**:1025–1027.

Smithburn, K. C., A. J. Haddow, and A. F. Mahaffy. 1946. A neurotropic virus isolated from *Aedes* mosquitoes caught in the Semliki forest. *Amer. J. Trop. Med.*, **26**:189–208.

Smithburn, K. C., A. F. Mahaffy, and J. H. Paul. 1941. Bwamba fever and its causative virus. *Amer. J. Trop. Med.*, **21**:75–90.

Snodgrass, R. E. 1935. *Principles of Insect Morphology.* New York, McGraw-Hill, 667 pp.

Snodgrass, R. E. 1944. *The Feeding Apparatus of Biting and Sucking Insects Affecting Man and Animals.* Smithsonian Misc. Coll., Vol. 102, No. 7 (Publ. no. 3773) Wash. D.C. Smithsonian Inst. 113 pp.

Snodgrass, R. E. 1946. *The Skeletal Anatomy of Fleas.* (*Siphonaptera*). Smithsonian Misc. Coll. Vol. 104, No. 18, Washington, D.C.: Smithsonian Inst. (Publ. No. 3815), 89 pp.

Snodgrass, R. E. 1948. The *Feeding Organs of Arachnida, Including Mites and Ticks.* Smithsonian Misc. Coll., Vol. 10. No. 10. Wash. D.C. Smithsonian Inst. (Publ. No. 3944). 93 pp.

Snodgrass, R. E. 1952. *A Textbook of Arthropod Anatomy.* Ithaca, New York, Comstock Publ. Co., 363 pp.

Snodgrass, R. E. 1953. *The Metamorphosis of a Fly's Head.* Smithsonian Misc. Coll. 122 (3), 25 pp.

Snodgrass, R. E. 1959. *The Anatomical Life of the Mosquito. Smithsonian Misc. Coll.* 139 (8), 87 pp.

Snow, W. E. 1958. Production and control of floodwater mosquitoes incidental to water level operations on reservoirs of the Tennessee Valley Authority. *Proc. 10th Internat. Congr. Entom. Montreal.* pp. 745–750.

Sommerman, K. M. 1962. Alaskan snipe fly immatures and their habitat (Rhagionidae: *Symphoromyia*). *Mosquito News*, **22**:116–123.

Sommerman, K. M., R. I. Sailer, and C. O. Esselbaugh. 1955. Biology of Alaskan black flies (Simuliidae, Diptera). *Ecol. Monographs*, **25**:345–385.

Sommerman, K. M., and R. P. Simmet. 1965. Car-top insect trap with terminal cage in auto. *Mosquito News*, **25**:172–182.

Sonenshine, D. E., and E. L. Atwood. 1967. Dynamics of feeding of the American dog tick *Dermacentor variabilis* (Acarina: Ixodidae). *Ann. Entom. Soc. Amer.*, **60**:362–373.

Sonenshine, D. E., E. L. Atwood, and J. T. Lamb, Jr. 1966. The ecology of ticks transmitting Rocky Mountain spotted fever in a study area in Virginia. *Ann. Entom. Soc. Amer.*, **59**:1234–1262.

Soper, F. L. 1936. Jungle fever: A new epidemiological entity in South America. *Rev. Hyg. Saude Pub.*, **10**:107–144.

Soper, F. L. 1955. Yellow fever conference. *Amer. J. Trop. Med.*, **4**:571–661.

Soper, F. L. 1958. More about malaria eradication. *Mosquito News*, **18**:53–58.

Soper, F. L. 1958. The 1957 status of yellow fever in the Americas. *Mosquito News*, **18**:203–216.

Soper, F. L., and D. B. Wilson. 1943. *Anopheles gambiae in Brazil 1930–1940.* New York, The Rockefeller Foundation, 262 pp.

Soroker, R. H. 1958. Pigeon fly problem in southern California. *Calif. Vector Views*, **5**:46.

Souza, G. S. 1587. *Tratado Descriptivo do Brazil em 1587, orba de Gabriel de Souza.* Rio de Janeiro: Typographia universal de Laemmert, 120 pp. (Cited by França, C., in *Trans. Roy. Soc. Trop. Med. Hyg.*, **15**:58–60).

Sparrow, H. 1958. Étude du foyer éthiopien de fièvre récurrente. *Bull. WHO*, **19**:673–710.

Spencer, F. J. 1961. Tick-borne disease in Virginia, 1949–58. An ecological note. *Amer. J. Trop. Med.*, **10**:220–222.

Spieksma, F. T. M., and M. I. A. Spieksma-Boezeman. 1967. The mite fauna of house dust with particular reference to the house-dust mite *Dermatophagoides pteronyssinus* (Trouessart, 1897) (Psoroptidae: Sarcoptiformes). *Acarologia*, **9**:226–241.

Splitter, E. J. 1950. *Theileria mutans* associated with bovine anaplasmosis in the United States. *J. Amer. Vet. Med. Ass.*, **117**:134.

Stage, H. H., C. M. Gjullin, and W. W. Yates. 1937. Flight range and longevity of floodwater mosquitoes in the lower Columbia River Valley. *J. Econ. Entom.*, **30**:940–945.

Stahnke, H. L. 1944. Scorpions of the United States. *Turtox News*, **22**:20–22.

Stahnke, H. L. 1956. *Scorpions.* Poisonous Animals Research Laboratory, Arizona State University, Tempe, Arizona, 35 pp. Revised edition.

Stahnke, H. L. 1967. Scorpiology. *Turtox News*, **45**:218–223.

Stahnke, H. L., and B. D. Johnson. 1967. *Aphonopelma* tarantula venom, *In* F. E. Russell and P. R. Saunders, *Animal Toxins.* New York, Pergamon, pp. 35–39.

Stahnke, H. L., and R. H. Larson. 1968. Obtaining venom from centipedes. *Turtox News*, **46**:172–173.

Stampa, S. 1959. Tick paralysis in the Karoo areas of South Africa. *Onderstepoort J. Vet. Res.*, **28**:169–227.

Stark, H. E., and V. I. Miles. 1962. Ecological studies of wild rodent plague in the San Francisco Bay area of California. VI. The relative abundance of certain flea species and their host relationships on coexisting wild and domestic rodents. *Amer. J. Trop. Med.,* **11**:525–534.

Stefferud, A. (Editor). 1956. *Animal Diseases.* Washington USDA Yearbook of Agric., U.S. Govt. Printing Office.

Steinhaus, E. A. 1946. *Insect Microbiology.* Ithaca, New York, Comstock Publ. Co., 763 pp.

Steinhaus, E. A. (Editor). 1963. *Insect Pathology. An Advanced Treatise.* New York, Academic Press, Vol. 2, 661 pp; Vol. 2, 689 pp.

Stephens, J. W. W., and H. B. Fantham. 1910. On the peculiar morphology of a trypanosome from a case of sleeping sickness and the possibility of its being a new species (*T. rhodesiense*). *Proc. Roy. Soc. London,* Ser. B, **83**: 28–33.

Steve, P. C., and J. H. Lilly. 1965. Investigations on transmissability of *Moraxella bovis* by the face fly. *J. Econ. Entom.,* **58**:444–446.

Steward, J. S. 1937. The occurrence of *Onchocerca gutturosa* Neumann in cattle in England, with an account of its life history and development in *Simulium ornatum* Meig. *Parasitology,* **28**:212–218.

Stewart, M. A. 1927. A means of control of the European hen flea *Ceratophyllus gallinae* Schrank. *J. Econ. Entom.,* **20**:132–134.

Stewart, M. A. 1929. A case of dermal myiasis caused by *Phormia regina* Meig. *J.A.M.A.,* **92**:798–799.

Stewart, M. A. 1937. Phasmid injury to the human eye. *Canad. Entom.,* **69**:84–86.

Stiles, C. W. 1905. *A Zoological Investigation into the Cause, Transmission, and Source of Rocky Mountain Spotted Fever.* Washington, Pub. Health and Marine Hosp. Service of the U.S. Hyg. Bull. No. 20. 121 pp.

Stiles, C. W., and L. L. Lumsden. 1911. *The Sanitary Privy.* U.S.D.A. Farmer's Bull. 463, 32 pp.

Stiles, G. W. 1939. *Anaplasmosis in Cattle.* U.S. Dept. Agr. Circ. No. 154 (revised) 10 pp.

Stirrat, J. H., J. McLintock, G. W. Schwindt, and K. R. Depner. 1955. Bacteria associated with wild and laboratory-reared horn flies, *Siphona irritans* (L.) (Diptera: Muscidae). *J. Parasit.,* **41**:398–406.

Stockdale, H. J., and E. S. Raun. 1960. Economic importance of the chicken body louse. *J. Econ. Entom.,* **53**:421–423.

Stoffolano, J. G., Jr., and W. R. Nickle. 1966. Nematode parasite (*Heterotylenchus* sp.) of face fly in New York State. *J. Econ. Entom.,* **59**:221–222.

Stohler, H. R. 1961. The peritrophic membrane of blood sucking Diptera in relation to their role as vectors of blood parasites. *Acta Trop.,* **18**:263–266.

Stokes, A., J. H. Bauer, and N. P. Hudson. 1928. The transmission of yellow fever to *Macacus rhesus:* Preliminary note. *J.A.M.A.,* **90**:253–254.

Stokes, G. M. 1967. A preliminary report on a potential new mosquito control weapon. *Proc. Papers 23rd Amer. Mosquito Contr. Assoc.,* p. 122.

Stone, A. 1930. The bionomics of some Tabanidae (Diptera). *Ann. Entom. Soc. Amer.,* **23**:261–304.

Stone, A. 1938. *The Horseflies of the Subfamily Tabaninae of the Nearctic Region.* U.S. Dept. Agric. Misc. Publ. 305. 171 pp.

Stone, A. 1961. A synoptic catalog of the mosquitoes of the world, supplement I. (Diptera-Culicidae). *Proc. Entom. Soc. Wash.,* **63**:29–52.

Stone, A. 1963. A synoptic catalog of the mosquitoes of the world. Supplement II. *Proc. Entom. Soc. Wash.,* **65**:117–140.

Stone, A. 1964. *Simuliidae, and Thaumaleidae. Insects of Connecticut. Part VI. The Diptera or True Flies of Connecticut.* State Geol. Nat. Hist. Survey Conn. Bull. 97. 126 pp.

Stone, A. 1967. A synoptic catalog of the mosquitoes of the world, supplement III. *Proc. Entom. Soc. Wash.,* **69**:197–224.

Stone, A., *et al.* 1965. *A Catalog of the Diptera of America North of Mexico.* U.S. Dept. Agr. Agr. Handbook 276. 1,696 pp.

Stone, A., K. L. Knight, and H. Starcke. 1959. *A synoptic catalog of the Mosquitoes of the World* (*Diptera, Culicidae*). Entomol. Soc. Amer. Thomas Say Foundation: Vol. 6. 358 pp.

Stone, B. F. 1963. Parthenogenesis in the cattle tick, *Boophilus microplus. Nature,* **200**:1233.

Strandtmann, R. W., and G. W. Wharton. 1958. *A Manual of Mesostigmatid Mites Parasitic on Vertebrates.* College Park, Maryland. Institute of Acarology, Contribution No. 4. 330 pp.

Strickland, R. K., and R. R. Gerrish. 1964. Distribution of the tropical horse tick in the United States, with notes on associated cases of equine piroplasmosis. *J. Amer. Vet. Med. Assoc.,* **144**:875–878.

Strode, G. K. (Editor). 1951. *Yellow Fever.* New York, McGraw-Hill, 710 pp.

Sudia, W. D., and R. W. Chamberlain. 1962. Battery-operated light trap, an improved model. *Mosquito News,* **22**:126–129.

Sulkin, S. E., R. A. Sims, and R. Allen. 1966. Isolation of St. Louis encehaplitis virus from bats (*Tadarida b. mexicana*) in Texas. *Science,* **152**:223–225.

Sulkin, S. E., C. L. Wisseman, Jr., E. M. Izumi, and C. Zarafonetis. 1955. Mites as possible vectors or reservoirs of equine encephalitis in Texas. *Amer. J. Trop. Med.,* **4**:119–135.

Surcouf, J. 1921. *Diptera, Family Tabanidae.* Genera Insectorum, P. Wytsman, Brussels, Fasc. 175.

Suter, P. R. 1964. Biologie von *Echidnophaga gallinacea* (Westw.) und Vergleich mit andern Verhaltenstypen bei Flöhen. *Acta Trop.,* **21**:193–238.

Sutton, E., and D. R. Arthur. 1962. Tick feeding in relation to disease transmission. *Symp. Zool. Soc. Lond.* No. 6, p. 223–252.

Swaminath, C. S., H. E. Shortt, and L. A. P. Anderson 1942. Transmission of Indian kala-azar to man by the bites of *Phlebotomus argentipes,* Ann. and Brun. *Indian J. Med.,* **30**:473–477.

Sweatman, G. K. 1957. Life history, non-specificity, and revision of the genus *Chorioptes,* a parasitic mite of herbivores. *Canad. J. Zool.,* **35**:641–689.

Sweatman, G. K. 1958. On the life history and validity of the species in *Psoroptes,* a genus of mange mites. *Canad. J. Zool.,* **36**:905–929.

Swellengrebel, N. H., and L. Otten. 1914. Experimentelle Beiträge zur Kenntnis der Uebertragung der Pest durch Flöhe und Laüse. *Centralbl. Bakteriol.,* **74**:592–603.

Tarshis, I. B. 1958. A preliminary study on feeding *Ornithodoros savignyi* (Audouin) on human blood through animal-derived membranes (Acarina: Argasidae). *Ann. Entom. Soc. Amer.,* **51**:294–299.

Tarshis, I. B. 1961. Laboratory and field studies with sorptive dusts for the control of arthropods affecting man and animal. *Exptl. Parasitol.,* **11**: 10–33.

Tarshis, I. B. 1964. A sorptive dust for control of the northern fowl mite. *Ornithonyssus sylviarum,* infesting dwellings. *J. Econ. Entom.,* **57**:110–111.

Tarshis, I. B., and W. D. Ommert. 1961. Control of the spinose ear tick, *Otobius megnini* (Duges), with an organic phosphate insecticide (naled) combined with a silica aerogel. *J. Amer. Vet. Med. Assoc.*, **138**:665–669.

Tashiro, H., and H. H. Schwardt. 1949. Biology of the major species of horse flies of central New York. *J. Econ. Entom.*, **42**:269–272.

Tay, J., and F. Biagi. 1961. Accidentes por animales venenosos. *Rev. Facultad Medicina U.N.A.M.*, **3**:811–819.

Taylor, F. H., and R. E. Murray. 1946. *Spiders, Ticks and Mites Including the Species Harmful to Man in Australia and New Guinea.* Serv. Publ. Dept. Hlth. Austral. No. 6, 275 pp.

Taylor, R. M., T. H. Work, H. S. Hurlbut, and F. Rizk. 1956. A study of the ecology of West Nile virus in Egypt. *Amer. J. Trop. Med.*, **5**:579–620.

Telford, A. D. 1963. A consideration of diapause of *Aedes nigromaculis* and other Aedine mosquitoes (Diptera: Culicidae). *Ann. Entom. Soc. Amer.*, **56**:409–518.

Tempelis, C. H., and M. F. Lofy. 1963. A modified precipitin method for identification of mosquito blood-meals. *Amer. J. Trop. Med.*, **12**:825–831.

Temple, J. U. 1912. Acute ascending paralysis or tick paralysis. *Med. Sentinel*, **20**:507–514.

Theiler, G. 1962. *The Ixodoidea Parasites of Vertebrates in Africa South of the Sahara (Ethiopian region).* Proj. S. 9958, Rept. to Director of Vet. Services, Onderstepoort, 260 pp.

Theiler, G. 1964. Ecogeographical aspects of tick distribution, *in* Davis, D. H. S. (Editor), *Ecological Studies in South Africa.* The Hague, W. Junk, pp. 284–300.

Theiler, G., and L. E. Salisbury. 1958. Zoological survey of the Union of South Africa. Tick survey X, XI. *Onderstepoort J. Vet. Res.*, **27**:599–610.

Theiler, M., and W. G. Downs. 1963. Oropouche: The story of a new virus. *Yale Sci. Mag.*, **37**(6): 10–12, 26.

Thevasagayam, E. S., and K. Tharumarajah. 1962. Fly-breeding in night soil trenches, and its reduction by the use of green vegetation. *Ann. Trop. Med. Parasit.*, **56**:127–129.

Thomas, L. A. 1963. Distribution of the virus of western equine encephalomyelitis in the mosquito vector, *Culex tarsalis. Amer. J. Hyg.*, **78**: 150–165.

Thomas, L. J., and A. R. Cahn. 1932. A new disease of moose. *J. Parasit.*, **18**:219–231.

Thomas, W. P. 1960. Notes on a preliminary investigation into the habits and life cycle of *Copris incertus* Say (Coprini: Coleoptera) in New Zealand. *N.Z.J. Sci.*, **3**:8–14.

Thorp, R. W., and W. D. Woodson. 1945. *Black Widow, America's Most Poisonous Spider.* Chapel Hill, Univ. North Carolina Press. 222 pp.

Thorpe, B. D., R. W. Sidwell, D. E. Johnson, K. L. Smart, and D. D. Parker. 1965. Tularemia in the wildlife and livestock of the Great Salt Lake Desert Region, 1951 through 1964. *Amer. J. Trop. Med.*, **14**:622–637.

Thorsteinson, A. J. 1958. The orientation of horse flies and deer flies (Tabanidae, Diptera): The attractance of heat to tabanids. *Entom. Exp. Appl.*, **1**:191–196.

Tictin, J. 1897. Zur Lehre von Rückfalltyphus. *Zbl. Bakt. Abt.*, **21**:179–186.

Tigertt, W. D., and others. 1962. Studies on the virus of Venezuelan equine encephalomyelitis in Trinidad, W.I. I, II, III. *Amer. J. Trop. Med.*, **11**:822–843.

Tinkham, E. R. 1953. Control of eye gnats by soil larvicides. *Proc. Papers Calif. Mosquito Control Assn.*, **21**:67–68.

Tinkham, E. R. 1956. Bite symptoms of the red-legged widow spider (*Latrodectus bishopi*), *in* Buckley and Porges, *op. cit.*, pp. 99–100.

Todd, F. M. 1909. *Eradicating Plague from San Francisco. Report of Citizens Health Committee.* San Francisco, C. A. Murdock Co., 313 pp.

Tokunga, M. 1962. Biting midges of the genus *Culicoides* from New Guinea. *Pacific Insects*, **4**:457–516.

Tokunga, M. 1963. Supplementary Study to New Guinea biting midges of the genus *Culicoides. National Taiwan Univ. Plant Protection Bull.*, **5**:119–143.

Townsend, C. H. T. 1913. The transmission of verruga by *Phlebotomus. J.A.M.A.*, **61**:1717–1718.

Traub, R. 1950. Siphonaptera from Central America and Mexico. *Fieldiana, Zool.*, **1**:1–127.

Traub, R., and M. A. C. Dowling. 1961. The duration of efficacy of the insecticide dieldrin against the chigger vectors of scrub typhus in Malaya. *J. Econ. Entom.*, **54**:654–659.

Traub, R., L. P. Frick, and F. H. Dierks. 1950. Observations on the occurrence of Rickettsia tsutsugamushi in rats and mice in the Malayan jungle. *Amer. J. Hyg.*, **51**:45–76.

Traver, J. R. 1951. Unusual scalp dermatitis in humans caused by the mite, *Dermatophagoides. Proc. Entom. Soc. Washington*, **53**:1–25.

Travis, B. V. 1958. The role of the entomologist in medical and veterinary entomology. *Proc. Tenth Internat. Congr. Entom.*, **3**:697–701.

Trpiš, M. 1960. Stechmücken der Reisfelder und Möglichkeiten ihrer Bekämpfung (ökologische Studie). *Biol. Práce*, **6**(3), 137 pp.

Turner, E. C., Jr. 1965. Area control of the face fly using self-applicating devices. *J. Econ. Entom.*, **58**:103–105.

Twomey, N. R. 1966. A review of the biology and control of the German cockroach, *Blatella germanica* (L.) in California. *Calif. Vector Views*, **13**:27–37.

Uilenberg, G. 1963. Existence de *Ornithodorus porcinus* Walton, 1962 (Argasidae) à Madagascar. *Rev. Elev.*, **16**:147–150.

Usinger, R. L. 1934. Bloodsucking among phytophagous Hemiptera. *Canad. Entom.*, **66**:97–100.

Usinger, R. L. 1944. *The Triatominae of North and Central America and the West Indies and Their Public Health Significance.* U.S. Public Health Bull. No. 288, 83 pp.

Usinger, R. L. 1966. *Monograph of Cimicidae (Hemiptera—Heteroptera).* Thomas Say Foundation (Ent. Soc. Amer.), Vol. 7, 585 pp.

Vachon, M. 1953. The biology of scorpions. *Endeavour* **12**:80–89.

Van Emden, F. I. 1954. *Handbooks for the Identification of British Insects. Diptera Cyclorrhapha. Calyptrata* (1). Section (a). *Tachinidae and Calliphoridae.* Royal Entomological Society, London, 133 pp.

Varma, M. G. R. 1962. Transmission of relapsing fever spirochaetes by ticks. *Symp. Zool. Soc. London*, **6**:61–82.

Varma, M. G. R. 1964. The acarology of louping ill. *Acarologia*, **6**:241–254.

Veeder, M. A. 1898. Flies as spreaders of sickness in camps. *Med. Rec.*, **54**:429–430.

Vercammen-Grandjean, P. H. 1963. Valuable taxonomic characters of Trombiculidae, including correlations between larvae and nymphs, *in* Naegele, J. A. (Editor), *Advances in Acarology*, 1:399–407.

Verjbitski, D. T. 1908. The part played by insects in the epidemiology of plague. *J. Hyg.*, 8:162–208.

Vitzthum, H. G. 1943. *Acarina*. 7 Lieferung. Dr. H. G. Bronn's Klassen und Ordnungen des Thierreichs, 5:913–1011. Akademische Verlagsgesellschaft. Becker und Erler Kom. Ges.

Vockeroth, J. R. 1954. Notes on the identities and distribution of *Aedes* species of northern Canada, with a key to the females (Diptera: Culicidae). *Canad. Entom.* 86:241–255.

Wade, C. F., and J. G. Rodriguez. 1961. Life history of *Macrocheles muscaedomesticae* (Acarina: Macrochelidae), a predator of the house fly. *Ann. Entom. Soc. Amer.*, 54:776–781.

Wagner-Jevseenko, O. 1958. Fortpflanzung bei *Ornithodorus moubata* und genitale Uebertragung von *Borrelia duttoni*. *Acta Trop.*, 15:118–168.

Waldbauer, G. P. 1962. The mouth parts of female *Psorophora ciliata* (Diptera, Culicidae) with a new interpretation of the functions of the labial muscles. *J. Morph.*, 111:201–215.

Waldron, W. G. 1962. The role of the entomologist in delusory parasitosis (entomophobia). *Bull. Entom. Soc. Am.*, 8:81–83.

Walker, E. M. 1922. Some cases of cutaneous myiasis with notes on the larvae of *Wohlfahrtia vigil* (Walker). *J. Parasit.*, 9:1–5.

Wallace, J. B., and E. C. Turner, Jr. 1964. Low-level feeding of ronnel in a mineral salt mixture for area control of the face fly, *Musca autumnalis*. *J. Econ. Entom.*, 57:264–267.

Wallwork, J. A., and J. G. Rodriguez. 1961. Ecological studies on oribatid mites with particular reference to their role as intermediate hosts of Anoplocephalid cestodes. *J. Econ. Entom.*, 54: 701–705.

Walsh, J. D., and J. P. Jones, Jr. 1962. Public health significance to the cone-nosed bug, *Triatoma protracta* (Uhler), in the Sierra Nevada foothills of California. *Calif. Vector Views*, 9:33–37.

Walton, G. A. 1962. The *Ornithodoros moubata* superspecies problem in relation to human relapsing fever epidemiology. *Symp. Zool. Soc. London*, No. 6, pp. 83–156.

Walton, G. A. 1964. The *Ornithodoros* "moubata" group of ticks in Africa. Control problems and implications. *J. Med. Entom.*, 1:53–64.

Warburton, C. 1920. Sarcoptic scabies in man and animals. *Parasitology*, 12:265–300.

Warburton, C. 1922. The warble flies of cattle. *Parasitology*, 14:322–341.

Warburton, G. W., and H. S. Fuller. 1952. *A Manual of the Chiggers*. Entomol. Soc. Washington, Mem. 4, 185 pp.

Ward, R. A. 1962. Preservation of mosquitoes for malarial oocyst and sporozoite dissections. *Mosquito News*, 22:306–307.

Warner, R. E. 1968. The role of introduced diseases in the extinction of the endemic Hawaiian avifauna. *Condor*, 70:101–120.

Warren, M., D. E. Eyles, and R. H. Wharton. 1962. Primate malaria infections in *Mansonia uniformis*. *Mosquito News*, 22:303–304.

Warren, M., and R. H. Wharton. 1963. The vectors of simian malaria: Identity, biology, and geographical distribution. *J. Parasit.*, 49:829–904.

Waterhouse, D. F. 1966. Bushfly repellents. *Austral. J. Sci.*, 28:351.

Waterhouse, D. F., and H. Irzykiewicz. 1957. An examination of proteolytic enzymes from several insects for collaginase activity. *J. Insect Physiol.*, 1:18–22.

Waterman, J. A. 1938. Some notes on scorpion poisoning in Trinidad. *Trans. Roy. Soc. Trop. Med. Hyg.*, 31:607–624.

Watt, J., and D. R. Lindsay. 1948. Diarrheal disease control studies. I. Effect of fly control in a high morbidity area. *Public Health Rep.*, 63:1319–1334.

Watt, K. E. F. 1962. Use of mathematics in population ecology. *Ann. Rev. Entom.*, 7:243–260.

Weber, N. 1959. The sting of the harvesting ant *Pogonomyrmex occidentalis* Cresson. *Entom. News*, 70:85–90.

Webster, L. T., and F. H. Wright. 1938. Recovery of eastern equine encephalomyelitis virus from brain tissue of human cases of encephalitis in Massachusetts. *Science*, 88:305–306.

Weinbren, M. P., and P. J. Mason. 1957. Rift Valley fever in a wild field rat (*Arvicanthis abyssinicus*): A possible natural host. *S. Afr. Med. J.*, 31:427–430.

Weisel, G. F. 1952. Animal names, anatomical terms and some ethnozoology of the Flathead Indians. *J. Washington Acad. Sci.*, 42:345–355.

Weiser, J. 1959. Unterlagen der Taxonomie der Mikrosporidien. *Trans. 1st Int. Conf. Insect. Path. Biol. Control*, pp. 277–285.

Weiss, K. E. 1957. Rift Valley fever. A review. *Bull. Epizootic Dis. Africa*, 5:431–458.

Weiss, K. E., D. A. Haig, and R. A. Alexander. 1956. Wesselsbron virus—a virus not previously described, associated with abortion in domestic animals. *Onderstepoort J. Vet. Res.*, 27:183–195.

Weitz, B. 1956. Identification of blood meals of bloodsucking arthropods. *Bull. WHO*, 15:473–490.

Weitz, B. 1960. Feeding habits of bloodsucking arthropods. *Exp. Parasit.*, 9:63–82.

Weitz, B. 1963. The feeding habits of Glossina. *Bull. WHO*, 28:711–729.

Welch, H. E., and I. A. Rubtsov. 1965. Mermithids (Nematoda: Mermithidae) parasitic in blackflies (Insecta: Simuliidae). Taxonomy and bionomics of *Gastromermis boophthorae*. *Canad. Entom.*, 97:581–596.

Weller, B., and G. M. Graham. 1930. Relapsing fever in Central Texas. *J.A.M.A.*, 95:1834–1835.

Wenk, P., and G. Schlörer. 1963. Wirtsorientierung und Kopulation bei blutsaugenden Simuliiden (Diptera). *Z. tropenmed. Parasit.*, 14:177–191.

West, L. S. 1951. *The Housefly*. Ithaca, N.Y., Comstock Publ. Co., 584 pp.

Weyer, F. 1960. Biological relationships between lice and microbial agents. *Ann. Rev. Entom.*, 5: 405–420.

Weyer, F. 1964. Experimentelle Übertragung von Rickettsien auf Artropoden. *Z. Tropenmed. Parasitol.*, 15:131–138.

Wharton, G. W., and H. S. Fuller. 1952. *A Manual of the Chiggers*. Ent. Soc. Washington Mem. 4. 185 pp.

Wharton, R. H., J. F. B. Edeson, T. Wilson, and J. A. Reid. 1958. Studies on filariasis in Malaya: Pilot experiments in the control of filariasis due to *Wuchereria malayi* in East Pahang. *Ann. Trop. Med. Parasit.*, 52:191–205.

Wheeler, C. M. 1938a. Progress of spirochaete infection in the developmental stages of the host tick, *Ornithodorus hermsi* Wheeler. *Amer. J. Trop. Med.*, 18:413–419.

Wheeler, C. M. 1938b. Experimental infection of *Ornithodorus turicata* (Duges) with a Brazilian strain of *Trypanosoma cruzi* Chagas. *Proc. Soc. Exp. Biol. Med.*, **38**:191–193.

Wheeler, C. M., and J. R. Douglas. 1941. Transmission studies of sylvatic plague, *Proc. Soc. Exp. Biol. Med.*, **47**:65–66.

White, E. B., and E. F. Legner. 1966. Notes on the life history of *Aleochara taeniata*, a staphylinid parasite of the house fly, *Musca domestica*. *Ann. Entom. Soc. Amer.*, **59**:573–577.

Whitesell, K. G. 1965. Large scale granular parathion pre-treatment of a duck club area in the Colusa mosquito abatement district. *Proc. 33rd Ann. Conf. Mosquito Control Ass.*, pp. 56–57.

Whitsel, R. H., and R. F. Schoeppner. 1966. Summary of a study of the biology and control of the valley black gnat *Leptoconops torrens* Townsend (Diptera: Ceratopognoidae). *Calif. Vector Views*, **13**:17–25.

Wichmann, R. W., and D. J. Vincent. 1958. Cnemidocoptic mange in the budgerigar (*Melopsittacus undulatus*). *J. Amer. Vet. Med. Ass.*, **133**:522–524.

Wiesenfeld, S. L. 1967. Sickle-cell trait in human biological and cultural evolution. *Science*, **157**:1134–1140.

Wijers, D. J. B. 1958. Factors that may influence the infection rate of *Glossina palpalis* with *Trypanosoma gambiense*. I. The age of the fly at the time of the infected feed. *Ann. Trop. Med. Parasit.*, **52**:385–390.

Wilcocks, C. 1959. Summary of recent abstracts. VIII. Typhus group of fevers. *Trop. Dis. Bull.*, **56**:1001–1006.

Wilcox, Aimée. 1942. *Manual for the Microscopical Diagnosis of Malaria in Man*. U.S. Pub. Health Ser. Nat. Inst. Health Bull. No. 180. 39 pp.

Wilde, J. de. 1962. Photoperiodism in insects and mites. *Ann. Rev. Entom.*, **71**:1–26.

Wiley, A. J. 1958. Distribution of the common brown tick in Kenya. *E. Afr. Agric. J.*, **24**:53–56.

Wilkinson, P. R. 1957. The spelling of pasture in tick control. *Aust. J. Agr.*, **8**:414–423.

Wilkinson, P. R. 1962. Selection of cattle for tick resistance, and the effect of herds of different susceptibility on *Boophilus* populations. *Aust. J. Agr. Res.*, **13**:974–983.

Wilkinson, P. R. 1964. Pasture spelling as a control measure for cattle ticks in southern Queensland. *Aust. J. Agr. Res.*, **15**:822–840.

Wilkinson, P. R. 1965. A first record of paralysis of a deer by *Dermacentor andersoni* Stiles and notes on the host potential of deer in British Columbia. *Proc. Entom. Soc. B.C.*, **62**:28–30.

Wilkinson, P. R. 1967. The distribution of *Dermacentor* ticks in Canada in relation to bioclimatic zones, *Canad. J. Zool.*, **45**:517–537.

Wilkinson, P. R., and J. E. Lawson. 1965. Difference of sites of attachment of *Dermacentor andersoni* Stiles to cattle in southeastern Alberta and in south central British Columbia, in relation to possible existence of genetically different strains of ticks. *Canad. J. Zool.*, **43**:408–411.

Wilkinson, P. R., and J. T. Wilson. 1959. Survival of cattle ticks in central Queensland pastures. *Aust. J. Agr. Res.*, **10**:129–143.

Willett, K. C. 1962. Recent advances in the study of tsetse-borne diseases, *in* Maramorosch, K., *Biological Transmission of Disease Agents*. New York, Academic Press, pp. 109–121.

Willett, K. C. 1963. Trypanosomiasis and the tsetse fly problem in Africa. *Ann. Rev. Entom.*, **8**:197–214.

Williams, F. X. 1931. *The Insects and Other Invertebrates of Hawaiian Sugar Cane Fields*. Exper. Sta. Hawaiian Sugar Planters Assoc., 400 pp. (p. 279).

Williams, L. L., Jr. 1937. Mosquitoes and malaria. *J. Econ. Entom.*, **30**:20–26.

Williams, R. W. 1946. A contribution to our knowledge of the bionomics of the common North American chigger, *Eutrombicula alfreddugesi* (Oudemans) with a description of a rapid collection method. *Amer. J. Trop. Med.*, **26**:243–250.

Williams, R. W., and H. W. Brown. 1945. The development of *Litomosoides carinii*, filariid parasite of the cotton rat in the tropical rat mite. *Science*, **102**:482–483.

Wilson, F. 1960. *A Review of the Biological Control of Insects and Weeds in Australia and Australian New Guinea*. Tech. Commun. Commonw. Inst. Biol. Contr. No. 1, 102 pp.

Wilson, F. 1963. *Australia as a Source of Beneficial Insects for Biological Control*. Tech. Commun. Inst. Biol. Contr. No. 3, 28 pp.

Wilson, L. B., and W. M. Chowning. 1902. The so-called "spotted fever" of the Rocky Mountains. A preliminary report to the Montana State Board of Health. *J.A.M.A.*, **39**:131–136.

Wilson, W. H. 1904. On the venom of scorpions. *Records Egyptian Govt. School. Med.*, **2**:1–44.

Wingo, C. W. 1964. The status of *Loxosceles reclusa*, the brown recluse spider, as a public health problem. *Proc. N. Centr. Branch. Entom. Soc. Amer.*, **19**:115–118.

Wirth, W. W., and F. S. Blanton. 1959. Biting midges of the genus *Culicoides* from Panama (Diptera: Heleidae). *Proc. U.S. Nat. Museum*, **109**: 237–482.

Woke, P. A. 1937. Comparative effects of the blood of man and of canary on egg production of *Culex pipiens* Linn. *J. Parasit.*, **23**:311–313.

Wolfe, H. R., and W. F. Durham. 1963. *Orchard Mouse Control With Endrin Sprays*. Wash. State Univ. Ext. Circ. 282.

Wood, D. M., B. V. Peterson, D. M. Davies, and H. Gyorkos. 1963. The black flies (Diptera: Simuliidae) of Ontario. Part II. Larval identification, with descriptions and illustrations. *Proc. Entom. Soc. Ontario*, **93**:99–129.

Wood, F. D. 1934. Natural and experimental infection of *Triatoma protracta* (Uhler) and mammals in California with American human trypanosomiasis. *Amer. J. Trop. Med.*, **14**:497–517.

Wood, S. F. 1942. Observations on vectors of Chagas' disease in the United States. I. California. *Bull. Calif. Acad. Sci.*, **41** (2 pt.):61–69.

Woodall, J. P., M. C. Williams, P. S. Corbet, and A. J. Haddow. 1964. The isolation of Sindbis virus from the mosquito *Mansonia* (*Coquillettidia*) *fuscopennata* (Theobald) in Uganda. *Ann. Trop. Med. Parasit.*, **58**:383–389.

Woodward, T. E., and W. F. Turner. 1915. *The Effect of the Cattle Tick upon the Milk Production of Dairy Cows*. U.S. Dept. Agr. Bur. Animal Industry, Bull. No. 147, 22 pp.

Woody, N. C., and H. B. Woody. 1955. American trypanosomiasis (Chagas' disease), first indigenous case in the United States. *J.A.M.A.*, **159**:676–677.

Woolley, T. A. 1961. A review of the phylogeny of mites. *Ann. Rev. Entom.*, **6**:263–284.

Work, T. H. 1962. Kyasanur Forest disease—an infection of man by a virus of the RSS complex in India. *Proc. 6th Intern. Congr. Trop. Med. Malar.*, **5**:180–196.

Work, T. H. 1963. Tick-borne viruses. A review of an arthropod-borne virus problem of growing importance in the tropics. *Bull. WHO*, **29**:59–74.

World Health Organization. 1961. *Specifications for Pesticides. Insecticides, Rodenticides, Molluscicidies, Herbicides, Auxiliary Chemicals, Spraying and Dusting Apparatus.* 2nd ed., 523 pp.

World Health Organization. 1964a. *Genetics of Vectors and Insecticide Resistance. WHO* Tech. Rept. Ser. No. 268, 40 pp.

World Health Organization. 1964b. *Equipment for Vector Control. Guide to Major Items—Specifications—Use Descriptions—Field Tests.* Geneva, 200 pp.

Wu, L. T., J. W. H. Chun, R. Pollitzer, and C. Y. Wu. 1936. *Plague, a Manual for Medical and Public Health Workers.* Shanghai, Weishengshu Nat. Quar. Service, 547 pp.

Yamada, S. 1932. Observations on a house-infesting mite (*Liponyssus nagayoi* n.sp.) which attacks human beings, rats, and other domestic animals, with brief notes of experiments regarding the possibility of the plague transmission by means of this mite. *Far East. Assoc. Trop. Med., Trans. 8th Congr.*, **2**:358–372.

Yamamoto, R. T., and E. Jensen. 1967. Ingestion of feeding stimulants and protein by the female housefly, *Musca domestica* Linnaeus. *J. Insect Physiol.*, **13**:91–98.

Yao, H. Y., I. C. Yuan, and D. Huie. 1929. The relation of flies, beverages, and well water to gastrointestinal diseases in Peiping. *Nat. Med. J. China*, **15**:410–418.

Young, M. D. 1948. Adaptability of exotic malaria parasites to indigenous anophelines. *Proc. 4th Intern. Cong. Trop. Med. Malar.*, pp. 672–680.

Young, M. D., D. E. Eyles, R. W. Burgess, and G. M. Jeffery. 1955. Experimental testing of the immunity of negroes to *Plasmodium vivax. J. Parasit.*, **41**:315–318.

Yunker, C. E., and J. Cory. 1967. Growth of Colorado tick fever (CTF) virus in primary tissue cultures of its vector, *Dermacentor andersoni* Stiles (Acarina: Ixodidae), with notes on tick tissue culture. *Exp. Parasit.*, **20**:267–277.

Zimin, L. S. 1951. *Muscini, Stomoxydini*, (in Russian) Fauna U.S.S.R.: Diptera, 18, No. 4:1–285.

Zimmerman, E. C. 1948. *Insects of Hawaii.* Vol. 3, *Heteroptera.* Honolulu, Univ. of Hawaii Press, 255 pp.

Ziprkowski, L., E. Hofshi, and A. S. Tahori. 1959 Caterpillar dermatitis. *Israel Med. J.*, **18**:26–31.

Zumpt, F. 1950. Fifth preliminary study to a monograph of the Stomoxydinae. Key to the Stomoxydinae of the Ethiopian region, with descriptions of a new Haematobia and a new Rhinomusca species from Zululand. *Ann. Inst. Med. Trop. Lisbon*, **7**:397–426.

Zumpt, F. 1965. *Myiasis in Man and Animals in the Old World.* London, Butterworths, 267 pp.

Zumpt, F., and H. E. Paterson. 1953. Studies on the family Gasterophilidae with keys to the adults and maggots. *J. Entom. Soc. South Africa*, **16**:59–72.

Index

Boldface numbers indicate primary discussion in text.
Italic numbers indicate pages on which illustrations appear.